ITEM 021 342 859
D0490917

BTEC NATIONAL

Book 2

Children's Care, Learning + Development

Sandy Green
Sally Foster
Sue Kellas

UXBRIDGE COLLEGE
LEARNING CENTRE

Nelson Thornes

Text © Sandy Green, Sally Foster and Sue Kellas 2008
Original illustrations © Nelson Thornes Ltd 2008

The right of Sandy Green, Sally Foster and Sue Kellas to be identified as authors of this work has been asserted by them in accordance with the Copyright, Designs and Patents Act 1988.

All rights reserved. No part of this publication may be reproduced or transmitted in any form or by any means, electronic or mechanical, including photocopy, recording or any information storage and retrieval system, without permission in writing from the publisher or under licence from the Copyright Licensing Agency Limited, of Saffron House, 6–10 Kirby Street, London, EC1N 8TS.

Any person who commits any unauthorised act in relation to this publication may be liable to criminal prosecution and civil claims for damages.

Published in 2008 by:
Nelson Thornes Ltd
Delta Place
27 Bath Road
CHELTENHAM
GL53 7TH
United Kingdom

08 09 10 11 12 / 10 9 8 7 6 5 4 3 2 1

A catalogue record for this book is available from the British Library

ISBN 978 0 7487 8198 0

Cover photograph by Ian Shaw/Alamy

Illustrations include artwork drawn by Angela Knowles, Peters and Zabransky UK Ltd and Pantek Arts Ltd

Page make-up by Pantek Arts Ltd, Maidstone, Kent

Printed and bound in Slovenia by Delo tiskarna by arrangement with Korotan – Ljubljana

Contents

Introduction

Early years practitioners work with children in a variety of care and education settings, in schools, nurseries, pre-schools, crèches and hospitals, and in the home as childminders and nannies. There are also opportunities within after-school clubs and playschemes. This is an exciting time to be early years practitioner as there is greater interest than ever before in supporting children in the earliest years. Opportunities to support children within the classroom have also increased as inclusion is the accepted preference for many children with an additional need. If you enjoy being with young children and are enthusiastic about training and development then this course will introduce you to an interesting and challenging career, providing you with opportunities to learn about all the key areas and supporting you within a range of settings to help you gain practical experience.

How do you use this book?

Covering seven of the most popular specialist units from the new 2007 specification, this book has everything you need if you are studying BTEC National Certificate or Diploma in Children's Care, Learning and Development. Simple to use and understand, it is designed to provide you with the skills and knowledge you need to gain your qualification. We guide you step-by-step towards your qualification, through a range of features that are fully explained over the page

Which units do you need to complete?

BTEC National Children's Care, Learning and Development Book 2 provides coverage of seven specialist units for the BTEC National Certificate or Diploma. To achieve the Certificate, you are required to complete seven core units plus further specialist units that provide for a combined total of 720 guided learning hours (GLH). To achieve the Diploma, you are required to complete seven core units plus further specialist units that provide for a combined total of 1080 guided learning hours (GLH). Together *BTEC National Children's Care, Learning and Development Book 1* and *Book 2* provide you with coverage of the following:

BTEC National CCLD Book 1 **Core and Specialist Units**	***BTEC National CCLD Book 2*** **Specialist Units**
Unit 1 **Positive Relationships for Children's Care, Learning and Development***	Unit 11 **Diet and Nutrition for Children**
Unit 2 **Positive Environments for Children's Care, Learning and Development ***	Unit 12 **Physical Activities for Children**
Unit 3 **Promoting Children's Development***	Unit 14 **Psychological Perspectives on Children's Behaviour**
Unit 4 **Reflecting on and Developing Practice for Children Aged 0-8 Years***	Unit 17 **Supporting Children's Numeracy Skills**
Unit 5 **Protecting Children***	Unit 18 **Supporting Children's Literacy Skills**
Unit 6 **Promoting Children's Rights***	Unit 27 **Meeting Additional Requirement for Children's Care, Learning and Development**
Unit 7 **Children's Learning Activities and Play***	Unit 35 **The Development and Care of Babies and Children Under Three Years**
Unit 8 **Research Methodology for Children's Care, Learning and Development**	
Unit 9 **Promoting Healthy Development and Living for Children and their Families**	

Is there anything else you need to do?

1. Talk to others about their work and listen to their guidance and advice on practice, qualification and personal development.
2. Familiarise yourself with all relevant curriculum frameworks and guidance.
3. Keep yourself up to date with current thinking and ideas by reading the many magazines and journals especially for the early years.
4. Use your observation skills to help you develop strategies for communicating, planning and managing behaviour, and for dealing with complex or difficult situations.
5. Never be afraid to ask for help or advice when you need it.

Turn over now for your guide to the features of this book.

We hope you enjoy your BTEC course – Good Luck!

Features of this book

Learning Objectives

At the beginning of each Unit there will be a bulleted list letting you know what material is going to be covered. They specifically relate to the learning objectives within the specification.

Grading Criteria

The table of Grading Criteria at the beginning of each unit identifies achievement levels of pass, merit and distinction, as stated in the specification.

To achieve a **pass**, you must be able to match each of the 'P' criteria in turn.

To achieve **merit** or **distinction**, you must increase the level of evidence that you use in your work, using the 'M' and 'D' columns as reference. For example, to achieve a distinction you must fulfil all the criteria in the pass, merit and distinction columns.

UNIT 11

Diet and Nutrition for Children

This unit covers the following objectives:

- Understand the principles of infant feeding and diet of children
- Understand the potential effects of diet on children's health
- Understand the principles of food safety

Supporting the diet and nutrition intake of babies and young children includes encouraging parents to provide healthy balanced foods at home and supporting the feeding choices of new mothers. Having an understanding of food groups and how foods support development will help you plan appropriately to meet children's energy needs as they change according to both growth and activity levels

grading criteria

To achieve a **Pass** grade the evidence must show that the learner is able to:	To achieve a **Merit** grade the evidence must show that the learner is able to:	To achieve a **Distinction** grade the evidence must show that the learner is able to:
P1 describe the key principles of breast and bottle feeding	**M1** plan a bottle feeding routine for a baby giving explanations for each step	**D1** analyse the menu produced, from the point of view of nutrients, balance and the health of a childe
P2 describe the process of weaning and the feeding of older babies and young children	**M2** explain the importance of the process of weaning	**D2** evaluate the food safety practices in a children's setting
P3 describe the main considerations in presenting food to young children	**M3** produce a balanced menu for a three year old child for a week, justifying the choices	
P4 describe the potential effects of an unbalanced diet on babies and children		
P5 describe the principles of food safety and the potential effects of unsafe practice		

Diet and Nutrition for Children **UNIT 11**

activity
INDIVIDUAL WORK

P1

You have been asked to prepare a leaflet on feeding choices for your local antenatal class. This has to set out the advantages and disadvantages of both breast and bottle feeding and you should also include health, social, cultural and environmental factors in your information. It also needs to provide a suggested formula feeding routine giving step-by-step guidance for parents. Make clear any likely differences at each of the following (approximate) ages:

- from birth
- from around 3 months
- from around 6 months
- from around 12 months.

case study 11.1 **Janice**

Janice is shortly due to give birth to her first baby and is unsure which sterilising method to use. She is currently on maternity leave and is due to return to work when her baby is about 3 months old. Janice intends to breast feed for the first few weeks, moving her baby onto formula feeds by about 2 months as she will be working full time and this will be a more practical option for her. Janice has asked for your advice.

activity

1. What advice would you give Janice?
2. What are the advantages and disadvantages of the various sterilising methods?

remember

It is easier to make up enough feeds for the day in one go, if suitable refrigeration is available. This is particularly useful for families with twins or other multiples.

Lactation produces two stages of milk production. The fore milk is the milk the infant receives initially, which satisfies the initial thirst and hunger, whereas the hind milk, which is the richer type of milk, due to its higher fat content, offers longer term satisfaction for the infant. Breast feeding provides sufficient nutrition for an infant until around the age of 6 months. By this stage, the iron stores within the mother's milk, which were built up during pregnancy, have been used up and the process of **weaning** needs to begin.

Professional Practice

- Wash your hands thoroughly before you handle any feeding equipment.
- Prepare feeds on a cleaned surface.
- Have spare teats handy in case you drop one!

Link

For information on how to make up a formula feed, or how to sterilise feeding equipment, refer to pages 00 and 00

Progress Check

1. What nutritional factors can you think of that can affect the developing foetus?
2. Why is folic acid considered to be important for pregnant women?
3. Give examples of foods for each of the main food groups.
4. Why is breast milk considered to be best for babies?
5. What is the difference between fore milk and hind milk?
6. Why is weaning usually introduced at about 6 months?
7. Explain the advantages and disadvantages of breast feeding.
8. Explain the advantages and disadvantages of formula feeding.
9. Explain how you would encourage a 'fussy' eater.
10. What is the difference between a food allergy and a food intolerance?

Activities

are designed to help you understand the topics through answering questions or undertaking research, and are either *Group* or *Individual* work. They are linked to the Grading Criteria by application of the D, P, and M categories.

Case Studies

provide real life examples that relate to what is being discussed within the text. It provides an opportunity to demonstrate theory in practice.

An **Activity** that is linked to a Case Study helps you to apply your knowledge of the subject to real life situations.

Keywords

of specific importance are highlighted within the text and then defined in a glossary at the end of the book.

Remember

boxes contain helpful hints, tips or advice.

Professional Practice

boxes highlght any professional practice points relevant to the topic being covered

Links

direct you to other parts of the book that relate to the subject currently being covered.

Progress Checks

provide a list of quick questions at the end of each Unit, designed to ensure that you have understood the most important aspects of each subject area.

Dedications

Thanks to John as always for his love, and to family, friends and colleagues for their continued interest, support and encouragement. With fond memories too of the many children and students I have worked with, who each have added to my own learning.

To Sally and Sue, thank you for your contributions to this book.

Sandy Green

Sally Foster would like to thank friends and colleagues at Norton Radstock College for their support and expertise.

Sue Kellas would like to thank Terry, Mark and Joe for their patience and support, Zoe for initial encouragement and Ali.

Acknowledgements

The authors and publishers would like to thank the following for permission to reproduce the following material:

DfES, Jeffrey W. Hull, National Strategies Publications, QCA

Crown copyright material is reproduced with the permission of The Controller of Her Majesty's Stationery Office © Crown Copyright.

Every effort has been made to contact copyright holders, and we apologise if any have been overlooked.

Photo credits

Bubbles Photolibrary: Fig. 35.48

David Ashley/Corbis: Fig.12.14

Digital Vision PB (NT): Fig. 35.17

The Fragile X Society: Fig. 27.19

John Birdsall: Fig. 35.45

National Marfan Foundation: Fig. 27.6

Photodisc 41 (NT): Fig. 35.18

Rex Features: Figs 12.27, 27.20

Science Photo Library: Figs 27.1, 27.3, 27.4, 27.8, 27.18, 27.20, 35.2, 35.3, 35.6

UNIT 11 Diet and Nutrition for Children

This unit covers the following objectives:

- Understand the principles of infant feeding and diet of children
- Understand the potential effects of diet on children's health
- Understand the principles of food safety

Supporting the diet and nutrition intake of babies and young children includes encouraging parents to provide healthy balanced foods at home and supporting the feeding choices of new mothers. Having an understanding of food groups and how foods support development will help you plan appropriately to meet children's energy needs as they change according to both growth and activity levels.

grading criteria

To achieve a **Pass** grade the evidence must show that the learner is able to:	To achieve a **Merit** grade the evidence must show that, in addition to the Pass criteria, the learner is able to:	To achieve a **Distinction** grade the evidence must show that, in addition to the Pass and Merit criteria, the learner is able to:
P1 Describe the key principles of breast and bottle feeding page 10	**M1** Plan a bottle feeding routine for a baby giving explanations for each step page 10	
P2 Describe the process of weaning and the feeding of older babies and young children page 24	**M2** Explain the importance of the process of weaning page 24	
P3 Describe the main considerations in presenting food to young children page 28		
P4 Describe the potential effects of an unbalanced diet on babies and children page 32	**M3** Produce a balanced menu for a three year old child for a week, justifying the choices page 32	**D1** Analyse the menu produced, from the point of view of nutrients, balance and the health of a child page 32
P5 Describe the principles of food safety and the potential effects of unsafe practice page 35	**M4** Explain the potential effects of unsafe food practices in children's settings page 35	**D2** Evaluate the food safety practices in a children's setting page 36

Understand the principles of infant feeding and diet of children

Breast feeding

When caring for a newborn infant, a number of decisions need to be made. One of the most important is the choice of infant feeding. Research shows that breast feeding is by far the best option for the infant, although formula milks are an excellent alternative. However, breast feeding is not always the best choice for the mother, and this has to be taken into account too. The wishes of the mother, and any medical or social difficulties this may present for her, will need to be balanced against the nutritional needs of the child. For many people it comes down to personal choice and, as an early years professional, you must respect the choice each individual makes. If asked for your opinion, you should be able to outline the advantages and disadvantages of each feeding method.

Breast milk offers a degree of **natural immunity** to the infant through the mother's own immunity, and it is considered to be nature's 'designer food' because, as the infant grows, the mother's breast milk changes to meet her child's developing needs. The colostrum-rich early milk (a thick, yellowish substance with a high protein content, secreted prior to the mother's full milk production) offers some protection against common infections and is particularly important to newborn infants. Even when mothers are not intending to breast feed long term, they are encouraged to do so for the first few days to allow their babies to benefit from this.

For breast feeding to be successful, the mother needs to eat well and drink plenty of fluids. This helps her milk production. It is also affected by the infant's suckling. The more the baby feeds, the more milk is produced, on a supply-and-demand basis. Once the initial stages of breast feeding are passed, and any soreness or discomfort has been overcome, breast feeding is usually considered a pleasurable part of mothering.

Babies suckle for different lengths of time – some will take all they need in just a few minutes, while others will suck for far longer. Letting the baby decide the length of a feed maintains a balance and helps to prevent engorgement of the breasts. As the infant sucks her jaws press firmly on the mother's milk reservoirs around the areola area of the breast, stimulating the flow of the milk. At each feed, the baby initially receives the **fore milk**, which offers satisfaction in the short term, but the richer **hind milk** which follows often gives satisfaction for a longer period. It is usual for babies to feed from alternate breasts at alternate feeds.

For the first few months of life, most babies will need only milk feeds – either breast or bottle – to give them all the nutrients they need for their development. Throughout the first year there is a need for a high intake of milk to ensure that they receive sufficient calcium. This supports the development of healthy bones and teeth. Therefore milk remains an important part of an infant's diet even once they have started to enjoy solid foods too.

Fig 11.1 Breast milk offers the baby natural immunity

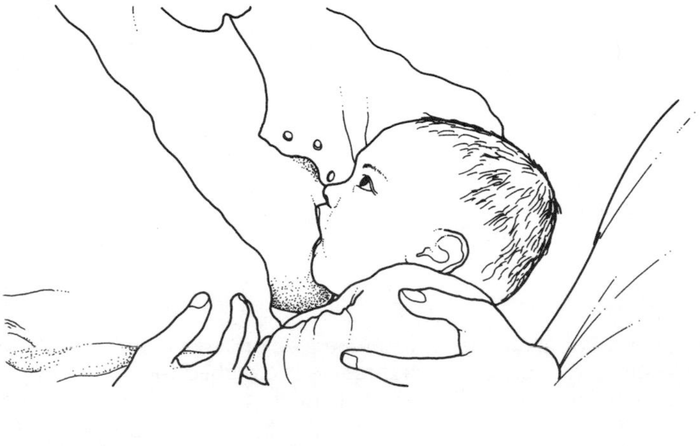

Preparation

As well as eating well, a lactating mother needs to be aware that whatever she eats will be passed on to her child. This includes alcohol, spicy food, medication and the effects of smoking. Medication should never be taken without checking that it is safe for the breast-feeding child too. This applies to cough and cold remedies as well as to prescribed items.

Breast-feeding mothers need plenty of support, especially in the early days and weeks. It can be very tiring as the mother is needed at each feed time and may have few uninterrupted rest periods. At times, breast feeding can be hard to establish and the sensitive support and encouragement of health professionals and early years workers can be crucial to whether a mother feels able to continue. Support can be given in the form of:

- encouragement
- help with positioning of the infant
- advice on length of suckling
- advice regarding 'latching' the infant on to the breast
- advice regarding removing the infant from the breast.

Each of these is necessary to establish a feeding process which is free from soreness and discomfort.

Professional Practice

- Feeding on demand allows babies to satisfy their hunger.
- If a baby sleeps well between feeds, it usually means they are getting sufficient nutrients.
- Regular weighing of babies allows mothers to monitor the sufficiency of their milk production and gives them peace of mind.
- Green, slimy stools may indicate that a baby is not getting enough feeds – longer or more frequent feeds may need to be encouraged.
- The breast-feeding mother needs to sit comfortably, with her back supported. The baby sucks with lips curled back and takes the whole of the areola (the pigmented area around the nipple) into the mouth.
- **Eye contact** is made between mother and child and as the baby develops they pat the breast contentedly.

remember

Breast feeding is always the best choice for a baby, although, as an early years professional, you should respect the choices made by mothers and offer support accordingly.

Process

A breast-feeding mother needs to be sitting comfortably with her back well supported. Ideally she will be relaxed, unhurried and uninterrupted. Most mothers feel the need to drink whilst feeding. A higher fluid intake is needed to maintain a good milk flow.

The infant usually 'roots' for the breast, but often needs help in latching on correctly and securely, especially in the earliest days. To encourage a sleepy or uninterested infant to suckle, the mother needs to:

- offer the breast to the infant
- keep the infant's head higher than their body
- squeeze a few drops of milk and touch them to the infant's lips
- talk gently using encouraging terms.

Once feeding has commenced, the mother should:

- continue to talk to and make eye contact with her baby
- be aware of sudden milk flooding from the breast, which can cause the infant to splutter and choke as they struggle to deal with the increased flow.

Following the first few minutes of feeding, the mother needs to interrupt the suction by gently inserting a clean finger into the infant's mouth. This will enable winding to take place, before continuing the feed. Winding should ideally be carried out again at the end of the feed before the infant settles to sleep.

Timing

Ideally babies should be fed on demand. This means that the infant is fed when they are hungry, which usually means they will take sufficient milk to keep them satisfied for the anticipated length of time (according to their age and weight). Most infants fed on demand are usually able to maintain a steady weight increase and a regular pattern of sleep. In a household where work, the school run, etc. has to be fitted into specified time slots, this is not always practical and sometimes an infant has to be woken and fed to fit in with the rest of the family.

Feeding a baby who is not necessarily hungry can at times be more challenging as the infant may be sleepy and less responsive, or they may take just a little and fall fast asleep again, needing to be 'topped up' again an hour or so later.

Most infants feed around every two to three hours initially, settling quite quickly into a three to four hourly routine. As their sucking gains in strength, they take in more milk at each feed and the time between feeds gradually lengthens, with the actual feeding time often getting shorter as hunger is satisfied more quickly.

Constituents of breast milk

Breast milk is largely made up of water and is therefore able to meet all the water requirements of a young infant even in hot climates. Mostly the various nutrition components, e.g. cholesterol, proteins, are not affected by the diet of the mother, but water-soluble vitamins, especially the B vitamins, can be affected. It is often recommended that mothers who follow a strict **vegan diet** take a vitamin B12 supplement to ensure that the infant receives a sufficient amount through her breast milk. Vitamin B12 is needed by the infant for optimal brain development.

Table 11.1 The constituents of breast milk

Constituent	Role
Docsohexanoic acid	Necessary for growth and development of the brain and retina, also for myelinisation of nervous tissue
Cholesterol	Enhances myelinisation of nervous tissue
Taurine	Important for bile acid function
Choline	May enhance memory
Enzymes such as lipases	Important for digestion of fats
Lactoferrin	Binds iron and transports it efficiently into the infant; prevents iron from being used by gut bacteria
Inositol	Enhances synthesis of surfactant in immature lung tissue
Poly- and oligo-saccharides	Inhibit bacterial binding to intestinal surfaces
Various proteins	Bind calcium and zinc for absorption by the infant; supply amino acids to the infant
White blood cells	Transmit maternal immunity to infant's immune system
Nucleotides	Building blocks of DNA, RNA and energy storage compounds; enhance formation of immunity to infection
Glutathione peroxidase, alkaline phosphatase, xanthine oxidase	Important in prevention of infection
Lactoferrin (above), lysozyme, secretory immunoglobulin A	Line intestinal surface, prevent bacterial attachment and infection

Link

Refer to Table 11.2 on page 7 for a comparison of breast milk and formula feeds.

Physiology of the breast

A woman's breasts begin to develop at puberty, influenced by the sex hormones. Each breast has a range of lobules, which each have ducts (called lactiferous ducts). These link to lactiferous sinuses, which in turn lead directly to the nipple, allowing the milk to be secreted to the sucking infant.

The nipple is surrounded by an area of skin known as the areola. The pigmentation of this area of skin darkens during pregnancy. The areola has a number of glands called Montgomery's tubules, which become larger during pregnancy. The fluid produced within them during pregnancy helps to keep the nipples supple.

Lactation (milk production)

Lactation occurs following a hormone 'trigger' from the brain following birth. This sends signals to the mother's breasts to start the lactation process. Initially, the breasts secrete

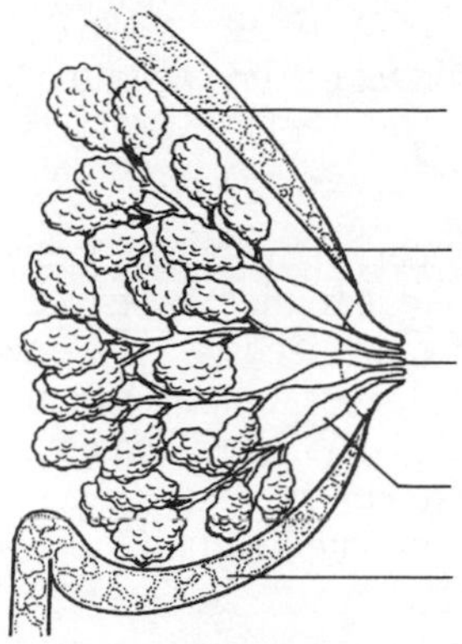

Fig 11.2 The structure of the breast

a thick, creamy substance called colostrum. This is very rich in protein and is produced in the later stages of pregnancy and for the first few days after birth, prior to the onset of the main milk supply (two to four days after birth). The high protein level in the colostrum is particularly beneficial to newborn infants as it is very nutritious and a small amount can supply the infant with sufficient energy needs in the early days when they sleep a great deal. Mothers are encouraged to breast feed for the first few days to enable their baby to benefit from this high protein intake, even if they intend to change over to formula feeding.

As breast feeding becomes established, the colostrum gradually lessens until the mother produces only the mature breast milk. This looks thin and watery and often has a bluish appearance. The nutritional quality is not reduced however; it has simply adjusted to the needs of the infant.

Fore milk and hind milk

Lactation produces two stages of milk production. The fore milk is the milk the infant receives initially, which satisfies the initial thirst and hunger, whereas the hind milk, which is the richer type of milk, due to its higher fat content, offers longer term satisfaction for the infant. Breast feeding provides sufficient nutrition for an infant until around the age of 6 months. By this stage, the iron stores within the mother's milk, which were built up during pregnancy, have been used up and the process of **weaning** needs to begin. Weaning helps the infant develop a healthy attitude to food for the future, as well as replenishing the iron supplies that have now been reduced, and nourishing the body in general.

Normal changes and common breast-feeding difficulties

For most women the process of breast feeding is a natural action which, after any initial minor issues, settles down into a pleasurable routine, offering closeness and an ideal opportunity for bonding. For a few women, problems can occur, both prior to breast feeding and once it has commenced. Problems that can occur include the following.

Inverted nipples

Some women have nipples that are not raised in the usual way and sometimes there is a need for the nipple to be 'drawn out' with finger and thumb, or through the use of a nipple shield worn inside bra cups on a daily basis for several weeks prior to the date of delivery. This helps prepare the nipple(s) for breast feeding.

Sore or cracked nipples

Soreness and cracked nipples often occur towards the end of pregnancy, and both cracking and soreness can occur in the early days of breast feeding. These problems can be helped by ensuring that the infant is positioned to the breast correctly, and by regular washing, drying and moisturising of the nipple area. Exposure to air can also be beneficial.

Leaking breasts

The woman's body responds to the sound of her child, and her breasts will often produce milk automatically at the sound of her infant stirring. Breast pads can be used to soak up any surplus milk. Again, keeping the nipple area dry and moisturised will help avoid problems arising.

Engorged breasts

This is a painful experience in which the breasts become over-full. It can be due to incorrect positioning of the infant on the breast or insufficient emptying of the milk supply. Allowing the infant to feed on demand will often help regulate the milk flow. It is important that breast-feeding women wear a well-fitting and supportive bra at all times.

Blocked ducts
The main cause of blocked ducts is incorrect positioning of the infant when feeding, or a lack of regular feeding taking place.

Mastitis
This is an inflammation of the breast or part of the breast. It is a very painful condition, and is often accompanied by fever. It can be due to the breasts becoming over-full or through insufficient feeding by the infant. The mother needs to relieve the painful breast first at each feed, until it improves, and offer frequent feeds until the situation has settled down. In severe cases, the mother may need antibiotics to relieve the inflammation. At times she might be advised to avoid feeding from the affected breast, but to express the milk by hand regularly to lessen the build-up and to continue the stimulation of the milk supply.

Insufficient milk supply
This can occur if breast feeding is regularly replaced by formula feeds, by incorrect positioning of the infant when feeding or if the mother is poorly nourished. It is important that all breast-feeding mothers have a nutritious diet and a high fluid intake.

Professional Practice

- All breast-feeding mothers need support and this is especially important when problems arise.

Advantages and disadvantages of breast feeding

Advantages of breast feeding
- The balance of breast milk nutrients is perfect for the infant.
- The milk 'matures' with the baby, constantly meeting their needs.
- Breast milk offers a degree of immunity against infection in the early weeks.
- Breast milk protects against eczema, asthma and jaundice.
- Breast feeding helps the mother to regain her figure more quickly.
- Breast-fed babies have less gastro-enteritis and fewer chest infections.
- Breast-fed babies tend to have fewer and less smelly nappies.
- There is a lower risk of diabetes later on.
- Breast milk is always 'on hand'.
- Breast feeding is cheaper overall – the milk is free!

Disadvantages of breast feeding
- Only the mother can feed, lessening the opportunities to involve siblings and others.
- The mother can become over-tired as she has to cover all the night feeds too.
- Cultural discretion needs may restrict where feeding can take place.
- There is no record of how much milk the infant has had; you judge by contentment.
- There is always a possibility of feeding problems such as mastitis, sore nipples, etc.
- The mother needs a good healthy diet.
- The mother needs support/feeding bras.
- Breast pads may also need to be bought.

Expressing breast milk

Many mothers choose to express some of their breast milk, which can be given in a bottle or cup, and this can be a useful solution to the question of how to continue breast feeding when returning to work. Breast pumps can be either manual or mechanical and they produce a vacuum which draws out the milk in much the same way as the baby's sucking. Battery or mains-operated pumps are far quicker to use than expressing by hand, and are suitable for expressing significant quantities.

Expressed milk can allow other family members to enjoy feeding the baby too. It can give the mother some time for herself and can alleviate any issues of embarrassment or cultural indiscretions regarding feeding in front of other people. Expressed milk needs to be kept in sterile containers and refrigerated until needed. Breast milk can be frozen (ice-cube trays are useful for this) and used in preparing solid food when the baby reaches the onset of mixed feeding. The usual sterilising procedures should be followed.

Link Refer to page 10 for information on sterilising methods.

Table 11.2 Comparison of human milk and formula milk

Nutrient factor	Breast milk contains	Formula milk contains	Comment
Fats	■ Rich in brain-building omega 3s, namely DHA and AA ■ Automatically adjusts to infant's needs; levels decline as baby gets older ■ Rich in cholesterol ■ Nearly completely absorbed ■ Contains fat-digesting enzymes, lipase	■ No DHA ■ Doesn't adjust to infant's needs ■ No cholesterol ■ Not completely absorbed ■ No lipase	Fat is the most important nutrient in breast milk; the absence of cholesterol and DHA, vital nutrients for growing brains and bodies, may predispose a child to adult heart and central nervous system diseases. Leftover, unabsorbed fat accounts for unpleasant smelling stools in formula-fed babies.
Protein	■ Soft, easily-digestible whey ■ More completely absorbed; higher in the milk of mothers who deliver preterm ■ Lactoferrin for intestinal health ■ Lysozyme, an antimicrobial ■ Rich in brain-and-body-building protein components ■ Rich in growth factors ■ Contains sleep-inducing proteins	■ Harder-to-digest casein curds ■ Not completely absorbed, more waste, harder on kidneys ■ No lactoferrin, or only a trace ■ No lysozyme ■ Deficient or low in some brain- and body-building proteins ■ Deficient in growth factors ■ Does not contain as many sleep-inducing proteins	Infants aren't allergic to human milk protein.
Carbohydrates	■ Rich in lactose ■ Rich in oligosaccharides, which promote intestinal health	■ No lactose in some formulas ■ Deficient in oligosaccharides	Lactose is considered an important carbohydrate for brain development. Studies show the level of lactose in the milk of a species correlates with the size of the brain of that species.
Immune boosters	■ Rich in living white blood cells, millions per feeding ■ Rich in immunoglobulins	■ No live white blood cells or any other cells. Dead food has less immunological benefit ■ Few immunoglobins and most are the wrong kind	When mother is exposed to a germ, she makes antibodies to that germ and gives these antibodies to her infant via her milk.
Vitamins and minerals	■ Better absorbed, especially iron, zinc and calcium ■ Iron is 50 to 75 per cent absorbed ■ Contains more selenium (an antioxidant)	■ Not absorbed as well ■ Iron is 5 to 10 per cent absorbed ■ Contains less selenium (an antioxidant)	Vitamins and minerals in breast milk enjoy a higher bioavailability, that is, a greater percentage is absorbed. To compensate, more is added to formula, which makes it harder to digest.
Enzymes and hormones	■ Rich in digestive enzymes, such as lipase and amylase ■ Rich in many hormones: thyroid, prolactin, oxytocin and more than 15 others ■ Varies with mother's diet	■ Processing kills digestive enzymes ■ Processing kills hormones, which are not human to begin with ■ Always tastes the same	Digestive enzymes promote intestinal health. Hormones contribute to the overall biochemical balance and well-being of baby. By taking on the flavour of mother's diet, breast milk shapes the tastes of the child to family foods.

Bottle feeding

Formula milk is an alternative to breast milk, and formulas available today mirror human milk as accurately as is possible. However, no artificial milk can ever be as ideal for a baby's stomach as breast milk. As the baby's nutritional needs change, parents or the primary adult carer need to decide when the next stage formula is required, whereas breast feeding copes with changes naturally, linked to the growth rate of the baby and their levels of hunger.

In early years settings, babies' feeds will usually be supplied ready prepared by the parents and will need to be stored in a refrigerator until needed.

Fig 11.3 The baby should be held securely, with good eye contact

Professional Practice

- Each baby must have their feeds labelled clearly and stored separately to avoid confusion or **cross-infection**.

Bottles

Making a formula feed

Preparation

You will need:

- formula feed
- bottle
- teats
- knife
- kettle of water, pre-boiled and allowed to cool
- sterilising equipment.

Professional Practice

- Wash your hands thoroughly before you handle any feeding equipment.
- Prepare feeds on a cleaned surface.
- Have spare teats handy in case you drop one!

Method

1. Boil the kettle in advance and allow the water to cool.
2. Remove bottle from the steriliser unit and rinse with boiled water.
3. Pour sufficient **cooled boiled water** into the bottle for the feed required, following the manufacturer's guidelines.
4. Check the level is accurate.
5. Open the tin of formula.
6. Using the scoop enclosed in the tin, add the correct number of scoops to the bottle. Level each scoop off with a flat knife.
7. If using straight away, put on the teat, ring and lid, and shake the bottle gently to dissolve the formula.

8 The feed is ready for use after checking the temperature is OK (see below).
9 If storing the feed for later, put a disc and ring on the bottle and shake gently to mix.
10 Remove disc and replace with upside-down teat (do not allow formula to touch the teat, as bacteria could begin to form).
11 Cover with disc and lid and refrigerate until needed.

Professional Practice

- It is important that the scoops of formula are level.
- Heaped scoops or packed-down scoops lead to over-feeding, and over-feeding can lead to excessive weight gain, high levels of salt intake and possible kidney strain.
- Using insufficient scoops of formula for the correct amount of water leads to under-feeding, and under-feeding can lead to poor weight gain and a hungry baby.
- A baby needs 75 ml of formula per 500 g of body weight (2½ fl oz per pound) in each 24-hour period.

remember It is easier to make up enough feeds for the day in one go, if suitable refrigeration is available. This is particularly useful for families with twins or other multiples.

remember Wash your hands thoroughly before feeding a baby or handling feeding equipment.

remember Always throw away leftover milk and never use the same bottle twice without sterilising.

Giving a formula feed

It is important to be prepared in advance, with everything that you might need easily to hand. You should be seated comfortably and able to give the baby your full attention. Often a baby will be more comfortable having their nappy changed prior to feeding, but individual routines will vary.

1 Have all equipment together and suitably covered. The bottle can be kept warm in a jug of hot water whilst you settle with the baby.
2 Hold the baby close to you, offering a sense of security and pleasure.
3 Test the temperature of the formula against the inside of your wrist. It should feel warm, not hot.
4 Check that the milk is flowing at the appropriate rate for the baby you are feeding. Several drops per second is usual, but rates do vary from baby to baby.
5 Encourage the onset of feeding by touching the teat against the baby's lips before placing the teat into the mouth. The milk should always cover the whole teat to stop the baby taking in excess air and becoming frustrated at not receiving enough milk at a time. If the baby is reluctant to suck, pull the teat gently, as the tension will often give them the impetus to suck harder.
6 About half-way through the feed, stop and wind the baby (see below).
7 Wind again when the feed is over and settle the baby down. They may need another nappy change.
8 When a baby has finished feeding, discard any remaining formula and wash the bottle thoroughly before placing it in a steriliser.

Winding

Winding a baby is the process of helping them release any trapped air taken in during the feeding process. The baby is best held in an upright position to allow the air to rise. Useful positions for this include:

- sitting the baby forward, resting against your hand, which allows you to rub or gently pat their back with your other hand
- placing the baby on your shoulder and rubbing or gently patting their back
- resting the baby along your forearm (very young babies only) and rubbing their back
- with some babies, laying them prone across your lap and rubbing their back works well.

Professional Practice

- It is always useful to have a cloth handy as many babies posset (regurgitate) some milk during the winding process.
- Remember to keep the head and neck of young babies well supported.

activity
INDIVIDUAL WORK 11.1

P1

M1

You have been asked to prepare a leaflet on feeding choices for your local antenatal class. This has to set out the advantages and disadvantages of both breast and bottle feeding and you should also include **health**, social, cultural and environmental factors in your information. It also needs to provide a suggested formula feeding routine giving step-by-step guidance for parents. Make clear any likely differences at each of the following (approximate) ages:

- from birth
- from around 3 months
- from around 6 months
- from around 12 months.

remember

A mother has the right to choose the feeding method that suits her needs and your information should simply inform and not judge or advise.

remember

Fully submerging items such as bottles means ensuring that all air bubbles are released – an air bubble leaves an area unsterilised and therefore a potential site for bacteria growth.

Fig 11.4 A microwave steriliser

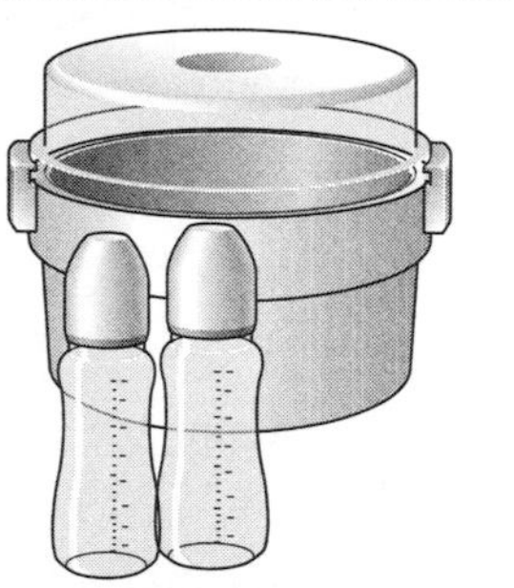

Sterilising techniques

Bottles and all other feeding utensils need sterilising to prevent illness occurring from the growth of bacteria. There are various **sterilising techniques** to choose from.

Cold-water sterilisers
This method of sterilising uses chemicals either in solution or tablet form. The steriliser needs to be filled to the required capacity and the solution added (or sterilising tablet allowed to dissolve) before adding bottles and other feeding equipment. Each bottle, teat or other item needs to be fully submerged, and held under water by a float. Sterilising takes 30 minutes from the time the last piece of equipment has been added. The solution needs to be replaced every 24 hours, and most tanks hold a large amount of feeding equipment.

Steam sterilisers
The steam-sterilising method is quick and efficient but is expensive and, once opened, the bottles need to be prepared within a short period of time, as opening the steriliser allows the potential growth of bacteria. There is a risk of scalding from the release of steam if the unit is opened whilst still very hot, so care must be taken. Steam sterilisers usually hold six or eight bottles at a time. They are ready for use within approximately 12–15 minutes from switching the unit on.

Microwave sterilisers
This method works on the same principle as the steam steriliser. The units usually only hold four bottles, but the method is quick. Metal objects cannot be placed in the microwave steriliser.

Boiling method
Boiling an infant's feeding equipment is cheap but no longer a popular choice. It has considerable potential for accidents owing to the large quantities of boiling water used. It can, however, give reassurance that equipment is clean and free from germs if no other form of sterilising is available. This method only needs 10 minutes of boiling time to be ready. All equipment must be fully submerged, as with the cold water method.

case study 11.1

Janice

Janice is shortly due to give birth to her first baby and is unsure which sterilising method to use. She is currently on maternity leave and is due to return to work when her baby is about 3 months old. Janice intends to breast feed for the first few weeks, moving her baby onto formula feeds by about 2 months as she will be working full time and this will be a more practical option for her. Janice has asked for your advice.

activity

1 What advice would you give Janice?
2 What are the advantages and disadvantages of the various sterilising methods?

Amounts

When measuring out formula milk powder, it is important that the scoops are levelled off with the flat side of a knife or something similar. Heaping a scoop up or packing the formula down is likely to lead to over-feeding, and over-feeding can lead to excessive weight gain, high levels of salt intake and possible kidney strain. It is equally important that you do not use insufficient formula for the amount of water used, as this can lead to an under-fed infant, and under-feeding can lead to poor weight gain and a hungry baby.

case study 11.2

Bronagh

Bronagh is a new student in the baby room at your nursery. She has been asked to calculate the amount of formula needed at each feed for the following babies:

- Earl, who weighs 5.5 kg and is having seven feeds in each 24-hour period
- Alfie, who weighs 8.0 kg and is having six feeds in each 24-hour period
- Lola, who weighs 9.5 kg and is having six feeds in each 24-hour period.

Bronagh has not done this before.

activity

1 How would you explain the formula to Bronagh?
2 Where/how would you advise her to check her calculations if ever she was unsure?

remember

A baby needs 75 ml of formula per 500 g of body weight (2½ fl oz per pound) in each 24-hour period.

Temperature

Some babies will take their bottles cold, but most prefer warmed milk. If you are making a bottle up to feed an infant immediately, test the temperature of the milk on your wrist. It should feel tepid. If you are using a bottle that has been made in advance and stored in the refrigerator, warm it by standing it in warm water. Again, test it on your wrist.

Professional Practice

- Never heat a bottle of milk in a microwave as hot spots can occur.

Constituents of formula milk

The following list shows the many ingredients of a typical formula milk:

- beta-caratene
- biotin
- calcium carbonate
- choline chloride
- copper sulphate
- cytidine 5'-monophosphate
- demineralised whey*
- dietary fibres (galacto oligosaccharide*, polyfructose)
- emulsifier (soya lecithin)
- ferrous sulphate
- fish oil
- folic acid
- inositol
- lactose*
- L-arginine
- magnesium chloride

- manganese sulphate
- nicotinamide
- pantothenic acid
- potassium citrate
- potassium iodide
- guanosine 5'-monophosphate
- skimmed milk*
- sodium chloride
- sodium selenite
- taurine
- thiamine
- uridine 5'-monophosphate
- vegetable oils
- vitamin A
- vitamin B6
- vitamin B12
- vitamin C
- vitamin D3
- vitamin K1
- whey protein concentrate*

*contains milk, fish, soya

Link

Refer to Table 11.1 on page 4 for the constituents of breast milk and to Table 11.2 on page 7 for a comparison of breast milk and formula milk.

Advantages and disadvantages of bottle feeding

Advantages of bottle feeding

- Feeding routines can be shared.
- Siblings can be more directly involved.
- It can be less tiring for the mother.
- Mother can leave her baby with someone else for a while, knowing that their feeding needs will be met.
- Formula feeds can now be bought already made up, making it an even easier process.
- It is easy to see how much milk has been taken at each feed.

Disadvantages of bottle feeding

- Formula milk lacks the immunological qualities of breast milk.
- There is always a risk of bacterial infection from teats, bottles, etc.
- Making up feeds correctly is vital to ensure a correct balance is achieved.
- Over-diluting feeds = a hungry baby.
- Over-concentrated feeds = an over-fed baby, potentially causing longer-term harm.
- Formula feeds need to be bought.
- A range of equipment is needed for both feeding and sterilising.

Link

For information on how to make up a formula feed, or how to sterilise feeding equipment, refer to pages 8 and 10.

case study 11.3

Sita

Muna is 2½ weeks old and his mother, Sita, has opted to breast feed. Muna has sucked strongly since birth and Sita's milk supply is good.

In the last few days Sita's nipples have become sore and her breasts are very full and lumpy. The milk seems very watery and Sita wonders if it is nutritious enough for her son.

The health visitor is due to visit today, and Sita intends to ask her about her concerns.

activity

1 What might be the cause of Sita's soreness?
2 How could the health visitor advise Sita on reducing the fullness of her breasts?
3 Should Sita be concerned about the nutritional content of her milk?

Weaning

Weaning is the process of introducing a baby to 'solid' food alongside their usual milk feeds. The onset of this process should be led by the individual baby's hunger needs, and health professionals now recommend this to start when the baby is around 6 months old. It is a good indicator that the infant is ready to start to be weaned when they begin to seem less satisfied with just breast or formula milk and are ready for their next feed more quickly.

Another important factor is that breast and formula milk do not contain sufficient iron for continued healthy development, and prolonged (exclusive) milk feeding will not provide enough of this important mineral. Initially, an infant has sufficient stocks of iron taken from the mother during pregnancy, and much earlier the baby's digestive system is not usually mature enough to cope with the components of solid food.

Gradual introduction of foods

Weaning should be a pleasurable experience for both carer and child, encouraging them to explore new tastes over a period of time. It should not be a situation of stress or tension. At times it can be difficult to get a baby interested in trying to take solids from a spoon, but it is important to keep on trying, without worrying about regular refusals. The baby will get there in time, and in the early stages of weaning the baby will still be having all of their milk feeds and so will not be losing out nutritionally.

Fig 11.5 Babies progress quickly onto other foods once they are used to taking food from a spoon

remember

Weaning should be introduced gradually, usually at midday, gradually building up to three 'meals' each day, plus early morning milk feed, and late evening or bedtime milk feed.

Professional Practice

- Milk remains an important part of the baby's diet and will remain so until they are at least a year old.
- The aim of weaning is to introduce babies to a variety of textures, tastes and experiences to integrate them fully into family mealtimes.
- Do not introduce weaning (or a new food) when the baby is unwell or tired.
- Offering half of the milk feed before the solids and half afterwards works well for most babies, but each baby is different and they will soon indicate their preference!

As the level of solid food intake increases, the milk feeds will decrease until the baby is having sufficient solid food at a mealtime to be satisfied with a drink of water to accompany it. Table 11.3 sets out a sample programme for weaning a baby.

Table 11.3 A suggested weaning plan

Age	Under 6 months	5–6 months	6–7 months	7–8 months	9–12months
On waking	Breast or formula feed	Breast or formula feed	Breast or formula feed	Breast or formula feed	Breast or formula feed – may now be ready to start drinking from a feeder cup
Breakfast	Breast or formula feed	Baby rice or cereal + breast or formula feed	Cereal + puréed fruit + bread or moist toast + breast or formula feed	Cereal, toast and fruit pieces + breast or formula feed	Cereal, toast + fruit + milk – often from a feeder cup
Midday	Breast or formula feed	Puréed vegetables, or mixture of meat or fish and vegetables + puréed fruit + breast or formula feed	Sieved or finely mashed fish or vegetables + mashed fruit + either breast or formula feed or drink of cooled boiled water	Less finely mashed fish or meat with vegetables+ fruit or milk dessert + drink of water	Variety of foods now usually enjoyed: fish, meat, poultry, rice, pasta, vegetables, etc., all chopped or well grated + fruit, yogurt or rice pudding + drink of water – again, often now in feeder cup
Tea time	Breast or formula feed	Puréed fruit + breast or formula feed	Fruit + milky dessert, moistened toast + breast or formula feed	Sandwiches, fruit pieces, fruit jelly + breast or formula feed	Sandwiches, fruit, yogurt, custard or rice pudding + milk in feeder cup
Late evening/ bedtime	Breast or formula feed	Breast or formula feed	Breast or formula feed	Breast or formula feed	Breast or formula feed often still offered

Professional Practice

- A Bristol University research project into children's development has shown that babies who are not introduced to mashed (rather than puréed) food by 10 months of age are likely to be fussier eaters later on in their life.

Types of foods

Most babies start with baby rice, which is bland in taste and very smooth. They usually progress quite quickly to other puréed foods once they are used to taking food from a spoon. Whenever possible, freshly prepared foods should be given, rather than packets, jars or tins, as this will enable the carer (you) to control what the baby is eating more fully, particularly regarding additives such as sugar, salt, colourings and preservatives. Preparing fresh food helps to integrate the baby into family mealtimes. Convenience foods are ideal as emergency options or when travelling and many commercially prepared foods now have symbols showing whether they are sugar-free, salt-free, gluten-free, and so on.

remember Young babies' sense of taste is less developed than adults and older children. They do not need strong flavours, nor do they need salt, sugar or other seasonings to enhance flavours.

Try preparing the following:

- stewed fruits, sieved or liquidised, with or without baby rice
- puréed carrot and potato
- puréed sweet potato and broccoli
- puréed yam and carrot
- well mashed banana.

The recent thinking by health professionals based on research into children's development recommends that babies are not introduced to solid foods until they are around 6 months old. Until quite recently most infants were given their first food experiences at around 4 months.

One of the main reasons for waiting until the child is 6 months is to try to reduce the level of food allergies among young children which have increased considerably in recent years, e.g. coeliac disease, nut **allergy**, lactose **intolerance**.

There will of course always be some infants that will need to start the weaning process earlier than others. No infant should be kept hungry simply to fit in with new thinking. Health visitors are always happy to advise parents and carers, and anyone with concerns should not hesitate to ask for their advice. Avoiding foods containing gluten is a sensible precaution for all infants under six months old.

Potential allergies

Allergies and intolerances are not the same, but each can cause a range of illness, discomfort and, in severe allergy cases, anaphylaxis which can be life threatening and needs urgent medical attention.

Allergy

An allergy is caused by an individual's immune system mistakenly believing that a food or substance (that is usually perfectly safe) is harmful. To counteract the 'harm', the system creates antibodies to fight it off and whenever the food or substance is identified it releases huge amounts of chemicals and histamines to try to protect the body. This can cause breathing difficulties, swelling of lips and throat, and in the worse cases total collapse and loss of consciousness. This is called anaphylaxis.

Nut allergy

Current thinking is that nuts or products containing nuts should be avoided completely, as early introduction to these has been linked to later development of nut allergy. However, some disagreement between researchers is emerging as this book reaches the final stages of production (autumn 2007). Therefore it is important that all early years practitioners should keep up to date with health guidlines regarding nuts and the potential for allergy reaction and reduction.

In some early years settings there is a blanket ban on all products containing nuts (e.g. peanut butter sandwiches) even when parents are sending packed lunches with their own child. This is to help prevent accidental contamination by children sharing a plate or swapping foods with friends.

Intolerance

An intolerance is where an individual's digestive system does not produce enough of a particular enzyme which is needed to digest a food properly. Common intolerances are gluten and milk.

Gluten intolerance

Carers should avoid giving babies foods containing gluten before 6 months of age even if the weaning process has started earlier than this. Gluten is a protein found in wheat, barley, rye and oats. There is a suspected link between early introduction of these products and the development of gluten-intolerance, known as coeliac disease, later on.

Fig 11.6 The gluten-free symbol

Coeliac disease

Coeliac disease is a condition affecting the lining of the small intestine. It is an immunological reaction to gluten, a protein found in wheat, rye and barley. Some people react badly to oats too. Children are usually diagnosed when they start to have solid food from about 6 months onwards.

Babies with coeliac disease fail to thrive in the usual way; they do not put on weight and are low on the centile charts. Young children become very unwell, lethargic and miserable, with abdominal bloating. Their stools are pale, fatty, smell unpleasant and are difficult to flush away.

Gluten-free foods considered to be the staples of a diet, such as flour, bread, pasta and plain biscuits, are available on prescription for children and adults who have a confirmed diagnosis of coeliac disease. There is also an increasing range of products to be found in supermarkets.

- A gluten-free diet is necessary throughout life.
- Gluten is found in many everyday foods and it takes time to identify all foods that need to be avoided.
- Guidance is given from a dietician to help establish a balanced diet.
- The charitable organisation Coeliac UK gives helpful advice and a regularly updated food list.
- Many supermarkets now display a gluten-free symbol on suitable foods.
- Since November 2005, new food laws require all forms of gluten to be indicated on packaging.
- Iron deficiency anaemia is a possibility due to malabsorption of food.
- Calcium deficiency can also be present, again due to malabsorption.

There is a familial tendency regarding coeliac disease, but it is not considered hereditary. Babies born into a family where coeliac disease has previously been diagnosed should be observed closely for early signs and some health practitioners recommend that gluten should ideally be withheld from their diet until their first birthday. In some cases, early exposure to gluten has been thought to have triggered the condition.

Coeliac UK: Suites A–D, Octagon Court, High Wycombe, Bucks HP11 2HS; 01494 437278; www.coeliac.org.uk.

Link

See Unit 35, page 341, for examples of centile charts and Unit 35, page 372 for more information about coeliac disease.

Milk intolerance

Milk intolerance is quite common in young children, but has often ceased by about 5 years of age. Some children are intolerant to cow's milk and some to a protein in the milk or to lactose. Common symptoms of milk intolerance are eczema, diarrhoea and vomiting.

Eczema

Eczema is due to an allergic reaction and is common amongst young children. It dries the skin, forming itchy inflamed areas which crack open and often weep. It is extremely unpleasant and causes great misery to many children. Fortunately the majority of children cease to be affected by eczema by the time they reach puberty. Some, however, continue to suffer from eczema, along with asthma (another allergic reaction).

Triggers for eczema vary between individuals, with common causes being dairy produce, washing powders and soaps. It can also be triggered or exacerbated by stress or excitement.

The initial signs of eczema usually appear between 3 and 18 months. It occurs initially on the face and scalp, the shins and forearms, and later it affects the backs of knees, inside of the elbow joints and at the ankles. Symptoms include:

- dry scaly skin which cracks and itches
- the itchy rash often weeps
- the sore areas crust over
- in the long term, the skin becomes thickened and leathery. Young children find it difficult to sleep due to the itching.

If a child develops itchy or sore areas of skin, they should be seen by a health professional to confirm or discount a diagnosis of eczema. Childcare staff need to be aware that a child's condition may become more acute in extremes of weather. They become very sensitive to changes in temperature.

- It is important to keep the skin softened, using an emollient cream.
- Emollients should be applied regularly throughout the day, and this is particularly important after a bath. It can often be helpful to cover the affected area with cotton tubular sleeves (bandages).
- Special bath oils can be used to help remoisten the skin, which naturally loses its oils through bathing.
- Affected children should not use normal soaps; there are special preparations available.
- Children should be taught to avoid any known trigger factors.
- Keeping fingernails cut short helps minimise scratching.

- Very young children may benefit from wearing cotton mittens at night.
- Loose cotton clothing helps the skin breathe and reduces chafing of the skin.
- Some children need prescribed products to help control the effects of eczema.
- Antibiotics, taken orally or as creams, may become necessary to counter the effects of secondary infections, caused by excessive scratching.
- Children with severe eczema can become the victims of teasing. Early years staff need to be ready to deal with this.

Many children with eczema are born into families where there are others with a range of allergic conditions.

Professional Practice

- Consideration is needed to ensure that children with eczema are not excluded from activities because of their condition.
- Applying creams to the affected areas during the day should be done without fuss and with some privacy.
- It is important to wear disposable gloves when applying the creams, to avoid any risk of introducing infection to the child and to prevent the absorption of corticosteroids into your own skin.

Lactose intolerance

Lactose intolerance is not usually seen in children. It tends to develop later on in life. Lactose intolerance is caused by the body lacking sufficient levels of the enzyme lactase to digest the lactose in milk and other dairy products.

Phenylketonuria (PKU)

Phenylketonuria is caused by a deficiency of the enzyme phenylalanine hydroxylase. This leads to build-up of phenylalanine in the affected individual's blood.

PKU is tested for by a blood test a few days after birth. To control the effects of this deficiency a strict diet needs to be maintained throughout life. Occasionally, babies with PKU can be breast fed if monitored very closely, but many mothers opt to give them specially prepared low phenylalanine formula feeds instead. As the child grows, there are a range of staple foods specifically low in phenylalanine (e.g. flour, pasta) available on prescription.

At around puberty the child will be re-checked for the deficiency. Some children will be able to adjust their diet a little at this point.

Cystic fibrosis (CF)

Cystic fibrosis is caused by a problem with a protein known as CFTR. It is the most common inherited condition in the UK and affected children will show symptoms very soon after birth. CF affects both lungs and digestive system and all children with CF need to take special pancreatic enzymes before they eat. These children need a high calorie, but low fat diet and they also need regular (percussion) physiotherapy every day to help keep their lungs clear.

Link

Refer to Unit 27, page 271, and Unit 35, page 372, for more about cystic fibrosis.

Professional Practice

- There are a range of other disorders that need a restricted or specialised diet. Many of these are linked to the metabolism affecting digestion and liver function. Examples include galactosaemia, fructosaemia and favism. You may find it helpful to research disorders involving diet and keep a note of where you can obtain information if a child with the condition comes into your care.

Diet of older babies and young children

Food groups

A good balanced diet is one which includes all the nutritional requirements for the growth, maintenance and development of the body. The food we eat helps us maintain and repair our body tissues, keeping muscles and organs functioning. It also helps to prevent infection and supplies us with our energy needs. A balanced diet should abide by the **principles of diet and nutrition** and include elements from each of the four **food groups**:

- proteins, which help growth, development and tissue repair
- carbohydrates, which provide energy
- vitamins, minerals and fibre, for general good health and the prevention of illness
- dairy products, which are high in calcium, enhancing and maintaining bones and teeth.

A fifth food group – fats and oils – are higher-level energy-giving foods which should be consumed sparingly by adults.

Many foods contribute to more than one food group, e.g. meat is a good source of iron, and pulses are a good source of fibre, but Figure 11.7 indicates where the main benefits of each food lie.

Fig 11.7 The food groups

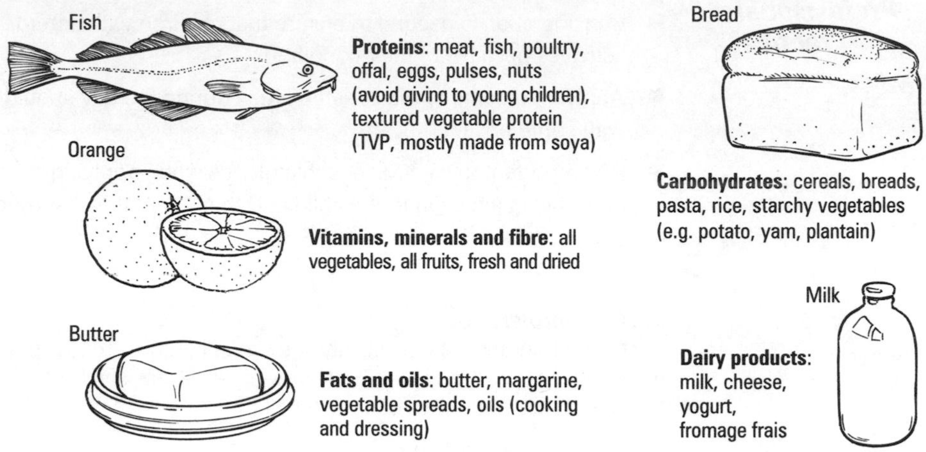

Fish
Proteins: meat, fish, poultry, offal, eggs, pulses, nuts (avoid giving to young children), textured vegetable protein (TVP, mostly made from soya)
Bread
Carbohydrates: cereals, breads, pasta, rice, starchy vegetables (e.g. potato, yam, plantain)
Orange
Vitamins, minerals and fibre: all vegetables, all fruits, fresh and dried
Milk
Butter
Fats and oils: butter, margarine, vegetable spreads, oils (cooking and dressing)
Dairy products: milk, cheese, yogurt, fromage frais

Our diets and nutrition intake will be influenced by:

- any special dietary requirement, e.g. an intolerance or allergy
- cultural guidelines and taboos
- personal or family diet choices, e.g. vegetarian or vegan diets
- personal preferences and taste.

Carbohydrates

Carbohydrates can be classified under three main headings:

- sugars
- starches
- fibre – soluble and insoluble.

Carbohydrates and needed for:

- energy and activity
- the maintenance of body temperature
- keeping the body's normal functions running smoothly.

Children need a good intake of energy-rich foods to enable them to play, explore and learn freely.

Carbohydrates are linked to the glycemic index (GI). Foods with a low glycemic index provide us with energy that is absorbed and used slowly within the body, providing us with energy over a long period of time. Foods with a high glycemic index give us a 'rush' of energy that will soon fade.

Low glycemic foods are therefore of greater value to both children and adults, especially at the start of the day. A breakfast of porridge (low GI) will give longer lasting energy levels than a bowl of rice crispies (high GI). It will also lessen the need for a mid-morning boost of energy from chocolate or similar.

Sugary foods mostly come under the heading of high GI and so should be eaten sparingly. Snacks of bananas, dried apricots or grapes are low GI and are therefore preferable.

Examples of starchy foods are breads, cereals, rice and pasta. Whole grains contain a higher level of fibre than refined grains. Fibre is needed to aid digestion and avoid issues such as constipation.

Fibre can be either soluble (e.g. oatmeal, legumes such as beans, peas and lentils, bananas, apples and oranges) or insoluble (e.g. wheat, rice, legumes, plus many vegetables and fruits). Too much insoluble fibre can fill children up too quickly and can also cause diarrhoea, flatulence and general tummy upsets.

Proteins

As Figure 11.7 shows, protein is mostly found in foods such as meat, fish, poultry, eggs, pulses and nuts. It is also found in textured vegetable protein which is mostly made from soya. Protein is needed to support the healthy growth and development of:

- muscles and connective tissues
- skin and hair
- the immune system.

It also plays an important role in our blood, helping to maintain good levels of haemoglobin and in helping with the control of our metabolism.

remember

Do not give nuts to very young children.

Although protein is found in both animal and plant sources, most meat-eating people will gain the greatest amount of protein from animal sources. Vegetarians and vegans need to ensure they have a sufficient intake of protein-rich foods to avoid deficiencies such as anaemia occurring. Soya, pulses, grains, seeds and nuts form an important part of the vegan diet, with eggs also contributing to a **vegetarian diet**.

Fats

Fats can be saturated, unsaturated or polyunsaturated.

- Saturated fat tends to be found in a solid form at room temperature, e.g. in butter and some margarines.
- Unsaturated and polyunsaturated fat is found in oils and oily fish such as sardines, salmon, etc.

Fat is needed by the body to help provide energy but care should be taken not to eat too much fat as this can cause weight increase and may contribute to health problems such as heart disease later on. Foods containing unsaturated fats are thought to help lower cholesterol levels and help to maintain general health and well-being.

Vitamins

Table 11.4 shows a range of everyday foods and where each vitamin can be obtained, the function each vitamin plays in the health and development of the body, together with potential problems linked to insufficient intake and brief additional notes where appropriate.

Table 11.4 The main vitamins

Vitamin	Food source	Function	Notes
A	Butter, cheese, eggs, carrots, tomatoes	Promotes healthy skin, good vision	Fat-soluble, can be stored in the liver; deficiency causes skin infections, problems with vision
B group	Liver, meat, fish, green vegetables, beans, eggs	Healthy working of muscles and nerves; forming haemoglobin	Water-soluble, not stored in the body, so regular supply needed; deficiency results in muscle wasting, anaemia
C	Fruits and fruit juices, especially orange, blackcurrant, pineapple; green vegetables	For healthy tissue, promotes healing	Water-soluble, daily supply needed; deficiency means less resistance to infection; extreme deficiency results in scurvy
D	Oily fish, cod liver oil, egg yolk; added to margarine, milk	Growth and maintenance of bones and teeth	Fat-soluble, can be stored by the body; can be produced by the body as a result of sunlight on the skin; deficiency results in bones failing to harden and dental decay
E	Vegetable oils, cereals, egg yolk	Protects cells from damage	Fat-soluble, can be stored by the body
K	Green vegetables, liver	Needed for normal blood clotting	Fat-soluble, can be stored in the body

Source: Beaver *et al*. (2001, p. 99)

Minerals

The body requires a range of minerals, the essential minerals and the trace minerals, in order for us to function fully. Table 11.5 sets out each mineral, showing where it can most easily be found in our everyday foods, the function each plays in the health and development of our body, together with potential problems linked to insufficient intake and brief additional notes.

Table 11.5 The main minerals

Mineral	Food source	Function	Notes
Calcium	Cheese, eggs, fish, milk, yogurt	Essential for growth of bones and teeth	Works with vitamin D and phosphorus; deficiency means risk of bones failing to harden (rickets) and dental caries
Fluoride	Occurs naturally in water, or may be added artificially to water supply	Combines with calcium to make tooth enamel more resistant to decay	There are different points of view about adding fluoride to the water supply
Iodine	Water, sea foods, added to salt, vegetables	Needed for proper working of the thyroid gland	Deficiency results in enlarged thyroid gland in adults, cretinism in babies
Iron	Meat, green vegetables, eggs, liver, red meat	Needed for formation of haemoglobin in red blood cells	Deficiency means there is anaemia causing lack of energy, breathlessness; vitamin C helps the absorption of iron
Sodium chloride	Table salt, bread, meat, fish	Needed for formation of cell fluids, blood plasma, sweat, tears	Salt should not be added to any food prepared for babies: their kidneys cannot eliminate excess salt as adult kidneys do; excess salt is harmful in an infant diet
Other essential trace minerals include: potassium, phosphorus, magnesium, sulphur, manganese and zinc.			

Source: Beaver *et al.* (2001, p. 100)

remember

- Young children need approximately 1 pint of milk each day to maintain healthy bone and teeth development.
- Young children often need a snack between meals to boost energy during active play. Always try to offer healthy snack foods rather than sweets and sugary foods.

A healthy diet offers a range of foods from each food group, ensuring that the diet is well balanced, and is not deficient in any area. Encouraging children to try foods from a range of cultures and from amongst seasonal fruits and vegetables will promote a healthy and diverse approach to diet throughout life.

A balanced diet

- Children need a diet that is high in protein and carbohydrates to meet their high energy needs. The carbohydrates should ideally come from starchy foods such as potatoes, breads and cereals.

Fig 11.8 How a balanced diet promotes health and development

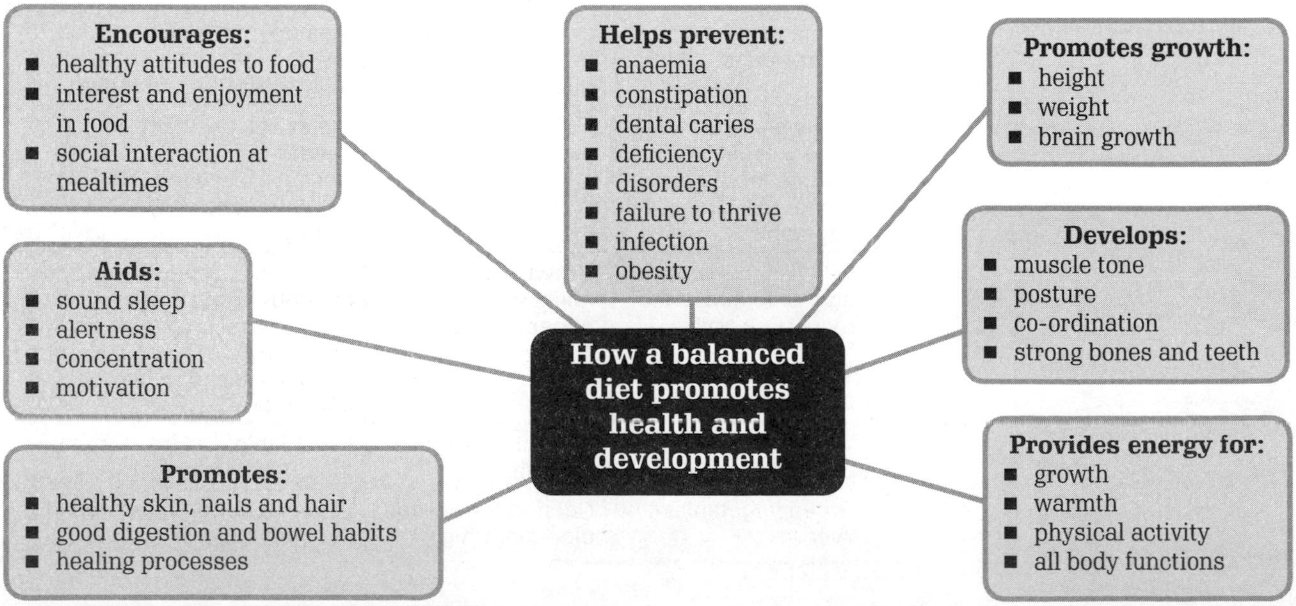
How a balanced diet promotes health and development
Encourages:
healthy attitudes to food
interest and enjoyment in food
social interaction at mealtimes
Helps prevent:
anaemia
constipation
dental caries
deficiency
disorders
failure to thrive
infection
obesity
Promotes growth:
height
weight
brain growth
Aids:
sound sleep
alertness
concentration
motivation
Develops:
muscle tone
posture
co-ordination
strong bones and teeth
Promotes:
healthy skin, nails and hair
good digestion and bowel habits
healing processes
Provides energy for:
growth
warmth
physical activity
all body functions

remember

Children have preferences too.

- Think about both colour and texture when planning meals, as an attractive meal will be more appealing, especially to a fussy or reluctant eater.
- Vary the meals that are offered to children, but do not offer more than one new food at a time.
- Large portions can be off-putting. It is better to have all of a small meal eaten, than half of a larger one, as it encourages good habits.

Identifying nutrients

Table 11.6 shows where the main food groups (proteins, carbohydrates, fibre and dairy) can be found within a five-day meal plan for a young child. Various vitamins and minerals can be identified throughout, using the tables on pages 19 and 20.

Table 11.6 Suggestions for healthy eating for young children

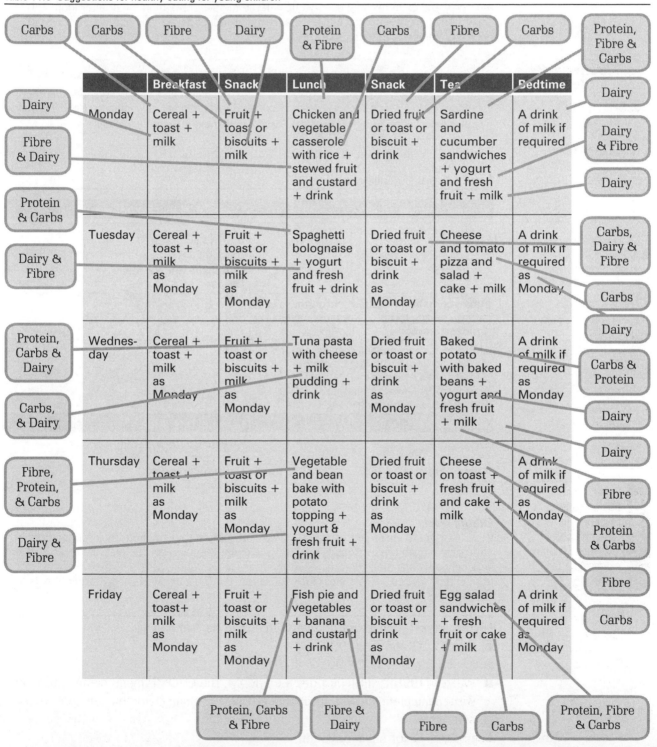

	Breakfast	Snack	Lunch	Snack	Tea	Bedtime
Monday	Cereal + toast + milk	Fruit + toast or biscuits + milk	Chicken and vegetable casserole with rice + stewed fruit and custard + drink	Dried fruit or toast or biscuit + drink	Sardine and cucumber sandwiches + yogurt and fresh fruit + milk	A drink of milk if required
Tuesday	Cereal + toast + milk as Monday	Fruit + toast or biscuits + milk as Monday	Spaghetti bolognaise + yogurt and fresh fruit + drink	Dried fruit or toast or biscuit + drink as Monday	Cheese and tomato pizza and salad + cake + milk	A drink of milk if required as Monday
Wednes-day	Cereal + toast + milk as Monday	Fruit + toast or biscuits + milk as Monday	Tuna pasta with cheese + milk pudding + drink	Dried fruit or toast or biscuit + drink as Monday	Baked potato with baked beans + yogurt and fresh fruit + milk	A drink of milk if required as Monday
Thursday	Cereal + toast + milk as Monday	Fruit + toast or biscuits + milk as Monday	Vegetable and bean bake with potato topping + yogurt & fresh fruit + drink	Dried fruit or toast or biscuit + drink as Monday	Cheese on toast + fresh fruit and cake + milk	A drink of milk if required as Monday
Friday	Cereal + toast+ milk as Monday	Fruit + toast or biscuits + milk as Monday	Fish pie and vegetables + banana and custard + drink	Dried fruit or toast or biscuit + drink as Monday	Egg salad sandwiches + fresh fruit or cake + milk	A drink of milk if required as Monday

Carbs
Carbs
Fibre
Dairy
Protein & Fibre
Carbs
Fibre
Carbs
Protein, Fibre & Carbs
Dairy
Fibre & Dairy
Protein & Carbs
Dairy & Fibre
Protein, Carbs & Dairy
Carbs, & Dairy
Fibre, Protein, & Carbs
Dairy & Fibre
Dairy
Dairy & Fibre
Dairy
Carbs, Dairy & Fibre
Carbs
Dairy
Carbs & Protein
Dairy
Dairy
Fibre
Protein & Carbs
Fibre
Carbs
Protein, Carbs & Fibre
Fibre & Dairy
Fibre
Carbs
Protein, Fibre & Carbs

Daily portions for children

As a guideline for planning the dietary needs of young children, a good daily balance would include:

- five portions of fruit or vegetables
- two portions of protein foods
- two portions of dairy foods plus 1 pint of milk
- four portions of carbohydrates.

Snacks

Most children will also need to be offered snacks. It is important that these are mostly nutritional and healthy. Some ideas are given in Table 11.7.

Snacks are an important part of a child's nutritional intake. Children use a lot of energy in their play and often need an energy boost in the middle of the morning or afternoon. This is particularly important if they are at a stage of developing particularly quickly physically, or becoming more active than usual.

Professional Practice

- It can be helpful to draw up a list of foods suitable to be offered as a snack. Examples would include toast, bananas, fresh fruit, dried fruit such as dates and apricots, and for older children seeds such as pumpkin and sunflower. (Be aware of choking hazard of offering seeds to younger children.) These can be held in your file and used as an easy reference source.

Table 11.7 Ideas for healthy snacks

Good as regular snacks	Occasional snacks, not regular
Fresh fruit: banana, orange, pear, kiwi, melon	Crisps Sweet biscuits Chocolate biscuits Chocolate and sweets Cakes
Raw vegetables (washed thoroughly): celery, carrot, tomato, cabbage leaves, Chinese leaves	
Dried fruits: raisins, sultanas, banana, dates and figs, apple rings, apricots Small cubes of cheese Sandwiches (savoury fillings) Pitta breads (savoury fillings)	
Healthy drinks	**Less healthy drinks**
Milk Water Milkshakes (fresh fruit) Fruit juices	Milkshakes (powdered) Squashes Carbonated drinks (cola, etc.)

remember

Snacks need to be nutritional to be of benefit to a child; this should set them a healthy example for the future.

Energy levels

It is important to ensure that children are getting sufficient energy from their foods. If they are eating a good range of foods then it is likely that they are, but the diet of a child who eats only a narrow range of foods needs greater consideration. Most energy is obtained from carbohydrates and proteins. Table 11.8 sets out the estimated energy requirements for children in the UK per day.

Further information on nutritional sources can be found in:

- Dare & O'Donovan (1996)
- Dyson & Meredith (2006)
- Walker (1998), which includes a CD-ROM, the CHOMP menu planner, to help with menu planning and nutritional advice for young children in all early years settings.

See page 412 for full information.

Table 11.8 Estimated average requirements (EARs) for energy in the UK (per day)

Age range	Males		Females	
	MJ	kcal	MJ	kcal
0–3 months (formula fed)	2.28	545	2.16	515
4–6 months	2.89	690	2.69	645
7–9 months	3.44	825	3.20	765
10–12 months	3.85	920	3.61	865
1–3 years	5.15	1230	4.86	1165
4–6 years	7.16	1715	6.46	1545
7–10 years	8.24	1970	7.28	1740

Source: Dare and O'Donovan (1996), p.7

Food preferences

It is important to remember that children, like adults, have preferences when it comes to foods. This may be by taste, smell or texture. It is worth trying to offer a food in an alternative way if it is clearly disliked by a child, e.g.

- Try giving raw grated carrot instead of cooked carrots.
- Make a simple potato rosti by mixing mashed potato with shredded green cabbage and adding a little grated cheese if either vegetable is disliked on its own.
- Try cutting meat into cubes if the child dislikes minced meat.
- Try puréeing vegetables and adding to or using instead of gravy.

Children should be encouraged, but never forced to try particular foods. It is important to keep meal times relaxed and a pleasant social occasion with as few distractions as possible. This gives positive messages to children about food and helps support a healthy attitude to eating as they develop. For a child who mostly eats the same foods every day, keep offering small amounts of other foods and encouraging them to try. At some point most children will, and many find they actually like the previously rejected foods.

Whenever practical, eat with the children. Seeing you eating and enjoying foods will often be sufficient encouragement. Talking about taste, texture, etc. can also be helpful, distracting thinking about refusal.

Potential effects of food additives

The use of **food additives** is claimed to outweigh the risks to health that may occur naturally in foods. Many people do not agree with this and try to keep consumption of additives to a minimum. This is easier said than done, as most bought foods have been affected in some way by additives.

Additives are used in foods to:

- keep them fresh and extend their shelf life
- provide foods out of their natural season
- keep foods free from disease
- make food look better, e.g. a better colour
- sweeten food or give it a certain taste
- enhance the overall flavour of food
- improve the nutritional content of food.

Additives include:

- antioxidants
- emulsifiers
- flavourings
- food dyes
- preservatives, e.g. sulphites and nitrites
- synthetic antioxidants
- thickeners.

There are over 4000 food additives and a diet high in processed food can mean a person eating 100 or more additives in just one day. Many additives have an E prefix, e.g.

- Colour additives are in the E100 group.
- Preservatives are in the E200 group.
- Antioxidants are in the E300 group.
- Emulsifiers, thickeners and gelling agents are in the E400 group.

Food can also be contaminated with chemicals during farming, through the use of pesticides and fertilisers.

There is significant concern that many additives contribute to and/or cause a number of health and behavioural problems. Examples include:

- insomnia
- aggression
- lack of concentration
- restlessness and inability to stay still
- inability to sleep or constantly disturbed sleep.

There are documented cases where children's behaviour has changed very quickly once processed foods are removed from their diet.

Professional Practice

- **When planning snacks and meals for children, choose fresh foods whenever possible to minimise the exposure to additives.**

activity
INDIVIDUAL WORK 11.2

P2

M2

1 a) Research weaning plans through parenting and child health magazines and books, or through the internet.

b) Using the blank table below as a guide, plan a week's menu for:

- a baby aged 6–7 months
- a young child aged 2 years.

Table 11.9 Planning a menu

Age/months	6–7 months	8–9 months	10–11 months	12 months
On waking				
Breakfast				
Lunch				
Tea				
Late evening				

2 Describe how you would introduce the weaning process to a baby and explain its importance in achieving a relaxed and healthy attitude to food in the developing infant. Give examples of how the foods you would offer would change over time according to the age of the infant.

Diet of older children

Older children, especially as they reach puberty, experience rapid growth and gain considerably in both muscle and bone. They need the same balance of foods from the four main food groups shown on page 17 with a lesser intake of fats and oils.

It is a natural part of growing up to eat out with friends, and older children and young people will often eat a diet high in saturated fats, due to an increase in fast foods and eating sporadically, often outside of family mealtimes. Eating habits can also be affected by peer pressure, not wanting to be different to others in their social group. In the short term this lifestyle is unlikely to do much harm, but prolonged periods of time without sufficient intake of fruit and vegetables, etc. can lead to a range of health problems, including anaemia, particularly in girls as they begin menstruation.

It is common for teenagers to have huge appetites, but often they try to satisfy their hunger with the wrong types of foods. Educating children about foods which give them energy can help them make informed choices later on.

Older children and young people should be encouraged to:

- eat starchy carbohydrates such as bread, rice, potatoes, pasta
- eat breakfast, preferably wholewheat cereals to give them slow-release energy to kick-start their day
- include plenty of fresh fruits and vegetables in their diet
- eat some protein every day, e.g. meat, eggs, pulses, fish
- have plenty of dairy produce, e.g. milk, yogurt, cheese
- drink at least eight glasses of water or other non-caffeine fluids per day
- take some form of exercise, whatever they enjoy best.

As teenagers, many young people become concerned about their body image. This is often through a skewed vision of themselves as they really are, leading to dieting when they are already of a good weight. Dieting unnecessarily can lead to anaemia, calcium and other mineral deficiencies. Slimming and eating disorders are quite common and need sensitive help from adult carers and health professionals.

Presentation of food and personal preferences

Most people can think of a time when they have been faced with a food that they dislike, or a huge meal when they are not really hungry. Both can be off-putting and affect the level of pleasure experienced at that time. It is therefore important that adults understand that children can also be overwhelmed by the sight of a large plate of food and repelled by food they really do not like. This can be helped partly through careful and thoughtful presentation.

remember

Once a child is in the habit of eating everything on their plate, the portion sizes of tiny eaters can be discreetly increased little by little.

To encourage young children, particularly the reluctant eater, try to ensure that:

- the plate looks attractive
- the food includes more than one colour
- the food includes more than one texture
- the meal is enough to satisfy hunger, but is not so much as to be off-putting.

Professional Practice

- Think how much better a plate looks if it contains chicken, peas, mashed swede and sweet potato, compared to a plate containing chicken, rice, sweetcorn and butter beans. The nutritional content will be similar, but the difference in colour appeal is vast.

Use of cutlery

It is important that children are given cutlery that they can manage. It is pointless to insist that all children from a certain age use a knife and fork, if clearly they eat better with a spoon. By all means provide a knife and fork as well, and encourage them to try. They will develop the skill eventually. Also, provide lightweight cutlery which is not too large for younger children, with plastic spoons and forks for babies and the youngest toddlers.

case study 11.4

Jenna and Beth

Jenna and Beth are discussing the following statements they have heard made to children:

- 'No, you can't have pudding unless your dinner is eaten up.'
- 'Everybody is given the same amount, otherwise it is not fair.'
- 'Of course you like peas, everyone likes peas.'
- 'You can have a drink after you have finished.'
- 'No, you're a coeliac, you can't have the pie.'

activity

1 What would concern you if you heard these statements being made?
2 What messages are being given to the children?
3 How would you feel if the statements were made to you during your meal?

Professional Practice

- Mealtimes should be a time of pleasure and socialising.
- Forcing a child to eat more than they want to may make them resent food, or even vomit.
- The pudding should be an integral part of the meal, not a prize for those who eat their dinner.
- Some children have far greater appetites than others, so will need larger portions.
- Making meals exciting can entice children to eat foods they may usually refuse.

Ways of making foods more interesting

To help children take an interest in food and also simply for fun, try making meals and snacks visually appealing, e.g. sandwiches can be cut into interesting shapes.

- Make sandwiches into boats: an oblong with two triangle sails (from one round of sandwiches).
- Use large pastry cutters: trees, stars, moons, and so on.
- Arrange food on plates into pictures: faces, clowns, cat with whiskers.
- Give meals exciting names: magic mash, nursery noodles, rocket of rice, planet of pasta.

Fig 11.9 Fun foods for children

Refer to Green (2005a) for further ideas (see the Bibliography on page 402).

Cultural and dietary needs

Children have their own preferences regarding food, which should be accommodated up to a point. A balance is needed between allowing a child to select what they eat or do not eat, and encouraging them to try a range of new and familiar foods. When preparing meals for children, dietary needs also need to be considered. This includes children with a food intolerance or allergy, family requirements such as vegetarian or vegan diets and **cultural food customs**. Table 11.10 sets out the food-related customs of a range of cultures; 'some' means that some people within a religious group would find these foods acceptable.

Table 11.10 Food-related customs

	Jewish	Hindu[1]	Sikh[1]	Muslim	Buddhist	Rastafarian[2]
Eggs	No blood spots	Some	Yes	Yes	Some	Some
Milk/yogurt	Not with meat	Yes	Yes	Yes	Yes	Some
Cheese	Not with meat	Some	Some	Possibly	Yes	Some
Chicken	Kosher	Some	Some	Halal	No	Some
Mutton/lamb	Kosher	Some	Yes	Halal	No	Some
Beef and beef products	Kosher	No	No	Halal	No	Some
Pork and pork products	No	No	Rarely	No	No	No
Fish	With fins and scales	With fins and scales	Some	Some	Some	Yes
Shellfish	No	Some	Some	Some	No	No
Butter/ghee	Kosher	Some	Some	Some	No	Some
Lard	No	No	No	No	No	No
Cereal foods	Yes	Yes	Yes	Yes	Yes	Yes
Nuts/pulses	Yes	Yes	Yes	Yes	Yes	Yes
Fruits/vegetables	Yes	Yes[3]	Yes	Yes	Yes	Yes
Fasting[4]	Yes	Yes	Yes	Yes	Yes	Yes

Source: Walker (1998), p. 68

'Some' means that some people within a religious group would find these foods acceptable.
1 Strict Hindus and Sikhs will not eat eggs, meat, fish, and some fats.
2 Some Rastafarians are vegan.
3 Jains have restrictions on some vegetable foods. Check with the individuals.
4 Fasting is unlikely to apply to young children.

Vegetarians and vegans

Many parents now choose for their children to eat a vegetarian diet, with a few following the stricter vegan diet. It is important that you understand what this involves.

Vegetarian diets

There are different levels of vegetarianism:

- The demi-vegetarian eats fish and eggs, but does not eat meat.
- The ovo-lacto-vegetarian eats neither meat nor fish.
- The lacto-vegetarian eats no meat, fish or eggs.

Vegetarians get some of their nutrients from different food sources, but this does not mean they do not get enough, e.g.

- Protein is gained from eggs, cheese, whole grains and legumes (beans, peas, sprouting seeds, etc.).
- Omega essential fats usually obtained from fish in a non-vegetarian diet are obtained by vegetarians (and vegans) through leafy green vegetables, nuts, seeds such as pumpkin, sesame, etc. and also through tahini and houmous. Vegetarians also gain these through egg yolks.

UXBRIDGE COLLEGE LEARNING CENTRE

Vegan diets

As well as avoiding meat, fish and eggs, vegans eat no foods or derivatives of animal produce at all, including:

- milk
- butter

- lard
- suet
- gelatine
- some food additives
- honey.

Many also avoid the use of animal products such as wool, leather, beeswax, etc. in their clothing or household products.

As with vegetarians, vegans obtain their nutrients from different food sources, e.g.

- Protein is gained from legumes (beans, peas, lentils, spouting seeds, etc.), and from soy, tofu and textured vegetable protein.
- Calcium is gained from tofu, blackstrap molasses, temph, rice milk, soy yogurt, and many green vegetables.

Seasonal variation

As a general rule, seasonal foods tend to be tastier, healthier and cheaper. Buying locally grown produce helps support the local economy and cuts down on 'food miles' travelled. Because of the effect of globalisation, in reality it is possible to buy most foods at almost any time of the year now in large supermarkets.

Globalisation also means that there is now easy access to a range of foods from around the world. This enables parents and practitioners to introduce new foods to children on a regular basis. Children who grow up experiencing a wide range of foods are more likely to develop a healthy attitude to trying new foods and have a broad food palette as adults.

Social aspects of eating

In today's busy society, many families do not eat together (often referred to as 'grazing'), and fewer than ever eat around a table. School or pre-school may be the only time a child experiences eating as a shared social occasion. Therefore ensuring that mealtimes in your setting are happy and relaxed, are times where the enjoyment of food is expressed, and there is the chance to chat to others and be part of a social group will provide an important learning opportunity for all the children, but especially those from 'grazing' families.

activity
INDIVIDUAL WORK 11.3
P3

1 Explain what you consider to be important when presenting food to young children.

2 Plan a midday meal for a group of 4-year-olds, ensuring that there are three colours and three textures within the meal. You can plan a meal from any culture you wish.

a) What have you included for colour?

b) What textures have you provided?

c) What food groups have you incorporated into your meal?

d) Are any food groups not represented? Is this a problem, do you think?

e) Explain your understanding of portion size and personal preferences.

Understand the potential effects of diet on children's health

Malnutrition

Malnutrition means there is an inability to meet the body's energy and nutritional needs. This inability can be due to a condition affecting malabsorption, such as Crohn's disease or coeliac disease. It can also be due to insufficient food or insufficient amounts of the right foods. Both **over-nutrition** and **under-nutrition** come under the collective heading of malnutrition.

Over-nutrition

The term over-nutrition is sometimes used to describe a diet in which the child is taking in higher levels of energy foods than they actually need. This leads to them being overweight and/or obese. Overweight children are often found to be part of a family where over-eating is the norm, therefore lifestyle clearly plays an important part in the health of these children.

Obesity in children is increasing, putting more and more children at risk of health problems both in childhood and for the future. Child obesity can lead to:

- high levels of fat in the blood
- high blood pressure
- snoring and strain on the heart
- joint problems
- diabetes type 2.

As adults, the risk of high blood pressure, coronary heart disease and some cancers is increased, with the additional strain on bones and joints causing mobility problems. Type 2 diabetes is also commonly seen.

Obese children are likely to:

- be continually tired
- have headaches and backache
- avoid exercise, potentially making the problem worse
- suffer from low self-esteem and poor body image
- suffer bullying from their peers.

Obesity is mostly caused by lack of exercise, poor food choices and over-eating. Very occasionally there is a medical reason for a child to be obese. Examples include:

- Prader-Willi syndrome where there is a problem with the control of hunger
- hypothyroidism where the metabolism works very slowly.

Under-nutrition

If a child's diet fails to provide sufficient energy through the consumption of carbohydrates and proteins, or there are insufficient vitamins and minerals in the diet, they are likely to be lethargic and fail to grow properly.

A poor diet and vitamin deficiency can lead to:

- lowered immunity
- increase in infections
- increase in illness in general.

Supplements can sometimes be used to help balance the vitamin and mineral intake, but these should not be taken in place of a healthy diet, and only on medical advice. Children on a vegan diet may need to supplement their diet with vitamin B12 as this is difficult to obtain from a plant-based diet.

Constipation

Children need fibre in their diet to ensure healthy bowel movements. A lack of fibre in the diet can lead to constipation. However, too much fibre is not recommended for young children as it can cause diarrhoea and bloating. If a child feels well, with regular bowel movements which cause them no distress or discomfort, it is an indication that they are having the right level of fibre intake for their needs.

Water

Water also plays an important part in our diet. It keeps us hydrated, it dilutes toxins and helps prevent constipation. Children should be encouraged to adopt the habit of drinking water, rather than fruit juices or other flavoured drinks. The amount needed daily will vary from person to person, and will also be affected by the time of year and overall temperature, and the level of activity being undertaken.

Water should be readily available to children throughout the day. Adults should be aware of any child who does not seem to drink regularly and encourage them to do so, especially during warmer weather and during or after physical activity and sport.

Specific nutrient deficiencies

Anaemia

Anaemia is due to a lower than ideal level of haemoglobin in the blood. Haemoglobin is the iron-containing part of the red cells that carries oxygen around the body. With anaemia there is less oxygen moving through the system leading to tiredness and general fatigue.

Good supplies of iron, vitamin B12 and folic acid are all needed to produce red blood cells.

- Anaemia is most often due to an insufficient intake of iron in the diet.
- In premature babies, it can occur due to a reduced store of iron, which is usually formed in the final weeks of pregnancy.
- Teenage girls can become anaemic due to heavy menstrual blood loss.
- Anaemia is commonly seen in individuals who have a condition that affects absorption such as Crohn's disease or coeliac disease.
- Anaemia is more common in vegetarians and vegans.

Rickets

Rickets is a deficiency of vitamin D. It is sometimes known as osteomalacia, osteodystrophy or renal rickets. The deficiency causes bones to soften and weaken due to a lack of the mineral calcium.

Rickets is not commonly seen in the UK today except in cases where a child is not exposed to sufficient sunlight (which helps the body to produce vitamin D), or there has been rapid growth without the increase of calcium to support it in the diet.

Rickets is occasionally seen in children with a malabsorption problem such as Crohn's disease or coeliac disease.

A lack of calcium and vitamin D can also lead to tooth decay.

Tooth decay

Tooth decay is caused by bacteria on the teeth. This occurs particularly when sweet or sticky foods have been eaten, or fizzy drinks consumed. It can be helped by a good intake of calcium and vitamin D together with good dental hygiene, i.e. brushing of teeth after meals, before bedtime and after eating sweets or drinking drinks such as lemonade or cola. It is important that children have regular check-ups at the dentist. Fluorination of the water in most areas of the UK is considered to help strengthen the outer surface of teeth.

Scurvy

Scurvy is a condition in which the gums bleed and wounds do not heal properly. It is due to a lack of vitamin C (ascorbic acid). In a diet including plenty of fruits and vegetables it is rarely seen.

Link

Refer also to the tables of vitamins and minerals on pages 19 and 20. These show the main functions and uses. In the UK, generally a deficiency in vitamins and minerals is uncommon.

Diabetes mellitus (type 1 diabetes)

Diabetes mellitus is an endocrine disorder in which the pancreas does not make enough insulin. Insulin helps the body to use and store sugar. When it is not used efficiently, the sugar overflows into the urine. It is often triggered following a severe viral infection. It is not an inherited condition, but there is a familial trait to diabetes.

Most children are diagnosed following a sudden onset of the two most common symptoms:

- extreme thirst
- frequently passing urine.

Also the breath may smell of pear drops.

Less obvious onset includes:

- tiredness
- constant lethargy
- weight loss
- loss of appetite
- urinary tract infection due to excessive sugar in the urine.

Medical diagnosis involving the testing of urine and blood for excessive sugar levels often followed by a short stay in hospital in order for the child's blood sugar levels to be stabilised and their dietary needs agreed and understood by parents.

Ongoing care:

- Insulin injections and a carefully controlled diet will be necessary for life.
- Checks on blood sugar levels are taken (at least) daily.

remember

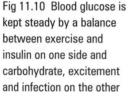

There are many hidden extras in processed foods, particularly sugar and salt. Whenever possible, offer fresh foods to children and do not provide salt or sugar on the table for them to add to their foods.

- Diet will be monitored by a dietician.
- A generally 'healthy heart' diet is needed (high fibre, low sugar, low fat).

The diet of a diabetic child needs to be monitored carefully. An imbalance of blood sugar levels can lead to either:

- hypoglycaemia (sweating and clammy skin – child needs to be given extra sugar or a boost of sugar), or
- hyperglycaemia (sugar levels are too high, so extra insulin is needed).

Signs of a hypoglycaemic attack include sweating, dizziness, confusion and rapid breathing. A snack or a glucose drink or something similar should be given to the child. It is important that someone remains with the child until they have stabilised. Illness, under-dosing on insulin and sudden growth spurts can all affect the blood sugar level balance.

See Keene (1999), page 259.

Fig 11.10 Blood glucose is kept steady by a balance between exercise and insulin on one side and carbohydrate, excitement and infection on the other

Common reasons for hypoglycaemia are:

- unusual exercise, e.g. extra games
- not enough carbohydrate, e.g. missed snack
- too much insulin, e.g. mistaken dose.

Common reasons for hyperglycaemia are:

- less exercise than usual, e.g. missed games
- not enough insulin, e.g. growing out of dose
- too much carbohydrate, e.g. extra snacks
- sudden excitement or strain, e.g. exams
- infection, e.g. cold.

Professional Practice

- Supplies of glucose tablets should be taken with you when you accompany a child with diabetes on any outing.
- Supplies should be readily available in the school or early years setting.
- Children with diabetes should be closely observed during exercise, particularly if they are trying something new.
- Contact numbers for parents should always be readily available.
- Staff working with a child with diabetes should be taught how to cope with their needs and any attacks.
- Privacy should be allowed when children need to test their blood sugar levels during the day.
- Catering staff need to be informed and be able to deal with special dietary needs.
- Good long-term dietary care will help prevent other ill health, such as heart, liver and vascular disease and eye disease.

Allergies

Link

Refer to pages 15–17 for food allergies and food intolerance.

Potential effects of additives

Link

Refer to page 23 for information on food additives.

activity
INDIVIDUAL WORK
11.4

P4

1 Produce a chart showing the main food groups and annotate it clearly to show how each food supports healthy development.

2 Draw up two daily meal plans for a baby, a toddler or a young child. Meal plan A will be a balanced diet, and meal plan B will be an unbalanced diet.

3 Explain why meal plan A is best and how the child is likely to be affected if their usual diet was unbalanced, as in meal plan B.

Professional Practice

- Try collecting labels from a range of frequently-used processed products that are enjoyed by children. Consider:
  - What proportions are the ingredients in?
  - How near to the top of the list are sugar or salt?
  - What does this tell you about processed foods?
  - What alternatives could you offer in their place?

activity
GROUP WORK
11.5

M3

D1

1 Using a chart like the one shown on page 14, plan a range of meals and snacks for a group of similarly aged children in a day nursery. Take into account their age, level of activity and the appropriate guidelines regarding EARs. National guidelines state that children in full day care (over 8 hours) should be provided with 70 per cent of the EARs by the setting. Assume that all the children in your chosen group are in this category.

2 Explain the balance and nutritional content of each meal, and in what ways they support an overall healthy diet for young children.

Understand the principles of food safety

Safe practice

Safe practice means:

- conforming to legislation and regulations
- working hygienically without taking risks
- ensuring that all staff handling food, or working in any environment in which food is stored, prepared, handled or delivered, are trained appropriately and understand standards and limitations, and how unsafe practice can affect health and also potentially the registration of the business.

There are many different laws and regulations to support **food safety**, including:

- Food Safety Act 1990
- Food Safety (General Food Hygiene) Regulations 1995
- Food Safety (Temperature Control) Regulations 1995
- Hazard Analysis Critical Control Point (**HACCP**).

Food Safety Act 1990

This Act is about ensuring that all relevant staff have attended and achieved a certified food-handling course. It requires that:

- no food unfit for eating is provided or sold
- food should not be described in an inaccurate or misleading way
- food must not cause illness to those handling or eating it.

Food Safety (General Food Hygiene) Regulations 1995

This Act is about effective management systems being in place to ensure that food is prepared and produced without risk to health, and that all staff follow the accepted hygiene principles regarding food handling.

Food Safety (Temperature Control) Regulations 1995

These regulations state:

- the stages of production in the food chain and appropriate temperature controls needed for each food type
- that each food must be kept at the correct temperature for its food type
- the foods which are exempt from regulations regarding specific temperature controls
- where flexibility is allowed regarding temperature controls.

Hazard Analysis Critical Control Point (HACCP)

This links to the general risk assessment that all early years settings should carry out and update regularly. Staff need to:

- identify any situation or activity where food hazards exist
- identify any situation or activity where food hazards are likely to occur
- identify when and how a hazard might occur and what needs to be done to ensure safety, i.e. what controls need to be put in place
- specify a person or persons who will monitor and review the controls that are put in place at regular intervals and also when there are any changes to the food operation at the setting.

Hygiene control

Safe hygiene practice includes personal hygiene, kitchen hygiene, temperature control and **pest control**.

Personal hygiene
Personal hygiene involves:

- regular hand washing throughout the day
- washing hands before all food preparation
- washing hands after any activity with the potential for bacterial spread, e.g.
  - nappy changing
  - using the toilet
  - coughing
  - sneezing
  - nose blowing
- use of bacterial soaps
- nails being kept clean and cut short
- cuts and sores covered at all times
- use of disposable gloves
- hair being kept tied back
- wearing clean, fresh clothes
- changing clothes as necessary for food preparation and cooking activities
- covering nose and mouth when coughing or sneezing, setting a good example to children

Kitchen hygiene

Kitchen hygiene involves:

- keeping surfaces clean and free from bacteria
- ensuring that all surfaces are unblemished and unchipped
- using separate boards for cooked and uncooked foods
- using separate knives for cooked and uncooked foods
- keeping floors thoroughly clean
- washing up as dirty utensils occur to eliminate additional bacterial growth
- whenever possible using a dishwasher as this is the more effective method to prevent bacterial growth
- wrapping all waste securely and emptying bins regularly
- regularly cleaning and defrosting refrigerators and freezers
- ensuring the temperature of a refrigerator is kept at 4–5° C (39–41° F)
- storing cooked foods at the top of the refrigerator with raw foods below
- minimal handling of all foods
- keeping foods well covered
- ensuring that use-by dates are adhered to
- serving re-heated food piping hot
- never re-heating foods more than once
- not keeping food warm for more than a few minutes.

Temperature control

Link

For guidance on temperature control, refer to the HACCP specifications on page 33.

Pest control

Pest control involves eliminating the risk of flies, cockroaches, mice, etc. by wrapping waste appropriately and ideally removing waste immediately, or emptying bins as soon as possible. It also involves the following:

- Any pets kept within the setting should be kept clean and away from the kitchen or any other food handling areas.
- Any animal or bird faeces should be cleaned up immediately and disinfected.
- Flies and wasps can be controlled by using insecticide strips.
- Aerosol-type fly sprays should not be used in the kitchen or anywhere where food is, due to the potential for chemical contamination.
- Hands should be washed carefully after handling pets or removing pests from the premises.
- There should be an established link with the local Environmental Health Department, who can be called upon for advice in the event of an infestation of mice, cockroaches, etc.

Effects of unsafe practices

Food contamination can be:

- chemical
- physical
- biological.

Chemical food contamination

Food can be contaminated chemically by:

- medicines and pesticides used in food production, e.g. in farming
- cleaning products, again used in food production, often in the machinery in which the food is produced
- cleaning products in the workplace.

Mostly chemical food contamination is accidental.

Physical food contamination

Physical food contamination can occur when something falls into food accidentally, e.g.

- a hair
- a fingernail
- a sticking plaster
- dirt
- jewellery
- a dead fly, etc.

remember

These types of hazards can be particularly dangerous when serving food to young children as a small 'foreign body' could become a choking hazard.

Despite even the most stringent processes to avoid this type of contamination, there will inevitably be occasions where it still occurs. However, every effort should be taken to avoid it, hence the food hygiene legislation and regulations above.

Biological food contamination

The body fights off potential food-related health problems through:

- the spleen which is a vascular organ with a large number of blood vessels, which filters out foreign bodies from the blood and produces antibodies
- the gut where good bacteria kills both good and bad bacteria when fighting infection, causing diarrhoea.

Microbiological (infectious) causes of illness are varied, and are the illnesses you will most often deal with as an early years worker. These germs (**pathogens**) can be roughly divided into five groups:

- bacteria – tough cells which rapidly multiply and thrive in the body's warm, moist conditions; treatable with antibiotics, e.g. ear infections and conjunctivitis
- viruses – parasites which invade other cells and then reproduce themselves; cannot be treated with antibiotics; can be relatively harmless or significantly serious, e.g. the common cold, influenza and chickenpox
- fungi – spread by contact with fungi spores; do no serious harm to humans but cause much irritation and discomfort; some harmless fungi are permanently with us; treatment with an anti-fungal product as necessary, e.g. for athlete's foot
- parasites – organisms spread by cross-infection; can be seen with the naked eye; many different varieties and difficult to eradicate once they have taken hold in a nursery or school class, due to cases of re-infection, e.g. scabies, head lice and threadworms
- protozoa – single-cell organisms; many cause human distress through illnesses such as severe stomach upsets, e.g. toxoplasmosis (often caught through handling cats or cat litter) and amoebiasis (causing diarrhoea).

Pathogens can enter the body in different ways. They can be:

- ingested – taken in through the mouth
- inhaled – breathed in through either the mouth or the nose
- inoculated – taken in through a break in the surface of the skin.

They can be spread by:

- direct contact – germs transmitted by touch, e.g. broken skin contacts, kissing and sexual activity
- indirect contact – germs left on surfaces subsequently in contact with another person
- droplet infection – air-borne germs spread through sneezing, coughing, and so on, as microscopic droplets are released into the atmosphere.

activity
GROUP WORK
11.6

P5

M4

1 Produce a booklet on food safety, describing the principles of safe food handling practice, and explaining clearly the potential effects of each point you have identified.
2 Make a poster (minimum size A3) showing the potential effects of poor food safety practice in a day nursery.

activity
INDIVIDUAL WORK
11.7

D2

Research the food safety practices carried out by staff in your current placement and evaluate them in a written report for an imaginary third party. Look back through this unit to help you decide what to include.

Food poisoning

The most common causes of **food poisoning**, accounting for around 90 per cent of cases, are:

- Staphylococcus aureus
- Salmonella species
- Clostridium perfringens
- Campylobacter
- Listeria monocytogens
- Vibrio parahaemolyticus
- Bacillus cereus
- Escherichia.coli (E. coli).

Table 11.11 shows where each bacteria is found, the symptoms it can cause and the storage or cooking temperature at which contamination can be prevented.

As you can see in the table, two of the main symptoms of food poisoning are diarrhoea and vomiting. This is often referred to as gastro-enteritis. You will need to know how to manage this illness.

Gastro-enteritis

Gastro-enteritis is the most common irritant of the stomach and intestinal lining.

- It is caused by bacteria and viruses.
- It can be spread in food due to poor hygiene during food handling.
- It can be spread by direct or indirect contact.

Gastro-enteritis in children sees them appearing unwell, lethargic and miserable before the onset of the main symptoms, which include:

- vomiting
- diarrhoea
- raised temperature
- loss of appetite.

Only clear fluids (cooled boiled water) should be given for 24 hours. Rehydration drinks may be used for children over the age of 1 year, particularly if symptoms are severe. Breast-fed babies should continue to be breast fed as usual. If there is no sign of improvement, medical advice should be sought, particularly in very young children.

Clear fluids, together with 'ice-pops' can give a child some sugar. Light foods should be offered when appetite returns. Diet drinks are not considered to be suitable.

Possible complications:

- Dehydration can easily occur in very young children and babies.
- If children cease to pass urine frequently, medical advice should be sought.
- Intravenous fluids may need to be given in severe cases.

There is no known incubation period. Strict hygiene is needed to try to minimise the spread of infection. Gastro-enteritis often 'sweeps' through families, nurseries and schools.

Table 11.11 Food poisoning bacteria

Bacteria	Description	Habitat	Types of food	Symptoms	Cause	Temperature sensitivity
Staphylococcus aureus	Produces a heat-stable toxin	Nose and throat of 30 to 50 per cent of healthy population; also skin and superficial wounds	Meat and seafood salads, sandwich spreads and high salt foods	Nausea, vomiting and diarrhoea within 4 to 6 hours. No fever	Poor personal hygiene and subsequent incorrect control or monitoring of temperature	No growth below 4°C. Bacteria are destroyed by normal cooking but toxin is heat-stable
Salmonella	Produces an intestinal infection	Intestinal tracts of animals and humans	High protein foods – meat; poultry, fish and eggs	Diarrhoea, nausea, chills, vomiting and fever within 12 to 24 hours	Contamination of ready-to-eat foods, insufficient cooking and recontamination of cooked foods	No growth below 4°C. Bacteria are destroyed by normal cooking
Clostridium perfringens	Produces a spore and prefers low oxygen atmosphere. Live cells must be ingested	Dust, soil and gastro-intestinal tracts of animals and humans	Meat and poultry dishes, sauces and gravies	Cramps and diarrhoea within 12 to 24 hours. No vomiting or fever	Improper temperature control of hot foods, and recontamination	No growth below 4°C. Bacteria are killed by normal cooking but a heat-stable spore can survive
Vibrio parahaemolyticus	Requires salt for growth	Fish and shellfish	Raw and cooked seafood	Diarrhoea, cramps, vomiting, headache and fever within 12 to 24 hours	Recontamination of cooked foods or eating raw seafood	No growth below 4°C. Bacteria killed by normal cooking
Bacillus cereus	Produces a spore and grows in normal oxygen atmosphere	Soil, dust and spices	Starchy food	Mild case of diarrhoea and some nausea within 12 to 24 hours	Improper holding and storage temperatures after cooking	No growth below 4°C. Bacteria are destroyed by normal cooking, but heat-resistant spore can survive
Listeria monocytogenes	Survives adverse conditions for long time periods	Soil, vegetation and water. Can survive for long periods in soil and plant materials	Milk, soft cheeses, vegetables fertilized with manure	Mimics meningitis. Immuno-compromised individuals most susceptible	Contaminated raw products	Grows at refrigeration (3– 4°C) temperatures. May survive minimum pasteurisation temperatures (72°C for 15 seconds)
Campylobacter jejuni	Oxygen sensitive, does not grow below 30°C	Animal reservoirs and foods of animal origin	Meat, poultry, milk and mushrooms	Diarrhoea abdominal cramps and nausea	Improper pasteurisation or cooking. Cross-contamination	Sensitive to drying or freezing. Survives in milk and water at 4°C for several weeks
Enteropathogenic E. coli	Can produce toxins that are heat stable and others that are heat-sensitive	Faeces of infected humans	Meat and cheeses	Diarrhoea, abdominal cramps, no fever	Inadequate cooking. Recontamination of cooked product	Organisms can be controlled by heating. Can grow at refrigeration temperatures

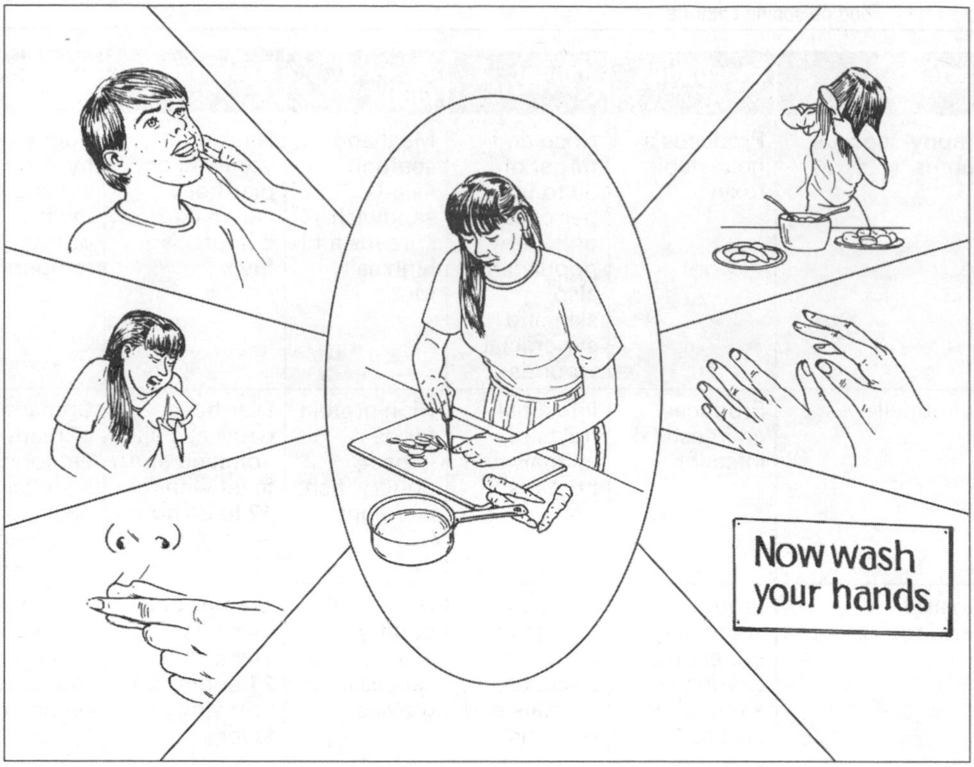

Fig 11.11 Good personal hygiene helps prevent cross-infection

Progress Check

1 What nutritional factors can you think of that can affect the developing foetus?
2 Why is folic acid considered to be important for pregnant women?
3 Give examples of foods for each of the main food groups.
4 Why is breast milk considered to be best for babies?
5 What is the difference between fore milk and hind milk?
6 Why is weaning usually introduced at about 6 months?
7 Explain the advantages and disadvantages of breast feeding.
8 Explain the advantages and disadvantages of formula feeding.
9 Explain how you would encourage a 'fussy' eater.
10 What is the difference between a food allergy and a food intolerance?
11 What does the term malnutrition mean? Give some examples.
12 Describe the symptoms of at least three vitamin and mineral deficiencies.
13 What are the main principles of safe food handling practice?
14 Why is temperature control important in food handling?
15 What is the difference between chemical, physical and biological food contamination?

UNIT 12 Physical Activities for Children

This unit covers the following objectives:

- Understand the anatomy and physiology of the growing child with reference to physical activity
- Be able to devise, justify, prepare, implement, monitor and evaluate a range of physical activities suitable for babies and children
- Understand adaptations to a selected range of physical activities for babies and children with additional needs

Physical activity helps a child to find out what their body is able to achieve, e.g. how fast it can move, how far it can twist or bend, whilst still retaining balance. It also helps them to understand their individual limitations and how these limitations change over time. Having opportunities to try out actions in a secure and supported environment will help children develop the confidence needed for them to attempt new actions and activities when situations arise for them to do so.

Physical activity does not need to be at a specified time or through a structured programme, although clearly physical education sessions will be part of the regular curriculum activity provided within the school environment, and are extremely important. Physical activity will naturally occur during a range of other activities. An example would be the development of balance being supported as children are encouraged to carry items that are larger than before, heavier than before, or perhaps contain liquid, e.g. a bucket of water from water tray to sand tray, a jug of milk to the table at snack time.

In this unit you will look at the workings of the body, how to provide activities to support healthy development and what modifications may be needed to accommodate a range of additional needs.

grading criteria

To achieve a **Pass** grade the evidence must show that the learner is able to:	To achieve a **Merit** grade the evidence must show that, in addition to the Pass criteria, the learner is able to:	To achieve a **Distinction** grade the evidence must show that, in addition to the Pass and Merit criteria, the learner is able to:
P1 Describe the structure, functions and arrangement of the body systems detailing the differences between mature and immature systems Page 59		
P2 Describe the effects of exercise on body systems and on growth and development Page 62	**M1** Explain the effects of exercise on growth and development Page 62	

To achieve a **Pass** grade the evidence must show that the learner is able to:	To achieve a **Merit** grade the evidence must show that, in addition to the Pass criteria, the learner is able to:	To achieve a **Distinction** grade the evidence must show that, in addition to the Pass and Merit criteria, the learner is able to:
P3 Describe how physical activities promote healthy development page 83	**M2** Explain how physical activities promote healthy development page 83	**D1** Evaluate the relative benefits of two different types of exercise in terms of promoting healthy development page 83
P4 Plan four age-appropriate physical activities with reference to safe practice and the relevant curriculum framework page 87		
P5 Implement, monitor and record the planned activities page 87	**M3** Explain how the activities carried out meet the relevant curricular objectives page 89	**D2** Evaluate the activities that have been undertaken and make recommendations for improvements page 89
P6 Describe ways to adapt the activities for children with additional needs page 96	**M4** Explain how the adaptations make the activities accessible and appropriate for children with additional needs page 96	**D3** Evaluate the role of the adapted activities in the promoting of healthy development and lifestyle for children with additional needs page 96

Understand the anatomy and physiology of the growing child with reference to physical activity

The body is a complex piece of human machinery. It involves many different parts, which in turn have many intricate roles to play to keep us functioning properly. The body is made up initially from cells, which change, combine and develop to form the finished article – us! Figure 12.1 illustrates this process.

Fig 12.1 The development of the body

Cells, made from atoms and molecules

↓

Tissues, formed from the cells

↓

Organs, formed from tissues

↓

Body systems, formed by organ function

↓

A functioning body powered by the body systems

Once formed, the body has a variety of needs. The most important of these are:

- food and nutrition
- water
- fresh air
- regular exercise.

The amount and quality of each of the above will impact directly on how well each part of the body develops, functions, and resists injury and infection.

Different parts of the body take different timescales to mature. Each of us as an individual will develop in a similar pattern, but the rate of development will vary. This will be decided partly on the bodily needs listed above, together with the influences of genetic inheritance, gender and opportunity.

Skeletal system

Functions

The **skeletal system** gives our body its overall shape. It is basically a framework of support for us. The skeleton enables us to move because it is jointed and it has (flexible) muscles that are connected to the ends of our bones. Without the skeletal framework there would be no protection for our internal organs, which can be very vulnerable, e.g.

- The skull protects the brain.
- The ribcage protects the heart, lungs, spleen, kidneys and liver.
- The spine protects the spinal cord.

Within the bones of the skeleton is the bone marrow. This is where all of our red blood cells are made, together with some of our white blood cells. There is also a constant exchange of calcium between the bone marrow and the blood, and it should be remembered that stocks of calcium can easily be lost from the bones if regular weight-bearing exercise is lacking.

There are two main parts to the human skeleton:

- the **axial skeleton**
- the **appendicular skeleton.**

Axial skeleton

The axial skeleton consists of those parts that lie along the main axis of the body. These are:

- the skull
- the vertebrae
- the ribcage
- the sternum.

Appendicular skeleton

These are the parts that are fixed to the axial skeleton in some way or other. They are:

- the pectoral girdle (shoulder)
- the pelvic girdle (hips)
- the arms (these move with the pectoral girdle)
- the legs (these move with the pelvic girdle).

There are a few main differences between the skeletons of men and women. On the whole, men tend to have slightly longer, thicker limb bones than women, with broader ribcages, larger teeth and a more angular jaw line. Women tend to have a broader pelvic girdle than men, one of the body's natural endeavours to prepare them for childbirth.

As children, boys are on average slightly taller and heavier than girls. This balance changes as childhood meets puberty, with girls growing at a faster pace, usually being around 2 to 2½ years ahead of boys in reaching the onset of puberty. Once growing ceases, boys, on average, will again be slightly taller and heavier than girls.

Fig 12.2 The human skeleton

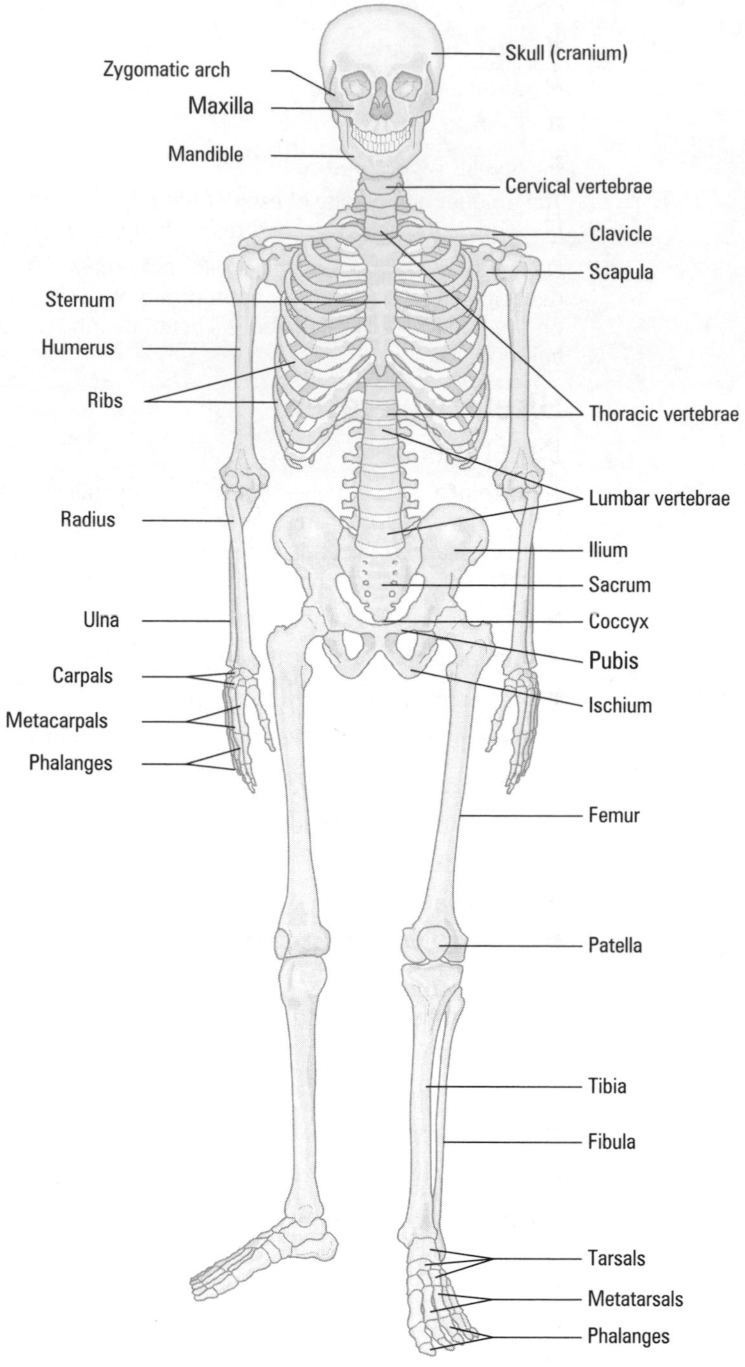

Classification of bones and joints

There are usually 206 **bones** in a typical adult skeleton. Look carefully at the diagram above and try to memorise the names and positions of each of the bones.

The axial skeleton is made up of 80 bones and the appendicular skeleton is made up of 126 bones. The division of bones in the axial skeleton is as follows:

- skull – 22 bones
- ossicles (the middle ear) – 6 bones
- hyoid bone (found in the throat) – 1 bone
- vertebral column (back bone) – 26 bones
- chest – 25 bones.

The division of bones in the appendicular skeleton is as follows:

- shoulder girdle – 4 bones
- arms – 6 bones

- hands – 54 bones
- pelvic girdle – 2 bones
- legs – 8 bones
- feet – 52 bones.

Children's bones are softer than adults, occasionally causing them to bend and splinter rather than break, following an injury. This is known as a greenstick fracture. At birth, a newborn infant has approximately 300 bones. Some of these bones have growing ends which gradually fuse together as they grow until the final count of 206 is reached when the child reaches full growth in their teens. Looking at the growth ends of children's bones helps specialist medical teams to determine how much more a child is likely to grow if there is a cause for concern.

Bone

Bone is an active tissue, not just a solid state. It needs a healthy diet to maintain a sufficient intake of calcium and vitamin D. Bone is made up of 50 per cent water and 50 per cent solids. Of the 50 per cent solid substance, 67 per cent is calcium carbonate and calcium phosphate, and 33 per cent gelatine and collagen.

Link

Refer to Unit 11, page 17 for information on a healthy diet and nutrient sources.

Joints

Bones are held together by muscles, ligaments and tendons. There are various types of **joints**, each helping us move in different ways.

Fixed joints

The bones of the pelvis and the skull are fixed joints. They are firmly fixed together allowing no movement.

Cartilaginous joints

These are areas of bone that are connected by cartilage. Cartilage is a tough, but slightly flexible, substance which allows just a little movement when under pressure. Examples would be where the ribs join the sternum, and the discs between the vertebrae in the spine.

The following joints are freely moving (synovial) joints:

Ball and socket joints e.g. shoulder

This is where the end of one bone is rounded and it fits neatly into the cup shape of the other bone. The hip bone is a good example of a ball and socket joint, as is the shoulder joint.

Hinge joints e.g. fingers

These joints work exactly as they sound – as a hinge, enabling movement in just one direction. Examples would be the knee joint and the finger joints.

Fig 12.3 Different types of joints

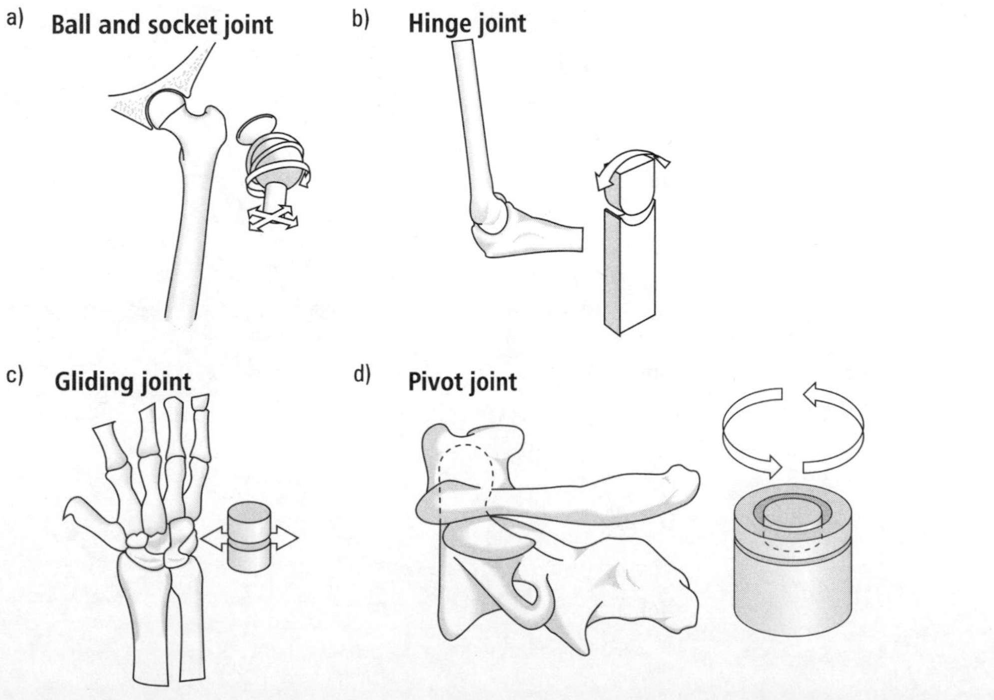

Gliding joints e.g. wrist or ankle
Gliding joints involve one bone sliding over another. The wrist and ankle joints are examples of gliding joints.

Pivot joints e.g. head turning
The head turning from side to side shows the pivot movement of one bone rotating alongside another.

Connective tissue

Bones are joined together by **connective tissue**, ligaments and tendons.

Smooth movements between joints are possible due to a substance called synovial fluid which is secreted from the lining of joints and helps lubricate them. Joints are strengthened by the muscles that surround them, the ligaments that link them together, and the strength of a capsule (the synovial capsule) that surrounds each joint to prevent the synovial fluid from seeping away.

Synovial joints can be summarised as follows:

- cartilage – helps to absorb shock
- synovial fluid – helps to reduce friction
- synovial membrane – secretes synovial fluid
- synovial capsule – keeps synovial fluid from seeping away
- ligament – joins the bones together
- tendon – joins muscle to bone, enabling movement.

Fig 12.4 The body's fulcrum

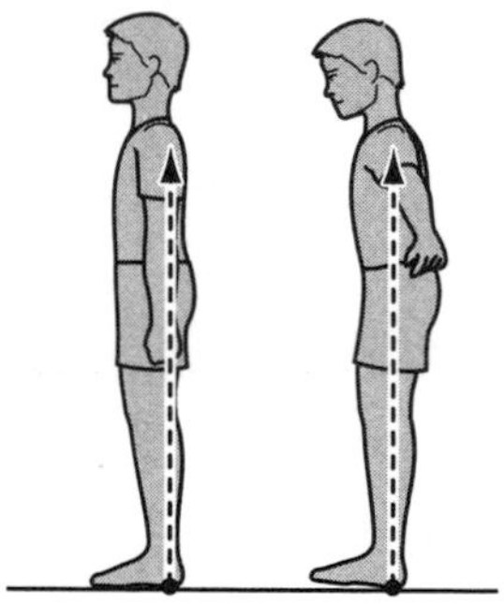

Movements and levers

The central point of something, i.e. its axis (balancing point), is also known as the fulcrum. The body's fulcrum is the centralised line when it is balanced in a state of equilibrium, i.e. it is balanced equally.

In making movements a child will change the 'load and effort' lever effect as they stretch and move around, changing their position to keep balanced.

There are three different levels of lever actions in the human body.

Lever action level 1
An example of level 1 is where the effort and load are on opposite sides of the fulcrum (the centre of balance), e.g. when standing up straight, the fulcrum point is not centrally through the skull (looking at it from the side). There is a greater skull mass in front of the fulcrum point (the load) than there is behind the fulcrum point (where the muscles and tendons exert the effort).

Fig 12.5 Lever action levels 1, 2 and 3

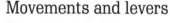

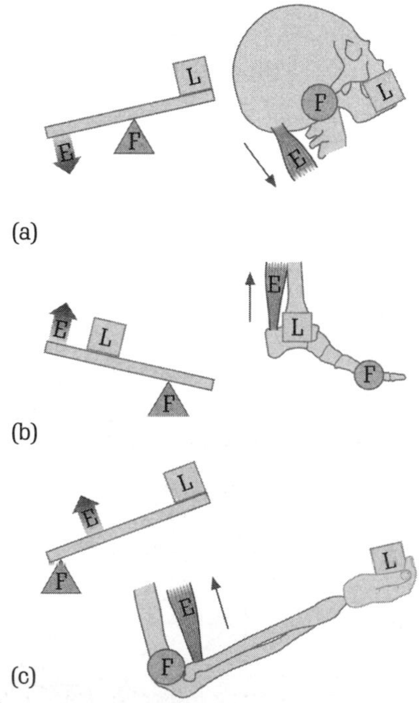

Lever action level 2
An example of level 2 is where the load is between the fulcrum and the effort, e.g. when standing on tiptoe the fulcrum point is at the toe and the load is the body's weight through the leg bones and the effort is seen in the muscles and tendons behind the heel.

Lever action level 3
An example of level 3 is where the effort comes between the fulcrum and the load, e.g. when holding a load, with arms held out in front the fulcrum point is at the elbow, the load is in the hand and the effort is seen in the muscles and tendons of the biceps.

Understanding how the balance is kept around the body's central axis (its fulcrum) is important when considering movement and exercise with children. There are two main types of movement involving balance:

- locomotion movements
- non-locomotion movements.

These, together with an understanding of co-ordination, will form the basis of many physical activities.

Link

Refer to pages 66–72 and 84 for activities involving co-ordination, locomotion and non-locomotion movements.

Effects of exercise on the growing skeleton

Having access to outdoor activity will help boost vitamin D levels, as the body generates this important mineral through exposure to natural sunlight. Providing children with garden or playground time on at least a daily basis will also encourage them to use and value fresh air and the outdoor environment in general. This sets up good habits for the future.

Regular exercise helps to keep joints mobile and supple. It helps prevents children becoming overweight or obese and usually makes individuals feel healthier and more energetic. Weight-bearing exercise helps to build up the body's calcium supply which improves bone density. Bone density is important to avoid health problems such as osteoporosis and osteopeania in later life.

Link

Refer to pages 66–69 and 84 for activities to support the health of the skeleton.

Muscular system

Functions

Muscles receive messages which travel from the brain down the spinal cord and along the peripheral nerves to whichever muscle is needed for the required movement. Movements such as walking involve the co-ordination of bones, muscles and nerves for successful movement to take place. Children with difficulty in co-ordinating such movements usually find finer movements even harder and are likely to need greater assistance to achieve specific movement aims.

Link

Refer to page 93 for information on cerebral palsy, a condition which affects movement and co-ordination, and also see Unit 27, page 279.

Types of muscle

There are muscles all over our body. They fall into three main groups:

- skeletal muscles (also known as voluntary or striated muscles), which are attached to the skeleton and work through the brain directing them
- cardiac muscle, which is the heart, the body's largest (and most important) muscle
- involuntary (unstriated) muscles, which work automatically without any conscious thought or action from the body. An example would be the walls of the intestine and how they absorb and deal with bodily waste products.

Muscle action and tone

Muscles are always in a slight state of contraction. This is known as our muscle tone. All muscles work in pairs or groups. They are never on their own. Muscles can only pull bones, not push them. Therefore, one muscle or group of muscles will pull a bone to move in one direction, and another muscle or group of muscles will pull it back again to the position it started in.

Movement takes place when a muscle on one side pulls harder than its corresponding muscle on the other side.

Muscles which bend a joint are called flexors, and muscles that straighten the joint out again are called extensor muscles, e.g.

- As you bend your elbow, the bicep (flexor muscle) bends the arm and the triceps (extensor muscle) straightens it again.
- As you bend your knee, the hamstring (flexor muscle) bends the knee and the thigh muscle (extensor muscle) straightens it again.

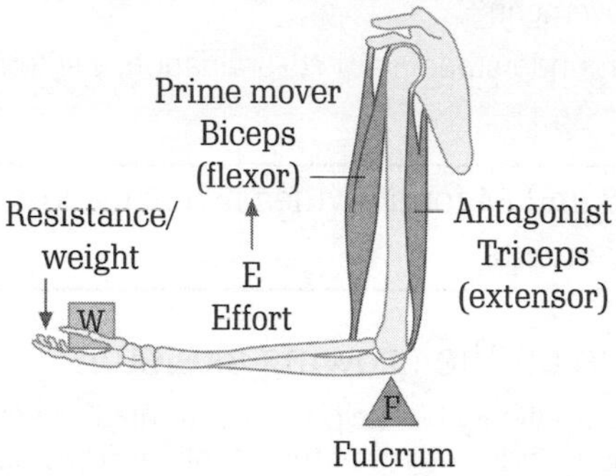

Fig 12.6 The flexor and extensor muscles in the arm

Isotonic and isometric contraction

Activities that involve movement are using muscles which contract and shorten (isotonic contractions). These actions help to strengthen muscles as you carry out the range of movements involved in any physical activity, e.g. dance, sport, swimming, etc.

Activity in which muscles contract but do not shorten (isometric contractions) do not enable any movement. These actions are about building up strength to push, pull, lift or bear weight.

Effects of exercise on growing muscles

- Exercise keeps muscles in good condition and helps to build on their strength. This includes the heart muscle too.
- It is important that exercise is suited to the level of fitness of each individual.
- Exercise helps to build up an individual person's stamina.
- Exercise should start off gently and be built up gradually.
- Exercise opens up the blood vessels in the muscles enabling them to draw on a good supply of blood, and therefore oxygen.
- Exercise helps build up the strength and size of muscles.

Fig 12.7a The location of major muscles

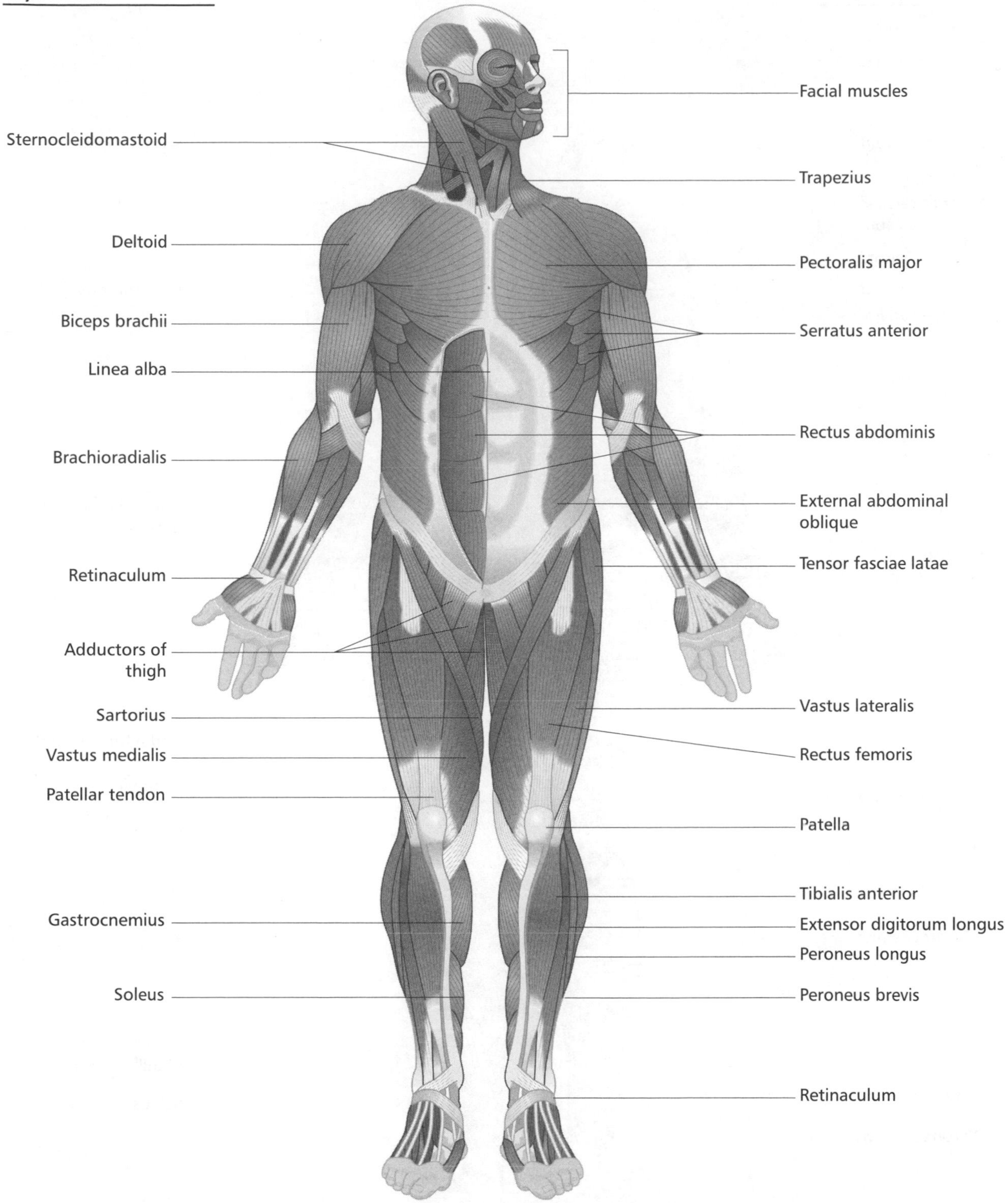
Facial muscles
Sternocleidomastoid
Trapezius
Deltoid
Pectoralis major
Biceps brachii
Serratus anterior
Linea alba
Rectus abdominis
Brachioradialis
External abdominal oblique
Tensor fasciae latae
Retinaculum
Adductors of thigh
Vastus lateralis
Sartorius
Rectus femoris
Vastus medialis
Patellar tendon
Patella
Tibialis anterior
Gastrocnemius
Extensor digitorum longus
Peroneus longus
Soleus
Peroneus brevis
Retinaculum

Fig 12.7b The location of major muscles

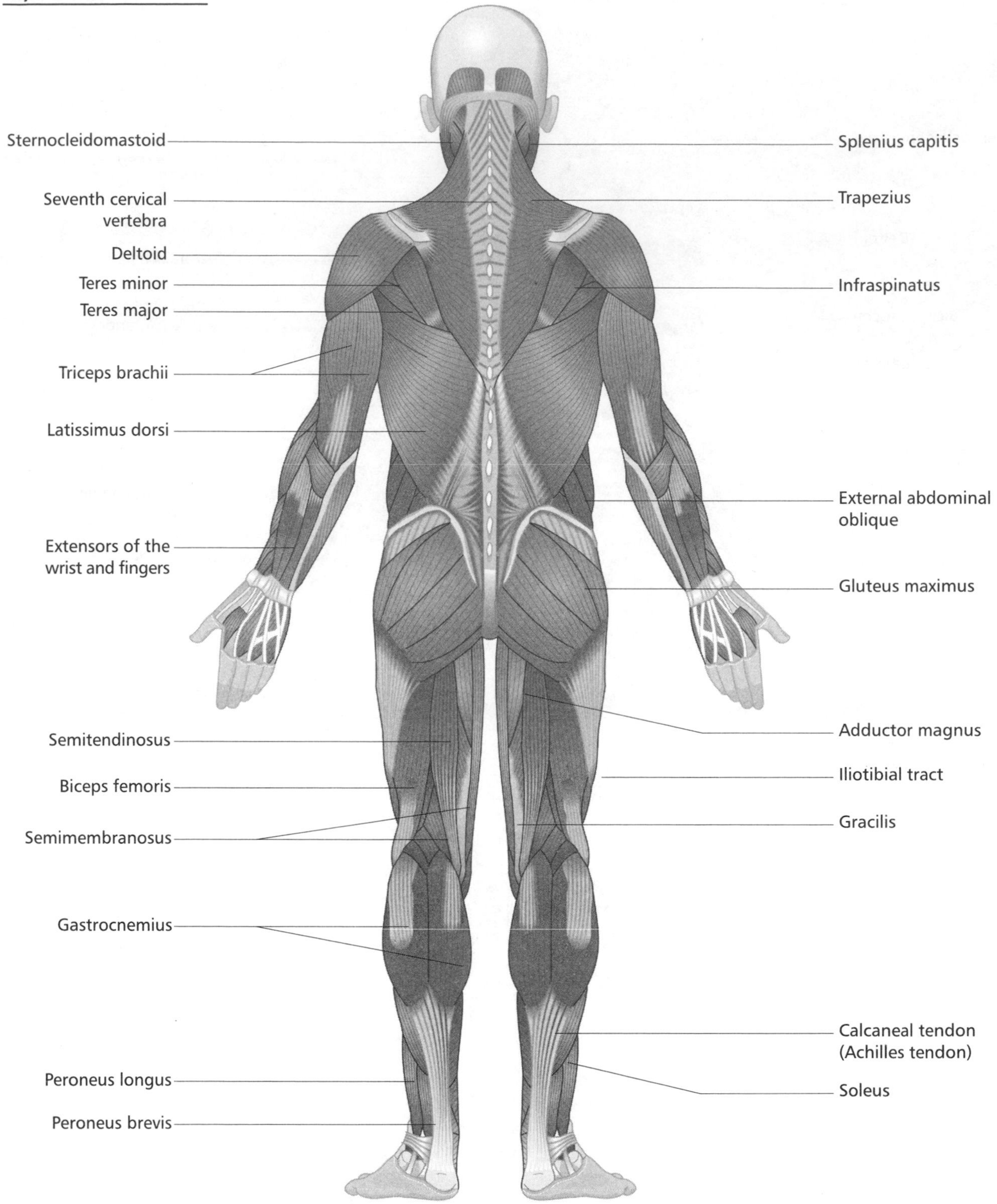
Sternocleidomastoid
Seventh cervical vertebra
Deltoid
Teres minor
Teres major
Triceps brachii
Latissimus dorsi
Extensors of the wrist and fingers
Semitendinosus
Biceps femoris
Semimembranosus
Gastrocnemius
Peroneus longus
Peroneus brevis
Splenius capitis
Trapezius
Infraspinatus
External abdominal oblique
Gluteus maximus
Adductor magnus
Iliotibial tract
Gracilis
Calcaneal tendon (Achilles tendon)
Soleus

Circulatory system

Structure and function of the heart

The heart's crucial function is to pump blood continuously around the body. It is about the size of a clenched fist and is the largest muscle in the body.

The heart is a hollow muscular organ which is divided into four chambers, with a muscular wall dividing the two sides. The upper chambers are the atriums and the lower chambers are the ventricles. Blood flows into the atrium which pushes the blood through a valve into the ventricle. The valve ensures that blood does not flow back into the atrium again.

The right side of the heart receives dark blood into its atrium from the veins. It is dark because its oxygen has been used up. The right atrium pumps this blood into the right ventricle, which in turn pumps it into the lungs where it receives oxygen. This re-oxygenated (bright red) blood flows from the lungs into the left atrium through a large vein. The atrium pumps the blood into the left ventricle and from here it is pumped through the aorta to the rest of the body.

Fig 12.8 The heart

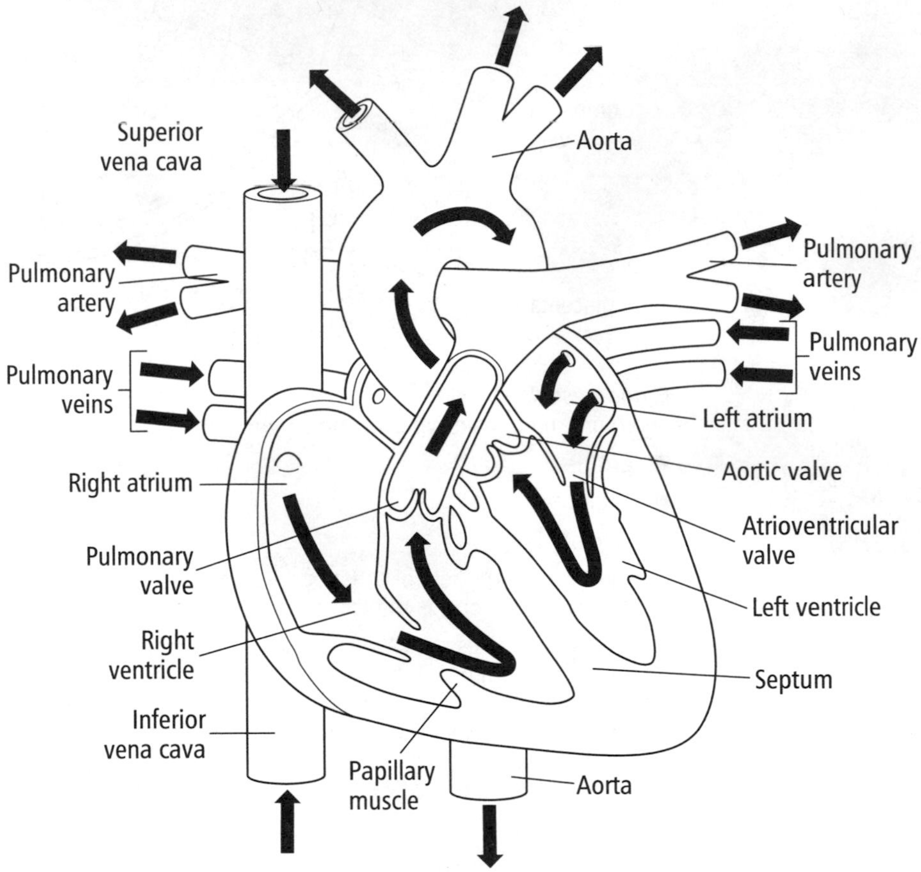

At birth, the newborn infant has to immediately begin to adapt to new body processes. She needs to use her lungs to breathe and her body's metabolism needs to begin to use its glycogen stores to generate heat. Significant changes also need to take place to the circulatory system. Whilst within the womb, the circulation of blood is short-circuited to avoid the lungs (which remain deflated until the first breath is taken). Circulation has been carried out via two channels, the foramen ovale, which connects the two atria of the foetus's heart, and the ductus arteriosus, which connects the pulmonary artery to the aorta. These need to close at birth in order for the usual gas exchange to occur through the normal process of double circulation.

Link
Refer to page 56 for information on glycogen.

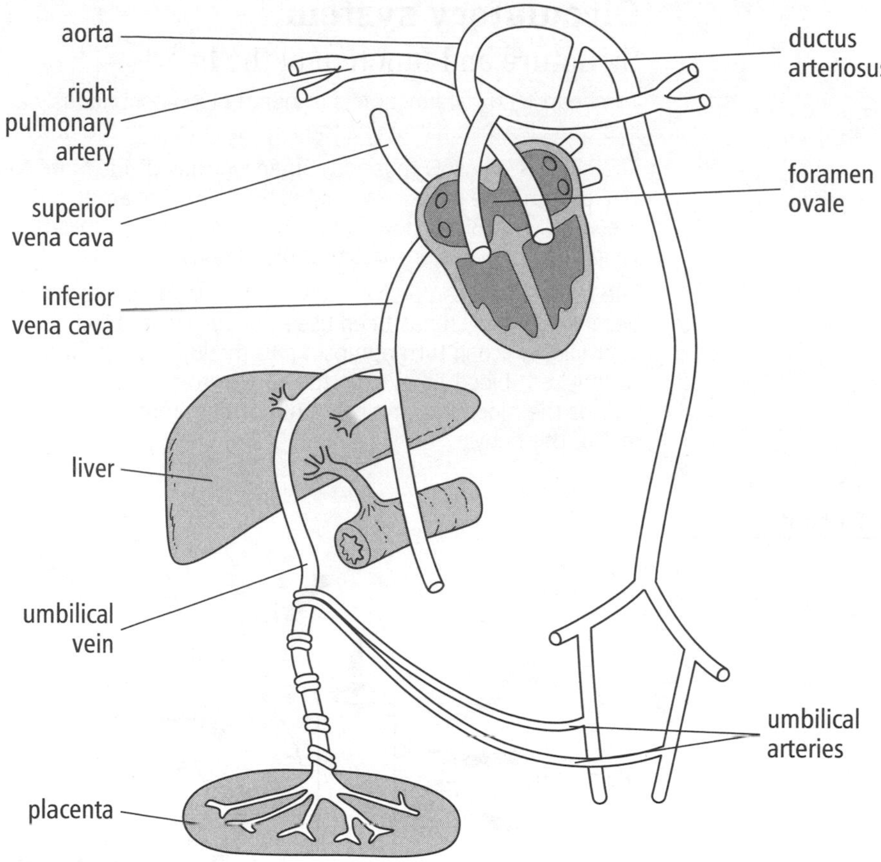

Fig 12.9 Important changes to circulation take place at birth

Blood vessels

There are three main types of **blood vessel**:

- arteries
- capillaries
- veins.

Arteries are the thickest of the blood vessels and they carry blood from the heart to the rest of the body. The aorta is the largest artery.

The smallest arteries are called arterioles. They carry blood to the capillaries. Blood in the arteries is bright red due to the presence of oxygen (there is one exception to this – the artery leading to the lungs). There are more than 100,000 km of capillaries in our bodies, forming a vast network through the body tissues. Capillaries are very thin blood vessels. Through their walls, oxygen and nutrients are passed into cells, and carbon dioxide and waste products are taken away. Blood from the capillaries flows into the veins.

Veins have thinner walls than arteries. Their job is to take blood back to the heart. They contain valves to prevent blood flowing backwards. The blood in veins is dark red, showing the presence of carbon dioxide, and less oxygen (again the exception is the vein carrying blood from the lungs to the heart).

Blood

Every function of **blood** is essential to living. It is made up of red blood cells and white blood cells, platelets and plasma.

- Red blood cells are often called erythrocytes. The haemoglobin found in these cells is responsible for carrying blood from the lungs to the heart.
- White blood cells are known as leucocytes. They are colourless and are fewer in number than red cells. The main job of the white cells is to engulf and destroy harmful bacteria or foreign particles which get into tissue or blood. Many white cells are killed off whilst fighting infection. This can be seen as pus in wounds.
- Platelets are tiny fragments of large cells. They help to clot our blood, preventing dangerous levels of bleeding. They also seal holes and tears in small blood vessels.
- Plasma is a straw-coloured liquid consisting mainly of water, containing a suspension of blood cells. It transports carbon dioxide from the organs to the lungs, urea from the liver

to the kidneys, hormones, soluble products of digestion from the small intestine and water to and from various parts of the body.

Blood can be either Rhesus positive (Rh pos), meaning that it contains rhesus factor, or rhesus negative (Rh neg), meaning that it does not. The presence of rhesus factor is important when giving and receiving blood, and also during pregnancy, as rhesus factor is inherited. If a baby's mother is rhesus negative and the father is rhesus positive, problems can occur if the infant inherits rhesus positive blood from its father. The mother's rhesus negative blood will develop antibodies against rhesus positive blood. The first infant born to the couple will be unaffected, but subsequent infants will be affected by the antibodies in the mother's blood fighting and destroying the red blood cells, causing blood-related problems such as anaemia and jaundice, and potentially death at birth without a blood transfusion. Mothers in this situation can be given an injection of a substance to prevent the reaction taking place during future pregnancies.

Blood varies from person to person, and everyone has a blood group. The main blood groups are A, B, AB and O.

- A person with the blood group O Rhesus negative is a universal donor and can be a donor to anyone in the ABO blood groups.
- A person with group A blood can donate blood to a person with AB blood, but not the other way round due to the reaction of blood to A and/or B antibodies.
- A person with AB Rhesus positive blood can receive blood from any donors in the ABO blood groups.

Blood pressure and pulse

Every time the heart beats, it pumps blood into the arteries. This is known as **blood pressure**. Blood pressure is measured using the following terms:

- systolic pressure
- diastolic pressure.

The systolic pressure measures the pressure just after the heart has contracted and the diastolic pressure measures the pressure after the heart has relaxed again. Blood pressure alters according to what the individual has been doing, e.g. exercise, stress and anger raise blood pressure and rest and lack of stress keep it lowered.

Average blood pressure differs according to age, gender and weight. It tends to increase with age. An average adult's blood pressure is around:

$$\frac{120}{80} \quad \begin{matrix}\text{(systolic pressure)}\\ \text{(diastolic pressure)}\end{matrix}$$

The pulse occurs when the wall of an artery is expanded by the gush of blood that is pumped through it each time the heart beats. The pulse can be felt in various places around the body. The easiest to find are those where there is a large artery close to the surface, e.g. the wrist, the neck, the groin.

Exercise and the growing circulatory system

Exercise that raises blood pressure is good for us. It gives our heart a workout and improves circulation generally.

Link

Refer to page 84 for activities that raise blood pressure in a healthy way.

Respiratory system

Respiration is another term used to describe breathing. It is our body's most instinctive action, and is the first thing we each do at birth.

Functions

The function of the respiratory system is to take oxygen into the body and expel carbon dioxide. This helps keep oxygen levels stable in the body. The **respiratory system** consists of three main parts:

- air passages
- lungs
- **diaphragm**.

Air passages and the gaseous exchange

The nostrils form the entrance to our nasal cavity and small hairs found there, called cilia, filter out dust, pollen and other impurities to prevent us breathing them in. The nasal cavity also warms and moistens the breathed-in air which assists it on its journey to the lungs.

As air passes down the throat to the larynx (the voice box), the epiglottis at the top of the larynx automatically prevents food from entering the larynx and getting into the lungs. As air passes through the larynx it helps us to vocalise due to the air passing over the vocal cords, causing them to vibrate.

Trachea

The trachea consists of strong rings of cartilage which help it to remain open at all times. This is necessary as closure of the trachea means that the respiratory system will fail.

Bronchi and bronchioles

The trachea branches into two bronchi, one for each lung. Each of the bronchi (the left and right bronchus) divides into smaller and smaller branches known as bronchioles. These, in turn, end in millions of microscopic air sacs called alveoli.

Alveoli

Each alveoli sac is surrounded by capillaries where an exchange of oxygen and carbon dioxide takes place. Oxygen is absorbed, and carbon dioxide is released. This is called the gaseous exchange.

Fig 12.10 The respiratory system

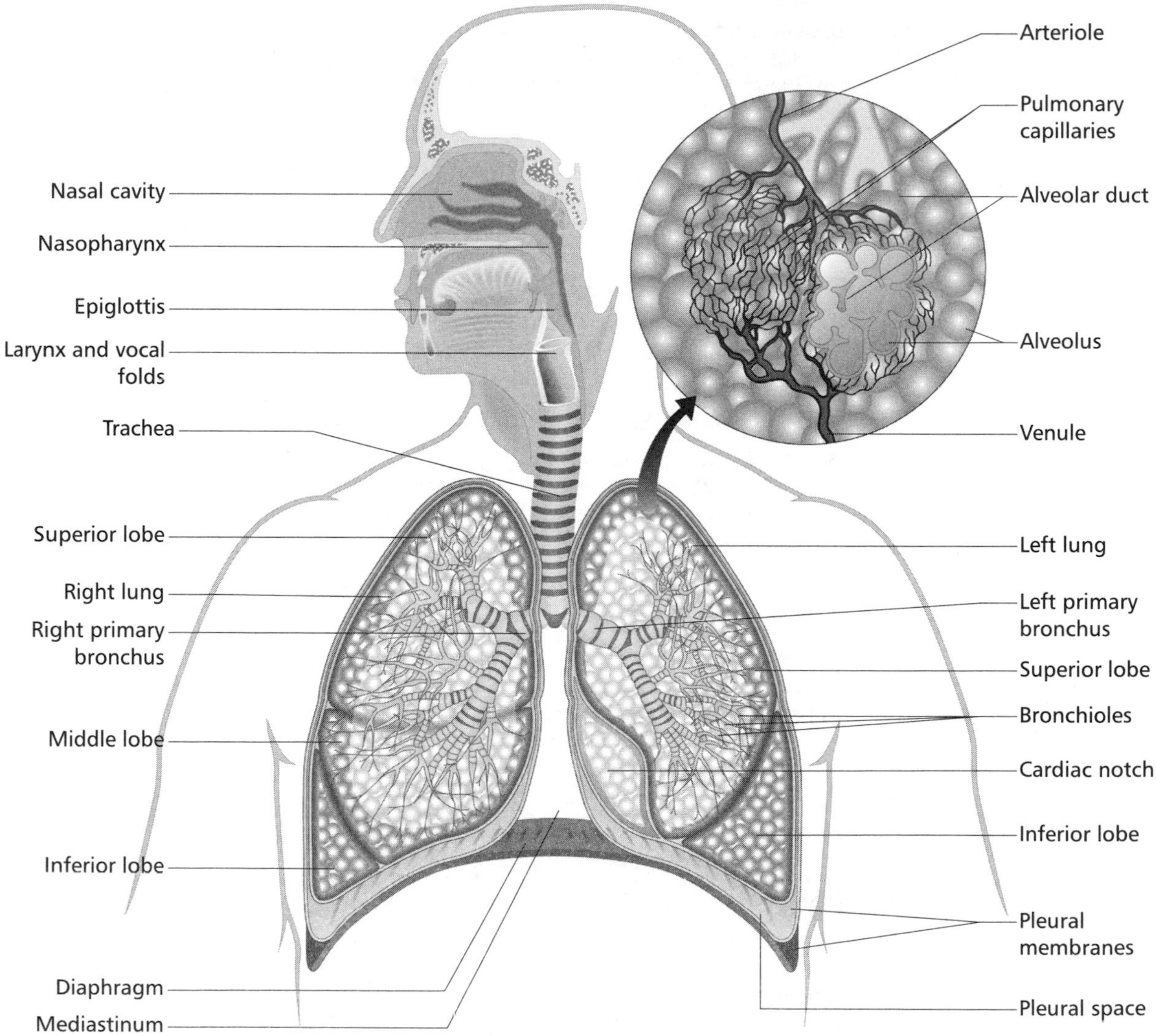

Mechanism of breathing

Lungs

The lungs are the major organs of the respiratory system and they take up most of the chest cavity. Lungs look and feel spongy due to the many bronchioles and millions of air sacs. The lungs are covered by a membrane, called pleura.

Pleura also lines the inside of the chest and the top of the diaphragm. It is smooth and moist to prevent friction as the lungs expand and contract, i.e. as we breathe.

The diaphragm

The diaphragm is a muscle found below the lungs sealing off the chest from the abdominal cavity. The lungs have no muscles of their own and their expansion and contraction depends on the movement of the diaphragm. Therefore it is the diaphragm, and not the lungs that is actually responsible for the process of breathing.

Breathing

The renewal of air in the lungs is caused by two types of breathing:

- **inspiration** – breathing in
- **expiration** – breathing out.

Our breathing is automatically controlled by the brain, which monitors the level of carbon dioxide in the blood. It is the growing level of carbon dioxide that makes the brain signal to the diaphragm to move, therefore causing the body to breathe in and take in the oxygen it needs.

Fig 12.11 Inspiration and expiration

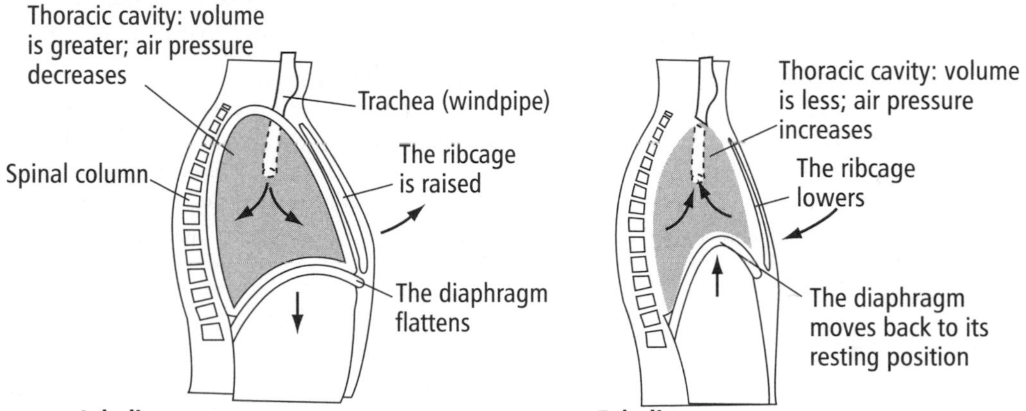

Inhaling
a) The intercostal muscles contract, lifting the ribs upwards and outwards.
b) The diaphragm muscles contract and the diaphragm flattens.
The movements increase the volume of the thoracic cavity. As a result the pressure of air inside the thoracic cavity decreases and becomes less than atmospheric pressure. Air, therefore, is drawn into the lungs.

Exhaling
a) The intercostal muscles relax,letting the ribs drop downwards and inwards.
b) The diaphragm muscles relax and the diaphragm returns to its resting position.
The movements decrease the volume of the thoracic cavity, helped by the elastic recoil of the ribs and diaphragm returning to their resting positions. As a result the pressure of air inside the thoracic cavity increases and becomes greater than atmospheric pressure. Air, therefore, is forced out of the lungs into the trachea.

Inspiration

The chest cavity is fully enclosed and during breathing it alters its shape and size. During inspiration, the diaphragm contracts, flattening and moving downwards. As it flattens, the intercostal muscles move the ribs upwards and outwards, further expanding the chest cavity. This expansion decreases the air pressure in the chest cavity, forcing air into the lungs.

A yawn is an extended inspiration, and a hiccup is a noisy inspiration, triggered by the muscle of the diaphragm going into an irregular spasm, causing a sudden sucking in of air. It is the air passing through the vocal cords that gives us the sudden hiccup sound.

Expiration
During expiration, the chest returns to its 'at rest' size and shape. The diaphragm relaxes and the ribs return to their original position. This increases the pressure in the chest cavity and forces the lungs to expel air.

Coughing is a forced expiration. The air is forced quickly through the vocal cords causing the coughing noise. Coughing can also help clear the lungs and bronchi of congestion, but this coughing of air can contribute to the spread of infection, through bacteria being present in the coughed-up air vapour.

Exercise and respiratory system

Exercise that involves breathing deeply is good for healthy lung development.

Link
Refer to page 84 for activities that help the respiratory system.

Nervous system

The nervous system can be divided into two main parts:

- the **central nervous system** – the brain and the spinal cord
- the **peripheral nervous system** – our 'automatic' nervous system.

Central nervous system

The central nervous system is protected by the meninges. This is a tough membrane that surrounds and supports the brain and spinal cord. The fluid centre of the meninges is known as cerebral spinal fluid. It protects the brain and spinal cord against shock.

The condition meningitis is an inflammation of the meninges.

Investigation of cerebral spinal fluid often takes place if a person is losing control of their legs, or has trouble with maintaining normal balance. It can help to identify if the myelin sheath that surrounds the spinal cord is breaking up, leaving areas unprotected and therefore vulnerable. Conditions such as multiple sclerosis can be indicated in this way.

The condition spina bifida is a developmental problem of the central nervous system.

The brain
The brain has a variety of crucial functions:

- It receives information via the senses and sends messages to other parts of the body.
- It controls the movements of our muscles.
- It is central to the various automatic body responses, e.g. breathing, digestion, circulation.
- It controls our intelligence, memory and the processing of conscious functioning, e.g. speech, thought, etc.

Fig 12.12 The brain

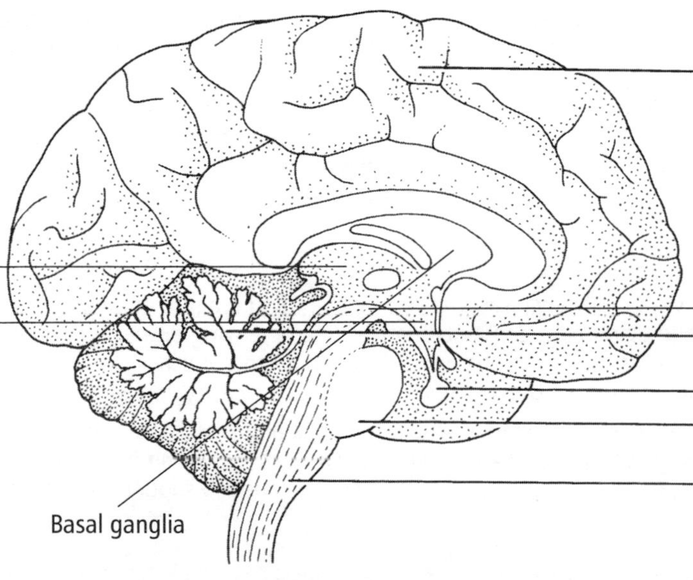

Fig 12.13 The transmission of energy

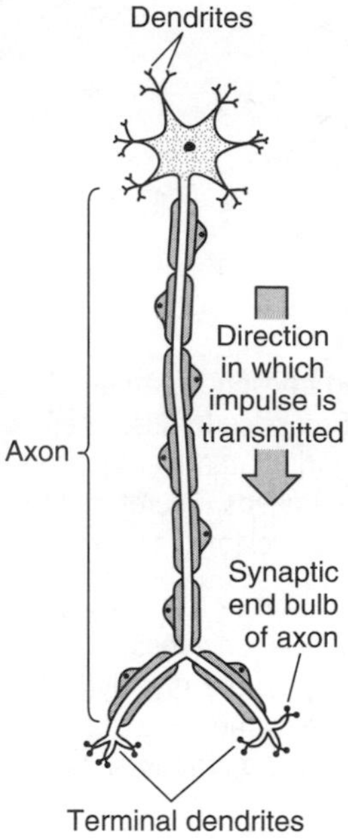

Peripheral nervous system

Each nerve cell (or neuron) is a bundle of axons and dendrites. Axons carry information away, and dendrites carry information towards. The transmission of nervous energy generated in the nerve cell is called the impulse and the point of transmission is called a synapse. Energy moves along the axon towards its destination, with the help of chemical substances called neuro-transmitters.

Nerves

The peripheral nervous system is divided into two parts:

- the sympathetic system which prepares the body for action, often referred to as 'fight or flight'
- the parasympathetic system which prepares the body to rest, and for processes such as reproduction and excretion.

The sympathetic and parasympathetic systems counteract and balance each other. Sympathetic nerves come from along the whole length of the spinal cord, whereas parasympathetic nerves start from the base of the brain and the lower end of the spinal cord.

Functions

The function of the nervous system is to recognise changes within, to or around the body (stimuli) and to co-ordinate an appropriate response. These responses result in messages passing rapidly from one part of the body to another. There are receptors to stimuli both outside and inside the body.

Exteroceptors respond to stimuli outside the body. These are:

- skin
- eyes
- ears
- nose
- taste buds.

Proprioceptors respond to stimuli inside the body. These are:

- our internal temperature gauges
- our receptor muscles.

The nervous system contributes to the smooth functioning of **homeostasis** in the body. Homeostasis includes:

- temperature
- blood pressure
- blood sugar levels
- chemical messengers, e.g. hormones.

There are nerves and hormones involved in all the processes needed to maintain each of the body's normal 'states'. For example, in maintaining temperature control there are nerves and hormones to:

- regulate oxygen and carbon dioxide within the lungs
- regulate the contents of the blood, removing unwanted substances
- deal with food and liquid within the intestines
- regulate the level of water and salts in the kidneys, removing urine and other waste products.

Link

Refer to Unit 27 for how to support children with physical conditions affected by the central nervous system, such as spina bifida.

Energy systems

We need energy for a variety of reasons, e.g. to:

- build and maintain body cells
- replace any heat lost from the body
- transport substances between cells
- help with specific functions, e.g. digestion and respiration.

The body has just one usable form of energy. It is known as ATP (adenosine triphosphate). All food has to be converted into ATP before any of the energy the food item can potentially provide can be released. Energy gained from food (chemical energy) is either changed into movement (kinetic energy) or stored as fat (potential energy).

How ATP is produced

Our body's cells produce ATP in three ways:

- ATP-PCr system
- glycolytic system
- oxidative system.

ATP-PCr system

ATP works together with another high-energy phosphate molecule called phosphocreatine (PCr) that also stores energy. ATP and PCr support the energy needs of muscles for just brief amounts of time. For example, the ATP-PCr system is used on its own during an athlete's short sprint race. It would not however be able to provide for prolonged energy needs. Therefore the following two systems are needed by the body for a more sustained energy release.

Glycolytic system

This system involves the breakdown of glucose in the body through special enzymes (glycolytic enzymes). The involvement of the ATP-PCr system *together with* the glycolytic system enables the body's muscles to produce an energy force even when the oxygen supply is limited. These two systems together supply energy needs during the early stages of high-intensity exercise.

Oxidative system

The oxidative system is the final stage of energy production. It uses oxygen and is therefore an aerobic process (see below). This system follows on from the glycolytic system and is used by the body during longer-term activity, providing a steady supply of oxygen to the body's muscles.

Energy values of food

The three main components of food are carbohydrate, fat and protein.

- Carbohydrate produces an energy value of 17 kj (kilojoules or calories) per gram.
- Fat produces an energy value of 39 kj per gram.
- Protein produces an energy value of 18 kj per gram.

If the total energy value of food consumed in a day is greater than the total energy value used in exercise and general physical activity, then the remaining (excess) energy will be stored as fat in the body.

Metabolism

Metabolism is the term used to describe the processes that take place in breaking down food and using it or storing it. Metabolism is influenced by gender, genetics, age and health. It is also affected by the percentage of muscle present.

- Females tend to have a slower metabolism than males.
- Fast or slow metabolism can be genetically inherited.
- The resting metabolic rate decreases with age.
- Conditions such as hypothyroidism can slow down metabolism, whereas hyperthyroidism can cause it to be faster than average.
- The higher the level of lean muscle in the body, the faster the metabolic rate is likely to be.

A small amount of body fat is however needed by the body to maintain health and it is used in the organs, muscles and central nervous system. Four per cent of the overall body weight is needed as 'essential fat' in these organs. It is clear that too much fat in the diet is bad for us, and as fat is less effective as an energy source, a diet high in carbohydrate (and also protein) is far healthier.

The body uses differing amounts of energy according to whether it is at rest, or active, and also according to what that activity might be. Each individual person has a basal metabolic rate (BMR) which is their minimum level of energy intake needed to keep the body functioning appropriately. Energy needs are measured in calories per second. The metabolic rate is influenced by activities such as:

- digestion
- temperature
- physical activity
- general day-to-day activity.

Digestion

The body's metabolic rate increases for several hours after eating. It also takes more energy to digest fat than it does to digest carbohydrate or protein. This is why athletes and sports people favour a high carbohydrate diet prior to a game or performance.

Temperature

The body uses more energy if it is cold to maintain its required temperature. This is why people tend to need a greater food intake during the winter months.

Physical activity

Both general day-to-day activity and planned exercise and physical exertion increase the use of muscle activity, and therefore increase the use of the body's energy stores. Again, this demonstrates why hunger is usual after exercising.

Fat distribution

Being overweight and having too much excess fat is clearly bad for our health, but where the fat lies is also important. Body shape plays a part in fat distribution, with people who carry most of their body fat around their abdomen and middle of their body (android or apple-shape people) being at greater risk of heart disease, diabetes, stroke, some cancers and high blood pressure than those who carry their excess fat on their hips and thighs (gynoid or pear-shape people).

Anaerobic and aerobic

As energy is released into the body from our food it is stored in a high-energy compound called adenosine triphosphate (ATP).

Energy can be released into the body either quickly for short amounts of time, or more slowly for sustained activity.

- The fast release of energy is the anaerobic power system where energy is used without the use of oxygen. It produces just two molecules of the compound ATP.
- The more endurance-related system which utilises oxygen is called the aerobic system. This provides around 38 molecules of ATP.

For an illustrated discussion of energy and the chemical make-up and processes used in energy production, you may find it helpful to refer to Honeybourne (2007) or to any good biology text.

Developmental

Differences between mature and immature systems

Physical development is maturational. Most children follow the same pattern in their development, even though they may reach each stage at slightly different ages. It is largely a process of one skill level building on the skills that have been learned before. Examples of this are the ways that physical development builds:

- From the simple to the complex – this means that a child learns simple actions such as starting to walk before they can learn more complex actions such as hopping, jumping or running.
- From **cephalo** to **caudal** – this can be defined as physical control starting at the head and moving down through the body. For example, head control is attained before the spine is strong enough for the infant to sit unsupported, and sitting unsupported is attained before they are able to stand.
- From **proximal** to **distal** – these terms refer to how a child develops actions near to the centre of their body before they develop control of the outer reaches of their body. For example, a child can hug and carry a large teddy bear before they are able to fasten teddy's clothing.
- From general to specific – the more generalised physical responses of an infant showing excitement when recognising a favourite carer gradually progress to become the facial smile of an older child greeting the same person.

Other examples of how the body's systems mature include:

- Bones – the hardening of bones is called ossification. These harden at different times, but again follow the same patterns as explained above, moving from the head downwards, and from the torso outwards. From this we can see that young children have a natural flexibility due to their bones being softer than older children and adults, but clearly this flexibility can easily be lost if it is not encouraged and nurtured through exercise.
- Muscles – the muscle fibres of young children are less well developed. They are soft and watery, gradually lengthening, thickening and becoming less watery throughout childhood, until adolescence when there is a sudden surge of muscle growth in line with the sudden growth spurt generally, i.e. puberty – changes in height and weight, and the development of secondary sexual characteristics. Although environmental influences such as lifestyle, diet and living conditions always play a part in development, genetic differences between boys and girls may also have an impact, with adult males having a greater muscle strength than adult females, influenced by the sex hormones.

Link

The activities set out from page 66 onwards show how children can be taught various movements and develop skills appropriately, illustrating the immature, intermediate and mature phases at Key Stage 1 of:

- walking
- running
- stopping
- jumping
- hopping
- skipping

Professional Practice

- Understanding how these skills develop will help you plan appropriate activities.

Links to all-round development

It should also be remembered that children have different body shapes, which can influence their physical development and also how they feel about their body. Some children are naturally 'springy' and light on their feet, whereas others are more physically awkward and heavy footed. Some children will be genetically predisposed to be tall or short, small framed or large framed.

All these factors can impact on physical ability and how all-round development is affected. This is particularly relevant as children reach puberty and adolescence. There can be enormous differences between the maturity of the bodies of children of the same age as the onset of puberty can vary by several years. For example, a boy of 15 who is the only one within his peer group who has not yet reached puberty and experienced the growth spurt, usual body changes and facial shaping that his friends have, is likely to feel self-conscious and need encouragement to feel good about himself. This can affect confidence to speak out, to volunteer and try new challenges, potentially holding him back both socially and intellectually.

Similarly, some girls will feel embarrassed by early breast development and growth, leaving them taller and often of a larger build than their peers, and conversely, others will find the late onset of puberty leaves them feeling unattractive and childlike compared to their peers.

Both situations can affect self-confidence and self-esteem, and again, can potentially impact on development in other areas too.

Later ages

The slowing down of all body processes is the ageing process. Ageing actually starts as soon as we have been born. The body becomes less able to cope with life's stresses. Examples include:

- deterioration of vision
- deterioration of hearing

- mental alertness diminishes
- skin loses its elasticity
- joints become less supple.

How the body ages

This can be summarised as follows.

- Eyes – muscles weaken, lenses deteriorate, causing long sightedness and sometimes cataracts.
- Taste and smell – taste buds decline and the sense of smell becomes less sensitive.
- Teeth – decay is possible due to caries, and in old age both jaws shrink.
- Lungs – the lungs shrink and become clogged and breathing capacity declines.
- Heart – the output drops, the heartbeat may become erratic and valves become rigid and may leak.
- Blood – flow decreases progressively and blood pressure rises in old age.
- Kidneys – blood becomes less well cleansed by the kidneys due to loss of filter units and the drop in blood flow.
- Ovaries – at menopause, the production of ova ceases and the output of sex hormones falls.
- Spleen – fewer antibodies are produced to fight micro-organisms in the blood stream.
- Height – average height decreases in old age, particularly when there is damage to the spinal discs causing a reduction in the size of gaps between bones of the vertebrae.
- Hair – loss of pigment causes hair to turn grey. It also thins and baldness is common in men.
- Hearing – some loss of hearing is common, particularly of the higher tones.
- Balance – the sense of balance declines.
- Brain – brain efficiency is impaired as brain cells decline in number and the blood flow drops.
- Bones – loss of calcium makes bones brittle, particularly common in women, and joints may stiffen with arthritis.
- Skin – a loss of elasticity makes skin thin, wrinkly and discoloured.
- Liver – the size of the liver diminishes as cell replacement declines and chemical processes slow down.
- Muscles – muscles feel weaker, partly from lack of use and partly due to a reduced blood supply.
- Arteries – the arteries harden and their walls thicken, speeding up the decline of the heart and other main organs.

In general, as the body ages it becomes more susceptible to disease, wounds heal less easily and illnesses that were minor at younger ages become far more serious.

activity
INDIVIDUAL WORK
12.1

P1

Produce a book showing each of the following:

- skeletal system
- muscular system
- circulatory system
- respiratory system
- nervous system
- energy system.

Make clear in your illustrations the differences between the immature and the mature systems.

Be able to devise, justify, prepare, implement, monitor and evaluate a range of physical activities suitable for babies and children

Basic framework for physical session

As with any planned activity, the adult setting it up usually needs to have some idea of the shape the activity will take, e.g.

- What is the overall aim?
- What preparation is needed?
- How will the activity start?
- What body actions will be involved, e.g. balance, movement, upper body work, lower body work, or a combination?
- What links (where applicable) will there be to other curriculum areas?
- How will the activity be wound down?

Warm-up

With physical activity, particularly as children get older and the actions they undertake are more strenuous and test their ability and agility to greater lengths, it is important that the body is prepared well, i.e. it needs to be warmed up.

Each physical session should usually start with a warm-up. This involves reflection on previous activities, a reminder of health and safety and some form of physical action that will help raise the core body temperature, loosen up the joints and increase blood flow to the muscles to help prevent strain or injury.

Reflective warm-up

Reflection is about thinking back to what has gone before and using that knowledge in the 'now'. When reflecting on a previous session or activity linked to the seaside you might, for example, encourage children to remember how they moved as the sea, the wind and the boats bobbing on the waves. This time you want them to think how seagulls might get fish for their dinner, how whales might come up for air, or how an octopus moves through the deeper water, encouraging them to compare and contrast movements and explore new ideas.

Health and safety warm-up

Children need to be reminded about their use of space. Encourage them to look around them and to identify a clear space in which they can turn without bumping anyone else. This is not an easy skill for some children to develop. Encourage them to observe the spacing of others and demonstrate and join in where needed.

Issues of speed need to be carefully considered. The supervising adult needs to keep it controlled. It is clearly unsafe for children to be imitating racing cars or planes, running at full speed around a hall or room.

You may need to remind children how to lift and carry certain items of equipment. Good manual handling techniques should be encouraged from the start.

Before any physical activity you should ask yourself:

- Are the children wearing suitable clothing and footwear for the activity?
- Is the space you are using safe and clear of obstacles?
- Is the space sufficient for the number of children and the activities planned?
- Do all the children understand how to use space, and have an awareness of others when moving?
- Do all children understand the rules and boundaries that have been set?
- Is any equipment being used the right size and weight for the children?

Physical action warm-up

Depending on what the main activity is going to be, examples would include:

- running on the spot
- taking weight on different body parts, e.g. toes, heels, buttocks
- standing on one leg
- lifting different body parts up high and stretching, e.g. stretching arms up as high as possible, lifting one leg up whilst using hands on floor to help balance.

Link

An example is given, linked to an activity idea, in case study 12.1 on page 73.

Fig 12.14 Warm-up exercises are important

Development of theme

Very few physical actions are introduced to children simply as an 'action'. They are introduced within the context of a theme, or are specifically linked to new knowledge, thinking or experience.

The following examples are by no means complete lists. There are many more ideas you could add to them.

In linking physical activity to a current theme on pond life, you could ask children to devise ways to move their bodies that would help them to:

- glide across the surface of the pond like a water-boatman
- hop from water lily to water lily like a frog or toad
- hover gracefully above the water like a damselfly
- swim like a fish
- wander over rocks and pebbles like a newt
- develop from being a tadpole to becoming a fully grown frog
- pretend to open as a water lily at dawn and close again at dusk.

In linking physical activity to a current theme on flight, you could ask children to:

- twirl like a helicopter
- rise up and down like a hot air balloon
- glide and then land as the hot air balloon
- fly like a plane
- swoop like a bird
- soar like an eagle.

In linking physical activity to a current theme on emotions, you could ask children to move showing feelings of:

- sadness
- happiness
- caution
- hesitancy
- worry

- anger
- pride
- embarrassment

encouraging them to stoop, dance, sway, etc.

Sometimes you will be aiming to get children to link skills together, forming a sequence, e.g. through the use of basic body actions to travel, jump, turn, gesture, be still.

It is important that any sequence you suggest is logical for the child's body (and understanding) to achieve.

Conclusion and wind-down activity

At the end of each physical session, children should be encouraged to slow down with gentle actions that calm both body and mind. A child who is still in the mindset of 'fast cars, roaring lions', etc. is likely to be less receptive to concentrating on what happens next in his day, than one who has 'parked his car in the car park, or left the lion asleep on a sunny rock'.

Winding-down actions could include:

- moving quietly around the room, until asked to be still
- working with a partner to 'mirror' each other's non-locomotion actions
- balancing carefully and remain in position
- gently swaying from side to side until asked to be still
- slowly curling up and then stretching, repeating each action three times.

Rest and recovery

Following extensive or strenuous activity, there should be opportunities for recovery. Planning a day that alternates between high physical activity and more passive activities will serve both the physical and mental needs of most children best.

activity
INDIVIDUAL WORK 12.2

P2

M1

Prepare a set of information cards to give to secondary school pupils.

- On one side describe the effects of exercise on the body's systems using visual images to support your text.
- On the reverse side, explain in detail the effects of exercise on growth and development.

Teaching basic skills

Most students on the BTEC National CCLD course will work with children aged from 0 to 8 years. This means that currently you will most likely be working with one of the following frameworks:

- Birth to Three Matters
  - Most early years settings will have a copy.
- Foundation Stage Curriculum
- Early Years Foundation Stage (EYFS)
  - All early years settings have copies.
- National Curriculum Key Stage.

Please note that from September 2008 the new Early Years Foundation Stage (EYFS) will become mandatory, although many early years settings started to work with it from 2007. The EYFS supports the development of children from 0 to 5 years. It builds on the guidelines of the Foundation stage Curriculum and Birth to Three Matters strategy, as part of Every Child Matters, Change for children. An overview of the main principles and themes of the EYFS are set out on p.155.

Full details of the EYFS can be found at www.dfes.gov.uk. The structure for the learning area Cummunication, Language and Literacy is included in Unit 18, p.226 and for Problem Solving, Reason and Numbering (formerly referred to as Mathematical Development) in Unit 17 p.156.

Within the Birth to Three Matters framework

The Birth to Three Matters framework focuses on the child rather than on any specific area or curriculum headings. It is divided into four main 'aspects'. These are:

- A strong child
- A skilful communicator
- A competent learner
- A healthy child.

The 'Healthy child' is the aspect most directly linked with physical activity. It is divided into four sections:

- Emotional well-being
- Growing and developing
- Keeping safe
- Healthy choices.

Fig 12.15 A healthy diet helps a child to be well nourished

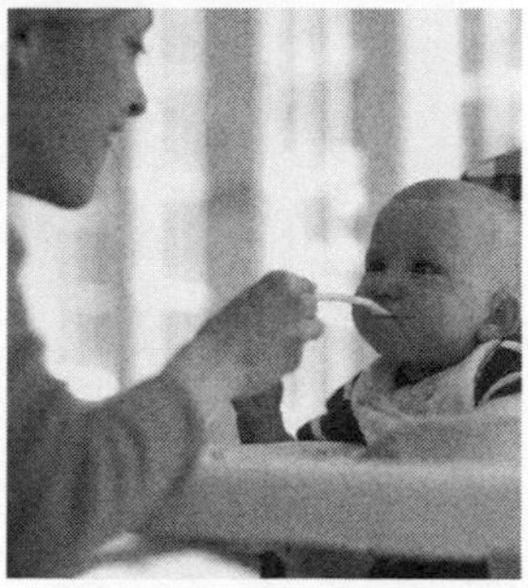

Within 'Growing and developing' it focuses on:

- Being well nourished
- Being active, rested and protected
- Gaining control of the body
- Acquiring physical skills.

These areas of focus are also seen throughout both the Foundation Stage Curriculum and the Physical Education programme within the National Curriculum.

Refer to a copy of the Birth to Three Matters framework for full details of each aspect.

Within the Foundation Stage Curriculum and the Practice Guidance for the EYFS

Both frameworks consider physical development and the Practice Guidance for the Early Years Foundation Stage as being about improving co-ordination, control, manipulation and movement. They are also about building confidence and self-esteem and enabling children to feel positive benefits from being healthy and active.

The QCA guidelines say that to give all children the best opportunities for effective physical development, practitioners should give particular attention to:

- Planning activities that offer appropriate physical challenges;
- Providing sufficient space, indoors and outdoors, to set up relevant activities;
- Giving sufficient time for children to use a range of equipment;
- Providing resources that can be used in a variety of ways or to support specific skills;
- Introducing the language of movement to children, alongside their actions;
- Providing time and opportunities for children with physical disabilities or motor impairments to develop their physical skills, working as necessary with physiotherapists and occupational therapists;
- Using additional adult help, if necessary, to support individuals and to encourage increased independence in physical activities.

(Based on material from the QCA Standards site for PE at Key Stage 1, www.dfes.gov.uk)

Early Learning Goals

The Early Learning Goals for physical development are:

- move with confidence, imagination and in safety
- move with control and co-ordination
- travel around, under, over and through balancing and climbing equipment
- show awareness of space, of themselves and of others
- recognise the importance of keeping healthy and those things which contribute to this
- recognise the changes that happen to their bodies when they are active
- use a range of small and large equipment
- handle tools, objects, construction and malleable materials safely and with increasing control.

Within the National Curriculum

The National Curriculum for PE at Key Stages 1 and 2 is divided into a number of units under the following physical activity headings:

- Dance activities
- Games activities
- Invasion activities
- Net/wall games
- Striking and fielding games
- Gymnastic activities
- Swimming activities and water safety
- Athletic activities
- Outdoor and adventurous activities.

In Year 1 it is usual for children to work through:

- Dance activities – unit 1
- Games activities – unit 1
- Gymnastic activities – unit 1.

In Year 2 it is usual for children to work through:

- Dance activities – unit 2
- Games activities – unit 2
- Gymnastic activities – unit 2
- Swimming and water safety – unit 1
- Athletic activities – unit 1 (possibly)
- Outdoor and adventurous activities – unit 1 (possibly).

These form the basic skills needed to enjoy a range of everyday physical activities and organised games. They have been designed to build up and develop skills year on year, introducing new areas of skill development as is felt appropriate for the understanding and physical development of the age range in each year group.

Within a mixed ability group not all aspects of all sessions can be attained by all children. As an adult leading an active session you will need to find ways of accommodating any children with additional needs within the framework of your session. An example would be to have:

- open activities, in which all children can get involved in the same activity
- modified activities, where the task as a whole is adapted to make the pitch easier or harder to suit the needs of individuals
- parallel activities, where children are presented with different activities from the same activity area, and use rules, structures and equipment that suit their needs
- included activities, where children take part together in an activity but different conditions apply to members of the group or class
- separate activities, where children need activities specific to their needs, and these are not the same as those given to the rest of the group or class.

(Based on material from the QCA Standards site for PE at Key Stage 1, www.dfes.gov.uk)

Within Key Stages 1 and 2

At Key Stage 1, the QCA Standards state that PE offers opportunities for children to:

- Become skilful and intelligent performers;
- Acquire and develop skills, performing with increasing physical competence and confidence, in a range of physical activities and contexts;
- Learn how to select and apply skills, tactics and compositional ideas to suit activities that need different approaches and ways of thinking;
- Develop their ideas in a creative way;
- Set targets for themselves and compete against others individually and as team members;
- Understand what it takes to persevere, succeed and acknowledge others' success;
- Respond to challenges in a range of physical contexts and environments;
- Take the initiative, lead activity and focus on improving aspects of their own performance.

- Discover their own aptitudes and preferences for different activities;
- Make informed decisions about the importance of exercise in their lives;
- Develop positive attitudes to participation in physical activity.

(Based on material from the QCA Standards site for PE at Key Stage 1, www.dfes.gov.uk)

The objectives for Dance Activities Unit 1 are that children should learn:
Section 1 – Acquiring and developing skills

- To explore movement ideas and respond imaginatively to a range of stimuli;
- To move confidently and safely in their own and general space, using changes of speed, level and direction.

Section 2 – Selecting and applying skills, tactics and compositional ideas

- To compose and link movement to make simple dances with clear beginnings, middles and ends;
- To perform movement phrases using a range of body actions and body parts.

Section 3 – Knowledge and understanding of fitness and health

- To recognise how their body feels when still and when exercising.

Section 4 – Evaluating and improving performance

- To talk about dance ideas inspired by different stimuli;
- To copy, watch, and describe dance movements.

(Based on material from the QCA Standards site for PE at Key Stage 1, www.dfes.gov.uk)

The objectives for Games Activities Unit 1 are that children should learn:
Section 1 – Acquiring and developing skills

- To be confident and safe in the spaces used to play games;
- To explore and use skills, actions and ideas individually and in combination to suit the game they are playing.

Section 2 – Selecting and applying skills, tactics and compositional ideas

- How to choose and use skills effectively for particular games.

Section 3 – Knowledge and understanding of fitness and health

- That being active is good for them and fun.

Section 4 – Evaluating and improving performance

- To watch, copy and describe what others are doing;
- To describe what they are doing.

(Based on material from the QCA Standards site for PE at Key Stage 1, www.dfes.gov.uk)

The objectives for Gymnastic Activities Unit 1 are that children should learn:
Section 1 – Acquiring and developing new skills

- To explore gymnastic actions and still shapes;
- To move confidently and safely in their own and general space using changes of speed, level and direction.

Section 2 – Selecting and applying skills, tactics and compositional ideas

- To copy or create and link movement phrases with beginnings, middles and ends;
- To perform movement phrases using a range of body actions and body parts.

Section 3 – Knowledge and understanding of fitness and health

- To know how to carry and place apparatus;
- To recognise how their body feels when still and when exercising.

Section 4 – Evaluating and improving performance

- To watch, copy and describe what they and others have done.

(Based on material from the QCA Standards site for PE at Key Stage 1, www.dfes.gov.uk)

Link
Refer to page 94 for ideas on adapting activities to accommodate a range of needs.

General body management

Fig 12.16 Developing actions

Core Movement Skills for Key Stage 1

There are a number of core movements that form the basis of the physical education curriculum. These are essential at Key Stage 1 and it is therefore important to clarify the essential aspects of each of these movements. They are broken down into stages which enables the teacher to facilitate and assess learning. It is important that you understand the basic movement skills involved in PE, and time spent studying these core movements will be time well spent.

Activity 1: Walking

Immature phase
In this phase there is an uneven, unco-ordinated stride pattern. The feet may be displaced inwards or outwards. The arms hang at the sides and do not assist the action. Bodily movement is not in an upright position.

Intermediate phase
In this phase the stride pattern is becoming co-ordinated. The feet placement begins to show lift and transference of weight. The arms begin to complement the leg action. The posture of the body is now beginning to show tension and the correct direction of movement.

Mature phase
The weight is transferred from one foot to the other with the toes pointing in the direction of travel. As one foot is placed on the floor the other one is raised slightly and so leaves contact with the floor before a reversal process takes place. The arms are at the sides swinging forward and back in opposition to the movement of the feet. The body is upright showing good posture.

Activity 2: Running

Immature phase
This stage is typified by an uneven unco-ordinated stride which has no flight phase. The leg action tends to be 'out and around' from the hip which enables the child to maintain balance more effectively. The arms tend to be held outward and have a small range of movement.

Intermediate phase

Fig 12.16 Developing actions

The support leg extends at take-off and thus increases the flight phase. The stride length also increases and the arms swing more vigorously vertically and with less horizontal movement.

Mature phase
The knee is raised high and swings forward quickly. The knee of the support leg bends slightly. There is a great increase in the flight phase and the length of the stride. The arms swing in opposition to the legs.

Activity 3: Stopping

Immature phase
There is difficulty in controlling the body. The child is unable to stop immediately at the appropriate point in a practice or game. There is a lack of reaction to visual or sound stimuli and minimal body tension. The movement of the arms and legs is inappropriate. The body is not at rest.

Intermediate phase
The child is able to respond to instruction but difficulties in maintaining whole body stillness are shown in slight upper body and head movement.

Mature phase
The two feet are placed firmly on the floor with the weight evenly distributed. Tension promotes stillness throughout the body with the head focusing on the direction of travel, creating an upright posture.

Fig 12.16 Developing actions

Activity 4: Jumping

Immature phase
The arms are not co-ordinated with the jump, they are simply used to maintain balance. The trunk is mainly projected upwards for height, but not forward for distance. At take-off and landing the child has difficulty in using both feet simultaneously.

Intermediate phase
The arms initiate the jump with upward movement. The trunk is again mainly vertical in movement. There is a greater extension from the hips, knees and ankles at take-off; these remain quite bent during flight.

Mature phase
The arms move backwards and then forwards just prior to take-off. The arms are held high throughout the jump. The trunk is propelled at 45°, giving major emphasis to the horizontal direction of the jump. The hips, legs and ankles are completely extended at take-off.

Activity 5: Hopping

Immature phase
The leg hardly leaves the floor. There is a complete lack of co-ordination with upper and lower body. The no-hopping foot can remain constantly in contact with the floor. The upper part of the body tends to lean forward. There is a complete lack of appropriate arm action to aid elevation and balance.

Intermediate phase
There is a hopping action but it is not easily maintained, due to lack of awareness of upper body and lower body movement. There is limited use of the arms to assist elevation and balance.

Fig 12.16 Developing actions

Mature phase
One foot is continually lifted from the floor. The knees are slightly bent to assist elevation of the body and to support landing. There is tension of the body, particularly the hopping leg. The posture is upright, with back straight. The head is facing forwards and the arms are by the sides with elbows bent to assist elevation and the balance of the hop. The non-hopping leg should be bent at the knee and held at that position during the hop to either assist hop or help elevation.

Activity 6: Skipping

This movement needs to be introduced after the progression of the hopping action.

Immature phase
There is a lack of co-ordination of the alternate leg and arm action. The body posture lacks tension and position to assist flight. The knees and toes are not straight or stretched.

Intermediate phase
There is an improvement in co-ordination but a lack of knee lift and poor leg position. There is limited spring in the elevation. The arms are by the sides and bent but have little movement to assist elevation. The movement becomes progressively more fluid.

Mature phase
The arms should be held away from the sides of the body and should be slightly bent with a forward, backward swing to help the momentum of the body. The body tension is similar to the hop. The leg action is an alternate movement from one foot to the other in which the whole body is stretched in the spring. The knees are straight and the toes are pointed towards the floor. It should be a fluent and rhythmic action.

Projecting objects

Fig 12.17 Developing actions

Activity 26: Throwing

The immature phase
In the immature phase there is very little movement of the trunk or legs, the action comes mainly from the arm. The arm action is in fact a pushing action from the elbow, and the follow through tends to be downward and forward.

The intermediate phase
During the intermediate phase, the arm prepares to throw by moving sideways, upwards and backwards, to a point where the ball is almost behind the head, at the same time the trunk rotates backwards. As the throw starts, the arm moves forward in a high position and the trunk moves backward on the non-throwing side. The forceful action of the arm causes the foot on the throwing side to step forward, as the wrist follows through propelling the ball forward and downward.

The mature phase
In the mature phase the arm is taken back as above, the throwing shoulder drops as the trunk rotates backwards taking the weight on to the back foot in the preparation phase. Then as the throw begins the hips rotate leading the shoulders, the elbow leads the wrist, and the weight moves from back to front. The thumb rotates downwards on release of the ball with the fingers being noticeably together.

Receiving objects

Fig 12.18 Developing actions

Activity 27: Catching

The immature phase
As the ball moves toward the child there is an initial avoidance reaction noted in the turning away of the head or the protection of the face with the arms. The arms at this stage are straight at the elbow, and there is limited movement until the ball makes contact. The child then attempts to scoop the ball into the chest. There is very little use of the hands in this stage of catching. The catch is inevitably poorly timed.

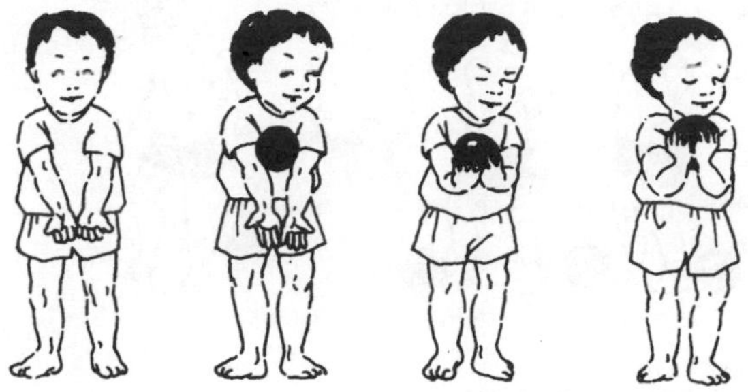

The intermediate phase
Avoidance reaction improves, with eyes closing when contact with the ball is made. At this stage the arms are held slightly bent in front of the body, and initial contact is attempted with the hands. The ball is still however scooped into the chest. Hands are held opposite to each other, fingers point toward the ball. The closing of the hands around the ball is poorly timed.

The mature phase
There is no avoidance reaction. The eyes follow the ball until contact is made. Fingers also point toward ball, and arms give on contact. Arms adjust position to flight of ball, and hands are cupped. The catch is well timed and hands clasp around ball on contact.

Footwork

Fig 12.19 Developing actions

Activity 25: Kicking

The immature phase
It is noticeable that in the immature phase, the leg tends to just kick at the ball, with very little follow through. There is also little help in kicking from the arms or trunk.

The intermediate phase
In the intermediate phase the child learns to bring the leg backwards in the preparation phase, keeping the leg bent until contact with the ball has been made.

The mature phase
During the mature phase the arm on the kicking side moves backward whilst the other arm moves forward. The movement of the kicking leg starts at the hip, with the non-kicking leg slightly bent at the knee. The leg swings through a long arc, toe is pointed on contact with the ball, after which the leg has a long follow through, at which point the non-kicking foot rises up onto its toes.

Professional Practice

- It should always be remembered that many activities can be carried out both indoors and outdoors.

Indoor activities

Creative movement and dance

Moving to music, responding to visual stimuli such as a painting, or expressing emotions are all examples of creative movement. Linking movement to a theme, e.g. the weather, offers opportunities to run like the wind, sway like a breeze, twirl as a tornado, billow like a cloud, etc.

case study 12.1

A dance session in a primary school

Miss Powton is helping her class to '... move confidently and safely in their own and general space, using changes of speed ...'.

- Her warm-up activity was for her class to sway gently from side to side, and round and round, remaining in one place, ensuring that they did not touch anyone else.
- In the main part of the activity the children were asked to at first be a flower, opening and shutting its petals, and then a bee buzzing around looking for nectar, alternating their actions as they moved around the room.
- At the end of the activity, Miss Powton asked them to be the bee that settled into the centre of the flower.

activity

1 Do you consider that the activity was suitable for the planned objective?
2 How else could this objective be met? Draw up a list of ideas.

Small and large play equipment

Manipulative skills and fine motor development can be helped through activities such as:

- construction
- small world play
- posting boxes
- stacking beakers.

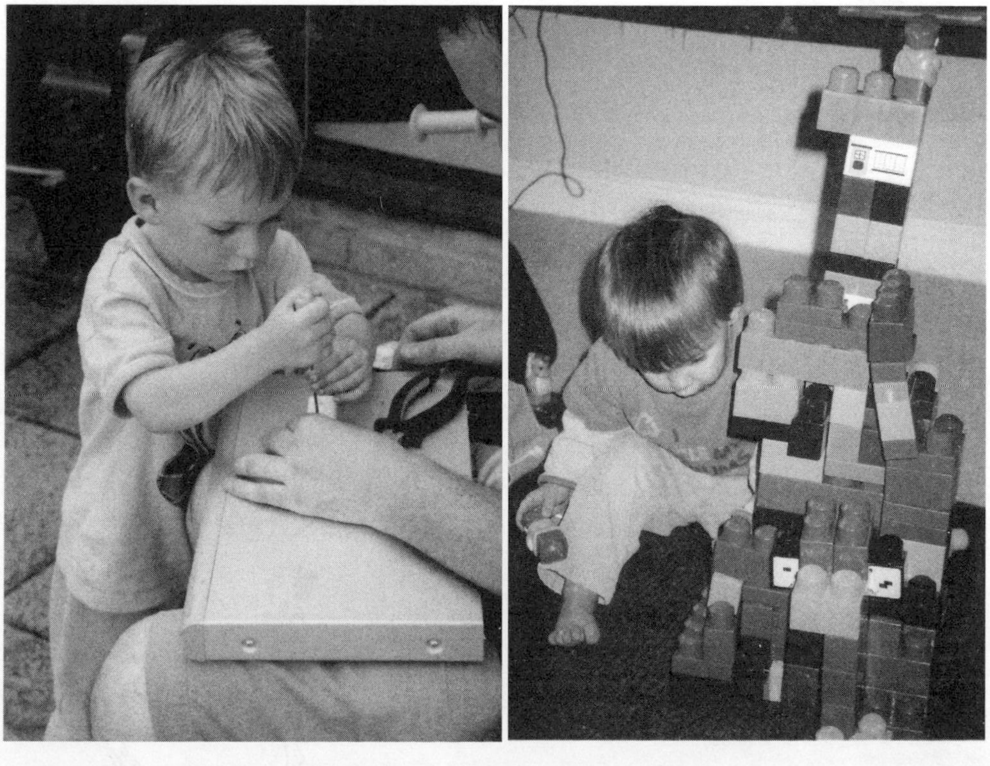

Fig 12.20 Harry and Alfie enjoy constucting

- jigsaw puzzles
- malleable materials such as clay, dough, sand, water
- art and craft materials such as crayons, painting, pencils, gluing, collaging, model making with papier mâché, boxes, etc.
- sewing, threading, weaving
- writing, both formally and informally during play, e.g. within role play settings
- playing musical instruments
- using keyboards: music and IT
- using small equipment such as magnifying glasses, binoculars, magnets, weighing scales, measuring sticks
- handling hoops, balls, quoits and beanbags
- skipping.

Large motor skills are helped through:

- dressing-up clothes
- tunnels to crawl through
- wheeled toys
- large hoops
- knocking down skittles
- balance beams
- stepping stones to walk across
- large-scale construction kits
- indoor gym equipment such as ropes, climbing frames, ladders, swing bars, poles, trampolines and springboards.

Gymnastic activities also involve large motor skills and can include:

- jumping activities
- stepping activities
- rolling actions
- sliding actions
- balances.

Fig 12.21 Developing actions

Activity 1: Jumping actions

A jumping action is one where the body is entirely off the ground and in the air for a moment. In all jumping actions:

1. Use arm swing to assist elevation.
2. Ensure the head and chest are up.
3. Ensure good body line, point toes and fingers.
4. Bend knees and ankles to receive weight on landing.

1a: Jump two feet to two feet

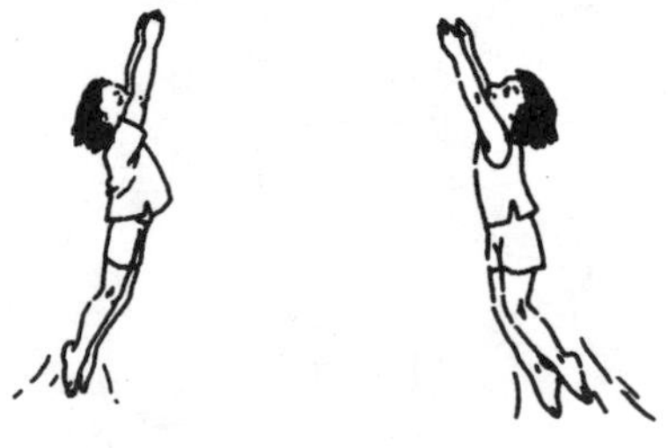

1b: Jump one foot to the other foot – a leap

1c: Jump one foot to the same foot – a hop

1d: Jump one foot to two feet – a take-off for flight

1e: Jump two feet to one foot

Jumping actions can be developed by changing bodyshape in the air or changing direction in the air, or by incorporating apparatus.

In all of these actions it is important to:

- prepare by making an arm swing
- make a shape when in the air
- straighten out before landing.

1f: Two feet to two feet – a star jump

1g: Two feet to two feet – a tuck jump

1h: One foot to the other foot – a turning jump

1i: Jumping two feet to two feet on to and off a bench

1j: Jumping one foot to two feet along the bench

1k: Jumping two feet to two feet along the bench

1l: Jumping one foot to the other – leaping along the bench

Jumping actions can be on to different body parts. In all these actions arm swing is very important to give momentum.

1m: Jumping from feet to hands – the bunny jump

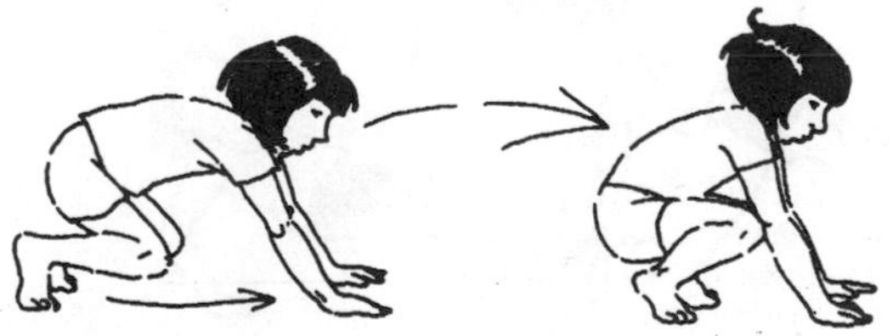

1n: Taking the bunny jump on to the bench

1o: Jumping on to bottom on a box top

Fig 12.21 Developing actions

1p: Jumping on to tummy on a box top

Activity 2: Stepping actions

A stepping action is one where different parts of the body come to the floor in turn, one after another. In these actions:

1 Concentrate on bodyline and tension.
2 Reach for the floor with the next body part.

2a: Crawling tummy down

2b: Crawling tummy up

2c: Rotating from tummy up to tummy down

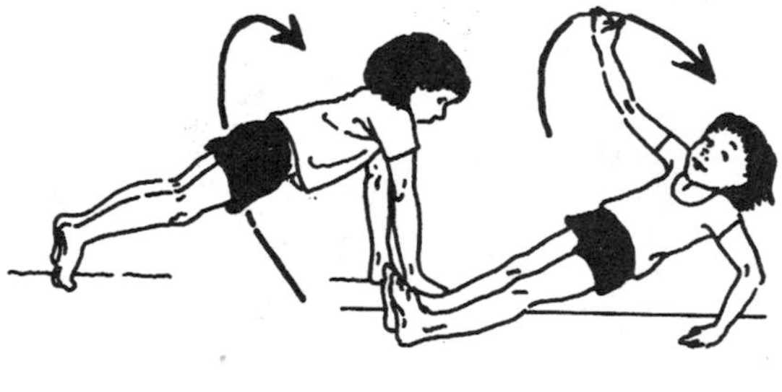

These actions can be developed by taking them across or along apparatus.

2d: Cartwheeling

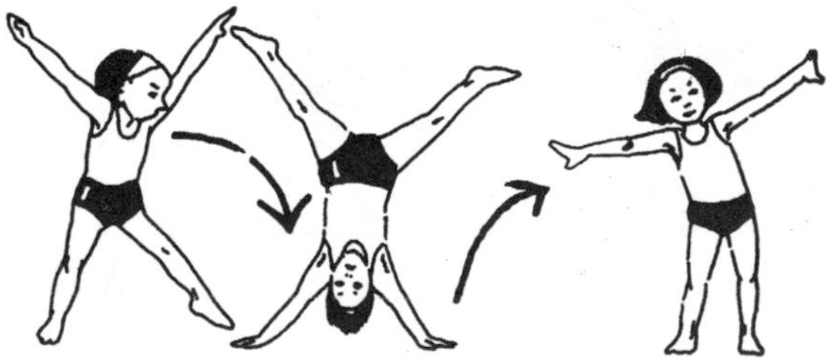

2e: Crawling along a bench

2f: Crawling over a bench

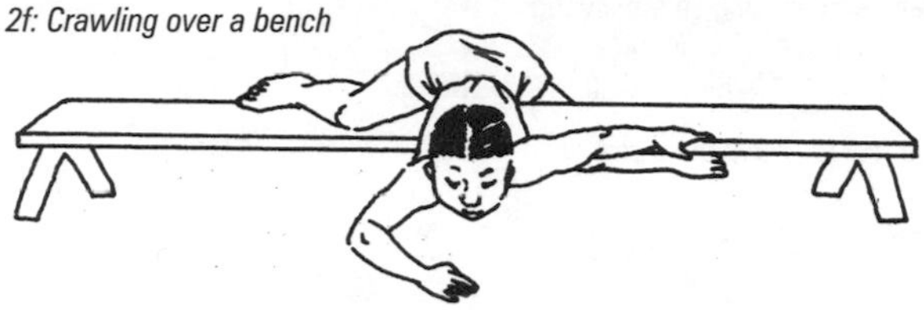

2g: Cartwheeling over a bench

Stepping actions can be developed by changing bodyparts.

2h: A stepping action with straight legs

2i: A stepping action with legs straddled

2j: A stepping action with body tucked

Fig 12.21 Developing actions

Activity 3: Rolling actions

A rolling action is one which takes the body over large surfaces and where there is continual contact with the floor. In all rolling actions:

1 Concentrate on body shape. If tucked, keep tight; if stretched, stretch fully.
2 Stress key points for each action as outlined.

3a: A pencil roll

3b: An egg roll

3c: A side roll

3d: A circle roll

Rolling actions can be developed to take you along, on to and off apparatus.

3e: A side roll on to a bench

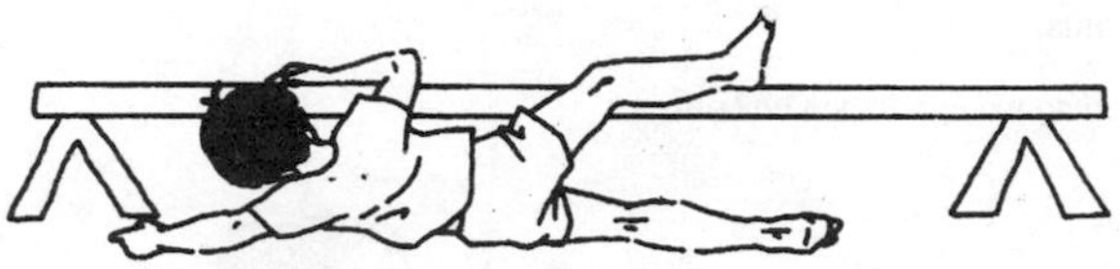

3f: A side roll along a bench

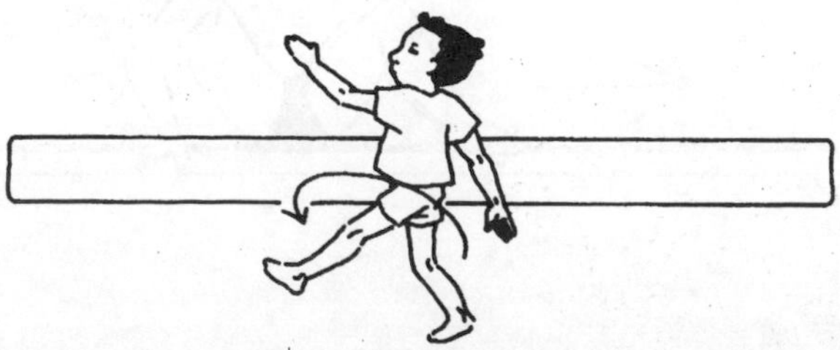

3g: A circle roll to come into contact with a bench

Fig 12.21 Developing actions

The following two rolls are not rolls which should be specifically taught at Key Stage 1 but reference to the correct performance will help if you have pupils who are able to perform these movements.

3h: A forward roll

3i: A backward roll

Activity 4: Sliding actions

A sliding action is one where the body remains supported on the same body part and there is continual contact with the ground. In all sliding actions:

1 Stress bodyline and tension.
2 Ensure attention to body shape: if tucked, ensure body is fully tucked; if stretched, ensure it is fully stretched.

4a: Sliding on back

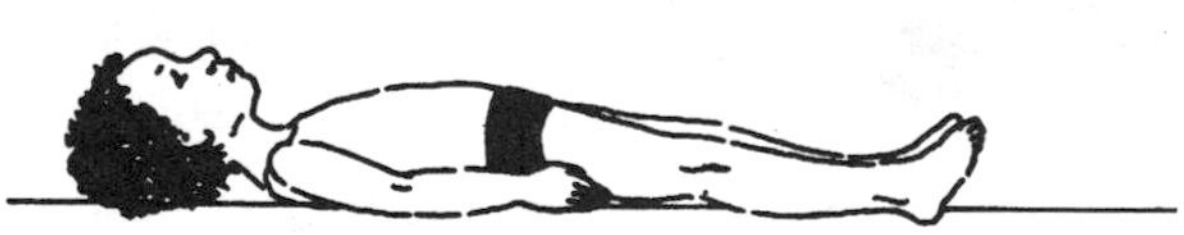

4b: Sliding on front

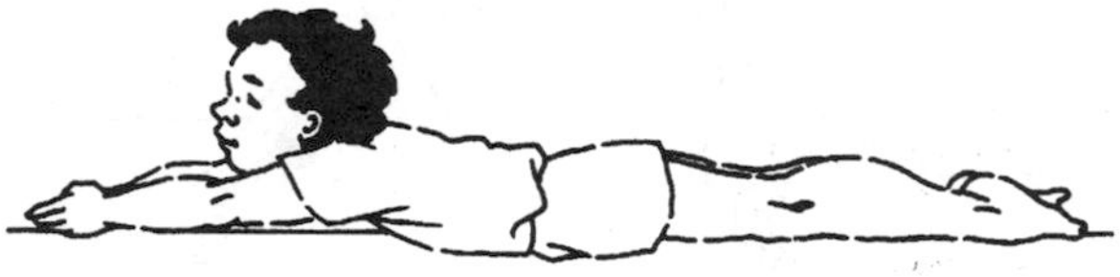

4c: Sliding on side

4d: Sliding on bottom

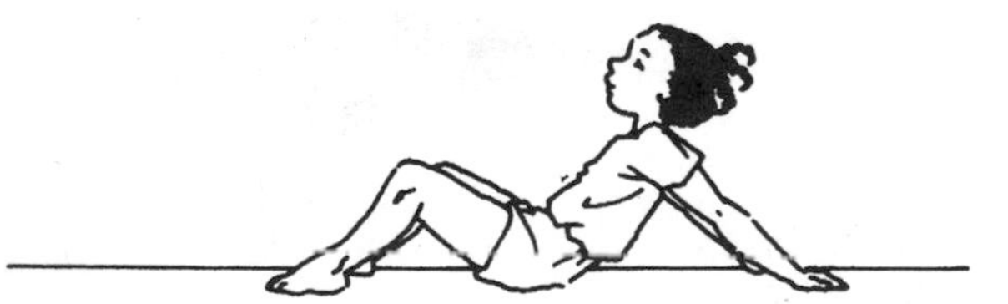

Sliding actions can be developed by changing body shape.

4e: Sliding on back in tucked shape

4f: Sliding in a V shape – legs straddled

Sliding action can also be developed by moving on to or coming off apparatus.

4g. Sliding along a bench on bottom

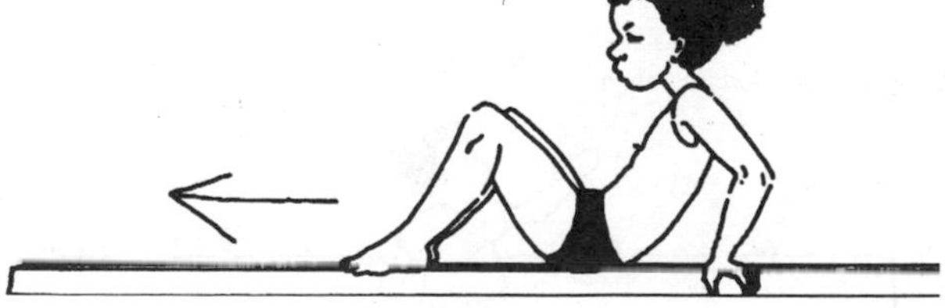

Fig 12.21 Developing actions

4h: Sliding off a box

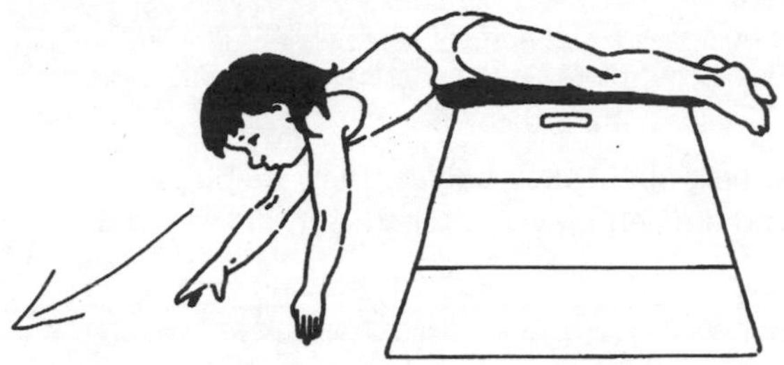

Activity 5: Balances

A balance is when the body is held still and good bodyline and body tension is maintained. In all balances:

1 Stress pulling away from the point of balance.
2 Stress the importance of the bodyline – point toes and fingers, keep head up.
3 Stress the importance of body tension, pull everything together.

5a: Body patches

5b: Body points

The earliest stage of all physical actions begin in babyhood as they are encouraged to reach, stretch and change position.

case study 12.2

Plum Tree Nursery baby room

Key worker Thelma wants to encourage 8-month-old Jamilla to reach for toys that interest her, as she currently waits for things to be passed to her, making urgent vocal sounds to get adult attention. Thelma provides hand-sized blocks and containers that make noises to tempt her, and places a basket next to her for putting them in.

In the next room, the toddlers are learning about their bodies. They are playing 'Heads, shoulders, knees and toes' and are getting very excited.

activity

1. What else would you do to encourage Jamilla to reach out and explore on her own initiative?
2. What would you have used as a warm-up action (to also get them focused) and as a wind-down action to calm the toddlers before lunchtime?

Games (individual, partner, group)

Apart from manipulative and motor skills, games help children learn about rules and boundaries, and about taking into account someone else, as they wait and take turns, share resources, learn to both lose gracefully and win gracefully. Examples include:

- board games, such as picture lotto, snakes and ladders, ludo, chess
- skill games, such as pick-up-sticks which need control and balance
- ring games, such as: Farmer in the den, There was a princess long ago, Here we go round the mulberry bush
- paired games, such as Row, row the boat, bouncing balls to a partner, rolling balls to a partner, skipping as a threesome with a long rope
- party-type games, such as statues, musical bumps, sleeping lions
- action games, such as Simon says, Head, shoulders, knees and toes.

Professional Practice

- **Ring games, paired activities and party-type games also provide a sense of belonging as well as helping with the development of physical skills such as spatial awareness, suppleness, flexibility, co-operative movement and a sense of timing.**

case study 12.3

Jazzy and Harry playing picture lotto

When playing picture lotto, Jazzy and Harry are learning to handle the small cards carefully, shuffling them initially, then spreading them out face downwards. As the game proceeds, they will be using precise manipulative skills as they carefully position picture cards on their individual game boards. Socially they are waiting and taking turns, helping each other identify who gets each card, and taking pleasure in each other's progress. Cognitive skills and language are seen as they discuss and describe each picture.

activity

1. What other suitable board games can you think of?
2. Jazzy is 6 and Harry is 4. How might their levels of concentration differ?
3. What other issues could possibly arise when children of differing stages of development play board games together?

Fig 12.22 Manipulative skills are used during board games too

Swimming for babies and children

Regular swimming helps babies and children gain confidence in the water. It is important for personal safety throughout life, and as it is a supported form of exercise (due to the buoyancy of water) it is a safe from of exercise if weight-bearing is an issue due to injury or health issues. It can be particularly helpful to children with mobility problems.

Fig 12.23 Regular swimming helps infants to gain confidence in water

remember Many activities that are traditionally played outside can also be enjoyed indoors too.

Outdoor activities

Providing time outdoors every day is beneficial for all-round health. However, it is not advisable to take very young children or those with health problems such as asthma out when it is very cold, or if it is foggy.

Small and large play equipment

This could include the use of:

- hoops, balls, quoits and beanbags
- skipping ropes
- tunnels and barrels

- wheeled toys: trikes, bikes, cars, tractor-trailers, scooters, wheelbarrows
- large hoops, hobby horses
- cones to run or ride in and out of
- skittles and games such as 'boules'
- ground level balance beam
- stepping stones to walk across
- outdoor gym equipment, such as ropes, climbing frames, ladders, swing bars, poles, trampolines and springboards
- sandpits
- gardening
- activities around a wildlife area
- ground games such as hopscotch.

Fig 12.24 Some games can be played either indoors or outside

Games (individual, partner, group, team)

- Ring games, such as Farmer in the den, There was a princess long ago, Here we go round the mulberry bush
- Paired games, such as Row, row the boat, bouncing balls to a partner, rolling balls to a partner, skipping as a threesome
- Party-type games, such as statues, musical bumps, sleeping lions
- Action games, such as Simon says, Head, shoulders, knees and toes

Athletics for babies and children

The use of obstacle courses can be a fun way to encourage a range of physical skills in mobile infants and young children. Useful items include:

- cones, to crawl or toddle in and out of
- tunnels or large cardboard boxes to crawl through
- soft play-type blocks to scramble over
- shallow slides for older babies and toddlers
- hoops or boxes to drop bean bags into
- lightweight blankets to crawl on tummies underneath (being careful that no one gets distressed).

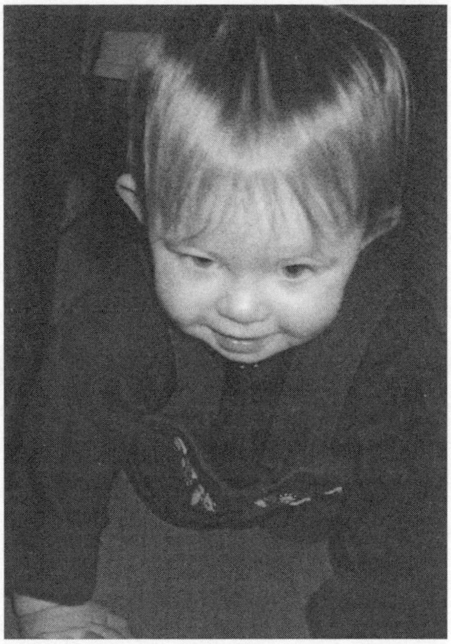

Fig 12.25 Babies and toddlers enjoy obstacle courses

activity
INDIVIDUAL WORK 12.3

P3

M2

D1

1. Produce a large A3 size poster showing how physical activity helps promote healthy development and lifestyle.
2. Choose three of the activities featured on your poster, and explain how they each promote healthy development and a healthy lifestyle, making clear differences and similarities between them.
3. Choosing two different forms of exercise, give a detailed evaluation of how they promote and support a healthy lifestyle, making clear how they compare and highlighting ways in which they differ.

Safety procedures

Appropriate supervision levels should always be maintained according to the ages and numbers of children. In a situation where this alters, perhaps due to one adult needing to leave with an ill or injured child, the situation should be re-assessed to ensure that the legal supervision levels are still in place. If the legal supervision ratios are in doubt, then the activity should cease and children return to a more passive activity until it is rectified.

Checks and maintenance of equipment

All equipment and resources should be checked regularly, and there should be a named person who carries this out. Many of these checks would come under the setting's risk assessment. Checks should be noted, showing dates, time and any concerns. If a concern is identified, the setting's procedures should be put into motion for responding. At times this may mean a piece of fixed equipment being put out of use temporarily, or certain resources remaining in the storage area.

remember Appropriate supervision levels should always be maintained according to the ages and numbers of children.

Safety surfaces need to be kept in good condition, and if they deteriorate for any reason, the equipment above them should be banned from use until repairs are made. All outdoor surfaces onto which a child could fall more than 60 cm must be impact-absorbing. Impact-absorbing playground surfaces (IAPs) must meet the BSEN 1177 safety standard. They include:

- loose-fill substances such as tree bark or sand (at least 30 cm deep)
- 'wet pour' rubber which sets to form a spongy surface
- special thick rubber tiles.

Playground activities

Most of the activities listed for outdoor play apply to playground play, together with games such as:

- May I cross the river, What's the time Mr Wolf
- free play games, such as touch, chase, on it, etc.
- ground games such as hopscotch
- hoops for basketball practice
- mini goal nets for practising kicking a football and shooting at goal
- sensory garden areas with places to sit quietly and chat to friends.

Promote healthy development and lifestyle

Activities to develop cardiovascular health (aerobic activities)

These types of activities are aimed at strengthening the heart, lungs and respiratory system, by increasing both heart rate and breathing. Examples include:

- running
- jumping
- hopping
- skipping
- dancing
- swimming
- team games like football or rounders
- sports using rackets like badminton, tennis, short tennis or squash (older children)
- obstacle races
- relay racing
- playing dodgeball.

Activities to develop balance, skill and co-ordination of large muscles

The following activities help with precise movement, controlled movements and synchronisation of movements:

- gymnastics
- dance
- running
- jumping
- hopping
- using balance beams
- turning rolypolys
- doing handstands
- turning cartwheels
- using climbing frames and large equipment
- obstacle courses.

Activities to develop flexibility, muscular strength and endurance

Activities to build strength focus mostly on muscles and joints. It also helps with balance. Weight carrying and weight lifting (older children only) can be helpful here. Flexibility is developed through stretching, e.g. through yoga or tai chi. Some schools and early years settings now include 'Yoga for children' within their physical curriculum plans.

Activities to support fine motor skill development

Link

Refer back to the list of small and large equipment on page 73 for a range of activities that support the development of fine motor skills.

Activities to support development of hand–eye co-ordination

Hand–eye co-ordination is needed for so many everyday actions. Activities to help it develop include:

- stacking toys, e.g. blocks, rings, beakers
- construction resources, both natural and commercial
- jigsaw puzzles
- sewing, threading and weaving, lacing cards and shoes
- activity songs and finger rhymes
- activities with a partner, e.g. rolling a ball to each other
- throwing and catching a ball, beanbag, quoit, etc.
- throwing a ball against a wall and catching it
- bat and ball games
- juggling.

Fig 12.26 Hand–eye co-ordination is needed here

remember

Foot–eye co-ordination is also important. Examples to support this include:

- kicking a football
- skipping
- hurdling
- jumping over small obstacles
- trampolining.

Activities that encourage co-operation, sharing and turn-taking among children

This could include activities such as:

- parachute games
- skipping in and out of a turned rope
- relay races.

Fig 12.27 Children learn to co-operate through group play

Fig 12.28 Physical skills + determination = success

remember Remember to value 'the great outdoors'. Children benefit from opportunities to climb and experience nature.

Long- and short-term effects of exercise on babies and children

Probably the best reason for encouraging exercise at the youngest age is to instil the habit of physical activity in children. This, together with a healthy diet, will enable children to develop their full potential regarding:

- muscle strength
- cardiovascular health
- stamina and endurance
- flexibility and suppleness
- good bone density.

Planning

When planning physical activity, you will need to:

- use any observations and assessments of children's abilities already recorded that are available to you
- know your overall aim, ensuring that you are setting realistic goals
- be inclusive, taking into account any additional needs a child may have

Link

Refer to page 90 for ideas and guidance on planning for and meeting additional needs.

- have some idea of the outcomes of what you have planned, e.g. how much the children are likely to achieve, or have built on their previous skill level, etc.
- link activities (where applicable) to your home country curriculum, e.g. Early Years Foundation Stage

Link

Refer to pages 62–65 for a brief outline of current frameworks for England.

- compose or plan moves or routines in advance, and build in opportunities (where applicable) for children to devise their own moves or routines
- write out your plans, using the pro forma favoured by your school or setting
- ensure that all children have appropriate clothing and footwear for all planned activities.

Risk assessment

Risk assessment involves taking into account:

- the outcomes of risk assessments for the area to be used in line with organisational policy
- the outcomes of risk assessment of the resources and equipment, again in line with organisational policy
- the age range of the children and the skill levels and limitations to be expected
- the staffing levels (statutory adult: child ratios must of course always be adhered to, but common sense dictates that some activities need an even higher level of supervision for them to be both safe and a meaningful experience for the children).
- previous assessments of children's individual skill level to help identify when it is appropriate to extend and challenge skills and build on experience.

activity
GROUP WORK
12.4

P4

In small groups – each group member on placement working with children within the same curriculum framework – plan four activities for children at your own current placements. Each activity needs to:

- be age-appropriate
- meet safe practice guidelines
- link to the relevant curriculum framework for the age group.

Ensure that you cover a range of different physical skills within your planned activities, and each of you will need to obtain relevant permissions from your placement supervisor regarding timings, resources, supervision levels, etc.

activity
INDIVIDUAL WORK
12.5

P5

1 Write up your plans for the four activities planned in the previous activity (P4), using the planning pro forma sheets from either your placement or tutor.
2 Carry out your activities within an agreed time span, agreed in advance with both your tutor and your placement.
3 Record the process of each activity clearly, to help you evaluate it later on.

Implementation

When planning and implementing activities you need to take into account:

- the equipment and numbers of personnel required
- what will be a suitable environment
- any health and safety issues
- how you will encourage and reward effort
- issues of inclusion.

Equipment and personnel required

- Supervision levels must always meet the statutory adult:child ratios.
- Any activity needing close one-to-one guidance is likely to require a higher adult:child ratio to ensure safety.
- All equipment and resources should be suitable for the age and size of the children using it.
- There should be sufficient resources for all children to have a meaningful experience without having to wait around for too long to actually use the resources.

Suitable environment

- There needs to be sufficient space for the activity to take place safely, without impacting on any other activity area.
- Some activities are best suited to outdoors, or indoors, or only outdoors, but in dry weather, etc. Sensible decision-making is always needed and alternative activities planned if implementation is ever doubtful.

Health and safety

- Risk assessments must be carried out in accordance with setting policy.
- Appropriate flooring is needed, e.g. impact-absorbent surfaces.
- Crash mats are needed when jumping off equipment is likely.
- Children need to understand 'Stop, stand still' and respond immediately. This is important in case an accident occurs, or a potential accident is identified.

Encouragement and reward

- Praise for effort is the best encouragement and reward you can give a child.
- Individual attention may be needed to help anxious children attempt new actions.
- Adult attention for working well with others and co-operating with requests is the best way of dealing with unwanted behaviour. If a child mostly gets your attention when they are not co-operating, you may actually be fulfilling their need, i.e. your attention.

Link

Refer to Unit 14 for more on behaviour management and positive reinforcement.

Inclusion

- You will need to consider the differing levels of skill and stages of development within the group you are working with.
- At times just simple changes to a planned activity will meet an individual child's additional needs. On other occasions you may need to plan an alternative approach altogether for a specific child, or group of children.

Link

Refer to page 94 for further guidance, and to Unit 27 for more information on supporting additional needs.

activity
INDIVIDUAL WORK 12.6

M3

D2

Imagine you have been asked to write an information sheet for new parents about physical activity within the school or early years setting where you are on placement.

1 Using the activities you planned and carried out for activities P4 and P5 as your main examples, explain to parents the aims of each activity and how they meet objectives within the curriculum framework.

2 For your placement portfolio, write an evaluation of each activity you planned and carried out, noting the success of each, any problems or drawbacks, and how you could improve on them further if you carried them out again at a future date.

remember

Some children will learn best visually. They need to be able to see the adult's actions, body language and facial expressions in order for them to fully understand what is required of them. Others focus on what they hear, so clear concise instructions are needed, repeated as necessary.

Provision for those children with specific needs

Teaching basic skills

Refer back to the basic skills illustrated on pages 66–79. You will see that each skill is shown in three stages: initially the immature approach, followed by the transition stage where the child has mastered the skill to an extent, but not yet fully, and then eventually the mature skill is shown. These simple first physical skills may need to be reinforced for far longer for some children, with adult demonstrations and mirroring of adult actions often preceding the planned activity as part of the warm-up, to remind the children of the actions required.

Simple arm movement exercises preceding the introduction of ball skills may help children with balance or locomotion difficulties to remember how their body moves, ready for joining in ball-throwing activities. Similarly, exercising legs in swinging motions will help prepare for kicking a ball. Some children will find a bar to hold onto helpful in helping them retain balance whilst kicking a ball.

Professional Practice

- At times advice and guidance will need to be sought from specialists such as physiotherapists, occupational therapists, speech and language therapists or educational psychologists. Often, a child will already be linked with them in one form or another, at other times information may be obtained through general enquiry.

Some children will need additional resources and equipment to enable them to take part in certain activities. The Special Education Needs Co-ordinator (SENCO) for the school or early years setting will usually be the person to take on responsibility for ensuring each child's equipment and resource needs are met.

Encouraging and monitoring children's progress and performance

Many children will have a one-to-one worker who will take on the main observation and recording of their development and progress. There may be pro forma sheets used specific to the setting, or specific to the child. If you are asked to add comments to these sheets, ensure that you only record facts. If you are uncertain about anything, ask for advice. The recorded comments are likely to be used in any reviews that take place regarding a child's progress and support needs. Misjudged comments could cause confusion and possibly impact on the type or level of help and support they receive.

As with all children, praise for effort is of extreme importance. At times, progress may be incremental and barely noticeable, but it is important that you acknowledge progress however slight, vocalising this and offering praise appropriately.

Evaluation

In making an **evaluation** of how successful your planning and implementation of an activity has been, you will need to consider:

- how well you used your observation skills
- how you could have improved the delivery of the activity
- whether you really did provide for the children's progress
- whether you should have included repeated skills, or whether the repeated skills you included were appropriate and sufficient
- how you could have improved further on weak areas
- how well the activity actually compared to the set objectives for activity
- whether you had set realistic goals, both for yourself, and for the children.

Understand adaptations to a selected range of physical activities for babies and children with additional needs

Acquisition of physical skills

Perceptual development

Perceptual development is about how an infant takes in information through their senses and interprets that information to help them make sense of their world. In young babies, we see responses made to visual stimuli, as the infant kicks and waves arms with pleasure and interest. Responses to auditory stimuli are noted as the infant turns to locate where each sound is coming from. Learning to regain the sense of touch is quickly sought by the infant who first makes contact with an object through their random kicking and waving movements, repeating the action over and over to obtain again the tactile, visual or auditory response that interests them.

The physical responses made to stimulation in this way help to maintain concentration, strengthen muscles and keep limbs flexible. An infant who has a sensory impairment, e.g. they are blind or have restricted vision, they are deaf or have limited hearing, will be likely to lose out on some of the stimulation usually experienced. This loss can impact on their all-round development, and therefore it is particularly important that babies and children with sensory impairment are provided with a highly sensory-orientated learning environment, designed to encourage, stimulate and develop all areas of learning, including motor development.

Children with visual sensory loss are likely to need help in locating resources and partners, and in positioning themselves appropriately for an activity. Vision plays a significant part in physical activity in helping children learn about spatial awareness and body movement and these children will need a great deal of help and support. It can be helpful to maintain a consistent layout of the room, resources and apparatus to help them build confidence and achieve some independence. Other children may need regular reminders about the importance of repositioning resources carefully and being aware of the needs of their peers.

Motor process

The usual process of motor development can be seen in Figure 12.29 and Table 12.1, each level of skill building on the other. As described on page 57, physical development moves from the simple to the complex, e.g. head downwards (cephalo to caudal), from the near body outwards (proximal to distal), and from generalised actions to specific.

Fig 12.29 The development of locomotion

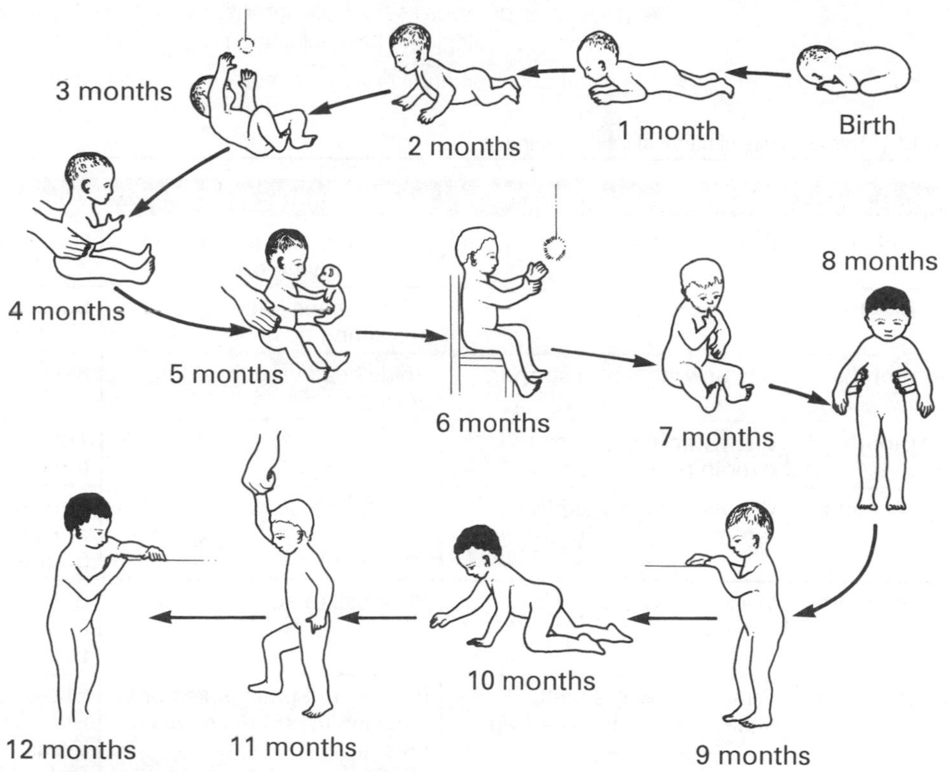

Fig 12.30 Development is from cephalo to caudal

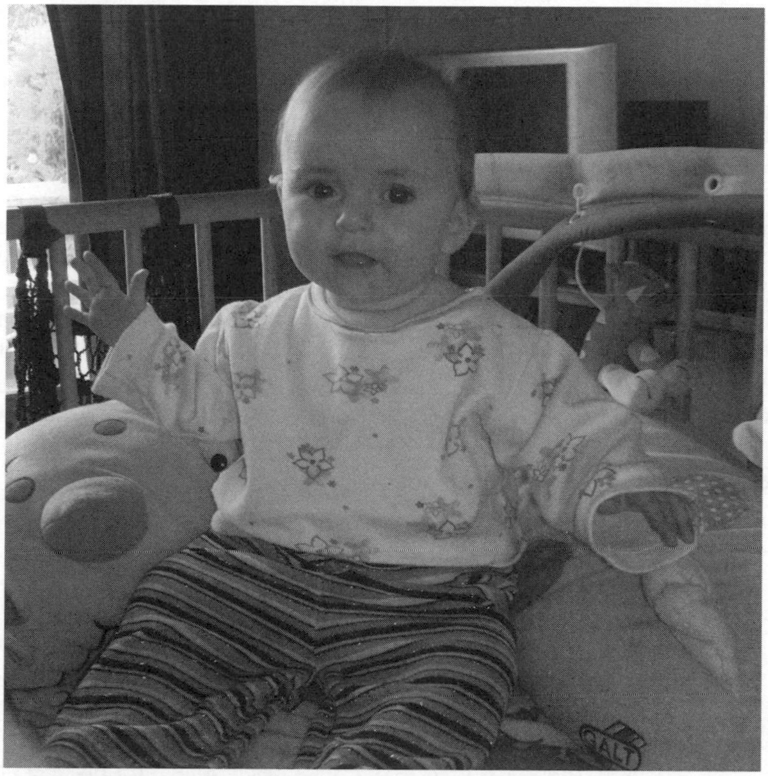

Classification of motor skills

Motor skills can be classified as locomotion skills, non-locomotion skills and manipulation.

- Locomotion is about movement, so locomotion skills are about the infant moving forwards in some way. This includes actions such as walking, crawling, running and hopping.
- Non-locomotion is movement that takes place whilst in one place. Non-locomotion skills involve actions such as bending, twisting, pulling something towards the body or pushing something away.

- Manipulation involves the fine motor skills, and manipulative skills include actions such as throwing or catching a ball, holding a pencil, a bat or a beanbag.

The usual developmental process of motor skills is shown in the table below.

Table 12.1 The sequence of motor skills development

Age	Locomotor skills	Non-locomotor skills	Manipulative skills
1 month	Stepping reflex	Lifts head; visually follows slowly moving objects	Holds object if placed in hand
2–3 months		Briefly keeps head up if held in a sitting position	Begins to swipe at objects within visual range
4–6 months	Sits up with some support	Holds head erect in sitting position	Reaches for and grasps objects
7–9 months	Sits without support; rolls over in prone; crawls		Transfers objects from one hand to the other
10–12 months	Crawls; walks grasping furniture, then without help	Squats and stoops	Some sign of hand preference; grasps a spoon across palm but poor aim of food to mouth
13–18 months	Walks backwards and sideways	Rolls ball to adult	Stacks two blocks; puts objects into small containers and dumps them
18–24 months	Runs (20); walks well; climbs stairs – both feet to a step	Pushes and pulls boxes or wheeled toys; unscrews lid on a jar	Shows clear hand preference. Stacks four to six blocks. Turns pages one at a time. Picks things up, keeping balance
2–3 years	Runs easily; climbs up and down from furniture unaided	Hauls and shoves big toys around obstacles	Picks up small objects; throws small ball forward while standing
3–4 years	Walks upstairs one foot per step; skips on both feet; walks on tiptoe	Pedals and steers a tricycle; walks in any direction pulling a big toy	Catches large ball between outstretched arms; cuts paper with scissors; holds pencil between thumb and first two fingers
4–5 years	Walks up and down stairs, one foot per stair. Stands, runs and walks well on tip-toes		Strikes ball with bat; kicks and catches ball; threads bead, but not needle. Grasps pencil maturely
5–6 years	Skips on alternate feet; walks a thin line; slides and swings		Plays ball games quite well. Threads needles; can sew a stitch
7–8 years	Skips 12 times or more	Rides two-wheeler bike, short distances	Writes individual letters
8 years+	Skips freely	Rides bike easily	

Source: Helen Bee, *The Developing Child*, 6th edition, © Allyn & Bacon, reprinted by permission

If normal motor development has not taken place, a child will be left without some of the methods of exploring and investigating that we take for granted, e.g. if they are unable to move independently, they are likely to miss out on opportunities for spontaneous investigation.

Motor development may be hindered by lack of muscle strength (and occasionally by having greater muscle strength than the child can cope with), by a lack of balance or co-ordination, or not having developed the skill to 'cross the mid-line', i.e. the child still needs to change hand to draw or write across a whole page, long after his peers have mastered this ability. This will result in 'clumsy' approaches to tasks, difficulty in paired or group work tasks as well as individual actions, potentially leading to frustration, disappointment and low self-esteem.

Factors affecting skill development

As an early years practitioner there are many conditions, both acquired and/or chronic, affecting children that you will work with and which you need to understand. Planning physical activity for such children will mean taking into account what they can do already, what you, they and their parents hope for them to achieve (this may form part of their individual education plan) and also how their health is on the day (for some children this can vary considerably on a day-to-day basis).

The following section gives just brief summaries of some of the most commonly seen conditions. There are many more conditions.

Link

Refer to Unit 27 where guidance is given on meeting a variety of needs, and also sets out the causative factors for various conditions and how they impact on the child.

You may also find it helpful to refer to Gilbert (2000) and to Dare & O'Donovan (2002). See the bibliography on page 412.

Cerebral palsy

Cerebral palsy is non-progressive and is most commonly seen from birth, often following a difficult delivery and a lack of oxygen. It can also occur early in gestation due to a range of problems, and occasionally occurs during early development. Children with cerebral palsy have problems with movement, balance and general posture. They have problems with muscle tone and the flexing and releasing of muscles, often causing jerky uncontrolled movements. Some children will have speech difficulties too, usually those who are most severely affected.

Children can be affected in three main ways with their condition being classified as:

- hemiplegia, where the paralysis and problems are mainly on one side of the body
- diplegia, where the legs are mostly affected, with far less effect to the upper body and upper limbs
- quadriplegia, where all four limbs are involved and also the muscles affecting oral skills are affected, therefore causing speech and feeding difficulties.

Apart from locomotion and non-locomotion difficulties, children with cerebral palsy are likely to need considerable help in taking part in activities that involve visual tracking (e.g. catching and throwing skills), as their jerky involuntary movements can make it difficult for them to identify and aim in the desired direction.

Spina bifida

Spina bifida is due to the failure of the spinal cord to close completely. It is a neural tube defect. There are differing levels of disability according to the severity of the defect:

- Spina bifida occulta – this is the most commonly found occurrence, and at this level there are rarely any problems. There may be a dimple or tuft of hair at the base of the spine. If the spinal cord has been caught within the vertebrae, there may be minor bladder control problems.
- Spina bifida cystica – this level of the condition is characterised by a swelling at the base of the spine, covered by a thin skin layer. This can be due to either:
    - Meningocele – the bulge of cerebral-spinal fluid simply needs protecting from knocks and unnecessary stresses. In most cases there is no damage to the nerves and only minimal disability.

  or:

    - Myelonmeningocele – in this level of the condition there is a gap in the outer part of the vertebrae and both the spinal cord and the meninges may protrude through. This causes paralysis and lack of sensation below the affected vertebra. There may also be bowel and bladder control problems. Surgery is usually carried out early in life to minimise the potential for infection and further damage.

Children with this most severe form of spina bifida often have little sensation in the lower body and muscles easily waste away without use. They are likely to need support from standing frames, walking aids and some children will be wheelchair bound for much of the day.

Muscular dystrophy

Muscular dystrophy is a genetically inherited condition that affects boys. It is not seen until around 2–3 years of age. Often the child begins walking much later than his peers and he may walk with wide unsteady steps. The condition causes progressive weakness of muscles and tightening of joints as the elasticity from tendons and muscles is lost. This affects walking and most other locomotion actions and there is a progressive increase in breathing difficulties and heart problems. Most children affected by this condition are wheelchair bound by their teens.

Children with muscular dystrophy benefit from activities that they can share with others on more equal terms, e.g. swimming, where the buoyancy of the water gives support to the body.

Asthma

Asthma is a condition of the lungs where there is a narrowing of the airways reducing the child's ability to breathe freely. The walls of the airways (the bronchioles) swell and become inflamed. It is often due to an allergic reaction. Individuals have their own 'triggers' that set off an asthma attack. These can include food items, dust, pollen and animals, but asthma can also be triggered by over-excitement, exercise and cold air.

An asthma attack can usually be alleviated by the use of medication via an inhaler, either as a preventative measure, used regularly throughout the day, or as a direct response to the onset of an attack. Each child will have their own regime and their own inhalers.

Children with asthma should have ready access to their inhalers, and teachers and early years practitioners should know where they can be located, and how and when they should be used. Supervising adults should be aware of which children are susceptible to asthma attacks linked to an increased level of activity and also the cold if physical activity is taking place outside. At times it will be appropriate to set different target levels for children with such conditions, particularly if they are already showing signs of a potential cold, etc. developing.

Sensory impairment

Sensory impairment can involve vision, hearing and understanding. Teachers and early years practitioners need to adjust their communication style to meet individual children's needs. For example, if a child is deaf or has limited hearing, then visual cues will be helpful in explaining procedures, timings and instructions (e.g. STOP or GO are easily understood by most children as they are distinctive, particularly if in colour). The use of sign language, Makaton, etc. may be helpful here.

Refer to Green (2007) for an outline of Makaton and various other forms of sign language.

A child with visual difficulties or limitations will benefit from a regular routine, structure and room layout. Supervising adults need to keep noise levels controlled to ensure that the child is able to hear all instructions, as they cannot rely on visually responding to the actions of others.

Where understanding is limited, clear instructions and careful supervision, particularly with reference to any situation where there could be potential dangers will be needed, e.g. when using climbing equipment. Guidance regarding dangers, rules and boundaries will need to be vocalised and emphasised repeatedly, often on a one-to-one basis with a specific child. The use of Makaton may again be helpful here if it is a communication form used by the child.

Adaptation of activities

Physical impairment

Each child's needs will of course have to be assessed individually, but as a general overview of how additional physical needs can be met, you may wish to consider the following bullet points and examples:

- Ensure that equipment and resources are not left lying around, potentially tripping up or being in the way of children.
- Focus on activities involving posture rather than movement for children who have very limited mobility, as posture is the forerunner to movement.
- For many children, it will be useful to focus on movement as a process in its own right rather than for a specific purpose or to achieve a goal.
- Try breaking actions down into smaller actions, talking through each stage and helping the child practise actions stage by stage until they are ready to try the planned action as a full sequence.
- Consider asking questions to help children identify space and distance before they attempt the planned action, e.g. How many steps will you need to take? Where will your next foot move to? Where will you need to stand to reach your partner/the wall/the A frame?
- Throwing bean bags into a box or hoop, or throwing quoits over a large cone will help develop a sense of space, distance and direction.

Examples:

- Joshua is 6 years old and has cerebral palsy. In PE his teacher is working with her class to find different ways of moving within a quadrant of the school hall, with a group of children in each quadrant. Joshua has erratic physical movements and so she has grouped Joshua with fewer children than there are in the other groups. This gives all the children in Joshua's group more space to move, whilst helping Joshua move and express himself as well as he can, lessening the likelihood of Joshua impacting on the space and actions of others.

- Toni is 5 and has osteogenesis inperfecta (also known as brittle bones). She has balance problems, due to damage to the bones in her inner ear. Her class are currently practising actions that involve balance during locomotion, e.g. hopping along a chalked line, walking along it with a beanbag balanced on their head. To help Toni to simply practise moving forward in a straight line, her teacher asks her to imagine a line right through her body, going from the top of her head right down to the floor. Toni focuses on this image as she moves. This focused thinking is helping Toni to walk along a chalked line, something she has not been able to achieve before.

Sensory impairment

Again, each child's needs will need to be assessed individually, but as a general overview of how sensory impairment needs can be met, you may wish to consider the following bullet points and examples:

- Use music to stimulate and gain attention.
- A ball with a bell inside will help visually impaired children locate it by sound.
- Use visual or tactile images, signs, etc. to denote specific areas, e.g. soft play area or nets for ball skills.
- Textured edges help guide children to stay within margins for team games.
- Visual clues show what action is needed, e.g. run/walk/jump/sit down.
- Use textured edges along the sides of the sandpit and garden area.
- Lights or a torch can indicate the start and finish of a piece of music.

Examples:

- Freddy is 5 and is profoundly deaf. He is physically very active and loves physical play such as obstacle courses and relay-type races. Freddy can easily take part in such activities by his teacher using a two-colour flashlight. Green tells him to start and red tells him he is on his last lap or final relay run. This simple method allows Freddy to be fully involved with no mention of his additional need.
- Carly is 6 and she is blind. She is quite a timid little girl who finds PE quite difficult at times as she finds the noise and speed of actions around her distressing. Since entering mainstream school a year ago, Carly has progressed very little, spending a lot of her time during PE at the edge of the room with her one-to-one support assistant. Carly's teacher this year has introduced her to using beanbags with bells inside. The support assistant now uses these with Carly, whilst the rest of her class are throwing and catching balls. She shakes them to help Carly identify which direction the beanbag will be coming from. Carly is gradually gaining confidence, as she can now hear the beanbag coming, and she also knows that if she does not catch it, and it hits her, it will not sting like the balls had done in the past.

Learning difficulties

As with each of the above, each child's needs will need to be assessed individually, but as a general overview of how the needs of children with learning difficulties can be met, you may wish to consider the following:

- Use creativity, e.g. music to stimulate interest and maintain attention.
- Mirrors can help the children actually see how their body is moving, keeping them focused.
- Modify the rules, limits, use of resources, etc. to suit individual needs.
- Consider carefully how children are partnered, ensuring that children who are easily distracted are paired with those who focus well, etc.

Examples:

- Pradeep is 3 and has moderate learning difficulties. He finds listening to instructions and responding to them very difficult. His key worker has produced some visual clue cards with images he understands. She has laminated these cards for durability both indoors and outside. When she wants Pradeep to listen, she holds up an illustration of an ear; when it is his turn to jump, during a team game, she holds up an image of a 'pin man' jumping. She also positions herself so that Pradeep can see her clearly whenever she speaks and uses hand gestures such as finger to lip, hand in the traditional STOP position, arm movements to show running, etc. to guide him during all activities. This works particularly well during active and physical play and the introduction of these visual clues has led to fewer bumps into other children and a more focused Pradeep.

- James can be quite disruptive. He is 4 years old and needs a lot of one-to-one attention. His key worker at nursery finds that giving James a clear personal instruction is a simple way of focusing him initially at the start of each physical activity, as he immediately has a specific purpose which curtails his excitement. For example, she might say 'James, please come and stand here, today you will be the middle person in my line of marching soldiers.' She then encourages a set number of children to line up in front of him, and more behind him. He has been immediately involved in the start of the activity in a controlled way, without automatically being 'first in line', etc. This simple type of action can often help to calm James' over-exuberant approach to something new, and James is able to enjoy a more meaningful experience, and the rest of his group are less disrupted.

activity
INDIVIDUAL WORK 12.7
P6
M4

Give examples of how you could adapt the activities carried out and discussed in activities P4 and P5 for children with a range of additional needs. Specify the additional needs you are referring to, and describe in detail the changes you could make.

activity
INDIVIDUAL WORK 12.8
D3

Using examples from your placement experience, explain how adapting activities to meet additional needs is important in promoting the healthy development and lifestyle of children with a range of specific needs.

Progress Check

1. Describe the four main needs of the human body.
2. Explain the difference between the axial skeleton and the appendicular skeleton.
3. Describe the different types of joint and where they can be found in the body.
4. Explain the different functions of ligaments and tendons.
5. Explain the difference between isotonic and isometric muscle contractions.
6. Describe the main functions of arteries, capillaries and veins.
7. What is meant by systolic and diastolic pressure when blood pressure is being measured?
8. What exteroceptors and proprioceptors can you explain and which respond to stimuli outside the body, and which inside the body?
9. What is homeostasis?
10. Explain the difference between anaerobic and aerobic exercise.
11. Give at least three examples of body systems, explaining their immature and mature states.
12. Give ten examples of physical activities suitable for children in the early years Foundation Stage, and ten for children within Key Stages 1 and 2.
13. Explain the importance of warm-up exercises and give examples.
14. Explain the importance of winding-down activities and give examples.
15. What needs to be taken into account when assessing risk prior to physical activity with young children?

UNIT 14

Psychological Perspectives on Behaviour in Children

This unit covers the following objectives:

- Understand the main theoretical perspectives of developmental psychology that explain how children's behaviour develops
- Understand how early relationships are formed
- Understand factors affecting the behaviour of children
- Understand different approaches to challenging behaviour
- Understand techniques for monitoring the effectiveness of implementing behaviour strategies

The unit gives an introduction to psychological perspectives of how behaviour develops and strategies that can be used to promote positive behaviour in children. You will gain an understanding of basic child psychology theory, which will enable you to carry out observations, activities and use behavioural intervention strategies and have a greater knowledge of the reasons for particular behaviour in children.

The unit considers the effect that early relationships can have on behaviour as well as transition stages during a child's development. You will look at theories and principles relating to child development and developmental psychology. You will consider a range of factors that can impact on children's behaviour and methods used to promote positive behaviour and reduce negative behaviour.

grading criteria

To achieve a **Pass** grade the evidence must show that the learner is able to:	To achieve a **Merit** grade the evidence must show that, in addition to the Pass criteria, the learner is able to:	To achieve a **Distinction** grade the evidence must show that, in addition to the Pass and Merit criteria, the learner is able to:
P1 Describe three debates in developmental psychology Page 100	**M1** Analyse one debate in developmental psychology Page 100	
P2 Outline the main psychological perspectives as applied to the understanding of the development of children's behaviour Page 114		
P3 Describe the role of early relationships in the development of children's behaviour Page 119	**M2** Use examples from work placement to explain how areas of early years practice are influenced by developmental theory Page 119	**D1** Analyse the contribution of the major developmental perspectives to early years practice Page 119

To achieve a **Pass** grade the evidence must show that the learner is able to:	To achieve a **Merit** grade the evidence must show that, in addition to the Pass criteria, the learner is able to:	To achieve a **Distinction** grade the evidence must show that, in addition to the Pass and Merit criteria, the learner is able to:
P4 Describe six factors that may affect children's behaviour Page 123		
P5 Outline four different behavioural management strategies Page 133		
P6 Identify a range of relevant support roles and agencies used in managing behaviour Page 133	**M3** Explain the potential effectiveness of four different behavioural management strategies Page 133	**D2** Evaluate the potential effectiveness of four different behavioural management strategies Page 133
P7 Describe methods that could be used to evaluate the effectiveness of behavioural management strategies Page 136	**M4** Explain the different methods used to evaluate the effectiveness of the behavioural management strategies Page 136	

Understand the main theoretical perspectives of developmental psychology that explain how children's behaviour develops

Within this section the main **theoretical perspectives** will be considered as well as the major psychological theories developed to understand ways that children learn. You will gain an initial understanding of:

- behavioural psychology
- **cognitive development**
- theories of language development
- how children acquire a sense of self.

When psychologists talk about 'behaviour' they mean it in a much wider sense than the normal concept of behaviour as simply being either good or bad. Psychologists talk about the study of behaviour in a broader way to include how children:

- learn
- form opinions
- act towards others.

Learning is linked to behaviour as children will show their understanding through the way they behave. It is vital for you to understand how children learn so that you can ensure your practice is effective.

Debates in developmental psychology

The nature–nurture debate

One of the main issues in development psychology revolves around the **nature–nurture debate**.

At one extreme of this are those people who think that an infant is completely shaped and developed by adult input. They feel that how a child develops and behaves is a reflection of the child's upbringing. This is the nurture viewpoint and might attribute blame or credit for a child's behaviour to his or her parents, school, television, etc.

In the past, philosophers such as John Locke and John Watson stated that newborn infants were blank slates that they could shape into any form they wanted using conditioning, rewards and punishments. This was always a controversial viewpoint and, since the discovery of DNA (deoxyribonucleic acid) and the rise of genetics, this view has fallen out of favour. Recent studies have linked genes to characteristics such as intelligence and behaviour as well as physical attributes. Most parents who have more than one child will say that different aspects of the infants' temperament are apparent from birth, indicating that temperament is at least influenced by genes. However, a person's temperament will be modified by environment and the particular circumstances that the infant is in.

Those who take the nature viewpoint believe that children's behaviour is shaped from the beginning by their genes and that each child will develop certain characteristics and that the role of the adult in shaping the character of the child is minimal. People who adopt this attitude would feel that there is little they can do to change things if they go wrong and that the only role of the adult is in giving support to help develop a child's innate potential.

The usual view these days is that a combination of both factors is responsible for development, with some aspects being much more linked to nature and others being influenced by nurture through upbringing and the environment.

case study 14.1

Ben

The form teacher is talking to the mother of Ben, a child in Year 10 of secondary school who has behavioural problems. The mother is divorced and finding it very difficult to cope with Ben's challenging behaviour. She explains to the teacher that there is nothing she can do with Ben as he takes after his father.

activity

1 Which viewpoint is she taking?

2 How might this attitude affect Ben?

In the case study above, you will be able to identify that the mother is taking the nature viewpoint in blaming Ben's behaviour on his father's genes. She may well have decided that she is unable to control Ben and feels helpless. The fact that the mother has adopted this viewpoint may mean that home life is chaotic and undisciplined for Ben and this will be contributing to him feeling unable to cope and perhaps showing this through challenging behaviour.

Later in this unit you will consider different theories of how children learn and will be able to link them to nature or nurture.

Consider your own personal situation. Think about your own family including parents, siblings, grandparents and half brothers and sisters, if you have them. What attributes do you share with others in your family? Have you been told that you look just like your grandmother or that you are good at art just like your father, for example? Make a list of the characteristics that you have which seem to be inherited.

Then consider the individual traits you have which appear to be unique to you. Are you very good at sports perhaps, where no one else in your family is?

How important do you think nature and nurture have been so far in your development? Are there aspects of your personality or abilities that you can definitely link to inherited factors and are there characteristics that are related to your upbringing?

Continuity v. discontinuity

Another aspect of developmental psychology is that of continuity versus discontinuity. Some psychologists see development as being a smooth continuous process with gradual changes in ability, skills and knowledge. Others see the process as being much less smooth, with new skills and knowledge appearing rather more suddenly in a series of distinct stages. The idea of continuity sees children as acquiring more of each skill as they grow older, whilst the discontinuity view sees skills emerging at certain points of development. You will see these different approaches in the theories of how children learn later in this unit.

Nomothetic v. idiographic

Within psychological approaches there are two opposing views of how to study people.

- The nomothetic approach looks at similarities between people as a way of establishing concepts about patterns of behaviour. This method tries to develop 'laws' and generalisations about people's behaviour. It relies on scientific experiments, often in laboratories, to test theories. The biological, cognitive and behaviourist approaches are examples of the nomothetic approach and Freud's ideas also fall within this area as he tended to view mental, unconscious processes occurring in everyone.

Link

Read about the cognitive and behaviourist approaches on pages 102 and 100. Freud's ideas are discussed on page 112.

- The idiographic approach looks at individuals and their unique characteristics, experiences and development. Therefore the idiographic approach is much more concerned with studies of individuals. Research has concentrated on interviews and observations and is much more holistic, taking in the whole person's experiences and views. An example of this approach, as you will see later, is the humanistic view.

Link

Read about the humanistic perspective on page 102.

activity
INDIVIDUAL WORK 14.1

P1

M1

1 Consider the three debates in developmental psychology discussed above.
   a) What do you understand by the nature–nurture debate?
   b) Explain the idea of development in terms of continuity or discontinuity.
   c) Describe the difference between the nomothetic approach and the idiographic approach.

2 Think about children you observe in your work placement setting and consider the different aspects of their behaviour. Which particular characteristics do you think are a result of the child's upbringing so far and which do you think are a natural progression? Do you think, for example, that the child would behave in the same way if he or she had different parents, lived in a different culture or didn't go to the setting you are in? Use your ideas to analyse the nature–nurture debate to show how each plays a role in a child's development.

remember

Each child has a distinctive genetic inheritance and differing cultural experiences and influences that will affect their development. There are many different family structures and lifestyles, with different priorities. Each child's experiences are unique and will shape their learning and development.

Principal psychological perspectives

There are many different approaches to explaining individual behaviour. Here we will begin to consider some of these theoretical perspectives.

The behaviourist perspective

The behaviourist perspective looks at learning as the result of conditioning and that behaviour is learnt by positive and negative **reinforcement**. All conditioning is a result of interactions within the child's environment so falls within the nurture viewpoint. It is easy to observe behaviourism as you will notice that children will repeat actions which draw a positive response from adults or their peers.

The social learning perspective

Social psychology looks at social aspects of development such as behaviour within a group, leadership, non-verbal behaviour and aggression. It concentrates on how the social environment and interactions with others influence behaviour and attitudes.

In reality, interplay of both biological and social factors is likely to shape individuals as a person's individual genetic inheritance combined with the particular environment will create a person's unique characteristics.

The role of gender

One part of the child's experience will relate to gender. Gender is an important consideration when thinking about behaviour.

Physical differences between males and females are biologically determined but these are accentuated in many cases by the way individuals choose to present themselves through clothes, hairstyles, make-up, etc. However the question about whether males and females are biologically programmed to behave differently is more contentious. Are males naturally more aggressive and females more passive or is this behaviour that is learnt? It is still true that in higher positions within politics, industry, higher education, sports, the judicial system, the police force and in almost every area you can think of, the senior posts are predominantly held by men. In contrast, women hold the majority of lower paid menial jobs. Perhaps part of the reason for this is that women have time off to have children. However with the mother likely to be the infant's main carer in the early years and female teachers more often than not teaching in infant classes, it could be that girls learn this female role from very early on and are already open to discrimination against women. There has been a lot of research that has shown that girls and boys are treated differently both by their parents and at school.

Fig 14.1 Avoid gender stereotyping of activities

Gender stereotyping

When referring to the sex of a person we are talking biology and genes, whereas gender refers to a social construction. Gender refers to the set of behaviours, expectations and attitudes that are part of society's role of being male or female.

Gender roles is an area of social psychology that relates how the genders may be treated and expected to behave. In our culture, men and women have quite different roles and are expected to behave in a certain way and have certain characteristics. Generally men are still expected to be strong, aggressive, have successful careers and not show their feelings, whilst women are expected to be gentle, caring and emotional. These stereotypes can start to appear in children from a very early stage.

Think about the way the media portrays women. Television and magazines usually show young and beautiful women with the emphasis on clothes, hairstyle and weight. What part do you think these images have on the way women behave? Or do you think that males and females are genetically different and that this is the reason for the difference in their behaviour and characteristics?

Read more about gender development in Jarvis (2001) – see the bibliography on page 412.

The psychodynamic perspective

This perspective takes the view that our behaviour and feelings as an adult have their roots in early childhood experiences. It places great importance on social relationships, particularly with parents, influencing how we feel and behave. It also stresses the importance of the unconscious mind in affecting our feelings and behaviour. The unconscious mind is influenced by past experiences and by innate instincts.

Link

The main psychodynamic theories that we will consider in this unit are those developed by Sigmund Freud (see page 112). Freud is a well-known psychologist who wrote in the 1890s to 1930s.

The humanistic perspective

The humanistic perspective stresses positive aspects of development and a person's potential for growth. It emphasises a person's unique experiences and values a person's feelings and thoughts.

The cognitive perspective

The cognitive perspective concentrates on how a child develops understanding of the world around him. The idea of cognition refers to different mental activities such as thinking, listening, speaking, learning and understanding. Theories of cognitive development often concentrate on development of intellectual skills.

Link

Piaget carried out a great deal of work on understanding cognitive development (see page 103). Other influential psychologists in this field that we will consider are Vygotsky (page 106) and Bruner (page 106).

The developmental perspective

The developmental perspective looks at child development and tries to explain behaviour in terms of the age and stage of development of the child.

It can be difficult to explain human behaviour and understand and identify why children, and adults, think and act the way they do. Each person has differing experiences which will influence their development as well as a unique genetic inheritance.

You can refer back to these summaries of the different approaches as you move on to read about the various theories on how children learn.

case study 14.2

Claudia

Claudia is 3 years old. She likes to dress herself but often gets her top on inside out and struggles with buttons. When her mother tries to help her, she gets cross and shouts out, 'No, me do it!'

activity

Do you think Claudia behaves this way because of her stage of development? Is it her personality? Or does she have a difficult relationship with her mother, possibly as a result of some part of her mother's personality?

The questions in the case study above are the sorts of questions that psychologists consider when looking at children's behaviour.

Applying the theories to child development

In this section you will consider how children develop cognitively, how they develop a sense of self as a separate identity to others, how they develop language and how socially accepted behaviour develops. In each area you will look at major psychological ideas and theories.

Cognitive development

The processes of thinking and understanding are skills that we take for granted. If the doorbell rings, you know that it means there is someone at the door and you know how to operate your mobile phone, use a computer, etc. All the skills you have are those you have learnt through cognitive development. If you did not have cognitive skills, you would not be able to make use of past experiences or plan future events. So cognitive development is concerned with how mental processes develop.

Two of the most influential psychologists who studied cognitive development in children were Jean Piaget and Lev Vygotsky.

Jean Piaget

Jean Piaget (1896–1980) was a Swiss psychologist who looked at how children developed their reasoning skills. A good deal of his research was on his own three children. He carried out detailed observations of them and his work has shaped our understanding of how children develop their intellectual skills and has contributed to changes in education.

Piaget believed that cognitive development occurred in stages and he saw children as being like 'inquiring scientists' who gradually made sense of the world around them. Piaget's research concentrated on how children learn and gain understanding of their environment to construct their own knowledge.

He saw children as constantly making constructions in their brains to understand something and reconstructing it to fit in with new information, so that they gradually developed an increased level of understanding. He felt that children had to be at a particular stage of development to be able to learn new concepts.

Piaget identified a four-stage process of cognitive development through childhood. Every child must go through each stage in the same order although at different rates. He did not say that children would all go through each stage at a particular age although there are indicated ages with each stage. He also said that some people would never reach the later stages.

Piaget's stages of cognitive development

1 Sensorimotor stage (0–2 years)

- Babies and toddlers learn by their own activity, movement and activities especially through their senses of sight, taste, smell, touch and hearing. At first everything a baby encounters is put into her mouth or held and examined closely.
- The infant develops understanding through **schema**. Schemas are mental constructions containing all the information a child has about a particular aspect of her world. For example an infant will develop a schema around her main carer and learn to recognise her mother as different to other people in her life. The concept of schema has been agreed and used by other psychologists as units of understanding. We have schema for people, objects, abstract concepts and actions.

Fig 14.2 Object permanence

- During this stage infants are egocentric as they see things from their own point of view and are unable to decentre to see something from someone else's point of view. Piaget was not suggesting that infants are selfish, only that they cannot see things from someone else's perspective. If you think of an infant covering their eyes and thinking that you cannot see them because they cannot see you, you will have an idea of this concept.
- Initially the infant shows no awareness of himself as an individual and does not seem to have a self-concept.
- Additionally the infant does not at first show an understanding that other people or things can exist without him. Piaget devised a test to see when infants understood that things exist when they are not in the infant's sight. He did this by hiding a toy under a blanket whilst the infant was watching. If the infant searched for the toy afterwards, Piaget took this as evidence that the infant had made a mental representation of the toy in his brain. He saw this as evidence of 'object permanence'. He discovered that infants started to search for the hidden toy from around the age of 8 months old and concluded that object permanence starts at around this age.

2 Pre-operational stage (2–7 years)

- At this stage children show evidence of thinking, but not logical thinking. The child is not able to perform mental operations, which is why it is called the pre-operational stage.
- Children begin to use symbolic behaviour such as pretend play, language and drawings. The use of symbols can be demonstrated well by the way children at this age will make use of objects as props and use them to represent something else. They will also role-play different people such as mummy and daddy.
- Children will continue to use schema to make sense of things. Children will use **assimilation** and **accommodation** to adapt their schema to new information. For example, if a child recognises the family pet terrier as a 'dog' and this is their schema for dogs and then sees a poodle he will assimilate poodles into the 'dog' schema. Therefore assimilation takes place when an existing schema can be adapted to contain new information. On the other hand, if a new experience is so different that it cannot be assimilated into an existing schema, then a new schema is created. So if the infant comes across a pet guinea pig, a new schema would need to be created!
- It is during this stage that Piaget pointed out that children would show several characteristic mistakes in their thinking. These include egocentrism, animism and centration.
- Piaget carried out research to demonstrate children's egocentrism by a test he made called the 'three mountain test' where he constructed a model of three mountains and asked children to consider what view someone would have who was seeing the mountains from a different position to them. Children under 7 were not able to realise that the view from another side would be different and chose the view that they could see as the one that would be seen by someone on another side. Children at this stage cannot see things from another person's perspective.

Fig 14.3 Piaget's three mountain experiment

- Animism is a child's belief that an object has feelings like a human. Piaget observed that children up to the age of about 4 gave life-like characteristics to inanimate objects. For example, they might tell their toys off for being naughty or draw a picture of the sun with a smiling face. By the age of 4, children have a good idea of what objects around them are alive and what are not alive.

Fig 14.4 Animism

- Centration refers to a child's ability to deal with only one criteria at a time. So if you gave a young child a box of different coloured toy cars and lorries and asked them to give you the blue lorries, the child would concentrate on one aspect only and pick either blue vehicles or lorries of any colour. According to Piaget the ability to decentre, i.e. consider more than one factor at a time, is only achieved in the concrete operations stage.
- Another well-known experiment that Piaget carried out demonstrated how far a child could understand **conservation**. Conservation is the understanding that objects are the same in quantity when their appearance has changed. Examples include putting equal quantities of water in two different shaped beakers and seeing if children can understand that they contain the same volume even though the water is higher up the taller, thinner beaker than the shorter, wider beaker. Similarly different arrangements of ten buttons would not be perceived as having the same number of buttons in a child who was unable to conserve. Piaget found that children under the age of 7 could not conserve.

3 Concrete operations stage (7–11 years)
   - During this stage children are able to understand ideas in a more logical way but still find it hard to understand abstract concepts.
   - Children at this stage are able to conserve and are able to decentre or think about more than one aspect of a situation.

4 Formal operations stage (age 12 to adult)
   - By this stage children are able to think in a much more abstract and logical way. They can use reasoning skills and be deductive by applying a general principle to a particular situation.
   - These skills are needed in maths and science.
   - By this stage children are much more flexible in the way they think.

Operations are the rules by which the world operates and Piaget suggested that children think in different ways at different stages because the operations of which they are capable change with age. Young children do not have operations so are pre-operational. First operations are concrete, meaning things that the child can see, and later operations are linked to abstract concepts.

Piaget's stages of development fit in closely with the ways children are taught and learn, with the emphasis on play in pre-school settings. More abstract ways of working and thinking, such as writing and mathematics, are developed after the age of about 6 or 7.

Piaget's work gives us a good deal of information about how children develop their intellectual skills and allows us to consider how they think and understand the world around them at different ages. Children's behaviour will always be linked to their level of understanding so expected behaviour should be appropriate for the age and stage of development. Knowledge of how a child can reason and think as they develop will give you more insight into age-appropriate behaviour.

Piaget's work has been of particular value for giving an understanding of how children develop cognitively and has been used as the starting point for further research into this area of child development.

Criticisms of Piaget

There have been a number of criticisms of Piaget's theory. For example, Margaret Donaldson (born 1926) believed that Piaget was wrong about what children could and could not understand at each of his stages.

Donaldson developed the idea of embedded and disembedded thinking. Embedded thinking is based in a familiar situation allowing children to understand a scenario that they are being asked about and have a better understanding of what is being asked of them. Disembedded thinking, where children were asked to think about something outside of their experience or which was more abstract, such as the three mountain experiment, caused children difficulty.

Donaldson was able to show that by setting the same task or question to children but expressing it in a way that they could understand, meant that they were more likely to be successful and so she concluded that children did not have a limit to their thinking at different ages. Donaldson's work has encouraged practitioners to look at what children can do rather than test them in formal ways. She has also stressed how important child-centred education is, ensuring things are presented to children in ways they can understand.

Lev Vygotsky

Lev Vygotsky (1896–1934) was a Russian psychologist who took a very different view to Piaget. Although he developed his ideas during the 1920s, they have only become prominent in recent times.

Vygotsky placed a great deal of importance of social relationships for learning whereas Piaget saw children as investigating and learning independently. Vygotsky saw communication as a vital part of learning with the child and adult talking about familiar experiences. He also saw communication as allowing a young child to make sense of situations, interpreting words, body language, expression, etc.

Vygotsky developed the concept of the **zone of proximal development (ZPD)**. This refers to the child's ability to learn with help, what the child can achieve now with adult support and then later do alone. He felt that two children may have similar levels of achievement without adult support but that they could achieve different, higher levels with adult instruction. He also described the importance of play, allowing children to do things which they cannot yet manage in real life.

In practice, the idea of the ZPD means observing carefully what a child can do alone and then planning activities which challenge them to develop further with the help of an adult or more competent child.

Vygotsky's influence has meant practitioners look at what a child is able to do and has placed importance on peer group learning and adult support to individual children.

Jerome Bruner

Bruner added to Vygotsky's ZPD the idea of **scaffolding**, with a more skilled child or adult assisting the learner. He did not agree with Piaget's stage approach to development and chose instead to consider the way that children represent ideas in their brains at different ages.

Bruner identified three types of representation at different ages and linked these to cognitive development:

1 **Enactive representation** stage – this was similar to Piaget's sensorimotor stage where a young infant learns by doing and learns the muscle actions needed for a particular activity.

2 **Iconic representation** stage – this develops at the age of 1 according to Bruner and involves the infant making a mental picture in his brain of something.

3 **Symbolic representation** stage – at around the age of 7, Bruner saw a child's thinking as moving on to this stage, where he or she can now use symbols for thinking, such as language, numbers and music. Bruner believed that the use of symbols came with the development of language and that language was thus very important for cognitive development.

Information processing approach

An alternative view to cognitive development is the information processing approach that compares a human brain to a computer. This approach considers how the memory works to gather, store, keep and then retrieve information. The three main processes involved in memory are encoding information, storage and then retrieval.

Practitioners use the information-processing model to consider what a child will need to understand to learn, how information can be linked to existing learning and how it can best be remembered and retrieved to solve new problems.

Aaron Beck and Albert Ellis

Two people who have been highly influential in the field of psychotherapy and cognitive styles of therapy are Aaron Beck and Albert Ellis. Cognitive therapy looks at people's psychological problems and the cognitive 'errors' they may have gained, especially their views of the self-worth, their lives and futures. These psychologists would help patients to discuss and explore their opinions and see that they could take a more positive approach.

Aaron Beck (born 1921) is still active and has used his methods of Cognitive Behavioural Therapy (CBT) to treat people who are suicidal, depressed or who have anxiety or personality disorders.

Albert Ellis (1913–2007) looked at ways to change people's behaviour using his method of Rational Emotive Behavioural Therapy (REBT). He realised that people often have irrational ideas about how their problems are limiting their lives. He used therapy to show his patients that their feelings were the result of habits brought about by conditioning rather than being realistic. For example, a child might feel that she is worthless because others treat her unkindly, but Ellis would show that there is no evidence for this. Therapists taking this approach could offer assertiveness training and role-play techniques to modify behaviour.

Encoding

Encoding refers to the ability to keep information in the working memory in the brain whilst using that information in a task. Current research into Attention Deficit Hyperactivity Disorder (ADHD) has shown a link to difficulties with encoding information. Studies of children who have difficulties in social situations and tend to be aggressive have shown that children with ADHD do not encode social cues as often as children who do not have ADHD. They also selected an aggressive response more often. Studies show that children with ADHD have difficulties in social problem-solving situations in encoding and generating appropriate responses.

Professional Practice

- Use these psychological theories to aid your understanding of child development and how to work with children.
- Consider the role of gender and make sure you are not modelling gender stereotypes.
- Encourage children to become more autonomous so that they develop self-esteem.
- Remember age-appropriate behaviour, e.g. is the child able to use moral reasoning yet?
- Think about how you can increase children's skills and knowledge by giving appropriate support.

Language development

Theorists have taken different views of how children acquire their linguistic skills. These fall into either the nature or nurture viewpoint.

Behaviourist perspective

The behaviourist perspective put forward by B.F. Skinner is a nurture viewpoint. He suggested that children learnt language by observing and imitating adults. The behaviourists' viewpoint is that children have to have language put into them by others. This view was popular in the 1920s.

Nativist perspective

During the 1960s there was a change in view when Noam Chomsky pointed out that children are able to put together sentences they have not heard before. Chomsky believed that language is an innate skill (nature viewpoint) and that we are born with the ability to speak language through what he termed a **language acquisition device**, including having the ability to produce all the sounds needed for any language and an understanding of grammar rules. This means we are able to learn a language much more easily than would otherwise be possible.

Prelinguistic, phonological and semantic skills

Language development is more than just learning to talk. During the first year of life children have to develop prelinguistic skills also known as emerging language. During this early stage infants learn to take turns when communicating, how to use non-verbal communication and how to interpret and use facial expression, body language, tone of voice and expression.

Children have to learn the phonological skills needed for the language they use. Children are born with the ability to make all the sounds needed for any language but later keep only those needed for their own language. In the English language there are 44 different sounds or phonemes. Children also have to learn the semantics or meaning of the language as well as the rules of grammar.

Link

See Unit 18, pages 187–197 for more about language development.

Development of self

A major area of children's social development is their perception of themselves. Children's awareness of themselves and their individual characteristics make up their self-concept. This sense of yourself is an intuitive knowledge. How much you like yourself is important for self-esteem. Evidence shows that low self-esteem causes problems for children.

Carl Rogers

Rogers developed the most famous concept on self-esteem. According to his view everyone has an idea of what his or her ideal self should be. If the image you have of yourself is the same as the image of your ideal self, then you will have a good self-esteem. Rogers felt that the development of self-esteem depends on unconditional positive regard from others and self-actualisation, i.e. fulfilling your potential. Consider the effect on a child's self-esteem of parents who do not give their children unconditional love and affection.

As children grow older they will spend a long time at school and although the parents or carers will play a major role in development of self-concept, children will also have to cope with situations where they are facing competition and the sense of achievement or failure in their academic and sports skills.

How far do you think a child's ability and achievement at school are linked to the sense of self-esteem they have developed at home? Do you think a child is more likely to do well at school if they have already developed a high self-esteem, or do you think that success at school can give a child a sense of self-esteem? What other factors can you think of which could affect a child's self-esteem?

You may have considered cultural factors, gender and physical attributes when you thought through the above points.

Abraham Maslow

Maslow developed a theory based on individuals being motivated through seeking to develop through five levels of need, known as a hierarchy of needs. The most basic needs are physiological needs relating to survival instincts of food, water and sleep. This is followed by safety needs for security, protection and safety, then belonging and love needs reflecting that we are social and need to feel loved. Higher up in Maslow's hierarchy of needs comes self-esteem needs, relating to the individual's sense of self-regard and how others view him. At the top of the hierarchy, Maslow placed self-actualisation needs; these are an individual's need for personal achievement and growth.

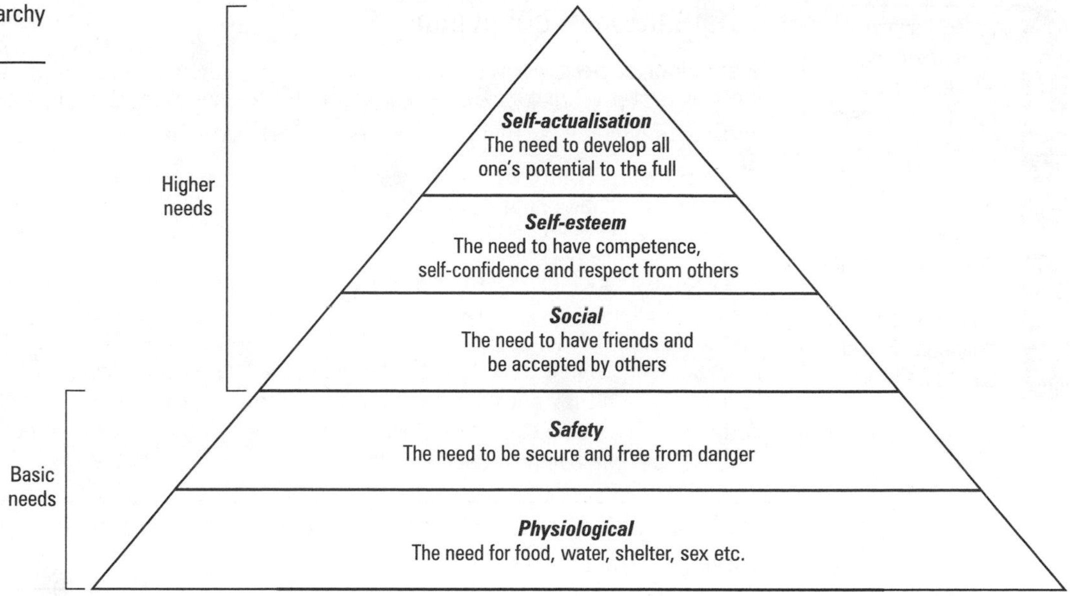

Fig 14.5 Maslow's hierarchy of needs

Maslow felt that a person could only go on to the stage of self-actualisation when the needs below this in his pyramid had been fulfilled. He also felt that the four needs below are deficiency needs, meaning that without these needs being met, a person cannot reach their full potential.

Consider how a child may be affected if his or her basic needs are not being met. How likely is a child to develop a sense of self-regard if his or her family do not have a secure home or there is not enough food or regular meals at home? How will a child be affected if they are not shown love and affection or if love is only given at certain times?

Maslow's approach is, perhaps, over-simple. People are able to achieve satisfaction in a number of areas at the same time and it is perhaps only in extreme conditions of poverty that a person's only motivation becomes the need for food and water.

Cognitive-developmental approach

Children's friendships form an important part of their lives and help children to develop cognitive and communication skills, as well as giving a sense of self-esteem and being of particular value when things are difficult for a child at home. Age-related changes in friendship have been investigated by child psychologists. Selman looked at children's understanding of friendships at different ages and concluded that early friendships are egocentric but later they develop a more sophisticated understanding of what a friend is and the relationship becomes more of an equal partnership.

Link See pages 114–119 for how children form their early relationships.

Environmental/learning theory

Bandura placed emphasis on the environment and social aspects of learning. His view would be that part of a child's development of self would be based on what they observed and imitated from others.

Link See page 111 for Bandura's experiment and how children imitated adult violence.

Interpersonal theories

Interpersonal theories consider the importance of the reaction of others in a child's development of self-esteem.

- Cooley was a sociologist who proposed the 'looking glass' theory in which the behaviour of others towards us acts as a looking glass or mirror to give us a reflection of ourselves. If people smile and enjoy spending time with us, this raises our self-esteem.
- Mead took the view that individuals have two aspects, the 'I' and the 'me', with the 'I' being the social responses of the individual and the 'me' being the responses and attitudes of others to the individual. Mead stressed the importance of communication with others for the development of self-esteem.

remember

A child's sense of self-esteem and self-worth is so important for their development that you should always work with children in ways that will help them develop a sense of value in themselves, confidence in their abilities and social skills.

Acquisition of behaviour

Behaviourist perspective

Behavioural psychology looks at learning from the viewpoint that all behaviour is learnt through conditioning. There are two types of conditioning:

- classical conditioning
- operant conditioning.

Classical conditioning

Classical conditioning is a method used in behavioural training where a naturally occurring stimulus is linked to a response. Then a neutral stimulus is added to the original situation and the added stimulus is conditioned and produces a response. The famous example of this is Pavlov's dogs where they were conditioned to salivate at the sound of a bell. Initially the dogs salivated when they got their food, but by introducing the sound of a bell as the dogs were fed, Pavlov was able to get the dogs to salivate when they heard the bell as they had learnt to associate the bell with being fed.

i

You can read more about Pavlov's research in Pennington et al. (2003)– see the bibliography on page 412.

Of course humans cannot be conditioned in the same way as dogs. However, this method is used in schools by creating a positive classroom environment to help pupils to feel more relaxed and to overcome any fears or anxieties. The calm environment aims to help pupils feel more comfortable and stress-free which in turn should lead to better behaviour. This contrasts sharply with how schools used to be run, with children ruled by fear of physical punishment or public humiliation.

Operant conditioning

Operant conditioning is a method of learning that operates by using a system of rewards and sanctions for different behaviour. B.F. Skinner (1904–90) was an American psychologist who carried out experimental research to find out about learning. The idea of operant conditioning is that children learn to link a particular behaviour with a consequence for that behaviour, either positive or negative. The consequence is known as a reinforcer.

- Positive reinforcers are favourable consequences that are used to encourage positive behaviour. For example, if a child receives a sticker for good behaviour, this would encourage the child to repeat the positive behaviour.
- Negative reinforcers involve the removal of unfavourable events after a particular behaviour is shown, again using reinforcers to encourage certain behaviour. An example here would be that a child is allowed to go out to play with the rest of the class once he has tidied up his table. To discourage negative behaviour, a punishment could be used.

Lovaas used the idea of operant conditioning to reinforce desired behaviour in children on the autistic spectrum. His early intervention programme used with children below the age of 5 is an intense, structured approach to teaching children social, self-help and language skills. Lovaas noted that behaviour had to be broken down into small steps and then clear and consistent reinforcement used to bring about change. Rewards are used, such as small pieces of food, a favourite toy to play with, and later social rewards such as praise and hugs.

i

You may be interested to read about the Lovaas behaviour modification technique on the National Autistic Society website at www.nas.org.uk/nas. You can also look at case studies of children whose behaviour has been modified using the Lovaas technique at www.lovaas.com.

Behaviour modification techniques are also used in other cases such as for children who have ADHD. Positive reinforcers are used to reward positive behaviour and to increase its frequency.

case study 14.3

Dwayne

Dwayne is a 10-year-old boy in Year 6 at primary school. He finds school work difficult and struggles in class. Dwayne never answers questions in class, does not get praised for his work and does badly in any class tests. At 10, he is already getting a sense of failure, the SATs tests are looming and he knows that he is below the national average and feels 'thick'. Recently Dwayne has started to become disruptive in class. The teacher gets very cross when he doesn't co-operate and he has been taken to one side and told off by the teacher several times recently.

activity

1 How might a pupil who is a low achiever at school respond to a teacher who tells him or her off for negative behaviour?
2 Why might the negative behaviour not decrease?

If the child does not get positive attention from the teacher then the telling off may be the only attention the teacher gives the pupil and the pupil may prefer this attention to none and so continue to behave in a negative way to gain more attention.

Social learning perspective

Behaviour may also be learnt through observation. Albert Bandura's view, in his **social learning theory**, is that we tend to forget the importance of modelling in how children learn behaviour, particularly when learning social skills. Bandura agreed that reinforcement is important but not always essential. He felt that children have an innate ability to imitate other people. This imitation is often not deliberate but unconscious as the child observes and notes behaviour and then copies it without thinking. Someone who plays a key part in the child's life is likely to be a role model. Often the child's parents and older siblings are the first role models and later peer group influences will influence behaviour.

Bandura carried out research to see if children would learn to behave aggressively if they observed aggressive behaviour. He used children between the ages of 3 and 6, both boys and girls, and they were exposed to adult role models who behaved in either an aggressive or non-aggressive way. The aggressive behaviour they observed involved the adult role model hitting a Bobo doll with a mallet and punching and kicking it whilst shouting out aggressive comments. Bandura found that children who were exposed to the aggressive role model and then put in a situation that would make them stressed, used exactly the same behaviour and were more aggressive than children who had not seen the role model. He also found that boys were more likely to copy modelling that they had seen by men and that boys displayed more aggressive behaviour than girls.

Fig 14.6 Bandura's Bobo doll research

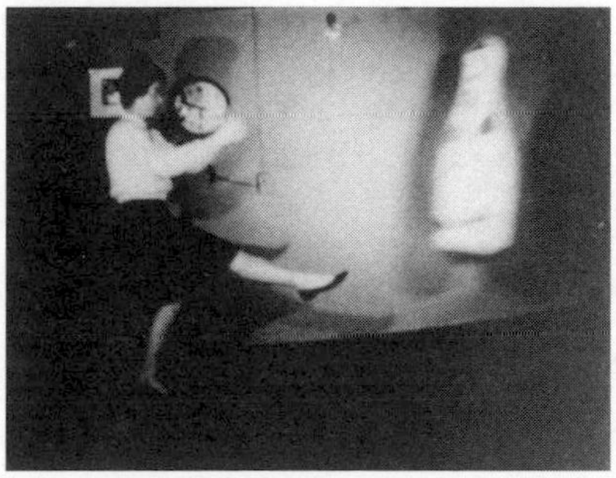

The most important factor in imitation of behaviour could be the response that the behaviour then brings. Bandura saw that children tend to seek same-sex models to imitate. This then brings us back to the effect of gender on behaviour, both the way that children will imitate same-sex adults and the reinforcement of behaviour that those role models may give.

How might a father react to seeing his son playing with a doll? What might the same father's reaction be to his son playing football for the school team?

Consider the role of the media in gender development. Have a look at soap operas, children's books and catalogues with children's toys in them. To what extent do you think they reinforce gender stereotypes?

Bandura's work is useful in helping us consider the importance of social contact in the development of social skills. His studies suggest that where children observe aggression in adults they are likely to imitate it, perhaps because they see it as socially acceptable if adults can behave that way.

Psychodynamic perspective

The psychodynamic approach for the acquisition of behaviour contrasts with the ideas of conditioning and social learning discussed above. This approach was developed by Sigmund Freud and is based on the ideas that our behaviour as adults is based on early childhood experiences and that early relationships, particularly with parents, are of great importance in determining how we feel about ourselves and behave. He felt that the unconscious mind has a large part to play in how we behave and how we feel and that the influences of the unconscious mind come from past experiences and from our instincts.

According to Freud, we have a number of levels to our personality:

- The id is present from birth and is driven by instincts. It is a survival instinct for food, comfort, warmth, sex, etc. The id is a completely selfish unconscious instinct, which does not take into account anyone else's needs or what effect your actions may have on anyone else.
- The second level of the personality starts to develop from about the age of 1. This level is called the ego and is a conscious level, which contains information that the child has about the world around him, how others behave and react to him. The ego will recognise that you cannot always do what you want as the consequences may be punishment or danger, and that learnt strategies may be more effective.
- At about the age of 6 the superego starts developing. This stage involves the child getting a sense of morality, knowing right from wrong and feeling guilty about doing the wrong thing. It also involves a less conscious process where a child has a sense of their ideal self usually based on his parents and this guides the child's behaviour.

An example to illustrate this would be a young child considering whether to take a chocolate bar out of the cupboard without asking. The id would say, 'Take it, you love chocolate', but the ego would say, 'You will get in trouble if you get found out. Don't take it.' The superego would say, 'Even if I don't get caught, I know it is wrong to take a chocolate bar without asking.'

So you can see that from the age of about 6 the id, ego and superego all play a part in the child's behaviour.

If the superego is based on the ideal self and the conscience, consider how similar this is to conditioning. What effect do you think the rewards and punishments parents have given their child have on the development of the superego?

Freud also proposed a stage theory of development during childhood. He proposed five stages of psychosexual behaviour (the oral, anal, phallic, latent and genital stages) and felt that if each stage was successfully completed it would result in a healthy personality. However, if an individual became stuck at a particular stage then there would be problems and the person would develop a fixation. For example, during the anal stage Freud believed that the child's achievement of toilet training and independence would complete this stage; however if the child experienced negative comments and the parents were too strict with toilet training, this could affect the child's personality, making him obsessive as an adult.

Development of personality

Freud

Freud's theory of personality development is one of the best known but also one of the most controversial, as at each stage of childhood, Freud saw pleasure-seeking based on sexual pleasure being the main influence on behaviour. Freud believed that personality is set by the age of about 5 and that early experiences play a large part in the personality a child develops.

There is more detail of Freud's theory of personality in Jarvis (2001) – see the bibliography on page 412.

Erikson

Another theory of personality development was developed by Erikson. His perspective is often known as psychosocial theory and is a stage theory but, unlike Freud or Piaget, Erikson's stages cover the entire lifespan. Erikson's stages were similar to Freud's as each stage involved overcoming a conflict or crisis. His main ideas are shown in Table 14.1.

Table 14.1 Erikson's eight stages of pychosocial development

Stage	Age	Central conflict
Trust v. Mistrust	Birth to 1 year	The child must develop a sense of trust with caregivers. If this crisis is not resolved, the infant may mistrust themselves and others. It is important for the infant to experience reliable care and affection to develop a sense of trust.
Autonomy v. Shame and doubt	1–3 years	At this age children learn some independence in a supportive home. If the child is successful, he will develop a sense of independence or autonomy. If the child is not supported to make choices and become independent, he will feel shame and doubt.
Initiative v. Guilt	3–5 years	In this pre-school stage, children develop more control over their environment. Success leads to a sense of initiative and failure to a sense of guilt if they exert too much power and experience disapproval.
Industry v. Inferiority	6–11 years (school age)	During this stage children have to learn how to cope in new social situations at school and with academic work. Failure may lead to feelings of inferiority and incompetence.
Identity v. Role confusion	12–18 years (adolescence)	Teenagers need to develop a sense of personal identity. Failure leads to confusion and this may be as a result of parents' demands and pressures.
Intimacy v. Isolation	19–40 years (young adulthood)	Young adults need to form loving, intimate relationships. Failure to do this leads to feelings of loneliness and isolation.
Generativity v. Stagnation	40–65 years (middle adulthood)	At this stage, adults need to create or nurture. This is normally by having children or creating something positive for the benefit of others. Success leads to feelings of accomplishment, whilst failure can lead to a feeling that life has no purpose.
Ego integrity v. Despair	65 to death (maturity)	Older adults need to look back with a sense of fulfilment in their lives. If the person was successful in the earlier stages, they can look back with a sense of integrity, whilst failure can lead to regret and despair.

Look at Erikson's stages of development during childhood and consider which are the important relationships at each stage. You can see that Erikson placed a good deal of value on social relationships.

case study 14.4

The Roberts Family

There are five children in the Roberts family. Lily is 9 months old, Jess is 2 years old, Zac is 4, Henry is 8 and Liz is 13.

activity

Using Erikson's first five stages, make a list of the key relationships each child in the family would need to be able to overcome the 'crisis' identified. In each case explain how negative social relationships could result in failure.

activity
INDIVIDUAL WORK 14.2
P2

Prepare a booklet for childcare workers that describes the major theoretical perspectives of development psychology relating to behaviour. You will need to explain:

- the behaviourist approach to learning, including classical and operant conditioning
- social learning theory, including Bandura
- Piaget's theory of cognitive development
- Vygotsky's zone of proximal development
- language development from the behaviourist and nativist (Chomsky) perspectives
- the importance of the development of self-esteem with mention of Rogers and Maslow.

Understand how early relationships are formed

Children's early relationships and their importance for a child's overall development is a relatively recent area of study in child psychology. Adults working with children need to understand the importance of attachment, the stages of attachment and the effects of separation on a child.

Theories of attachment

Child psychologists use the concept of attachment to describe the unique **bonding** that develops between a child and the main caregivers. Research has shown that the quality of these bonds will have an influence on how well the child is able to form relationships with other people.

Stages of attachment

Attachment is often described as a stage process. In one study of infants, Schaffer & Emerson (1964) looked at how infants reacted to separation from their main carer between birth and 18 months:

1 Asocial stage – at first, a newborn baby is attracted to human faces and voices and by 6 weeks onwards first smiles appear. At this stage the infant will accept comfort from strangers.

2 Indiscriminate attachments – from about 3 months an infant prefers to be in human company rather than alone and will enjoy being held by anyone, even a stranger. At the same time the infant will recognise familiar people and show pleasure in their company.

3 Specific attachments – from around 8 months the infant will have made specific attachments to main carers and will show distress when they disappear from sight. They will also start to become wary of strangers and even show fear if a stranger comes too close.

4 Multiple attachments – after this the child will start to form more, or multiple, attachments and this is a normal healthy part of the process of socialisation that children go through.

John Bowlby (1907–90) was the first psychologist to describe attachment. He explained attachment as a two-way emotional bond with each person depending on the other for a sense of security. Attachment is shown by the need to be close to the other person, distress on separation and pleasure at being together again. We form attachments throughout life but psychologists have studied the attachment that forms between the main carer and infant most closely. For infants the key characteristics of attachment include the main carer being a safe haven for the child to return to and a base from which to explore the environment.

Separation and deprivation

John Bowlby

Bowlby carried out research to study mental health needs of homeless and orphaned children after the Second World War. He found that the children were very distressed and put this down to the effects of separation from the key adults in their lives and identified psychological damage as a result of separation from their main carer. He called this maternal deprivation. Bowlby continued to study children and the bonds they made with adults. He believed that the early bonds children form with the main caregivers have a lifelong influence. His main idea was that mothers who were responsive to their infants gave the infants a sense of safety and security.

Bowlby felt that infants need the continuous presence of the main carer for the first one and a half to two years and described the lack of this in his maternal deprivation hypothesis. His work placed an emphasis on only one main attachment, although since then research by Schaffer and Emerson (1964) has shown that infants form strong attachments to others such as the father and siblings.

Bowlby also over-emphasised the importance of the mother as the main carer. At the time, after the Second World War, it was convenient for the government to encourage mothers to give up work so that there was sufficient work for men returning from war. Bowlby did later state that infants could form an attachment with someone other than the mother.

There has been controversy about the effects early day care may have on infants, but studies now show that good quality care can help children cope with separation.

Bowlby talked about deprivation, which is the temporary withdrawal of the main carer, rather than privation, which is the more serious lack of any attachment for the infant. These days psychologists believe that it is the lack of a secure attachment which can lead to the most serious consequences for a child.

Bowlby appears to be correct in identifying that a child's first attachment influences future development. However Bowlby over-emphasised the problems associated with delayed attachment or periods when a child is separated from his main carer.

Mary Ainsworth

Mary Ainsworth carried out research into attachment in the 1970s which expanded on Bowlby's work. Her 'Strange Situation' study showed how much attachment affects an infant's behaviour. In her work, children between the ages of 12 and 18 months were briefly left alone with a stranger and then reunited with their mothers. She looked at how securely the infants were attached to their mothers and how they reacted to being with a stranger. From this work, she described three types of attachment:

- secure attachment – children are able to show independence and continue to play when left with a stranger and react positively when their carer returns. These children are confident that the carer will return. They are also confident that their carer will provide comfort in times of need and will approach their carer for reassurance
- ambivalent or resistant insecure attachment – children are very distressed when their carer leaves them with a stranger and are not easily comforted when the carer returns. This attachment style is fairly uncommon and research suggests that it is the result of the carer not being available to the child when needed
- avoidant insecure attachment – children continue to play independently when the carer leaves, do not show distress at being left and do not make contact or show pleasure when she returns. These children do not show a preference between their main carer and a complete stranger. Research suggests that this may be a result of care that is abusive or neglectful. Children will not seek help and support from their carer if they have experienced punishment for doing so before.

Further research has shown that children who showed the secure attachment then went on to develop better intellectually and socially than the others. It does seem that the test measured more than just a child's personality, as personality could not explain how the infants reacted to the return of their main carer.

Ainsworth believed, like Bowlby, that the quality of the attachment the child forms depends on the quality of care from the main carer and how sensitive they are to the child's needs.

The Strange Situation seems to be a reliable way of identifying securely attached and insecurely attached infants. However the child's personality has to be a factor too in how they react to being separated from the main carer and left with a stranger.

Think of your own family or another family you know well. Is there any difference in the way siblings in the family react to being separated from the main carer? If you can identify differences, then it could suggest personality plays a part, as the main carer would be likely to treat the siblings in the same way.

Attachment theory based on the work of Bowlby and Ainsworth has been a big influence in child development. The key idea that a secure attachment to a primary carer during infancy provides great advantages for the child's later development has proved useful in understanding ways to provide appropriate care in nurseries and hospitals. Sensitive and responsive parenting styles are shown to be of particular importance in forming the main attachment. Professionals understand the importance of giving support to families where there is a risk of an infant being neglected or abused. On the other hand, the temperament of the child has to be considered as part of the picture of the type of attachment that is formed. Another issue is the pressure that some mothers feel is placed on them to stay at home full time with their infant rather than going to work.

Childhood experiences can be affected by abuse or neglect, which will affect attachment. Children may also be affected by other issues, such as separation from their main carer either by being in day care from infancy or through the death of a parent or the separation of parents.

Children in hospital

Robertson & Bowlby (1952) worked together to look at the experience of children in hospital. At the time it was felt that if children had good physical care whilst in hospital they would have few problems and parents had very limited access to their children whilst they were in hospital. However Robertson & Bowlby filmed a 2-year-old girl in hospital who was only having a minor operation and in hospital for a total of eight days. By the end of the treatment, the girl was extremely withdrawn and did not show trust to her mother.

Research by Robertson & Robertson in the 1940s looked at the short-term effects of deprivation when parents were not allowed to visit their children in hospital as they were told it would be too upsetting for the children. This meant long-term spells in hospital formed a kind of deprivation for children. Robertson & Robertson looked at how children coped with being separated from their mothers. They carried out observations and filmed the reactions of children. At first children showed extreme distress when the mother left them in hospital with a great deal of crying. Following this, the children were unhappy, showing misery and apathy. They did not take part in normal play activities. Finally the children would begin to play again but when their mothers returned they either ignored them or rejected them. Robertson & Robertson concluded that during separation the children were very distressed and when they returned home they were less attached, less happy and less affectionate than they had been previously.

This study has had a major influence on hospital visiting hours for children which are now extended, parents are encouraged to visit and children are prepared for hospital stays beforehand.

Day care is a daily routine for many young children as it is now common for both parents to work. There have been many studies into whether or not day care is harmful to young children. The conclusions of various studies seem to show that good quality childcare is not damaging to children if they have a close relationship with their main carers whilst at home.

remember

Deprivation = the temporary withdrawal of the main carer.
Privation = the lack of any secure attachment.

Privation

Research on privation has considered the effects of institutionalised care on children and how later adoption can reverse any damage. During the 1990s after the fall of Ceauşescu, there was a lot of interest in Romanian orphanages which were under-staffed and over-crowded. A lot of the orphans were adopted by Western families.

Michael Rutter (1998) looked at the progress of some of the orphans who were adopted by British families. He compared these orphans and their developmental progress with that of British children who had been adopted to compare the effects of maternal deprivation itself with general privation through neglect. He found that initially the Romanian orphans had delayed development and were very underweight whereas the British children were not. After four years the Romanian children's development was on a par with the British children who had been adopted. Rutter concluded that if children who have had early privation then receive good quality care the chances of healthy development are good. However not all the Romanian children caught up with the development of the British children and effects were more severe for children who had spent longer in institutional care.

For more information on Romanian orphans, see http://news.bbc.co.uk/1/hi/world/europe/4649383.stm

Isolation

Other cases where children have experienced privation and not formed a secure attachment are those where children have suffered serious abuse. There have been a number of cases which have been used for studies.

Kulochova (1972) looked at the case of identical twins, usually referred to as the Czech twins, whose mother died after their birth. The twins were in an institution for a year, fostered by an aunt for a further six months and then their father remarried and the boys were taken home. The stepmother was very cruel and they were kept locked in a dark room and beaten regularly. At the age of 7 they were rescued. At the time both were severely developmentally delayed and had no speech. They were terrified of adults. After two years of careful care, they were fostered by caring adults. By 14, they had no delay in their development and by 20 they were both of above average intelligence. They are now reported to be in successful relationships with their own children and have careers. In this particular case study, the twins had a positive outcome demonstrating that even in cases of severe privation where there is high quality care later the effects of privation can be overcome. However the twins were rescued at a relatively young age and also had each other throughout the years of abuse, which means that they had a close attachment with each other.

Find out about the very different case of Genie who was not discovered until she was 13 and had experienced severe abuse and neglect. The outcome for her was very different to that of the Czech twins. See www.feralchildren.com.

Development of attachment

Research into attachment has been the focus of much media interest and a source of interest and stress, particularly to mothers who return to work after having a baby.

The infant and carer should develop a strong attachment initially during feeding time and through the physical contact this brings, as well as when the infant is cuddled, changed and washed. The bond will depend on how sensitive and responsive the carer is. It is known that where the carer responds sensitively to the infant's efforts to communicate in different situations, such as crying, feeding and play, the infant will develop a secure, high-quality attachment to the carer.

There will obviously be individual differences in experiences including cultural variations and a variety of family situations. A child may also have to cope with separation, family arguments, overcrowding, maternal depression, etc.

Continuity hypothesis

It seems that the key issue for the development of attachment is how well any difficulties are handled and how continuity is ensured for the child.

Attachment continuity is the focus of many current studies looking at the effect of discontinuous attachments on children as they grow older. The conclusions are mixed, with some finding that continuous secure attachments are needed for children to be emotionally secure and other studies finding no significant difference. Clearly a disrupted and difficult childhood will have some effect on a child, but this could depend on other factors such as the child's own character and resilience.

Historical theories of child rearing styles

Nowadays, mothers are advised to breast feed their babies on demand, but until the 1960s this was considered bad for the baby. Advice about weaning, potty training and sleeping have also changed over time.

At the turn of the twentieth century, Dr Truby King's (1858–1938) system of child rearing included feeding an infant every four hours but not at night, early potty training at 10 months and leaving the baby outdoors wrapped up warmly in the fresh air even on cold days.

During the 1950s and 1960s, the name Dr Benjamin Spock (1903-98) was well known by parents. He advised them to trust their own instincts when caring for a baby and to be more flexible than previously. Although this seems normal advice today, at the time ideas about parenting were very different. Early parenting advice had recommended only occasional treats and strict supervision. Dr Spock did not agree with smacking children and at the time this was controversial. Spock introduced a more relaxed way of parenting and has been blamed by many people for a rise in immorality due to lax discipline in children.

Penelope Leach is known for her books offering childcare advice, which were popular during the 1970s and 1980s. Her advice to parents was to do things by the baby not the book, in other words she recommended caring for a baby on demand.

Sheila Kitzinger similarly recommended working with the child and gave advice about carrying the infant around in a sling whilst doing jobs, taking the infant into bed to sleep and using your instincts as a parent in caring for your infant. She argues against having a strict routine, leaving babies to cry and sleep training methods, feeling that these ways treat babies as if they are enemies not part of the family.

Konrad Lorenz (1903–89) studied animal behaviour and applied this to humans. For example, he noticed that greylag goslings would follow and attach themselves to the first moving object they saw, which would normally be the mother goose. This behaviour, called imprinting, ensures the gosling stays safe from harm. This innate behaviour ensures the species survives.

In one respect, Lorenz saw humans as different to animals and that was in the way their behaviour is influenced by positive feedback to encourage desired behaviour rather than negative feedback to stop unwanted behaviour.

Theories that inform current practice

Current best practice is to follow a child-led approach where the baby is fed on demand and given comfort and cuddles. Miriam Stoppard recommends not leaving a baby to cry but go immediately to the baby. This fits in with the idea of a secure attachment being the result of sensitive parenting.

Not all advice now recommends a child-led approach though. One book that has been very popular with parents recently is *Toddler Taming* by Dr Christopher Green, which takes a behaviourist approach to child rearing. Gina Ford is another popular childcare adviser and she recommends a much more strict routine for parents to use with infants. There are also a number of programmes on television these days giving advice on areas such as discipline.

i

Look at the advice given on the Super Nanny website at www.supernanny.co.uk.
Is the advice that is given child-led or does it follow a behaviourist perspective?

Talk to your parents and grandparents or other family members about the childcare advice that was popular when they were raising young children. Do you think that advice given to parents is consistent?

Role of the family

remember

Children will have different home experiences.

Positive early relationships, where a child is brought up by loving and responsive parents, will obviously give the child the best chance to go on to develop good relationships with others. However, you must bear in mind that children will have different home experiences and these must be considered. Some children live in a nuclear family that is made up of the parents and children, whilst others live within an extended family which may include grandparents, uncles, aunts, cousins, etc. Levels of family break-up and divorce now mean that more children live with one parent or in stepfamilies. Another point to consider is that most mothers now work and it is normal for a child to have two working parents not one. Cultural variations are an important consideration too. With more movement of people, there is no longer the support network of relatives and neighbours for all families.

If there are different attitudes to correct ways of discipline and child rearing in the family this can cause conflict and difficulties. A consistent approach is vital for a child's well-being.

With the changing nature of families and lack of support structures for many families, it can be extremely difficult for families to cope where there are additional problems. This means that some children are especially vulnerable to neglect or abuse.

Parents who were badly treated as children themselves are often unable to relate correctly to their own children and this affects the attachment formed. Some parents take good physical care of their children but are unable to give appropriate emotional support leading to problems such as disturbed behaviour for these children.

Within a family, it is important that there is a consistent approach when using any behavioural modification techniques. It is vital that both parents work together in a supportive way to ensure the child is not confused by difference or perceived conflict between the parents in the way discipline and rewards are used. The same applies to any childcare setting, such as a school, where there will be a behaviour policy and expected code of conduct. Staff need to work together to ensure consistency which will give children boundaries and security.

activity
INDIVIDUAL AND GROUP WORK 14.3

P3

M2

D1

1 a) Think about work placement experiences you have had and the ways in which children are expected to conform. What opportunities do the children have to think and choose for themselves and when are they expected to follow a particular behaviour?

b) Children will generally follow socially accepted rules and conform to rules of expected behaviour. As children grow older the influence of the social group they are in will be a huge factor in how they behave. Peer pressure can be a factor in a child either conforming or not conforming. Can you think of examples of peer pressure that will influence children in a way that will lead to them not conforming?

c) Prepare a report which should include the following points:

- the importance of a secure attachment
- opportunities for carers to form a secure attachment during the daily routine of an infant
- Bowlby's theory and additional research by others including Ainsworth
- how modern child rearing practices will support the development of attachments
- the role of the family in the development of early relationships.

2 a) For each of the theories covered so far, consider how they link to what you have experienced in your work placement. Work in small groups to draw up a list of ways in which practice links to theory and share your ideas with the class.

b) Write up your findings to cover this task. Possible ideas will include:

- the use of the behaviourist approach to manage behaviour
- key workers assigned to children in nurseries to aid attachment
- how the National Curriculum fits in with Piaget's theory of child development
- the use of teaching assistants in schools to support children's learning, which links to Vygotsky and Bruner.

3 Analyse the contribution of the major developmental perspectives to early years practice. The distinction criteria can be covered by a reflective account of the ways that theory has informed practice in early years settings. Build on from your examples for activity M2 by carefully linking theory and practice together.

Understand factors affecting the behaviour of children

There are many different factors that will have an effect on children's behaviour and we will consider some of the main ones in this section.

Approaches to behaviour

The approach taken to behaviour is of great importance. Language needs to be used carefully so that a child is not labelled as 'naughty'. Any comments should be worded in such a way that the child understands that the behaviour is not acceptable but that he is still liked, e.g. by saying 'I don't like your rude behaviour' rather than 'You naughty rude girl'. Whenever possible, positive directions should be given to address behaviour concerns, e.g. 'We walk in the corridor' rather than 'Stop running', or 'Listen please' rather than 'Stop talking'.

A great deal of emphasis has been put on using positive approaches with children rather than negative approaches. Comments on positive behaviour reinforce and reward that behaviour and encourage it, rather than focusing on the unwanted behaviour. 'Good listening', 'Well done for tidying away the toys', 'You are playing nicely', etc. are positive comments which will show children how you want them to behave.

Negative approaches may make a child feel negative about himself and can create a self-fulfilling prophecy whereby he acts in negative ways to gain attention or because he feels that he is a 'bad' child.

Where children have additional or special needs using a positive approach can be particularly important and effective and they will need a great deal of reinforcement of positive behaviour, perhaps using more visual means such as a sticker chart as well as verbal praise.

Reinforcement of positive behaviour with praise and rewards links to behaviourist theories of positive conditioning. Negative conditioning would result if a child received attention for negative behaviour rather than positive behaviour. This would lead the child to seek attention in the only way she knew how; by behaving badly. If a child receives positive attention for acceptable behaviour, this will lead to conditioning to repeat the desired behaviour to receive praise and other rewards.

Link

Strategies for dealing with challenging behaviour are discussed on page 125.

Steiner

Rudolf Steiner (1861–1925) wanted to establish a form of education which developed children's personal and social development and their spiritual side. He believed that children should be in a protective environment during the early years so that they could develop holistically. He disagreed with formal learning and instead saw great value in creative and imaginative play with simple activities and natural materials. He put emphasis on establishing relationships.

Steiner schools have a distinct way of teaching and learning which develops the child spiritually, physically, morally and academically. Social abilities are a priority. Formal teaching starts later in Steiner schools than is usual and there is greater emphasis on creative activities.

A less formal academic method of education might be more successful for many children and result in less behavioural problems at school. Many people feel that the National Curriculum is very intense and with tests from the age of 7 many children soon experience a sense of failure.

The approach is very different to the academic emphasis in mainstream schools in the UK. You can find out more about Steiner methods of education on the internet at www.steinerwaldorf.org.uk.

Transitions

Transitions can also have an influence on a child's behaviour. Any time of change can be difficult for a child and may result in challenging or withdrawn behaviour. When a child first starts in a childcare setting, he will not know the expected behaviour and may not have a great deal of experience of mixing with his peer group or know expected social behaviour.

Starting school can be an anxious time for a child, particularly for a child who hasn't been to a pre-school setting. Consider how difficult it could be for a child starting in a reception class who has had a very different home life to the other children in the class. If the child does not have experience of being with other children in a formal group situation, has a home life where conversation is not common and the child's upbringing has been chaotic, what problems might the child have adjusting to school?

Moving to a new setting can also be difficult, especially if the child has moved to the area and has no friends or has joined a new school mid-way through an academic year. Settings need to take a sensitive approach to help the child to settle in and make friends. Often a buddy system is used and the child is linked with another child until she is familiar with the school and has made friends herself.

Later on children will move from primary to secondary school and can again face challenges. It is usual for secondary schools to have a 'taster' day so that new pupils get a feel for the school before they start formally.

Puberty is another time of transition where children face hormonal and body changes as they grow from a child to an adult. Adolescent children may experience strong emotions and mood changes and need to be given sensitive support and understanding during this time. Teenagers will need to understand acceptable boundaries to behaviour, but this is a time when discussion and negotiation is appropriate as they can take more responsibility for their own actions.

Where a child's behaviour is noticeably different to normal, e,g. becomes aggressive or unusually withdrawn, there is often an underlying reason such as a life event which has affected their security. Events such as a family bereavement, family break-up or even the death of a family pet can have a devastating effect on a child and will need handling carefully according to the individual situation.

Physical factors

Physical factors include genetic influences; this may be a physical attribute such as height, hair colour, etc. or an inherited disorder such as Down's syndrome. Physical appearance may influence a child's behaviour if he feels disadvantaged in some way, perhaps as a result of unkind comments from peers. An inherited disorder on the other hand may result in delayed development compared to the 'norm' for the age group and the child would display behaviour which is more appropriate for a younger child.

Disabilities can also influence behaviour, e.g.

- A child with a physical disability might feel frustration if she cannot join in with activities with other children, whilst a child with brain damage might show age-inappropriate behaviour.
- A child with communication difficulties may also show behavioural differences; a child with a hearing impairment may not hear what he has been asked to do or may not understand social interactions within the peer group.
- A child with hearing loss may not even be aware of a conversation if he is not observing and lip reading a situation and would miss a great deal of the day-to-day banter which is so vital in social situations.
- Speech and language difficulties can also isolate a child; there are a variety of difficulties within this category, some of which are physical problems with forming words and others which are processing problems where the person has trouble encoding or decoding language.

In all cases the child will experience frustration and possibly anger at being unable to communicate easily. Finally the physical changes that occur during puberty, as mentioned previously, will influence behaviour.

Health-related factors

Health-related factors could also affect behaviour.

A variety of factors can affect a child even before it is born. During pregnancy, factors such as mother's diet, alcohol or drug intake, as well as stress levels, will all have an effect on the infant.

Birth trauma can result in problems for an infant. When the infant is born there is a great deal of pressure exerted on the baby's head as it travels through the birth canal and babies are often born with odd-shaped heads. Most babies' heads lose this shape and are happy and contented, but other babies have difficulty with sleep and crying. Sometimes cranial osteopathy is used to realign the skull bones. Other problems during birth can be a long delivery time with distress to the newborn, lack of oxygen, etc. Studies have linked birth trauma to developmental delays in children, possibly including ADHD and autism.

There may be problems relating to health during childhood; these may be due to inherited factors, disabilities, brain development or communication difficulties such as hearing loss or speech impairment.

Sometimes children have severe reactions to immunisation or the medication they take can affect behaviour. Children with ADHD are often prescribed Ritalin and this has proved controversial with some reports that the medication is needed to enable the child to conform to expected behaviour in school and dampen down over-activity, whilst other reports say it makes the child withdrawn and 'like a zombie'. A child with diabetes would display unusual behaviour if his blood sugar level was either too low or too high and would need careful monitoring to ensure appropriate treatment was given.

Hormones can also influence behaviour, e.g. during puberty.

case study 14.5

Mary

Mary is in her early forties and is pregnant. She is a heavy drinker and an intravenous drug user. Her baby is at risk from foetal alcohol syndrome and drug addiction.

activity

1 What are the possible dangers to the baby?
2 How might the baby's behaviour be affected?

Link

Unit 27 contains information on additional needs which you may find helpful.

The factors mentioned so far are all internal to the child, but external factors will also affect behaviour.

Socio-economic factors

Socio-economic factors will be important to a child. These include gender, social class, financial security, culture and ethnicity, the housing and environment of the family and socialisation.

As mentioned previously, a child who has no or little experience of early socialisation will find it harder to know appropriate social behaviour than a child who has experience of meeting other children.

Social class is also a factor to consider as educational settings tend to have middle-class teachers and other staff leading them. For a child from a working-class background, the norms of behaviour may be very different from those which are acceptable at school and the child will need to learn these new expectations, e.g. the child may observe swearing as part of everyday life at home but not at school.

Gender is another issue where differences may be apparent from the home culture or ethnic group. What issues might a boy have, whose home culture values males above females, who has not been encouraged to do things for himself but has always been helped with everything and considers it normal and right for females to serve males? How might his behaviour be affected?

Other factors to bear in mind are financial security, housing and the community the child lives in. Where a child experiences pressure at home, there will be stress and less security. A child may live with violence or bullying either in the home or wider community. Family influences will also be pivotal, including attitudes to education. The greatest influence on a child's schooling is the family interest and involvement. Children from lower socio-economic groups face extra hurdles to reach the same level of success in life as those from more advantaged groups. Gender is another issue where differences may be apparent from the home culture or ethnic group.

Family influences

Family situations vary enormously. Some children live in extended families whilst others live with just one adult. There may be siblings or step-siblings. Parenting styles and approaches to discipline vary greatly. Children may have space and opportunities to develop and become independent or may live in a crowded noisy home with no opportunities. Their diet may be nutritious and balanced or consist of junk food. Lifestyles and customs differ. Children may have role models to look up to who are positive or negative. Many factors could be relevant and unique to each child and how they behave. It is important for practitioners to value each child as an individual and not make judgements based on lifestyle or family circumstances. Where judgements are made about a child, they can result in a self-fulfilling prophecy where the expectations you have about a child are picked up by the child and then become reality. It is vital that you have realistic and fair but high expectations of all children whatever their situation.

case study 14.6

Naomi and Sanjay

- Naomi is 11. Her parents divorced when she was 6 and she lives with her father, his new partner and her four children who range in age from 2 to 15. They live in a three-bedroom flat on a crowded estate and do not have a car or the convenience of supermarkets nearby.
- Sanjay is a 6-year-old boy who lives with his parents, three younger siblings and his grandparents in a five-bedroom house on the edge of a pleasant town. Both his parents work, but his grandmother provides care and support at home. The family are financially comfortable and Sanjay has plenty of opportunities to participate in activities both in school and outside of school. Sanjay and his family are Hindus.

activity

1 What family factors may have an influence on Naomi's behaviour?
2 Make a list of factors that may influence Sanjay's behaviour.

Effects

Self-esteem

The effects of negative factors may be that the child develops low self-esteem and has a poor self-concept. The child may experience stress and be unable to cope well with life and even have depression. When a child lives with many difficulties, he or she may be unable to cope and handle emotions particularly as the child is likely to be powerless to change his or her circumstances.

Children who are unhappy show this through their behaviour. Some children will become withdrawn and avoid everyday activities and tend to escape into solitude. Some children will become clinging and demanding as a result of their feelings of insecurity. Others may spend excessive amounts of time on one activity such as playing a video game or may over-eat. Restless behaviour can be another sign of unhappiness. Children may also self-harm as a way of coping with their feelings.

Marginalisation, social exclusion and the cycle of deprivation

Children may also be affected by marginalisation and social exclusion. If children belong to social groups that are the target of stereotypes and discrimination, they will experience social separation and feel they have less worth socially than other children. People who are marginalised do not have equal access to resources and activities and live on the 'margins' of society being unable to participate fully in activities that other children have opportunities to be involved in.

Some families are unable to access education, health services and childcare fully, e.g. people with disabilities, mental health problems, addictions and some minority ethnic groups, in particular asylum-seekers and refugees. These groups often live in poverty and are unable to change their circumstances so experience a cycle of deprivation.

The whole issue of asylum-seekers coming to the UK has caused controversy in recent years with a lot of negative media coverage. Use the BBC website http://news.bbc.co.uk/1/hi/programmes/asylum_day **to look at the reality of life for asylum-seekers and the issues they face.**

Pro-social and anti-social behaviour

All these influences on a child will result in the development of behaviour which is either pro-social or anti-social.

- Pro-social behaviour is socially desirable behaviour, such as helping and conforming to expected behaviour.
- Anti-social behaviour refers to aggression and other undesired behaviour.

If you consider the range of circumstances a child may find themselves in, you can begin to understand ways in which his or her behaviour will be affected and possible outcomes.

activity
INDIVIDUAL WORK 14.4
P4

Nine-year-old Leon has just joined the local primary school in the middle of the spring term after moving into the area from another part of the country. He has a heavy accent and the other children find it difficult to understand his speech. His mother has moved to the area with him after fleeing an abusive marriage and they are currently living in a refuge for women and children in one room with a shared kitchen and bathroom. His mother is suffering from depression and they are on a low income. They have no family or friends in the area.

1 What kind of behaviour might you expect Leon to display?
2 What factors may affect Leon's behaviour?
3 How might Leon be supported during this transition time?
4 Use this case study as the starting point for writing your own report on six factors that may affect children's behaviour. You may like to consider children in work placement settings as case studies, but you will need to ensure confidentiality is maintained.

Understand different approaches to challenging behaviour

Conformity

Within any setting where there are a group of children, or in fact adults, there will be a level of social conformity. This is needed for the successful operation of the setting. Conformity refers to the expected behaviour of children in the setting. Children need to be helped to understand when they must follow expected patterns of behaviour and what is acceptable in social situations. If children were allowed to go entirely their own way in a setting, it would be very hard to manage the setting. On the other hand, rigid rules where children are not allowed any choices or independence will not support the child's development of autonomy and self-esteem.

Children normally feel the need for conformity, to have the sense of belonging to a group. Conformity can be to do with behaviour and attitude and also to choice of clothing and language, etc. Teenagers will often choose to conform to popular fashion trends to fit in with peer group norms. Some, however, will reject these norms and will deliberately assert their individuality by being non-conformist in most ways. Conformity is more likely when it ensures social approval and belonging. Reasons why children may choose not to conform would include trying to show individuality, gaining peer group approval, as well as underlying background factors mentioned previously which could result in a child not acting in socially accepted ways. Non-conforming would include aggression, swearing, etc.

Challenging behaviour

Challenging behaviour refers to any behaviour that puts the child or others at risk or prevents normal day-to-day life. This includes any anti-social actions such as aggressive, disruptive or destructive behaviours and distressed behaviour such as self-injury, e.g. head banging. Some children with additional needs may display challenging behaviour more often.

Anti-social behaviour

Anti-social behaviour can take many forms including defiance, violent outbursts, bullying, anger, aggression, biting, attention-seeking and other non-conforming behaviour. Anti-social behaviour will have a negative impact on other children around the child. Two- and 3-year-old children commonly have tantrums and this age group has gained the label 'terrible twos'. In fact children may continue to have tantrums until the age of 4 or 5. These tantrums are the result of strong emotions which the child cannot control, such as frustration, hunger, tiredness, being refused something or wanting attention.

Distressed behaviour in young children has been discussed earlier in this chapter and includes clinging, crying, fear and anxiety in young children.

Link

Look at page 116 where research by Robertson & Robertson considered distress in children who were in hospital and separated from their mothers.

Additional needs

Where children have additional needs they may need extra support in **managing behaviour**. For example, children on the autistic spectrum of disorders have difficulties with appropriate social behaviour and may be awkward, indifferent or avoid social situations. Children can be supported by being told 'social stories' to help them understand appropriate ways to behave. Practitioners also need to adjust their expectations of the child's behaviour to take into account the social stage of development the child is at which may well be at a lower stage than their biological age.

Children who are gifted and talented, as well as those with learning difficulties, will need consideration to ensure their needs are met. The gifted child will need challenging work and may need support with behaviour and forming relationships.

Strategies for dealing with challenging behaviour

Rewards and consequences

It is usual these days to use positive behaviour management, following the behaviourist approach, to reinforce desirable behaviour with a rewards system of verbal praise, stickers, house points, etc., whilst negative behaviour is discouraged with a series of sanctions. Advice to teachers and other practitioners is to focus on positive rather than negative behaviour and not to use negative language to describe the child's behaviour. Teachers and others are told not to label a child as 'naughty' or 'bad' and to explain why the behaviour is unacceptable instead, so that the child gets the message that you don't like their behaviour not that you don't like them.

Nowadays the normal view taken to challenging behaviour is that a child is exhibiting challenging behaviour because they are feeling angry or upset in some way and do not know how to handle their emotions. If a child continues to show difficult behaviour in school or another setting and does not respond to normal sanctions, it demonstrates that the child has emotional difficulties.

Since the child is already feeling angry and hurt, for them to experience anger and aggression from the adults who care for them will only make matters more negative. Verbal or physical punishment or exclusion will exacerbate things for a child who is already struggling.

Where practitioners establish an environment that is supportive and the peer group is taught to consider the feeling of others, the outcome is likely to be positive.

Find out about Jenny Mosley's Quality Circle Time approach to promoting positive behaviour by looking on the website www.circle-time.co.uk or reading up about it. Have you seen 'circle time' used in your work placements or other techniques such as 'time to talk'? How does the teacher use these sessions to encourage positive behaviour?

Social and emotional aspects of learning are developed in school so that children learn social, emotional and behavioural skills. In May 2005 the Department for Education and Skills introduced the SEAL (Social and Emotional Aspects of Learning) programme for all primary schools as a source of resources.

Information on SEAL can be found on the internet at www.teachernet.gov.uk/teachingandlearning/socialandpastoral.

Link SEAL is also discussed in Unit 27, page 302.

Where there are more specific types of behaviour problems, different strategies may be needed. Table 14.2 shows some common behaviour problems and strategies to deal with them.

Table 14.2 Common behaviour problems and strategies

Behaviour	Strategy	Possible reasons for behaviour
Attention-seeking	Try not to give the child attention for negative behaviour as this will reinforce the behaviour. Instead give praise when the child shows positive behaviour. Spend more time with the child in positive ways.	Attention-seeking behaviour is often a result of emotional difficulties and is a way for the child to get adult attention.
Biting	Give comfort to the child who has been bitten. Give praise to the child who has bitten later when they are behaving well. Supervise the child closely to ensure no further biting occurs.	Biting is common in young children up to the age of 3 and can be the result of frustration.

Behaviour	Strategy	Possible reasons for behaviour
Bullying	The child who is being bullied will need support as they will have emotional problems to cope with. The child who is doing the bullying will also need support to learn how to behave in a socially acceptable way.	Children who bully are often from homes where parents are aggressive and they have learnt that this is an effective way to get what they want. Bullies will need help to raise their self-esteem. Bullying is common in schools and all schools have an anti-bullying policy and zero tolerance of bullying or other abusive behaviour including racist or sexist behaviour. *Check the policies in your placement.*
Defiance, violent outbursts and aggression	At the time you will need to remove the child to a quiet place to have time out to calm down. It is normal for children to have tantrums around the age of 2 to 3. Later it is important to talk to the child about how they are feeling and ways to manage their feelings of anger or helplessness. There is no quick or easy solution to dealing with a child who acts this way regularly. They will need support and encouragement from those around them.	Children who are out of control are often sad and feel unsafe. They will be frightened by their own behaviour and need to find ways to manage their feelings.

Assertive discipline techniques

Canter and Canter (2001) recommended assertive discipline as a way of managing behaviour in the classroom. It is widely used and straightforward. Assertive discipline involves having clear expectations of behaviour with rules, rewarding positive behaviour and having consequences for negative behaviour. This method is used in schools in the UK where there are behaviour rules, rewards and sanctions as the consequences of positive and negative behaviour.

You will have seen rewards systems and sanctions in your work placement settings. Do you think these methods are effective in managing discipline?

The government has set legal requirements for school behaviour policies as shown below.

SCHOOL BEHAVIOUR POLICIES: LEGAL REQUIREMENTS

1. Section 61 of the School Standards and Framework Act 1998 requires a governing body to ensure that its school pursues policies designed to promote positive behaviour. In particular it:
   a. requires a governing body to make and review a written statement of principles to guide the Headteacher in determining measures for promoting positive behaviour; and
   b. where the governing body wants particular measures introduced or particular issues addressed, requires the governing body to notify the Headteacher and enables it to give further guidance.
2. In carrying out these functions the governing body must:
   a. have regard to guidance given by the Department; and
   b. before making or revising its statement of principles, consult the Headteacher and parents and carers.
3. The Headteacher must determine measures (which may include a code of conduct and its application) designed to secure an acceptable standard of behaviour and to promote self-discipline, proper regard for authority and respect for others. In particular these measures should aim to prevent all forms of bullying and racial harassment.

4. These measures should be consistent with the statement of principles made by the governing body and any specific notification or guidance it has given. These may go a long way towards defining an acceptable standard of behaviour. In so far as they do not, the Headteacher is responsible for defining the acceptable standard.
5. The measures determined by the Headteacher must be published as a written document, made generally known within the school and to parents and carers and, at least once a year, brought to the attention of all pupils, parents and carers and staff.

www.dfes.gov.uk/

Another part of this method is to use the 'broken record' technique where you acknowledge what a child is saying and then tell the child what you want them to do and then repeat this statement without adding any more demands, e.g. saying 'Yes, I know you would rather play with the sand but I need you to stop and sit down', 'Stop what you are doing and sit down', 'Stop and sit down everyone.'

Child empowerment and enabling the child to be proactive

When there are disagreements between children it can result in a physical fight between two children. It is useful to diffuse the situation initially perhaps using the 'broken record' technique above, but then you need to get to the root of the problem. The teacher needs to get details from everyone involved and listen to all sides so that everyone has the chance to explain what happened. It is worth using **active listening** techniques such as paraphrasing to show understanding. The teacher may then identify or help the children to identify possible misunderstandings that have occurred and then ask for suggestions about how the children could change what they did another time. Giving children empowerment and allowing them to be proactive in resolving an issue, although time-consuming, is time well used, especially where a child behaves in an aggressive or disruptive way regularly. Child empowerment puts the focus on the child to resolve difficulties.

Parent–child contracts

It is a requirement now for all schools to have a home–school agreement that parents sign to show their acceptance of it. Parents and schools are expected to work closely where there are issues of concern such as behavioural difficulties or bullying and other agencies may be involved too.

Rewards and consequences

Where there are particular individual behaviour challenges from some children, additional methods will be used to encourage positive behaviour. Examples include using a sticker chart where the child receives a sticker as a reward at the end of each lesson for good behaviour or comments in a daily record diary on how they have behaved in each lesson. This record would then be taken home so that the parent or carer could see how the child had managed their behaviour that day and rewards or sanctions could be applied at home.

Card, picture and badge communications

Children with special needs may need extra support in developing their social skills, including their behaviour and emotions.

case study 14.7

William

William is a pupil aged 9 with communication difficulties. He finds it hard to communicate his needs to staff at school, and when he is not understood he gets very distressed and runs around screaming. He has been given a more effective way of communicating his needs using picture cards that show activities he may want to do and objects he may want to use. These picture cards are kept in his tray so that he knows where they are and can get them easily. Now, when William wants something he is encouraged to select the picture card that shows what he wants and to give this to a member of staff.

If he cannot do the chosen activity at that time, the card is displayed on his pictorial timetable and he is able to do the activity at a more suitable time. This way William is learning to control his behaviour and to see that even if he cannot immediately have his request he will be able to later.

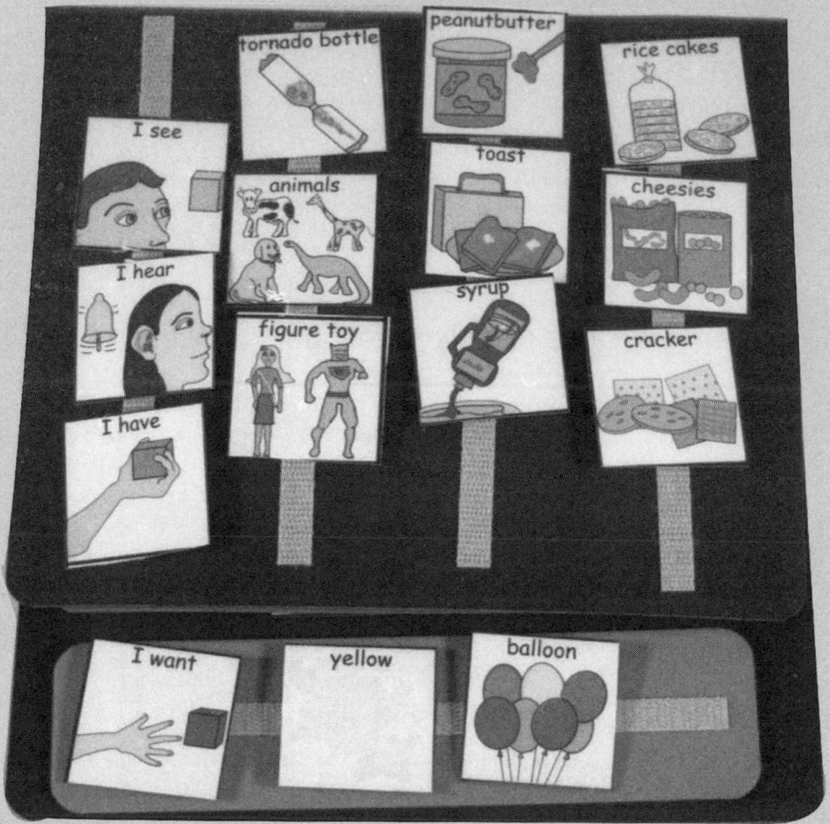

Fig 14.7 Picture Exchange Communication System: Picture Binder

activity

1 Why does William show distressed behaviour at times?
2 How have the childcare workers supported William?
3 Why is this method likely to help with William's development of social skills?
4 Can you think of any other ways they could support William?
5 Have you seen any methods in placement that you feel are effective for supporting children who have additional needs?

For more information about the Picture Exchange Communication system, refer to www.childrenwithspecialneeds.com.

Practitioners who work with children with additional needs will make greater use of picture cues to show incentives, for example to remind a pupil that once they have finished their work they can play on the interactive whiteboard.

Verbal and non-verbal communication

Verbal communication is used to manage behaviour, but non-verbal behaviour is just as important. In fact the first step to managing behaviour is often just 'the look', catching a child with eye contact to show you have noticed their behaviour. Body language and tone of voice also send out messages of approval or disapproval.

Specialist equipment and resources

Specialist equipment and resources, such as sensory equipment, can be used for children with special needs to enhance their play and learning experience. Some playgrounds incorporate musical instruments. Soft play equipment can be beneficial for children with physical disabilities.

Browse through a school supplies catalogue or a catalogue with equipment for special needs to see what specialist equipment is available. If you have been on placement in a special school then you can talk about equipment and methods of teaching and learning that you have seen and how effective they are. Have you come across multi-sensory learning techniques?

Counselling

Some children will need to be supported by counselling. Counselling services may be offered to teenage children through the county youth service. Anger management courses may be offered to teenagers or they may be able to have an adult mentor to give support.

Check to see what is available in your locality. Is there somewhere that young people can go to for confidential advice and support? Find out what your county council's youth service do.

What facilities are available in your area for younger children who may have self-esteem and behaviour problems? Find out about local schemes to support children with low self-esteem.

Colour/art therapy

Art therapy is sometimes used to support children's emotional development when they have problems. Art will enable a child to express their emotions when perhaps they cannot put them into words. Young children who are unhappy will often draw using very dark colours. A skilled counsellor could use the art work as a basis for discussion about feelings. Another idea is to have an angry wall and let older children draw on it to show their emotions.

Persona dolls

Persona dolls are used in schools and early years settings as a way of supporting inclusion and understanding another person's point of view. Persona dolls are large dolls dressed in appropriate clothing to represent a person from a particular cultural background or with a disability. Each doll has its own name and comes with a story. The dolls are used as a way of looking at diversity in a positive way.

Fig 14.8 A persona doll

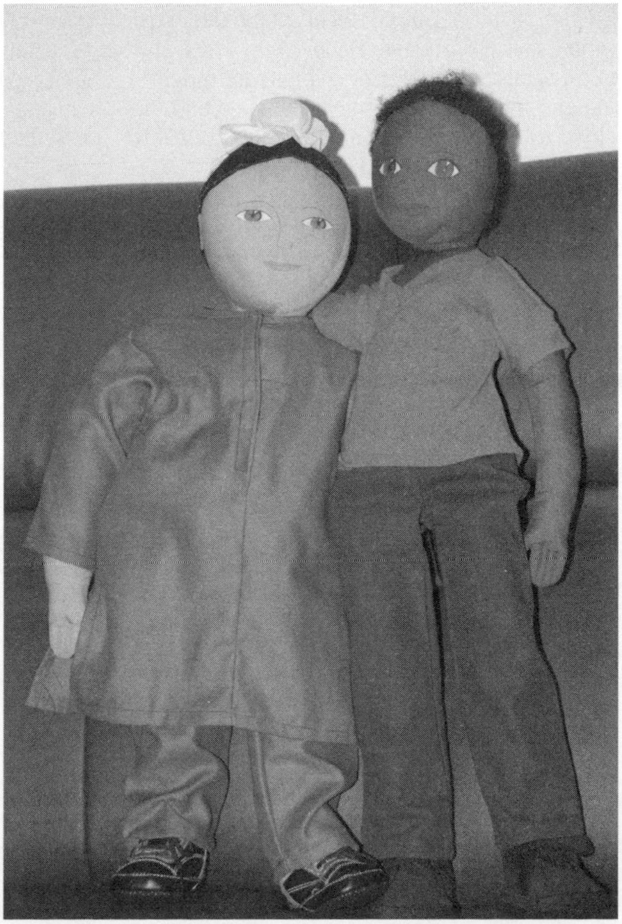

case study 14.8

Marik

The class teacher in Year 1 at St Mary's School was concerned that Marik, who had newly joined the class having arrived recently from Poland, was being excluded from the other children's games and that he was being verbally abused. The teacher encouraged an outgoing child, Joe, to become friendly with Marik and make sure he was not left out of playtime activities. She also explained to the class why their behaviour had been unacceptable.

A few days later in circle time, she talked to the class using a persona doll. To avoid putting Marik in the spotlight, the teacher used a boy persona doll with a disability and told the children how difficult life was for 'Simon' as he lived in a small flat with his mother and they had very little money. As he had a physical disability, it was difficult for him to get around and in and out of the flat. Worse still, he was feeling very unhappy because the children in his class were calling him names like 'Slow Simon' because he couldn't run around with them. The teacher talked to the children and asked them questions about how they thought Simon felt. The children were all able to empathise with Simon and offered suggestions and advice.

activity

1 Why do you think this would be an effective way for children to consider other people's feelings?
2 Piaget would argue that children aged 5 and 6 would be egocentric. How does his view fit in with this case study and what further perspective explains the children's ability to understand another's viewpoint?

Protective behaviours

Children are taught about personal safety and knowing how to protect themselves. In a programme called Protective Behaviours, which started off as a way of offering children protection against child abuse, children are taught to understand that they have the right to feel safe and that there is nothing that is so bad that they cannot talk to someone. Children are helped to identify who it would be safe to talk to. This programme is used in a variety of areas including in schools and youth work.

Find out more on the internet at www.protectivebehaviours.co.uk.

Buddy schemes

Other schemes to help children including playground buddy systems in schools or 'bully busters' where children can talk to another child about any problems they have.

Personal networks

Children may have a personal network established to support their behaviour. This may include a school learning mentor or out-of-school mentor, social worker, etc.

Circle of friends

Another approach is called 'circle of friends'. This technique to support a child who has social and behavioural problems involves creating a support network of other pupils for the child. These pupils consider ways to support the pupil and help avoid that pupil being isolated.

case study 14.9

Brian

Brian was isolated in his peer group at secondary school and other pupils talked about him as 'mad' and a 'nutter'. Brian had shown distressed and difficult behaviour at school. In the last term, eight children from his class were selected by the teacher and, together with an educational psychologist, they talked about ways to support Brian and show him they cared about him. The result has been that Brian has reacted less often to provocation, has not run out of the class so often and has started doing his work.

activity

1 How has this method helped meet Brian's social and emotional needs?
2 How do you think Brian used to feel about himself?
3 How might he be feeling now?

Link Circle of friends is also discussed in Unit 27, page 302.

Time out

'Time out' is another way of handling behaviour. A member of staff, such as a teaching assistant, may pick up warning signs from a pupil that she is losing control of her behaviour and remove the child for time out to calm down. If the child is older, they may be given responsibility to recognise their emotions and ask for time out themselves.

Work placement policies

Students on work placement will always be expected to adhere to a code of conduct for acceptable behaviour and with regard to health and safety in the work setting.

Parent empowerment

Parent empowerment strategies are often used to support parents with appropriate ways to handle behaviour management in the family.

Parent support groups and nurture groups

Parent support groups can involve parents meeting up with other parents to talk and share ideas, e.g. Gingerbread is a support group for lone parents, or experienced parents sharing their ideas and giving understanding to parents who are experiencing problems.

Nurture groups operate to support families with children that have emotional and behavioural difficulties in school. The aim of nurture groups is to support children in school and their parents.

For more information on nurture groups, look on the website www.nurturegroups.org.

Holistic educational therapy

Holistic educational therapy also involves offering support to children with emotional and behavioural difficulties and their families. A holistic approach will consider all aspects of the child and family and seek to resolve all issues.

Family therapy

Family therapy centres on offering behavioural therapy for families which will include counselling for behavioural and emotional difficulties and family issues.

Family therapy has been developed as a technique to support the whole family not just the child. The family attend therapy sessions together and the therapist is then able to observe interactions within the family, how problems are caused which affect the child and how the child in turn creates problems within the family. This approach can be helpful in cases of alcoholism, violence or gambling within the family.

When families break up children are resilient to change and can even benefit from being away from a stressful environment, so long as they have the love and support of both parents. However if the parents start to use the children as a way of getting at their ex-partner or there are other problems such as socio-economic factors, these can have a knock-on effect for the child. Family therapy can help where there are difficulties including behavioural problems such as attention or over-activity or emotional disorders.

Look at the Family Therapy UK website to find out about the areas family therapists work in: www.familytherapy.org.uk. This site also has useful handouts on behaviour and different special needs which you can download.

Support roles and agencies

There is a wide range of support agencies and specialist staff to give support with ways of approaching challenging behaviour. These include:

- health visitors
- school nurses
- educational psychologists
- clinical psychologists
- child and family services
- children's services
- educational social workers
- support teachers, e.g. peripatetic teachers who support children with hearing impairments
- speech therapists.

There are a variety of approaches to managing behaviour. The local education authority (LEA) will have a behaviour support unit where trained and experienced staff are able to visit local schools and observe children with difficulties, assess possible problems and give advice on strategies to use. Educational psychologists will also be available to assess individual children's needs. Counsellors may also be used.

Multi-agency teams, known as Behaviour and Education Support Teams (BESTs), combine professionals from the fields of education, health and social services and are used to promote social and emotional well-being for children, school attendance and positive behaviour. They are used to target children and families who are identified as being at risk of developing emotional and behavioural problems.

If a child is identified as having special educational needs (SEN) and given a statement of special needs, then they are likely to have a teaching assistant assigned to give one-to-one support. Other children are likely to benefit from the presence of a teaching assistant to give learning support. Nursery nurses work with young children.

Some schools have a learning mentor scheme where an adult mentor is responsible for a small group of children rather than a form teacher having to oversee 30 children. With this scheme, if a child needs support or is having difficulties, it is much easier for the mentor to liaise with the family and teachers in the school, to act as an advocate for the child and to help them overcome problems.

You may have seen Brain Gym being used in placements. This is a physical activity programme involving exercises. It was developed to help children with difficulties such as dyslexia, dyspraxia and ADHD concentrate and improve their behaviour and attention.

Confidentiality

Remember the need for **confidentiality** when working with children. Children with challenging behaviour will often have an underlying difficulty. You may find a child discloses child abuse to you and you will need to know the procedure and practice for this in the workplace setting. You will often be aware of sensitive information. This has to be passed on to the child protection officer and others on a strict need-to-know basis, but otherwise you should never discuss information about children and their families with anyone.

activity
INDIVIDUAL AND GROUP WORK 14.5

P5
M3
D2

1 You are now ready to write a report about behaviour management strategies. For P5 you need to outline four different behavioural management strategies from those mentioned above. Consider the strategies that could be most effective in the case of a very young child in a pre-school setting, a child within an infant class, a child with special needs and a child in a secondary school.

2 To gain M3 you should explain the potential effectiveness of each of your four strategies discussed for P5.

a) Discuss in small groups the strategies you have seen in placement and how effective each method has been.

b) Write up an explanation of how each method could be used in an effective way. Explain the types of situation and child that is likely to benefit from the method. You will need to consider the age and stage of development of the child, any special needs or additional needs, any health issues and family circumstances.

3 You need to evaluate the potential effectiveness of the four methods you have chosen. You will need to consider in detail when each method is likely to be effective and why and when it would not be appropriate to use the method or it might be less effective. Consider the suitability of each method to different children. For example, a method which gives responsibility for behaviour in a proactive way would be appropriate for a teenager but not to a very young child. A younger child is more likely to respond positively to a sticker chart than an older child. Children with special needs often need a more visual method and detailed explanations of the consequences of their behaviour might not be suitable for the level of understanding of the child.

Link this to what you have seen in practice and what you feel is effective for different ages or children with different needs or personalities.

activity
INDIVIDUAL WORK 14.6

P6

For P6 you need to identify a range of relevant support roles and agencies used in managing behaviour. Carry out research to find out what support services are available and used in your area and briefly explain what they are and how they are used. You may like to speak to your work placement supervisor to find out what services the setting uses to support behaviour management and how they access these services.

Understand techniques for monitoring the effectiveness of implementing behavioural strategies

Observation

Observation is used in order to assess behavioural problems and also as a way of monitoring changes.

In a school, it can be helpful for support staff to carry out observations to monitor overall levels of disruptive behaviour, such as how often pupils shout out, interrupt each other, argue, approach the teacher to settle disputes, etc. Observations can be used to get detailed information where the teacher feels a particular child is being disruptive to pinpoint exactly what is happening and identify the specific behaviour of the child.

One strategy, which was recommended by the Department for Education and Skills, came from Skinner and Bandura and is known as the ABC method of analysing behaviour. Any behaviour can be broken down using this method into three parts:

- **A**ntecedent – what happens before the behaviour to trigger it
- **B**ehaviour – the behaviour itself
- **C**onsequence – what happens after the behaviour.

The consequences of behaviour are not always obvious, but it could be that the child is actually getting attention this way, whether negative or positive, or feeling relief from stress which has built up. Observing and keeping details of what has been observed helps build up an idea of what is happening.

Observation can show the exact behaviour a child is showing, when it occurs, how often and what happens immediately before and after the behaviour.

The approach can then be used to modify behaviour by using an appropriate antecedent such as a clear instruction to produce a suitable behaviour and then a consequence that rewards the child, such as verbal praise, which increases the likelihood of the behaviour being repeated. This method could be used to teach a child with autism or ADHD more appropriate social behaviour.

Being able to identify specific behaviour enables practitioners to share methods of managing and modifying the behaviour using a consistent approach. Later observations can assess how much the behaviour has changed and improved. Carrying out observations will give data to show patterns of behaviour and change rather than staff just having a feeling that a child is behaving in a certain way or that behaviour has altered. However observations are time-consuming.

Link

For more information on different methods of observation, see Unit 35, page 354.

Consultation

A great deal of information is gathered about a child by consultation, using questionnaires or getting reports from all personnel involved with a child. This is the case when a child is identified as having special educational needs. There is a graduated response to meeting the child's needs involving collecting information about the child, assessing the child's strengths and weaknesses and discussing with parents and practitioners how to support the child.

Support professionals will be consulted and offer advice and reports as needed, according to the child's needs. Professionals might include specialist teachers, a behaviour specialist, paediatrician, etc. Behavioural profiles might be gathered from observations in the classroom, playground and home setting to identify possible patterns and triggers for certain behaviour.

Very often the school or childcare setting will liaise with outside professionals to get further advice on ways to support a child. For example, a specialist behaviour support worker would be able to offer a school advice and suggestions on ways to handle challenging behaviour.

If a child has a statement of special needs, there is a legal requirement that the statement is reviewed annually to monitor progress and make changes to provision as necessary. The annual review will be an opportunity for all people involved with the child to give input including the child and parents.

Link

Special educational needs and the statementing process are discussed in Unit 27, page 318.

Collecting data

Practitioners working on a day-to-day basis with children with behavioural issues will need to keep detailed records and collect data. Data collected will often be qualitative, giving a descriptive account of behaviours, such as a diary, but some data will be quantitative, showing frequency of behaviours, such as a behaviour chart.

Sources of data include:

- Records will include personal diaries that record daily events concerned with the child including behavioural issues. The teaching assistant working on a one-to-one basis with a child may keep such a diary.
- There may be a home–school communication diary where the teaching assistant and teacher share information with the child's parents relating to the child, e.g. what the child has done at school that day, what they have enjoyed, any behavioural issues, etc. This is especially useful where a child is unable to communicate verbally and gives parents and practitioners a better idea of what the child has done.
- Within the setting there will be reward charts and for a child with behavioural problems there may be a more detailed reward chart.
- Settings will also have logbooks for recording any incidents of behaviour of particular concern, e.g. racist comments must always be logged and bullying would always be taken

seriously. If a child's behaviour raises any possible concern about the child's welfare, this will also be recorded by the Child Protection Officer.

Link

Refer to Green (2007), Unit 5, for details of child protection systems.

It is usual for schools to set each child individual targets or Individual Action Plans (IAPs), say for literacy and numeracy, and a general target; this may relate to behaviour, e.g. putting your hand up to answer questions in class not shouting out the answer.

Where a child has been identified as having additional needs, the school will draw up an Individual Education Plan (IEP) for the pupil setting out targets and how these targets will be met. Very often these targets will relate to behaviour; where this is the case the document may be called an Individual Behaviour Plan (IBP).

The targets are reviewed on a regular basis and the plans are updated to set new targets where the original targets have been met.

Link

IEPs are discussed in Unit 27, page 318.

The emphasis on partnerships with parents in Every Child Matters means that there should be effective communication with parents about their child. This means regular meetings, a home–school communication book, if appropriate, and practitioners who are approachable so that parents or carers feel comfortable talking to them on a day-to-day basis. Very often practitioners are busy in the morning but can usually find time at the end of the day to talk to parents or should make an appointment for a convenient time to talk through concerns.

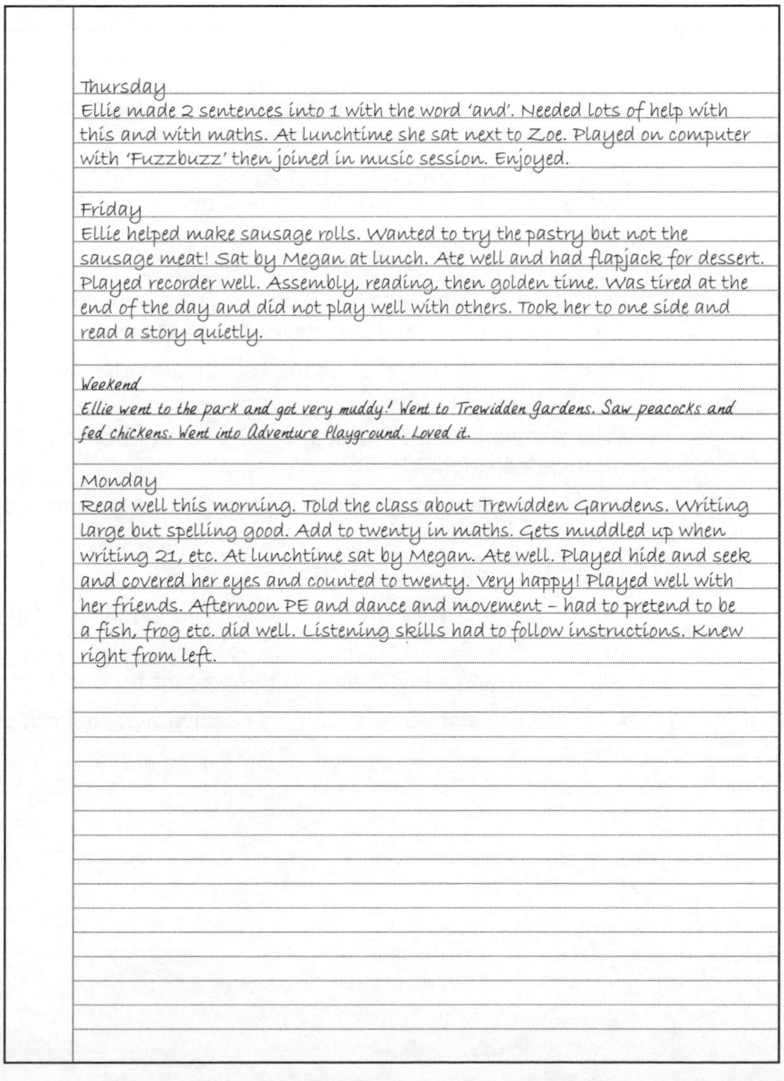

Thursday

Ellie made 2 sentences into 1 with the word 'and'. Needed lots of help with this and with maths. At lunchtime she sat next to Zoe. Played on computer with 'Fuzzbuzz' then joined in music session. Enjoyed.

Friday

Ellie helped make sausage rolls. Wanted to try the pastry but not the sausage meat! Sat by Megan at lunch. Ate well and had flapjack for dessert. Played recorder well. Assembly, reading, then golden time. Was tired at the end of the day and did not play well with others. Took her to one side and read a story quietly.

Weekend

Ellie went to the park and got very muddy! Went to Trewidden Gardens. Saw peacocks and fed chickens. Went into Adventure Playground. Loved it.

Monday

Read well this morning. Told the class about Trewidden Garndens. Writing large but spelling good. Add to twenty in maths. Gets muddled up when writing 21, etc. At lunchtime sat by Megan. Ate well. Played hide and seek and covered her eyes and counted to twenty. Very happy! Played well with her friends. Afternoon PE and dance and movement – had to pretend to be a fish, frog etc. did well. Listening skills had to follow instructions. Knew right from left.

Fig 14.9 A parent–school communication book

Limitations of these methods

Remember that any one method alone is likely to be limited and that the most effective way to monitor how effective the implemented behaviour strategies is will be a combination of methods and a holistic approach that means having a good knowledge of the child and monitoring the child on a daily basis. Changes are likely to be slow and practitioners need to be sensitive and patient.

activity
INDIVIDUAL WORK 14.7

P7

M4

1 a) How can observation be used to monitor behaviour and to assess the effectiveness of behaviour management strategies?

b) How could consultations with parents or carers provide information on the effectiveness of the behaviour strategies used?

c) Why would it be good practice to keep a diary or behaviour log to record a child's behaviour – both positive and negative – each day in the setting?

d) Explain how Individual Action Plans are used to set targets for a child's behaviour.

2 Prepare a report that explains the different methods used to evaluate the effectiveness of behavioural management strategies. Add details of methods used in your placement settings. You may wish to talk to your supervisor about how they observe children, methods they use to collect data on children's behaviour and how they set targets. You will also need to find out how children and parents/carers and other professionals are involved in consultations, particularly for children who are on School Action, School Action Plus or who have a statement of special needs. Within the report you will need to mention that no single method will be effective alone and the need for a holistic approach to monitoring behaviour.

Progress Check

1 Why might society's expectations of gender roles have an impact on behaviour and how would you avoid gender stereotyping in childcare settings?

2 How does a school's reward system link to conditioning? What does a child learn to link to positive behaviour and how does this encourage the child to repeat the desired behaviour?

3 A child has learnt that when he throws a tantrum his mother sits with him and comforts him until he falls asleep. This has reinforced his behaviour and he continues to have tantrums regularly. What might be a better approach?

4 Give examples of when a setting could inadvertently condition negative behaviour and how to avoid this.

5 Why is it important for a child's self-esteem to encourage him or her to become more independent?

6 Use the attachment theory to explain why early years settings often assign a key worker to each child.

7 What do we mean by conformity?

8 How might peer pressure influence a child's behaviour in either a positive or negative way? Give examples.

9 Why is a strong early attachment important for a child's development?

10 Give examples of ways to support positive behaviour in children with additional needs.

UNIT 17

Supporting Children's Numeracy Skills

This unit covers the following objectives:

- Understand the development of children's numeracy skills
- Understand current national initiatives and curriculum guidance relating to the development of numeracy skills
- Be able to develop a range of activities that can be used to support children's understanding and use of number, shape, space and measure

This unit provides an overview of how numeracy and the use of number develops, with reference to a range of theories. It explains the usual stages of development, thinking and understanding. It should, of course, always be taken into account that, as with all aspects of development, each child progresses at their own pace. Guidance on planning and meeting additional needs is included, with a variety of activities used as examples. Reference is made to relevant curriculum frameworks and legislation, and to the contexts within which children learn best.

grading criteria

To achieve a **Pass** grade the evidence must show that the learner is able to:	To achieve a **Merit** grade the evidence must show that, in addition to the Pass criteria, the learner is able to:	To achieve a **Distinction** grade the evidence must show that, in addition to the Pass and Merit criteria, the learner is able to:
P1 Describe two different theories of how understanding of mathematical concepts develop in children Page 142	**M1** Compare and contrast the two theories using practical examples Page 142	
P2 Describe the stages in the development of children's mathematical understanding Page 143		
P3 Describe the role of the adult in developing children's numeracy skills Page 144		
P4 Describe the influence of one piece of legislation/curriculum guidance on supporting the development of children's numeracy skills Page 178	**M2** Explain how the identified legislation/curriculum guidance is used in an early years setting to promote children's numeracy skills Page 178	**D1** Evaluate the effectiveness of national initiatives in promoting children's numeracy skills Page 178

To achieve a **Pass** grade the evidence must show that the learner is able to:	To achieve a **Merit** grade the evidence must show that, in addition to the Pass criteria, the learner is able to:	To achieve a **Distinction** grade the evidence must show that, in addition to the Pass and Merit criteria, the learner is able to:
P5 Develop two activities to promote children's number skills Page 182	**M3** Implement one of the activities to promote children's number skills Page 182	
P6 Develop two activities to promote children's understanding of shape, space and measure Page 184	**M4** Implement one of the activities to support understanding of space, shape and measure Page 184	**D2** Evaluate the effectiveness of the two implemented activities Page 185

Understand the development of children's numeracy skills

Relevant theories

Many adults throw up their hands in despair at the thought of using mathematics, because they consider that they are 'no good at it'. A very negative mindset has developed in many people and, as early years practitioners, it is important to help children develop an 'I *can* do it' approach, rather than an 'I *can't* do it' approach, to using number and developing mathematical skills. It is also important to remember that many aspects of mathematics are about solving problems, and that we all take our preferred, and often differing, approaches to doing so. This reminds us that there is no one fixed way of doing something and that we each have our own learning styles.

How children develop an understanding of mathematical concepts

To understand numeracy and the development of mathematical understanding, it is important to consider the thinking of some of the most well-known theorists. These include Jean Piaget, Lev Vygotsky, Jerome Bruner, Tina Bruce and Chris Athey.

Jean Piaget

Jean Piaget has been an important theorist in helping adults to focus on the minds of children and how their understanding develops, but in more recent times some of his findings have been challenged. Piaget considered that children's thinking moves through four main stages, each stage building on the one before:

1 Sensorimotor stage (0–2 years)
2 Pre-operational stage (2–7 years) divided into:
- Pre-conceptual stage (2–4 years)
- Intuitive stage (5–7 years)

3 Concrete operational stage (7–11 years)
4 Formal operational stage (from around 12 years).

Link Refer to Unit 14, page 103, for an explanation of each of these stages.

Piaget believed that children develop knowledge concepts by using and building on previous experiences. Initially children will represent their thinking physically in their actions, then moving on to symbolic representations.

He considered that they gradually adapt these concepts, which he called schemas, to establish new understanding. An example would be a child initially seeing a coin and understanding it is a one pence piece because it is round, made of metal and brown. Typically the child would use the term 'money'. This experience, reinforced over time, will eventually move him on to understanding that other coins are also round, made of metal and that they can be either brown or silver. They are, however, all referred to as money. He will learn that a coin is part of the money system, and gradually understand that there are other forms of money (notes, cheques and debit cards, all used as payment for Mummy and Daddy's shopping). Piaget called this process assimilation and accommodation.

Piaget considered children to be active learners who learn best through doing (discovery learning). He felt it was important that they had access to a range of materials and resources to help them experiment and find out for themselves. The above example of a child learning about money will therefore be supported by role play activities involving shops, tills and going shopping. Using coins for counting, adding and taking away will also help reinforce both use of money and its value.

Piaget is also well known for his thinking on conservation. He believed that children in the pre-operational stage were unable to conserve, and cited the outcomes of several 'experiments' to support this. Figures 17.1 and 17.2 show his findings.

Fig 17.1 Conservation: example A

Preoperational children say that the two rows have the same number of pennies.

Preoperational children say there are more pennies in the longer, fourth row.

Fig 17.2 Conservation: example B

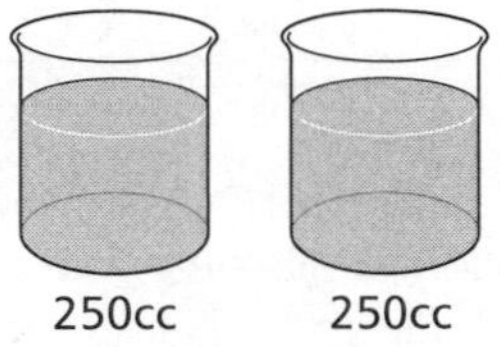

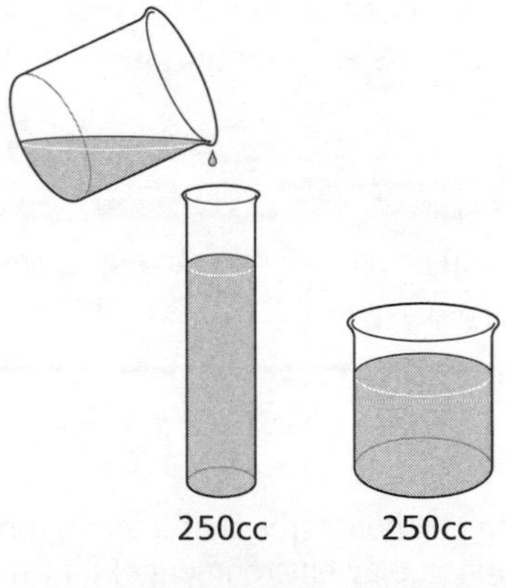

In Example A, the child was shown two identical rows of pennies and was asked if they were the same. The pennies in the second row were then spaced apart and the child was asked if there were still the same number of pennies.

If the child was able to conserve, they would answer that there were the same number. If the child could not conserve, they would answer that there were more pennies in the longer row.

In Example B, the child was shown two identical beakers of water and asked if they contained the same amount. After watching the adult pour the water from one beaker into a taller beaker, the child was asked if the amount of water in the beakers was still the same. If the child could conserve, they would answer that the amount of water remained the same. If they could not conserve, they would state that the amount of water was different – that there was more water in the taller beaker.

In a further example, the child was shown two identical balls of play dough and asked if they were the same amount. Having seen the adult roll one ball into a sausage shape, the child was asked if the amount of play dough was still the same. If the child could conserve, they would answer that the balls of play dough were still both the same size. If they could not conserve, they would think that the sausage shape was made from a greater amount of play dough.

Lev Vygotsky

Like Piaget, Lev Vygotsky believed that children learn best by doing. The main difference between their thinking was Vygotsky's belief in the importance of social interaction between a child and an adult, or more able peer. Vygotsky believed that discussion, sensitive questioning and guidance from a more able 'other' could help a child reach a higher level of understanding than they are likely to have reached on their own. He called this their zone of proximal development.

Jerome Bruner

Jerome Bruner describes a child's development of thinking in what he terms 'three modes'. These are:

- the enactive mode, where the child learns through first-hand experiences (like Piaget's discovery learning).
- the iconic mode, where the child is able to form mental images and use memory.
- the symbolic mode, where the child expresses their understanding through a range of mediums.

Bruner's thinking about a child's learning builds on the work of Vygotsky. He uses the term 'scaffolding' to describe how an adult can support a child, offering support to help them move to the next stage in their understanding, and then gradually removing the support structure, leaving them more able than they were beforehand.

Chris Athey and the development of schema

Chris Athey has built upon Piaget's thinking of schema. Her observations and research have shown that children spend specific passages of time focusing on a particular area of interest and learning, practising and exploring a concept from all angles. This exploration builds upon their understanding, moving them onto the next stage in their learning. Examples would include a child who repeatedly lines up objects, e.g. dolls and teddies, cars and other vehicles, their cutlery at lunchtime, their items of clothing along the sofa in the morning. It may also be seen in their paintings or drawings, with the creation of rows of splodges, dots, lines, etc.

case study 17.1 Jasmine

Jasmine, aged 2 years 9 months, showed a fascination with shapes. She delighted in people helping her make circles, squares and 'tangles' (rectangles) with any items she could find. Jasmine demonstrated a clear enclosure schema, wrapping up herself, her dolls, and other items such as crayons, bricks and empty cups. She also liked to surround things with a circle of bricks.

activity

1 What other activities would you expect Jasmine to enjoy, linked to this schema?

2 What activities would you offer Jasmine?

Learning through play

Practitioners working with young children agree that learning opportunities are at their best when provided within a well-planned play environment. Tina Bruce (1991) refers to the Plowden Report of 1967 and how it gave play 'central status' in the education of young children. This central status was also upheld by the Rumbold Committee Report of 1990 (section 89) which read:

> 'Young children learn effectively in a number of ways, including exploring, observing and listening. Playing and talking are, for young children, two principal means of bringing together a range of these activities. We believe that effective curriculum implementation requires careful attention to be given to providing fully for these.'

The report goes on to say (section 91) that:

> 'Play that is well planned and pleasurable helps children to think, to increase their understanding and to improve their language competence. It allows children to be creative, to explore and investigate materials, to experiment and to draw and test their conclusion. Such experience is important in catching and sustaining children's interests and motivating their learning as individuals and in co-operation with others.'

This promotion of play has continued with successive governments and through to the development of the present frameworks guiding and supporting early years practitioners in their work.

Link

Refer to page 152 for an overview of different frameworks.

Tina Bruce

Tina Bruce has been an important contemporary influence on the promotion of play. She uses the terms free-flow, or ludic, play to describe what she considers to be the only true concept of play – a form of play that allows children to learn by discovery.

> 'Games help children to understand external pressures and constraints; free-flow play helps children to see the function of rules for themselves'
>
> Bruce (1991)

Bruce illustrates her definition of free-flow play as follows:

> Free-flow play = Wallowing in ideas, feelings and relationships + Application of competence and technical prowess that has already been developed

Bruce's 12 features of free-flow play are summarised as:

- It is an active process without a product.
- It is intrinsically motivated.
- There is no external pressure to conform.
- It is about lifting the 'players' to their highest levels of functioning, involving creativity and imagination.
- It involves reflection, the wallowing in ideas.
- It actively uses previous first-hand experiences.
- It is sustained and helps us to function ahead of our real-life ability levels.
- It allows control, using competence previously attained.
- It can be initiated by child or adult, but adults need to be aware of not imposing rules, or directing activity.
- It can be a solitary experience.
- It can be in partnership with others.
- It brings together what we learn, feel and understand.

(Bruce 1991)

If you are interested in reading more of Tina Bruce's thinking, refer to the bibliography and suggested reading section on page 412 for details.

Janet Moyles

Another important contributor to the thinking on play is Janet Moyles. She developed the idea of the play spiral (Figure 17.3). This spiral clearly shows how children move in and out of different modes of play (directed and free play), each stage building on the previous one as their learning develops.

If you are interested in reading more of Janet Moyles' thinking, refer to the bibliography and suggested reading section on page 412 for details.

Link

Refer to page 178 for more general information on play, its importance in a child's learning process and examples of activities to support numeracy and mathematical development.

Fig 17.3 Moyles' play spiral

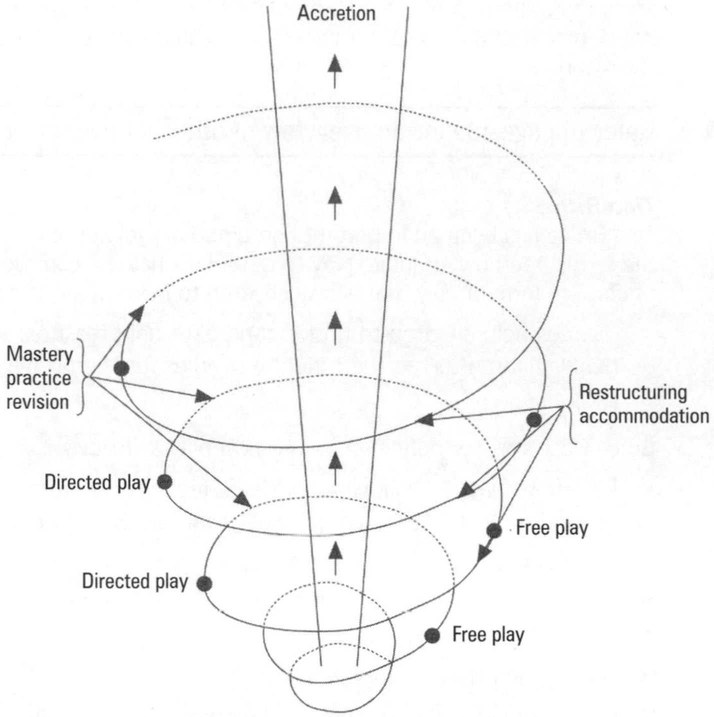

activity
INDIVIDUAL WORK 17.1

P1

M1

1. Imagine you have been asked to talk to a group of parents at your placement about the ways in which their children are developing mathematical understanding. Produce two information cards, one for each of two theories of your choice. Give a clear explanation of each theory, and provide examples for the parents of how each theory is supported within the setting.
2. Together with your two information cards, draw up a written comparison of the two theories. Again, use examples from your placement.

Sequences and stages

Understanding of the stages of children's mathematical understanding

From birth, infants begin to develop the sense of interest and enquiry needed for their mathematical development. For example:

- Immediately after birth, babies look around them and respond to events, e.g. smell mother's breast, start rooting for a feed. This is an example of early cause and effect.
- In the early weeks, their feet kick and their fists wave, occasionally touching an item that brings a reward, e.g. a mobile moves, the teddy swings, a bell jingles, etc. Again, cause and effect.
- In time they become eager to hold an object, temporarily experiencing its properties (hard/soft, big/small, etc.) and then …
- As their hands gain strength they take each object to their mouth, exploring them orally. This is soon followed by passing objects from hand to hand, and then eventually to purposefully releasing them.
- Parents and carers use mathematical vocabulary during domestic routines: 'one arm, two arms', 'one sock, two socks', 'what a big boy', 'up you come', 'one more spoonful', 'all gone', 'down you go', etc. These everyday vocalisations help introduce and reinforce the early concept of one-to-one correspondence, the familiarity of the terms and numbers, paving the way for the infant to respond to and use them themselves later on.
- The various toys and household objects babies come into contact with help them explore size, shape, texture and surface temperature.

- Once crawling begins, infants start to experience distance and, once able to stand, they can be seen trying to gauge how far it is to the next solid furniture item, as they make their first steps.
- As toddlers, they learn to master push-along toys, initially bashing into door frames and other objects, but eventually gaining an understanding of space, direction and orientation.
- Early water play sees children simply splashing, filling and tipping (all useful learning experiences), but this soon turns into more purposeful experimenting, with the child trying out different sized containers (size, measure and early conservation experience), using pumps (the concept of pressure and force).
- As children are introduced to rhymes and stories involving number, they begin to make sense of what actually is meant by the number one, what actually is two, etc. They need plenty of practice and reinforcement through the repetition of singing old favourites like 'Five currant buns', through regular stories using number, and through practical activities involving the grouping of numbers, adding one more, taking away, etc. as their understanding develops.
- As a child moves on in their thinking, they gradually develop an understanding of more abstract concepts.

remember

Children do not follow a neatly set pathway in their learning and much will be based on the experiences they receive.

Link

Refer to page 138 for the thinking of Piaget, Vygotsky, Bruner, etc., to page 156 for an overview of the Early Learning Goals for Problem Solving, Reasoning and Numeracy (part of the Early Years Foundation Stage, EYFS) and to page 164 for the outline of the National Primary Framework for Mathematics. These each show a generally accepted progression of how mathematical thinking develops.

activity
GROUP WORK 17.2
P2

As a group you have been asked to give a presentation on mathematical development to another group of students. You will need to:

1. Gather together a range of objects and/or pictures that illustrate each stage in a child's mathematical development.
2. Prepare an explanation for each stage.
3. Deliver the presentation and be able to answer questions.

The role of the adult

The role of the adult in planning and implementing opportunities to develop numeracy skills is to:

Fig 17.4 The role of the adult

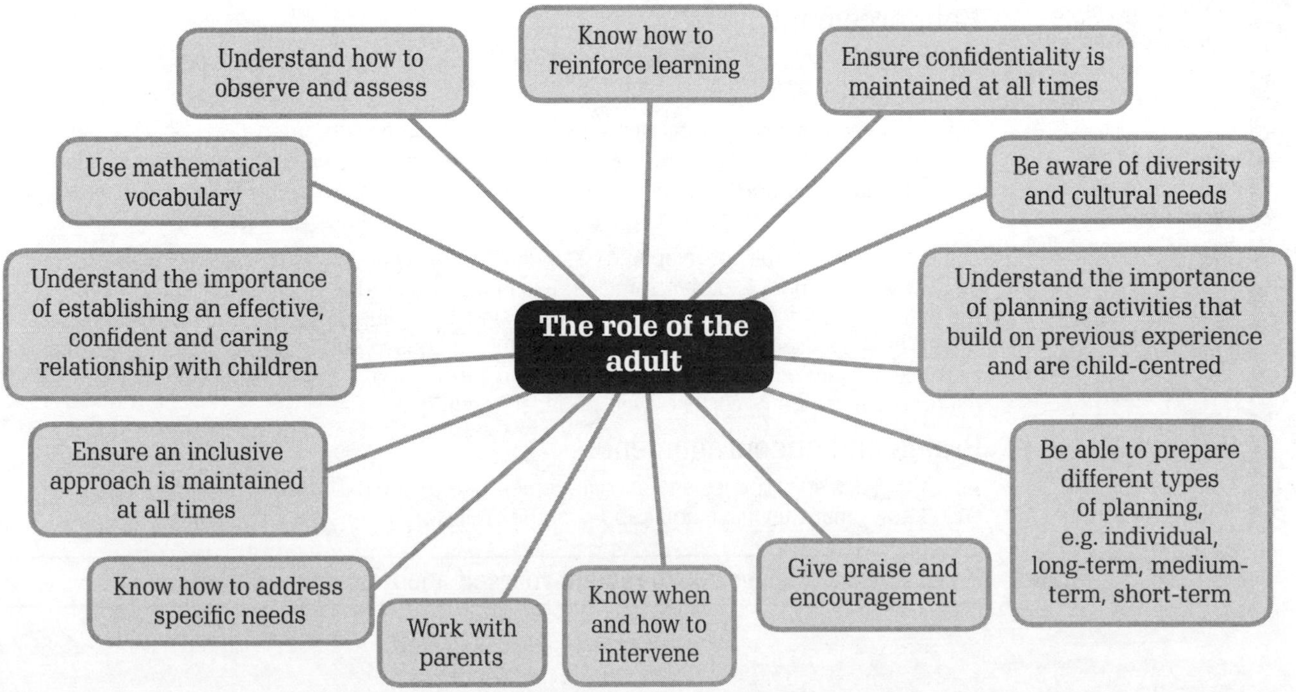

activity
INDIVIDUAL WORK 17.3
P3

Using the spidergram above as a guide, write a description of three occasions where you have personally supported the development of numeracy during your placement experience. Try to include an example from three different age ranges and/or three types of settings, e.g. nursery, school, childminder.

Using mathematical vocabulary

Each of us uses mathematical language every day as we discuss and describe amounts, measurements, position and shape, and as we order, shop, cook and work. When working with children the use of these terms in context reinforces their learning, helping them associate meaning with actions. The simple habit of vocalising what is happening within the setting provides children with additional and important opportunities to consolidate and further develop their understanding, e.g. 'We are all sitting in a lovely circle', 'What a lot of hoops, let's count them', 'The largest is on the bottom and the smallest is on the top', 'Everyone turn to the right', etc.

Link

Refer to page 178 for activities and ideas on supporting children's understanding and use of number, and to page 182 for ideas linked to supporting understanding of shape, space and measure.

Observation and assessment

remember
It is important that a group of children is not simply taught through one learning style.

Using a range of observation methods, individual children's progress should be followed and recorded according to the setting's procedural practice. This helps identify any specific areas of need, the areas of numeracy in which they are less able (if any) and also their preferred learning style. In early years settings, this will usually be carried out by a child's key worker, using the benchmarks of the appropriate curriculum or guidance structure, e.g. the Early Years Foundation Stage (EYFS). In school this would usually be the class teacher, but could also be carried out by the classroom assistant, with assessment linked to the Primary National Strategy and National Curriculum, as appropriate..

i

The Early Years Foundation Stage will be mandatory from September 2008 for all early years settings receiving government funding. A similar strategy called the Foundation Phase will be in place in Wales, covering the age range 3–7 years.

remember
Assessment helps practitioners ensure that every aspect of the relevant curriculum is being covered. Using observations and assessments to inform planning helps guarantee that a child's needs are being identified and that strategies to support those needs and help children achieve a planned goal are included in future sessions or activities.

Reinforcement

Reinforcement is about repeating elements of learning to help consolidate them for the child or group.

Children need practice in using numbers, both their names and order as in counting, and in their use, e.g. one-to-one correspondence. Both aspects are fundamental to all mathematical learning. As stated above, an environment in which children are regularly exposed to the use of mathematical vocabulary in context will support and reinforce their learning.

Some children naturally develop understanding of new concepts more quickly than others, and some need more experience-related examples to help them. This was clearly seen in the differing findings regarding ages at which understanding takes place of Jean Piaget and Margaret Donaldson. Piaget's initial experiments in conservation found children to be unable to conserve until much later than those of Donaldson, who phrased her questions to directly relate to the children's current levels of understanding

Praise and encouragement

As with all activities, praise and encouragement are a vital part of the learning process. If a child knows that they have adult approval they will work to ensure it continues.

Link

Refer to Unit 14, page 100 to remind yourself about positive reinforcement.

Working with parents

In schools teachers have limited time to spend with each child on an individual basis and for a child who takes a little more time than others to grasp a concept, or consolidate new learning, additional time spent outside of the classroom can be invaluable. Good links with parents help to actively encourage them to help their own child reach their potential. Giving even very young children 'homework' is now commonplace and most children enjoy sharing these experiences with their family. Examples could include:

- Find as many things at home the same length as your hand.
- Identify objects of a specific shape around the home.
- Write family names in order of height, shortest first.

The importance of planning activities that build on previous experience and are child-centred

Mathematical concepts build upon each other. For example, a child needs to know his number names and understand the 'two-ness' of the number two, before he is able to make a collection of objects, e.g. two of each colour brick, bear, etc. Similarly, he needs to understand two-dimensional shapes before he is expected to work with three-dimensional shapes.

The introduction of puzzles with graded levels of difficulty is a good example of how the same activity progresses based on previous learning. Initially the youngest infants may be given a two- or three-piece wooden shape that fits together and comes apart again. Next, play-tray type puzzles with pieces to lift out and replace help develop shape discrimination, together with hand–eye co-ordination and fine motor skills. Once a child has mastered this stage, they move on to understand the concept of the puzzle making an overall picture. The number of pieces and the complexity of the portrayed image can now be increased.

Many children learn best through a hands-on approach (kinaesthetic learning), therefore, the more opportunities there are for children to 'do' rather than simply 'see' or 'hear', the more successful the learning will be.

Awareness of diversity and cultural need

remember

It is important to speak clearly at all times.

remember

Many languages do not follow the left to right written convention, as found in written English. This applies both to letters and numbers, so this is an additional concept for a child to learn.

Some children will be learning English as an additional language. Again, it will be important in helping them understand and consolidate their learning of numeracy to introduce and embed mathematical language within appropriate contexts. The use of both two-dimensional and three-dimensional visual images will be helpful, providing concrete examples to help them.

When asking questions, an action or display of objects to accompany your words will usually be helpful. For example:

- holding up a handful of coins during shop play when asking, 'How much will we need to pay?'
- drawing a shape in the air with your finger when stating its name
- pointing to the cutlery at snack time, and then at each member of the group whilst asking, 'How many knives and forks will we need?'
- using gesture to confirm position when using terms such as behind, in front of, next to, etc.

Children need to have plenty of opportunities to listen to the mathematical vocabulary. Useful activities include whole group times (where children are grouped or divided up into certain numbers), the regular inclusion of number rhymes and counting games such as 'Five speckled frogs sitting on a speckled log', etc. These all help consolidate learning.

Professional Practice

- **Posters and number lines are available in dual languages. These can help non-English speaking parents to support their child's learning and show that a family's heritage language is valued.**
- **Asking a child's parents to help the whole class or group learn to count in their heritage language can also be beneficial, and fun for all.**

Children who are learning more than one language at a time are usually slower in their general language development. This is likely to impact on their verbal numeracy too, but as with all language development, children can normally understand more than they can vocalise.

Types of planning: individual, long-term, medium-term, short-term

Planning for the long term provides practitioners with a broad overview of the main themes they wish to cover. This type of planning is not usually followed rigidly, it is flexible according to need and circumstance. Written long-term plans are useful as a basis for all staff to refer back to, reminding them of how the period of time (e.g. a school year) is intended to be approached. In the Foundation Stage, long-term planning ensures that all six areas of learning are given sufficient attention both in allocated time, and in regularity, in order for children to have meaningful learning experiences and for them to make progress appropriately.

Short-term planning is more likely to focus on day-to-day planning or weekly plans, or as a block of two to three weeks, as often used in the Primary Framework for Mathematics (see page 164). Short-term planning should be taking into account the observations and informal assessments made of children during previous activities and use them to inform the next stage of the planning.

remember
One of the most important aspects of planning is to ensure that intended activities gradually introduce new concepts and build upon prior learning.

Medium-term planning is used by some, but not all practitioners. It provides a secure link between the long-term and the short-term plans, e.g.

- Long-term planning may cover a whole academic year in a school, e.g. divided into the five main blocks of the National Primary Framework for Mathematics.
- Medium-term planning may be linked to each of the terms within the school year, or to each of the five main teaching blocks.
- Short-term plans will refer to the weekly and daily planning of each unit of each main teaching block.

Link
Refer to page 170 for an outline of the National Primary Framework for Mathematics.

Professional Practice

- In many nursery and pre-school settings, long-term plans may simply cover the main 'terms' of autumn, spring and summer, with short-term planning covering small topics within each season.
- There is no hard and fast rule regarding written planning, but each school or early years setting will have their preferred 'in-house' method. Be sure to check the requirements of each setting where you are on placement, or in which you work.

Link
Examples of planning sheets are set out on page 176, to accompany the overview of the National Primary Framework for Mathematics.

Importance of establishing an effective, confident and caring relationship with children

Building up relationships with children and their families is a fundamental part of the role of every teacher and early years practitioner. If an adult has a secure and positive relationship with a child, then it is likely that the child will feel able to ask questions, express their worries and feel able to 'try' without fearing making mistakes. An adult who upholds confidentiality and is known to do this will receive the trust of parents. This effective relationship enables practitioners to have a better understanding of:

- when and how to intervene in the learning of each individual child
- the inclusive needs of individual children
- how they can address each child's **specific needs**.

It will also enable them to raise concerns with parents about a child's progress, knowing that the parent will usually trust them and their judgement and be willing to explore options and take advice from other professionals, knowing that it will be carried out within a framework of confidence and professionalism.

Specific needs

Meeting children's individual learning needs involves a careful assessment of the ways in which they learn best, what aspects of learning they find difficult and why that might be. Sometimes parents and practitioners have advance warning that a child may face difficulties, e.g. if a specific condition or chronic illness has already been identified and a known pattern regarding learning and development is usual. Examples that affect numeracy include developmental delay, congenital conditions and illness such as hearing and sight loss, dyscalculia and dyslexia. Practitioners need to know where they can obtain information on conditions they meet for the first time. This ensures that they meet a child's needs from the outset of their involvement in their care and education.

Developmental delay

Developmental delay is the term used whenever an infant or child is consistently behind in meeting the normal developmental milestones. This may be due to congenital conditions, illness or poor nutrition and/or the effects of drugs, tobacco or alcohol whilst still within the womb. Occasionally, an infant is simply small in size and develops very slowly.

Developmental delay can be due to sensory, physical, genetically inherited, social or environmental reasons.

All children showing signs of developmental delay will be closely monitored by health professionals and appropriate interventions made where it is considered necessary.

Congenital conditions and illness

If a child is born with a condition already present, it is referred to as being **congenital**. These conditions are mostly identified at birth, e.g. Down's syndrome and some forms of cerebral palsy. Some are identified within the first few weeks, e.g. blindness or vision impairment, profound deafness or hearing loss, as reactions by the infant differ to what is expected of them. Others are identified through specific testing, e.g. the distraction hearing test carried out at around 8 months, and the otoacoustic emissions test (that has mostly taken over from the distraction hearing test), which is carried out before an infant reaches 4 weeks old. Children with congenital problems can be helped to reach their full potential through a carefully planned programme of activities designed to stimulate and compensate for any known sensory loss.

Children who are blind or are visually impaired can be helped by:

- tactile experiences to help them develop understanding through touch
- an environment that enriches all their senses
- a rich spoken environment, with adults talking to them throughout each activity, domestic routine or experience, naming, describing, explaining, etc.
- rhymes and songs, musical boxes, musical instruments and listening to music
- mathematical vocabulary used within context, e.g. counting when doing up buttons
- listening to stories, both orally and through tapes/CDs, enjoying repetition and familiarity, and learning to predict, to anticipate, to understand the process of stories told either orally or through auditory media
- input from **Portage** workers in the earliest years.

Children who are deaf or have a hearing impairment can be helped by:

- a rich visual environment which encourages them to look carefully and with pleasure
- an environment that enriches all of their senses
- an environment where written text and numerals are used widely, labelling items all around them, helping them make links between spoken (or signed) numbers and printed numerals
- learning sign language or a signing system such as Makaton
- the use of sorting trays to help them group items into twos, fives, etc. for themselves
- books of all types, picture books in both colour and black and white, to help them count, group and grade items by size, length and height
- input from Portage workers in the earliest years.

Dyslexia

Dyslexia is a neurological disorder caused by a slight impairment to sensory pathways. It affects reading, both its fluency and its accuracy, and this impacts on numeracy skills too as it can also affect writing and both number recognition and formation.

Children who are dyslexic have normal levels of intelligence. Their difficulties with reading, writing, etc. often appear as an inconsistency in a child who is otherwise bright, inquisitive and able. Dyslexia is a lifelong disorder, but children can be taught strategies to help them deal with it and overcome any limitations it may have posed to people in the past.

Children with dyslexia can be helped by:

- patience and plenty of time to complete work and activities
- visual or oral clues alongside written text where appropriate
- one-to-one guidance from practitioners on developing organisation skills
- an environment with minimal distractions to help concentration
- the use of coloured overlays, usually in yellow, which help them in reading the written text and instructions for problem-solving and numeracy activities
- opportunities to use alternative ways to provide answers or express themselves
- additional use of concrete objects within activities
- specific work on sequencing
- input from an educational psychologist.

Dyscalculia

Dyscalculia is often found alongside dyslexia. It is a lifelong condition, but can be managed quite well with appropriate support. Children who have dyscalculia have problems with sequencing, both in number use and in time (past and present events). They have difficulty in understanding concepts, order and rules. They find dealing with money challenging and also, as they get older, have difficulty grasping the concepts of music such as sight reading and the fingering layouts for playing a musical instrument.

Physically, children with dyscalculia have poor co-ordination and struggle with quick physical changes in direction as in dance, movement and exercise classes.

Memory is often poor, with children frequently seeming absent-minded, losing or mislaying items, having difficulty in remembering the rules of a game or managing to keep score. Also, remembering the sequence of steps in a dance or movement routine is difficult for them.

Children with dyscalculia can be helped by:

- patience and plenty of time to complete work and activities
- visual or oral clues alongside written text where appropriate
- one-to-one guidance from practitioners on developing organisation skills
- an environment with minimal distractions to help concentration
- returning to foundations of learning to remind, support and consolidate understanding
- additional use of concrete objects within activities
- numeracy and mathematical activities being as practical as possible
- specific work on sequencing and time frames
- using calculators to check own calculations
- using commercial learning aids
- input from an educational psychologist.

Professional Practice

- Dysgraphia can be an associated difficulty for children with dyscalculia.

Link

Refer to Unit 18, page 219, for information on dysgraphia.

Dealing with difficulties in ways which do not undermine the child's confidence

Every child needs to feel good about themselves in order to achieve their potential. A child's difficulty or disability should not overshadow who they are as an individual. It is important to see them as a child first and foremost, and as a child with X, Y or Z as an additional need, after. Sometimes adults make assumptions about a child's ability, based on what they can or cannot do in another aspect of their learning. This can be dangerous. In making an assumption, rather than observing and assessing ability, you may plan inappropriately for a child's needs, either providing him with challenges that are too great, potentially knocking his confidence as he struggles to cope, to keep up with peers or to achieve, or conversely, assuming that a child will not be able to do something so leave them under-challenged, unstimulated and bored, potentially leading to an unmotivated child who lacks enthusiasm for new experiences.

The manner in which children are paired up or grouped for tasks can help or hinder progress. Again, this should be linked to levels of challenge, but take in account issues of personality, age, learning styles and interests.

Link

See Unit 18, page 198 for information on learning styles.

Professional Practice

- Sometimes simple aids can help a child, e.g. having access to counting blocks or number rods will help a child practically as they will achieve more easily, but also, this will help them mentally, boosting their self-esteem as they manage to 'keep up' with their peers better.

When and how to access help

A child may benefit from an assessment by another professional if their progress slows down and seems to stop, if they are making only minimal progress despite already having a programme of learning specifically set up for them by current staff, or if they are working at a level considerably below that of their peers. The Special Educational Needs Co-ordinator (SENCO) is always the first port of call. It is their role to make appropriate contacts, and, along with parents, help develop a programme of intervention for any child who needs it.

Link

Refer to Unit 27, page 320, for more information on meeting additional needs and the role of SENCOs.

Understand current national initiatives and curriculum guidance relating to the development of numeracy skills

There is a range of relevant legislation and curriculum guidance to support the development of children's numeracy skills either directly or indirectly. This includes:

- Children Act 1989 and 2004
- Continuing the Learning Journey 2005
- Childcare Act 2006
- Warnock Report 1978
- Code of Practice 2001
- Every Child Matters: Change for Children
- Birth to Three Matters – Will be completely replaced by EYFS in September 2008
- Foundation Stage Curriculum – Will be completely replaced by EYFS in September 2008
- Primary Framework for Literacy and Mathematics
- Early Years Foundation Stage (EYFS) – Mandatory from September 2008.

Legislation

Children Act 1989 and 2004

The Children Act 1989 and its update of 2004 legislates for the all-round health, development and safe living of young children. It sets out minimum requirements for staffing numbers, staffing qualifications, the state of resources within the care and learning environment, and how children's needs should be met. The regulatory body Ofsted oversees the maintenance of standards of both care and learning, and has the powers to act if these standards are not met. Ofsted inspection teams ensure that all areas of care, stimulation and learning, as set out by the Birth to Three Matters strategy and the Foundation Stage Curriculum, are fully met. Mathematics and general numeracy skills are significant aspects of each of these.

Childcare Act 2006

The Childcare Act 2006 includes specific updates on the Children Act 2004. It asks for local authorities and their local partners to reduce inequalities for young children in their areas by providing an integrated service for children and their families, part of the ethos of Sure Start. Each local area should have sufficient provision for care and learning for all the children aged 3 and 4 of parents who wish to take it up. A free minimum amount of provision for all 3- and 4-year-olds is set out.

Section 12 of the Act highlights the newly extended age range (now up to age 20 years) for which parents have a right to obtain information for their child. This includes language skills and the use of advocates and interpreters where appropriate.

Sections 39–48 of the Act introduces the **Early Years Foundation Stage (EYFS)**, and explains how it builds on the Birth to Three Matters, Foundation Stage Curriculum and the National Standards for Day Care and Childminding. It explains how the new EYFS will support an integrated provision for children from birth through to 5 years, and makes reference to the adjusted Ofsted Childcare Register standards.

Warnock Report 1978

In 1978 Mary Warnock headed the first enquiry for almost 90 years into the 'education of handicapped children and young people'. The focus of the enquiry was on children's rights to an education, whatever their disability, and the importance of seeing the child as a child first and foremost, and as a child with a disability second.

The report concluded that although around 20 per cent of children might have a special educational need (SEN), either ongoing or temporary, many of this group of children could be successfully educated in a mainstream setting. It concluded that it was inappropriate to place all children with a SEN in a 'special' school or unit. Each child's needs would be assessed individually in conjunction with the child's parents.

Much of the 'old' terminology (e.g. remedial, sub-normal) was discontinued following the Warnock Report, with terms such as 'mild', 'moderate' or 'severe' learning difficulties, and 'children with specific learning difficulties' being the favoured terms. It proposed that labelling should be avoided whenever possible and also that children should not be categorised as either having or not having a handicap or disability as this causes an unnecessary division.

The term 'specific learning difficulties' would often be used to describe the needs of children with conditions such as dyslexia, dysgraphia, visual or auditory loss. These children have an identified specific need that can be targeted specifically with appropriate strategies. The report recommended that relevant resources and equipment should be included in the classrooms for children with specific learning difficulties, e.g. hearing aids, tactile learning materials.

The term 'special educational need' (SEN) came into use following the report along with the five-stage process of assessment.

The report also highlighted the importance of early years provision for all children, again whenever practical, within a mainstream setting.

There have been many more legislative papers and acts since the Warnock Report in 1978. Each paper has attempted to build on the foundations of Mary Warnock and her enquiry team.

Link

You may find it of interest to research further using the internet. Also, refer to Unit 27, page 320, for more on supporting the additional needs of children.

Code of Practice 2001

The Code of Practice 2001 responded to the Education Act 1996, providing teachers, teaching assistants and all other early years practitioners with practical guidance on how to meet the needs of children considered to have a SEN. Regarding the support and development of numeracy skills, the following paragraphs (summarised below) of the Code of Practice are particularly relevant.

Provision in the early years

- 4.8 Children making slower progress may include those who are learning English as an additional language or who have particular learning difficulties. It should not be assumed that children who are making slower progress must, therefore, have special educational needs. But such children will need carefully differentiated learning opportunities to help them progress and regular and frequent careful monitoring of their progress.

Statements for children under 2

- 4.48 It is rare for a child under the age of 2 to be given a statement, but Portage and/or specific peripatetic services should be made available for children identified as being blind or deaf, or having either a visual or auditory impairment.

Moving to primary school

- 4.54, 4.55 The needs of a child who enters school, having had a considerable level of support (e.g. from Portage or similar), but without a statement should be carefully considered, in both the context of their current learning and in the wider context of the home environment and circumstances to establish if their difficulty is linked to any family issue. A record of their progress and needs should be passed on to the school, with agreement of their parents. The school will then be alerted to potential support needs for that child.

Communication and interaction

- 7.55, 7.56, 7.57 These paragraphs raise the point that children with SENs are more able in some areas than in others, and that their communication needs may be 'both diverse and complex'. It should be remembered that communication can impact directly on numeracy skills development. The Code of Practice states that children may require some or all of the following:
  - flexible teaching arrangements
  - help in acquiring, comprehending and using language
  - help in articulation
  - help in acquiring literacy skills
  - help in using augmentative and alternative means of communication
  - help to use different means of communication confidently and competently for a range of purposes, including formal situations
  - help in organising and co-ordinating oral and written language
  - support to compensate for the impact of a communication difficulty or learning in English as an additional language
  - help in expressing, comprehending and using their own language, where English is not the first language.

Children may be supported through School Action Plus or, if acceptable progress has not been made following receipt of this support over a period of time, statutory assessment will be considered.

Link

Refer to www.everychildmatters.gov.uk for information on:

- Early Years Action
- Early Years Action Plus
- School Action
- School Action Plus.

Cognition and learning

- 7.58, 7.59 This section refers to severe and profound difficulties, and also to specific learning difficulties such as dyslexia, which is often found alongside dyscalculia. It states that these children may require:
    - flexible teaching arrangements
    - help with processing language, memory and reasoning skills
    - help and support in acquiring literacy skills
    - help in organising and co-ordination of spoken and written word to aid cognition
    - help with sequencing and organisational skills
    - help with problem solving and developing concepts
    - programmes to aid improvement of fine and motor competencies
    - support in the use of technical terms and abstract ideas
    - help in understanding ideas, concepts and experiences when information cannot be gained through first-hand sensory or physical experiences.

LEA support services

- 10.7 The Code of Practice describes how local education authorities (LEAs) can provide advice on teaching techniques, classroom management and appropriate resources and materials. Also direct teaching or practical support for teachers, specialist teaching assistants and specialist help.

Based on DfES Special Educational Needs Code of Practice 2001

You may wish to read through the Code of Practice in more detail. Most college libraries will have a copy.

Curriculum guidance

Curriculum guidance and frameworks to support all-round health, education and well-being are provided for both before and throughout compulsory schooling. All children attending any care or education setting that meets the criteria to receive government funding, will be supported through government strategy or curriculum guidelines. At present these frameworks include:

- Birth to Three Matters – Will be completely replaced by EYFS in September 2008
- Foundation Stage Curriculum – Will be completely replaced by EYFS in September 2008
- Early Years Foundation Stage (EYFS) – Mandatory from September 2008
- National Curriculum.

The strategies for England are set out below, together with website links for each home country within the UK.

Each geographical area of the UK has its own home country curriculum and strategy for care and learning. The following websites may be of interest:

- England – www.dfes.gov.uk
- Wales – www.learning.wales.gov.uk for the Cwricwlwm Cymreig
- Scotland – www.scotland.gov.uk
- Northern Ireland – www.ccea.org.uk for the Northern Ireland Curriculum for Mathematics

Continuing the learning journey (2005)

This was a package of inset training materials to support practitioners in successfully helping children make the transition between the foundation stage and key stage 1.

The package aimed to:

- 'Establish an understanding of the principles of the foundation stage
- Show how these principles can be used to ensure an effective transition into key stage 1

- Promote continuity in learning by ensuring that year 1 teachers are aware of children's achievements and can implement the next stage in their learning
- Show how information from the foundation stage profile can be used to support school development.'

www.qca.org.uk

Professional Practice

- **Continuous Professional Development (CPD) is important to all teachers and practitioners. There are various inset packages and training sessions available. The example above is just one of many. There will be others within your local area, and also within each setting you work within. Undertaking CPD throughout your career will keep you up to date with new thinking and ensure that your practice remains appropriate and meets the needs of all the children you work with.**

Birth to Three Matters (2003)

Although this framework will be replaced by the EYFS by September 2008, this summary will help you understand how aspects of the curriculum frameworks have developed. Refer to EYFS overview on p.155. The Birth to Three Matters framework was not intended to be a formal curriculum as such but was designed as a framework for effective practice that would inform work with the under-3s. There had long been an increasing awareness of the importance of the first three years of life for development and this has been supported by neurological research studies. The framework was designed to inform the practice of anyone working with the under-3s regardless of the nature of the setting and it has four main aspects:

- A strong child
- A skilful communicator
- A competent learner and
- A healthy child.

Each aspect was further broken down into key components that inform the delivery of care and early learning. These are:

- A strong child
  - Me, myself and I
  - Being acknowledged and affirmed
  - Developing self assurance
  - A sense of belonging
- A skilful communicator
  - Being together
  - Finding a voice
  - Listening and responding
  - Making meaning
- A competent learner
  - Making connections
  - Being imaginative
  - Being creative
  - Representing
- A healthy child
  - Emotional well-being
  - Growing and developing
  - Keeping safe
  - Healthy choices.

These aspects and components were to be used to inform and structure innovative and imaginative care for the very youngest children. Babies are 'born to learn' and benefit from a rich, stimulating and emotionally supportive environment. Most provision for them was to be found within baby units or separate baby rooms. There is some evidence to suggest that they benefit from time spent with older babies and young children, but they also need a discrete and appropriate environment where there is a high ratio of qualified staff. The different aspects and components of the Birth to Three Matters framework could be used to inform daily care activities as well as more structured learning opportunities. It could be used equally by practitioners in day nurseries, family homes, children's centres and by childminders.

The aspect of 'a competent learner' was clearly the most directly relevant aspect of the strategy in the development of children's numeracy skills, but the general well-being of the whole child also contributes.

A useful series of books to refer to is Harpley & Roberts (2006).

Foundation Stage Curriculum

Although this framework will be replaced by the EYFS by September 2008, this summary will help you understand how aspects of the curriculum frameworks have developed. Refer to EYFS overview on p.155. The early years curriculum is one part of a range of connected strategies for children's services and was based on six main areas of learning:

- personal, social and emotional development
- communication, language and literacy
- mathematical development
- knowledge and understanding of the world
- physical development
- creative development.

Settings that implemented the **Foundation Stage Curriculum** successfully centered their practice on play and the holistic development of the individual child. Each of the areas of learning has Early Learning Goals that are measurable, but it also values everything a child does in the setting as the curriculum included 'everything children do, see, hear or feel in their setting, both planned and unplanned' (QCA, cited in Drake, 2001).

All settings offering the Foundation Stage Curriculum and achieving satisfactory inspection outcomes from Ofsted received funding for their 3- and 4-year-olds from a finance source known as the Nursery Education Grant.

The Foundation Stage Curriculum was offered from the age of 3 until the child began to follow the National Curriculum. The principle of the Foundation Stage Curriculum were:

> 'supporting, fostering, promoting and developing children's:
>
> - Personal, social and emotional well-being: in particular by supporting the transition to and between settings, promoting an inclusive ethos and providing opportunities for each child to become a valued member of that group and community so that a strong self-image and self-esteem are promoted;
> - Positive attitudes and dispositions towards their learning: in particular an enthusiasm for knowledge and learning and a confidence in their ability to be successful learners;
> - Social skills: in particular by providing opportunities that enable them to learn how to co-operate and work harmoniously alongside and with each other and to listen to each other;
> - Attention skills and persistence: in particular the capacity to concentrate on their own play or on group tasks;
> - Language and communication: with opportunities for all children to talk and communicate in a widening range of situations, to respond to adults and to each other, to practise and extend the range of vocabulary and communication skills they use and to listen carefully;
> - Reading and writing: with opportunities for all children to explore, enjoy, learn about and use words and text in a broad range of context and to experience a rich variety of books;
> - Mathematics: with opportunities for all children to develop their understanding of number, measurement, pattern, shape and space by providing a broad range of contexts in which they can explore, enjoy, learn, practise and talk about them;

- Knowledge and understanding of the world: with opportunities for all children to solve problems, make decisions, experiment, predict, plan and question in a variety of contexts, and to explore and find out about their environment and people and places that have significance in their lives;
- Physical development: with opportunities for all children to develop and practise their fine and gross motor skills and to increase their understanding of how the body works and what they need to do to be healthy and safe;
- Creative development: with opportunities for all children to explore and share thoughts, ideas and feelings through a variety of art, design and technology, music, movement, dance and imaginative and role-play activities.'

QCA (2000), pages 8–9

Early Years Foundation Stage (EYFS)

The EYFS principles which guide the work of all practitioners are grouped into four distinct but complementary themes:

- A Unique Child
- Positive Relationships
- Enabling Environments
- Learning and Development.

A Unique Child recognises that every child is a competent learner from birth who can be resilient, capable, confident and self-assured. The commitments are focused around development; inclusion; safety; and health and well-being.

Positive Relationships describes how children learn to be strong and independent from a base of loving and secure relationships with parents and/or a key person. The commitments are focused around respect; partnership with parents; supporting learning; and the role of the key person.

Enabling environments explains that the environment plays a key role in supporting and extending children's development and learning. The commitments are focused around observation, assessment and planning; support for every child; the learning environment; and the wider context – transitions, continuity, and multi-agency working.

Learning and Development recognises that children develop and learn in different ways and at different rates, and that all areas of learning and development are equally important and inter-connected.

Within Learning and Development there are six areas of learning covered by the early learning goals and educational programmes. These are:

- Personal, social and Emotional Development
- Communication, Language and Literacy
- Problem Solving, Reasoning and Numeracy
- Knowledge and Understanding of the World
- Physical Development
- Creative Development.

Each of these areas must be delivered within a broad range of contexts, through planned purposeful play, with a balance of adult-led and child-initiated activities.

Read through the following pages to help you understand the guidance for Problem Solving, Reasoning and Numeracy.

Numbers as Labels and for Counting

	Development matters	Look, listen and note	Effective practice	Planning and resourcing
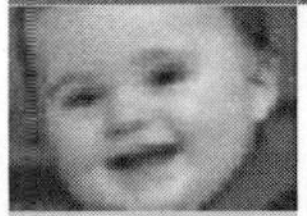 Birth-11 months	■ Respond to people and objects in their environment. ■ Notice changes in groupings of objects, images or sounds.	■ Responses to people and objects. ■ The attention that young babies give to changes in the quantity of objects or images they see, hear or experience.	■ Identify the people, toys and experiences that babies enjoy. ■ Talk about the things that babies notice when they are in different places such as the garden, the changing area or where they have meals.	■ Display favourite things in a lively, bright environment so that a young baby can see them. ■ Provide a small group of the same objects in treasure baskets, as well as single items, for example, two fir cones or three shells.
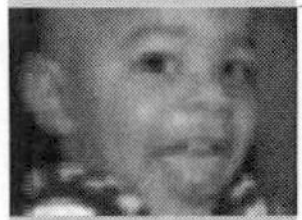 8-20 months	■ Develop an awareness of number names through their enjoyment of action rhymes and songs that relate to their experience of numbers. ■ Enjoy finding their nose, eyes or tummy as part of naming games.	■ Preferences for particular rhymes and action songs that relate to number. ■ The pictures of familiar things, in books, that babies recognise and point to, such as a ball or a teddy.	■ Sing number rhymes as you dress or change babies, for example, 'One, Two, Buckle My Shoe'. ■ Move with babies to the rhythm patterns in familiar songs and rhymes. ■ Encourage babies to join in tapping and clapping along to simple rhythms.	■ Collect number rhymes which are repetitive and are related to children's actions and experiences, for example, 'Peter Hammers with One Hammer'. ■ Use song and rhymes during personal routines, for example, 'Two Little Eyes to Look Around', pointing to their eyes, one by one. ■ Collect number and counting rhymes from a range of cultures and in other languages. This will benefit all children and will give additional support for children learning English as an additional language.
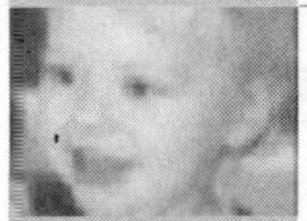 16-26 months	■ Say some counting words randomly. ■ Distinguish between quantities, recognising that a group of objects is more than one.	■ Awareness of number during play, such as the number words used and when and why they use them. ■ How children notice or choose a larger quantity.	■ Use number words in meaningful contexts, for example, "Here's your other mitten. Now we have two". ■ Talk to young children about 'lots' and 'few' as they play.	■ Provide varied opportunities to explore 'lots' and 'few' in play. ■ Equip the role-play area with things that can be sorted in different ways. ■ Provide collections of objects that can be sorted and matched in various ways.

Problem Solving, Reasoning and Numeracy

00012-2007BKT-EN
© Crown copyright 2007

Numbers as Labels and for Counting

	Development matters	Look, listen and note	Effective practice	Planning and resourcing
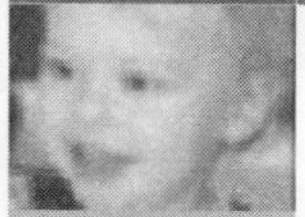 16-26 months	■ Gain awareness of one-to-one correspondence through categorising belongings, starting with 'mine' or 'Mummy's'.		■ Talk about young children's choices and, where appropriate, demonstrate how counting helps us to find out how many. ■ Give opportunities for children to practise one-to-one correspondence in real-life situations. ■ Talk about the maths in everyday situations, for example, doing up a coat, one hole for each button. ■ Tell parents about all the ways children learn about numbers in your setting. Have interpreter support or translated materials to support children and families learning English as an additional language.	■ Provide resources that support children in making one-to-one correspondences, for example, giving each dolly a cup.
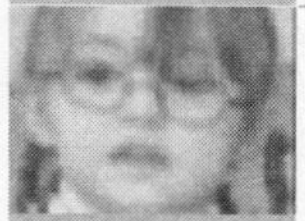 22-36 months	■ Have some understanding of 1 and 2, especially when the number is important for them. ■ Create and experiment with symbols and marks. ■ Use some number language, such as 'more' and 'a lot'. ■ Recite some number names in sequence.	■ How young children show their understanding of number labels such as 1, 2, 3. ■ The contexts in which young children use marks and symbols. ■ Situations that prompt children to talk about numbers. ■ The numbers children recite spontaneously in their games. ■ Children matching one thing with another, for example, glasses and straws. ■ Children putting things in order of 'turn'.	■ Show children how we use counting to find out 'how many'. ■ Talk about how the symbols and marks you make stand for numbers and quantities. ■ Ask questions such as "Would you like one sandwich or two?". ■ At mealtimes, talk about portions of food so that children learn about quantities, such as 'enough', 'more', 'how many'.	■ Introduce number labels to use outdoors for car number plates, house and bus numbers. ■ Create a 'number rich' environment in the home play area. Introduce numbers as they are used at home, by having a clock, a telephone and a washing machine.

00012-2007BKT-EN
© Crown copyright 2007

Numbers as Labels and for Counting

	Development matters	Look, listen and note	Effective practice	Planning and resourcing
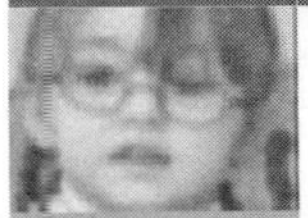 22-36 months			■ Encourage parents of children learning English as an additional language to talk in their home language about quantities and numbers.	■ Keep a diary with the children about their favourite things. Talk about how many like apples, or which of them watches a particular TV programme at home.
 30-50 months	■ Use some number names and number language spontaneously. ■ Show curiosity about numbers by offering comments or asking questions. ■ Use some number names accurately in play. ■ Sometimes match number and quantity correctly. ■ Recognise groups with one, two or three objects.	■ Children knowing that different numbers have different names. ■ Children using the names for numbers accurately. ■ The range of numbers that children refer to, and why they use certain numbers. ■ Children's guesses about numbers of things and their ability to check them. ■ Accuracy in the use of ordinals (first, second, third and so on). ■ The strategies that children use to match number and quantity, for example, using fingers or tallying by making marks.	■ Use number language, for example, 'one', 'two', 'three', 'lots', 'hundreds', 'how many?' and 'count', in a variety of situations. ■ Model and encourage use of mathematical language by, for example, asking questions such as, "How many saucepans will fit on the shelf?". ■ Allow children to understand that one thing can be shared, for example, a pizza.	■ Give children a reason to count, for example, by asking them to select enough wrist bands for three friends to play with the puppets. ■ Enable children to note the 'missing set', for example, "There are none left" when sharing things out. ■ Provide number labels for children to use, for example, by putting a number label on each bike and a corresponding number on each parking space. ■ Include counting money and change in role-play games.
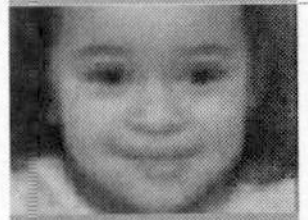 40-60+ months	■ Recognise some numerals of personal significance. ■ Count up to three or four objects by saying one number name for each item. ■ Count out up to six objects from a larger group. ■ Count actions or objects that cannot be moved. ■ Begin to count beyond 10.	■ The personal numbers that children refer to, such as their age, house number, telephone number or the number of people in their family. ■ Instances of children counting an irregular arrangement of up to ten objects.	■ Encourage estimation, for example, estimate how many sandwiches to make for the picnic. ■ Encourage use of mathematical language, for example, number names to ten: "Have you got enough to give me three?".	■ Provide collections of interesting things for children to sort, order, count and label in their play. ■ Display numerals in purposeful contexts, for example, a sign showing how many children can play on a number track. ■ Use tactile numeral cards made from sandpaper, velvet or string.

00012-2007BKT-EN
© Crown copyright 2007

Numbers as Labels and for Counting

	Development matters	Look, listen and note	Effective practice	Planning and resourcing
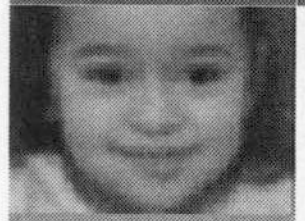 40-60+ months	■ Begin to represent numbers using fingers, marks on paper or pictures. ■ Select the correct numeral to represent 1 to 5, then 1 to 9 objects. ■ Recognise numerals 1 to 5. ■ Count an irregular arrangement of up to ten objects. ■ Estimate how many objects they can see and check by counting them. ■ Count aloud in ones, twos, fives or tens. ■ Know that numbers identify how many objects are in a set. ■ Use ordinal numbers in different contexts. ■ Match then compare the number of objects in two sets.	■ Children's methods of counting out up to six objects from a larger group, for example, when children do a jigsaw together and share out the pieces, counting to check everyone has the same number. ■ How children begin to represent numbers using fingers, marks on paper or pictures. ■ Children's recognition of numerals. ■ How children use their developing understanding of maths to solve mathematical problems, for example, solving a debate about which of two piles of pebbles has more in it.	■ Ensure that children are involved in making displays, for example, making their own pictograms of lunch choices. Develop this as a 3D representation using bricks and discuss the most popular choices. ■ Add numerals to all areas of the curriculum, for example, to a display of a favourite story, such as 'The Three Billy Goats Gruff'. ■ Make books about numbers that have meaning for the child such as favourite numbers, birth dates or telephone numbers. ■ Use rhymes, songs and stories involving counting on and counting back in ones, twos, fives and tens. ■ Emphasise the empty set and introduce the concept of nothing or zero.	■ Create opportunities for children to experiment with a number of objects, the written numeral and the written number. Develop this through matching activities with a range of numbers, numerals and a selection of objects. ■ Use a 100 square to show number patterns. ■ Make number games readily available and teach children how to use them. ■ Display interesting books about number. ■ Play games such as hide and seek that involve counting. ■ Use rhymes, songs and stories involving counting on and counting back.
Early learning goals	■ **Say and use number names in order in familiar contexts.** ■ **Count reliably up to ten everyday objects.** ■ **Recognise numerals 1 to 9.** ■ **Use developing mathematical ideas and methods to solve practical problems.**			

00012-2007BKT-EN
© Crown copyright 2007

Calculating

	Development matters	Look, listen and note	Effective practice	Planning and resourcing
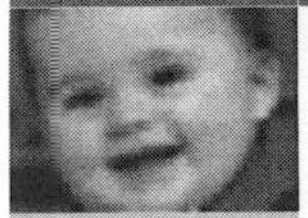 Birth-11 months	■ Are logical thinkers from birth.	■ How they enjoy games when objects are shown, then hidden away.	■ Talk to babies about what you are doing and what is happening.	■ Let babies see and hear the sequence of actions you go through as you carry out familiar routines.
 8-20 months	■ Have some understanding that things exist, even when out of sight. ■ Are alert to and investigate things that challenge their expectations.	■ Babies' interest in looking for things that disappear from sight. ■ Babies' persistence in trying to achieve something they have managed before, such as lifting the lid on a box that has previously popped open.	■ Play games such as peek-a-boo or comment when a puppet pops out of a sock. ■ Talk to babies about puzzles they encounter such as how to get their sock back from where it has fallen, asking whether they can do it or if they might need help.	■ Provide lift-the-flap books to show something hidden from view. ■ Provide a variety of interesting displays for babies to see when they are looking around them, looking up at the ceiling or peering into a corner.
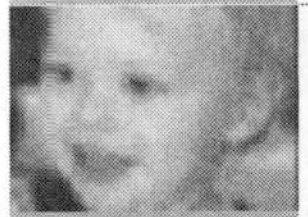 16-26 months	■ Are learning to classify by organising and arranging toys with increasing intent. ■ Categorise objects according to their properties.	■ Occasions when young children gather things together, such as collecting several books or lining up cars. ■ Children's interest in helping when an adult sorts the fruit at snack time, for example, putting all the apples together.	■ Foster children's ability to classify and compare amounts. ■ Use 'tidy up time' to promote logic and reasoning about where things fit in or are kept.	■ Encourage children, when helping with domestic tasks, to put all the pieces of apple on one dish and all the pieces of celery on another for snacks. ■ Use pictures or shapes of objects to indicate where things are kept and encourage children to work out where things belong.
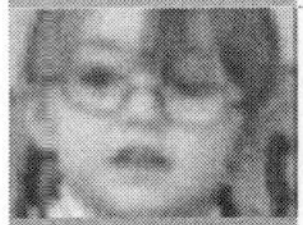 22-36 months	■ Begin to make comparisons between quantities. ■ Know that a group of things changes in quantity when something is added or taken away.	■ The deductions children make about whether there is some juice left, or whether it is 'all gone'. ■ Children's attempts at estimation and their efforts to check by counting.	■ Help children to organise their ideas by talking to them about what they are doing. ■ Play games which relate to number order, addition and subtraction, such as hopscotch and skittles.	■ Provide props for children to act out counting songs and rhymes. ■ Provide games and equipment that offer opportunities for counting, such as skittles.

Problem Solving, Reasoning and Numeracy

The Early Years Foundation Stage
Practice Guidance

00012-2007BKT-EN
© Crown copyright 2007

Calculating

	Development matters	Look, listen and note	Effective practice	Planning and resourcing
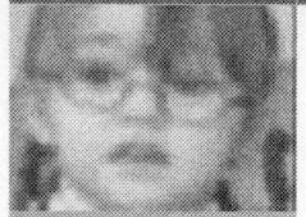 22-36 months		■ How children engage with simple counting songs and games, for example, 'Five Currant Buns'. ■ When children begin to know about dividing things equally into two groups.	■ Sing counting songs and rhymes which help to develop children's understanding of number, such as 'Two Little Dickie Birds'.	■ Plan to incorporate a mathematical component in areas such as the sand, water or other play areas.
 30-50 months	■ Compare two groups of objects, saying when they have the same number. ■ Show an interest in number problems. ■ Separate a group of three or four objects in different ways, beginning to recognise that the total is still the same.	■ The strategies children use that show they are working out whether a group of objects is the same or different. ■ How children work out a solution to a simple problem by using fingers or counting aloud.	■ Demonstrate language such as 'same as', 'less' or 'fewer'. ■ As you read number stories or rhymes, ask, for example, "How many will there be in the pool when one more frog jumps in?". ■ Use pictures and objects to illustrate counting songs, rhymes and number stories. This will benefit all children and be particularly supportive to children learning English as an additional language.	■ Create opportunities for children to separate objects into unequal groups as well as equal groups. ■ Provide story props that children can use in their play, for example, varieties of fruit and several baskets like Handa's in the story *Handa's Surprise* by Eileen Browne.
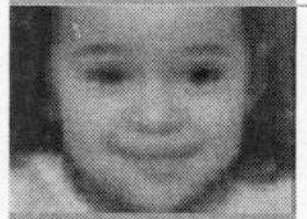 40-60+ months	■ Find the total number of items in two groups by counting all of them. ■ Use own methods to work through a problem. ■ Say the number that is one more than a given number. ■ Select two groups of objects to make a given total of objects. ■ Count repeated groups of the same size.	■ Methods children use to answer a problem they have posed, for example, "Get one more, and then we will both have two". ■ How children find the sum of two numbers. ■ The variety in responses when children work out a calculation. ■ The ways children count repeated groups of the same size, for example, counting the number of socks in five pairs.	■ Show interest in how children solve problems and value their different solutions. ■ Make sure children are secure about the order of numbers before asking what comes after or before each number. ■ Discuss with children how problems relate to others they have met, and their different solutions.	■ Encourage children to record what they have done, for example, by drawing or tallying. ■ Use number staircases to show a starting point and how you arrive at another point when something is added or taken away. ■ Provide a wide range of number resources and encourage children to be creative in thinking up problems and solutions in all areas of learning.

© Crown copyright 2007

Calculating

	Development matters	Look, listen and note	Effective practice	Planning and resourcing
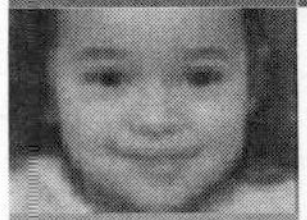 40-60+ months Early learning goals	■ Share objects into equal groups and count how many in each group. ■ **In practical activities and discussion, begin to use the vocabulary involved in adding and subtracting.** ■ **Use language such as 'more' or 'less' to compare two numbers.** ■ **Find one more or one less than a number from one to ten.** ■ **Begin to relate addition to combining two groups of objects and subtraction to 'taking away'.**	■ How children share objects, for example, sharing eight crayons equally among four children and knowing that each child has two crayons. ■ Children working out what remains if something is taken away.	■ Encourage children to make up their own story problems for other children to solve. ■ Encourage children to extend problems, for example, "Suppose there were three people to share the bricks between instead of two". ■ Use mathematical vocabulary and demonstrate methods of recording, using standard notation where appropriate. ■ Give children learning English as an additional language opportunities to work in their home language to ensure accurate understanding of concepts.	■ Encourage children to make links between cardinal numbers (quantity) and ordinal numbers (position). ■ Make number lines available for reference and encourage children to use them in their own play. ■ Help children to understand that five fingers on each hand make a total of ten fingers altogether, or that two rows of three eggs in the box make six eggs altogether.

00012-2007BKT-EN
© Crown copyright 2007

Problem Solving, Reasoning and Numeracy

Shape, Space and Measures

	Development matters	Look, listen and note	Effective practice	Planning and resourcing
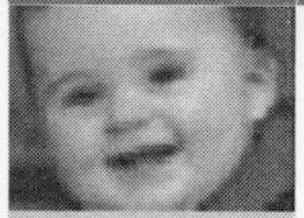 Birth-11 months	■ Develop an awareness of shape, form and texture as they encounter people and things in their environment.	■ Babies' explorations of space through their movements, for example, by rolling from back to front. ■ How babies begin to be aware of distance, as they grasp and reach out.	■ Talk to babies about things that interest them, describing particular features, such as the patterns formed when sunlight filters through the leaves on to the ground.	■ Display things to look at that encourage their interest in movement, such as a spiral.
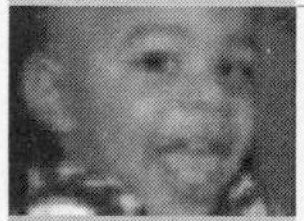 8-20 months	■ Find out what toys are like and can do through handling objects. ■ Recognise big things and small things in meaningful contexts.	■ Instances of babies' investigation of objects and space such as looking for hidden objects or putting things in and taking them out of containers. ■ How they hold out their arms wide to gather up a big teddy and bring hands together to pick up a small ball.	■ Play games that involve curling and stretching, popping up and bobbing down. ■ Encourage babies' explorations of the characteristics of objects, for example, by rolling a ball to them. ■ Talk about what objects are like and how objects, such as a sponge, can change their shape by being squeezed or stretched.	■ Provide a range of objects of various textures and weights in treasure baskets to excite and encourage babies' interests. ■ Look at books showing objects such as a big truck and a little truck; or a big cat and a small kitten. ■ Use story props to support all children and particularly those learning English as an additional language.
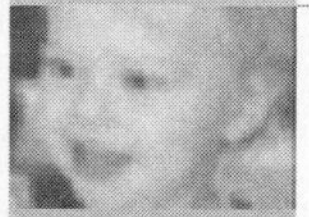 16-26 months	■ Attempt, sometimes successfully, to fit shapes into spaces on inset boards or jigsaw puzzles. ■ Use blocks to create their own simple structures and arrangements. ■ Enjoy filling and emptying containers.	■ Children's strategies as they select and fit shapes in a puzzle or balance blocks on one another. ■ Children's interest in and familiarity with the shapes of everyday objects.	■ Talk to children, as they play with water or sand, to encourage them to think about when something is full, empty or holds more. ■ Help young children to create different arrangements in the layout of road and rail tracks. ■ Highlight patterns in daily activities and routines. ■ Help children to touch, see and feel shape through art, music and dance.	■ Provide different sizes and shapes of containers in water play, so that children can experiment with quantities and measures. ■ Offer a range of puzzles with large pieces and knobs or handles to support success in fitting shapes into spaces.

00012-2007BKT-EN © Crown copyright 2007

Shape, Space and Measures

	Development matters	Look, listen and note	Effective practice	Planning and resourcing
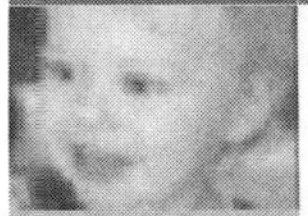 16-26 months			■ Encourage children to create their own patterns in art, music and dance.	
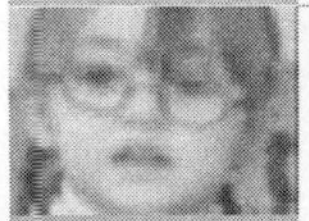 22-36 months	■ Notice simple shapes and patterns in pictures. ■ Begin to categorise objects according to properties such as shape or size. ■ Are beginning to understand variations in size.	■ Observations made by children relating to shapes or patterns. ■ When children begin to use some words that describe time, amount and size, for example, when children say things like "me bigger" to a smaller friend.	■ Talk about and help children to recognise patterns. ■ Draw children's attention to the pattern of square/oblong/square which emerges as you fold or unfold a tablecloth or napkin. ■ Be consistent in your use of vocabulary for weight and mass. ■ Sort coins on play trays into interesting arrangements and shapes; sort them into bags, purses and containers. ■ Measure for a purpose, such as finding out whether a teddy will fit in a bed.	■ Collect pictures that illustrate the use of shapes and patterns from a variety of cultures, for example, Arabic designs. ■ Provide opportunities for children to measure time (sand timer), weight (balances) and measure (non-standard units). ■ Vary the use of volume and capacity equipment in the sand, water and other play areas to maintain interest.
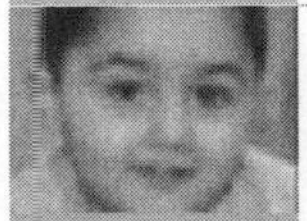 30-50 months	■ Show an interest in shape and space by playing with shapes or making arrangements with objects. ■ Show awareness of similarities in shapes in the environment. ■ Observe and use positional language. ■ Are beginning to understand 'bigger than' and 'enough'.	■ Children's skills in matching shapes and in completing puzzles. ■ Children's recognition of shapes in the environment, for example, that a roof has a triangle at one end. ■ Children's ideas about why something is the correct size, for example, a piece of paper to wrap a gift.	■ Demonstrate the language for shape, position and measures in discussions, for example, 'ball shape', 'box shape', 'in', 'on', 'inside', 'under', 'longer', 'shorter', 'heavy', 'light', 'full' and 'empty'. Find out and use equivalent terms for these measures in home languages. ■ Encourage children to talk about the shapes they see and use and how they are arranged.	■ Have large and small blocks and boxes available for construction both indoors and outdoors. ■ Play games involving children positioning themselves inside, behind, on top and so on. ■ Provide rich and varied opportunities for comparing length, weight and time.

© Crown copyright 2007

Shape, Space and Measures

	Development matters	Look, listen and note	Effective practice	Planning and resourcing
 30-50 months	■ Show interest in shape by sustained construction activity or by talking about shapes or arrangements. ■ Use shapes appropriately for tasks. ■ Begin to talk about the shapes of everyday objects.	■ How children apply their understanding of shape and space, for example, knowing they need one flat shape and one that is 'pointy'. ■ Children's use of mathematical names for shapes, such as 'circle' and 'triangle'.	■ Value children's constructions by helping to display them or take photographs of them. ■ Organise the environment to foster shape matching, for example, pictures of different bricks on containers to show where they are kept.	■ Use stories such as *Rosie's Walk* by Pat Hutchins to talk about distance and stimulate discussion about non-standard units and the need for standard units. ■ Show pictures that have symmetry or pattern and talk to children about them.
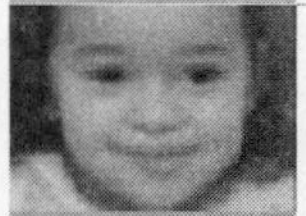 40-60+ months	■ Show curiosity about and observation of shapes by talking about how they are the same or different. ■ Match some shapes by recognising similarities and orientation. ■ Begin to use mathematical names for 'solid' 3D shapes and 'flat' 2D shapes, and mathematical terms to describe shapes. ■ Select a particular named shape. ■ Show awareness of symmetry. ■ Find items from positional or directional clues. ■ Order two or three items by length or height. ■ Order two items by weight or capacity. ■ Match sets of objects to numerals that represent the number of objects.	■ Children's interest in and observation of shapes, such as how some are the same or different. ■ How children match some shapes by recognising similarities and orientation, for example, Stevie looked at a rhomboid, saying, "It looks like a boat". Picking up a triangle, she says, "This one's different… it's only got three points". ■ How children select a named shape for a particular purpose. ■ Children's use of positional or directional clues, for example, "We had to come round the park and past the shops". ■ Children's ordering of two items by length or height, for example, comparing the length of zips on coats: "Too long for your coat".	■ Ask 'silly' questions, for example, show a tiny box and ask if there is a bicycle in it. ■ Play peek-a-boo, revealing shapes a little at a time and at different angles, asking children to say what they think the shape is, what else it could be or what it could not be. ■ Make books about shape, time and measure: shapes found in the environment; long and short things; things of a specific length; and ones about patterns, or comparing things that are heavier or lighter. ■ Be a robot and ask children to give you instructions to get to somewhere. Let them have a turn at being the robot for you to instruct.	■ Provide a range of boxes and materials for models and constructions such as 'dens', indoors and outdoors. ■ Provide examples of the same shape in different sizes. ■ Have areas where children can explore the properties of objects and where they can weigh and measure, such as a cookery station or a building area. ■ Plan opportunities for children to describe and compare shapes, measures and distance. ■ Provide materials and resources for children to observe and describe patterns in the indoor and outdoor environment and in daily routines, orally, in pictures or using objects. ■ Provide a range of natural materials for children to arrange, compare and order.

00012-2007BKT-EN
© Crown copyright 2007

Shape, Space and Measures

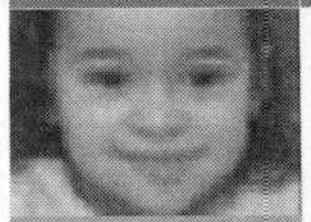

	Development matters	Look, listen and note	Effective practice	Planning and resourcing
40-60+ months	■ Sort familiar objects to identify their similarities and differences, making choices and justifying decisions. ■ Describe solutions to practical problems, drawing on experience, talking about own ideas, methods and choices. ■ Use familiar objects and common shapes to create and recreate patterns and build models. ■ Use everyday language related to time; order and sequence familiar events, and measure short periods of time with a non-standard unit, for example, with a sand timer. ■ Count how many objects share a particular property, presenting results using pictures, drawings or numerals.	■ Children's identification of a mathematical problem involving shape, space or measures and the ways they solve them. ■ Children's use of positional language, for example, "I'm near the end of the path". ■ Words children use to describe comparisons and measures such as 'greater', 'smaller', 'heavier' or 'lighter'.	■ Introduce children to the use of mathematical names for 'solid' 3D shapes and 'flat' 2D shapes, and the mathematical terms to describe shapes. ■ Ensure children use everyday words to describe position, for example, when following pathways or playing with outdoor apparatus.	
Early learning goals	■ **Use language such as 'greater', 'smaller', 'heavier' or 'lighter' to compare quantities.** ■ **Talk about, recognise and recreate simple patterns.** ■ **Use language such as 'circle' or 'bigger' to describe the shape and size of solids and flat shapes.** ■ **Use everyday words to describe position.**			

Problem Solving, Reasoning and Numeracy

00012-2007BKT-EN
© Crown copyright 2007

Shape, Space and Measures

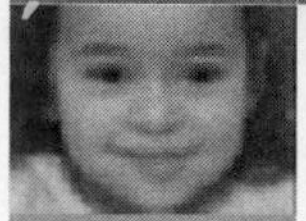

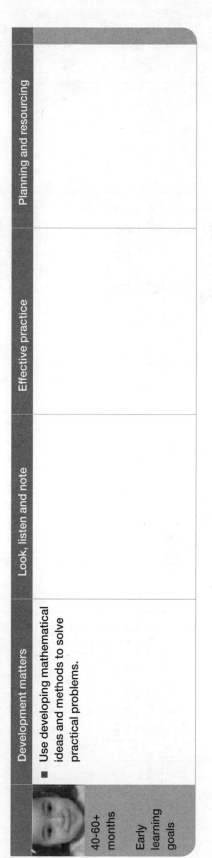

	Development matters	Look, listen and note	Effective practice	Planning and resourcing
40-60+ months Early learning goals	■ Use developing mathematical ideas and methods to solve practical problems.			

00012-2007BKT-EN © Crown copyright 2007

Assessment of learning will be recorded through the use of the Early Years Foundation stage profile. The following example is taken from the assessment profile of a child who moved through the (old) Foundation Stage Curriculum, before the EYFS. Although headings may now differ slightly, it will give you an idea of how an assessment profile might be set out.

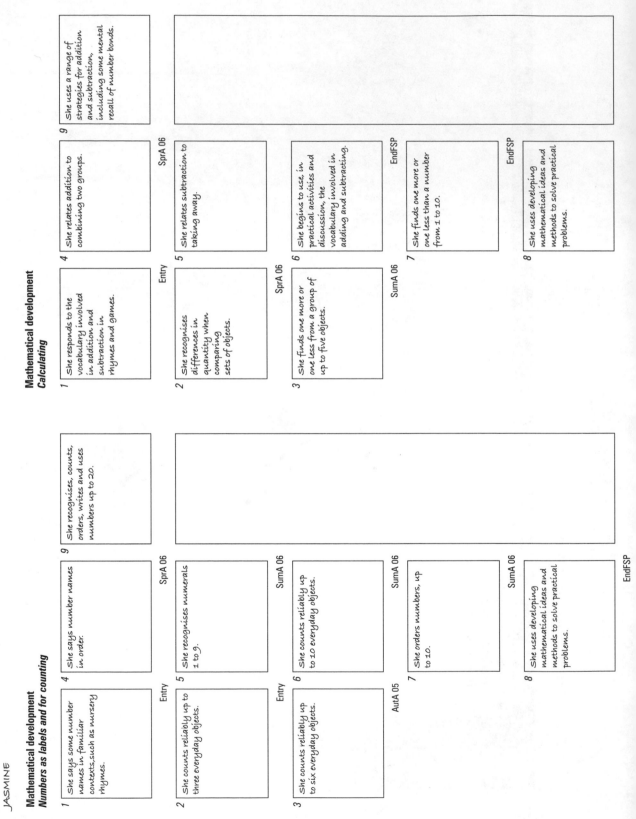

Fig 17.5 An example of a child's assessment profile for mathematical development

JASMINE

Mathematical development
Numbers as labels and for counting

1 She says some number names in familiar contexts,such as nursery rhymes. — Entry

2 She counts reliably up to three everyday objects. — Entry

3 She counts reliably up to six everyday objects. — AutA 05

4 She says number names in order. — SprA 06

5 She recognises numerals 1 to 9. — SumA 06

6 She counts reliably up to 10 everyday objects. — SumA 06

7 She orders numbers, up to 10. — SumA 06

8 She uses developing mathematical ideas and methods to solve practical problems. — EndFSP

9 She recognises, counts, orders, writes and uses numbers up to 20.

Mathematical development
Calculating

1 She responds to the vocabulary involved in addition and subtraction in rhymes and games. — Entry

2 She recognises differences in quantity when comparing sets of objects. — SprA 06

3 She finds one more or one less from a group of up to five objects. — SumA 06

4 She relates addition to combining two groups. — SprA 06

5 She relates subtraction to taking away.

6 She begins to use, in practical activities and discussion, the vocabulary involved in adding and subtracting. — EndFSP

7 She finds one more or one less than a number from 1 to 10. — EndFSP

8 She uses developing mathematical ideas and methods to solve practical problems.

9 She uses a range of strategies for addition and subtraction, including some mental recall of number bonds.

Fig 17.5 An example of a child's assessment profile for mathematical development

JASMINE

Mathematical development
Shape, Space, Measures

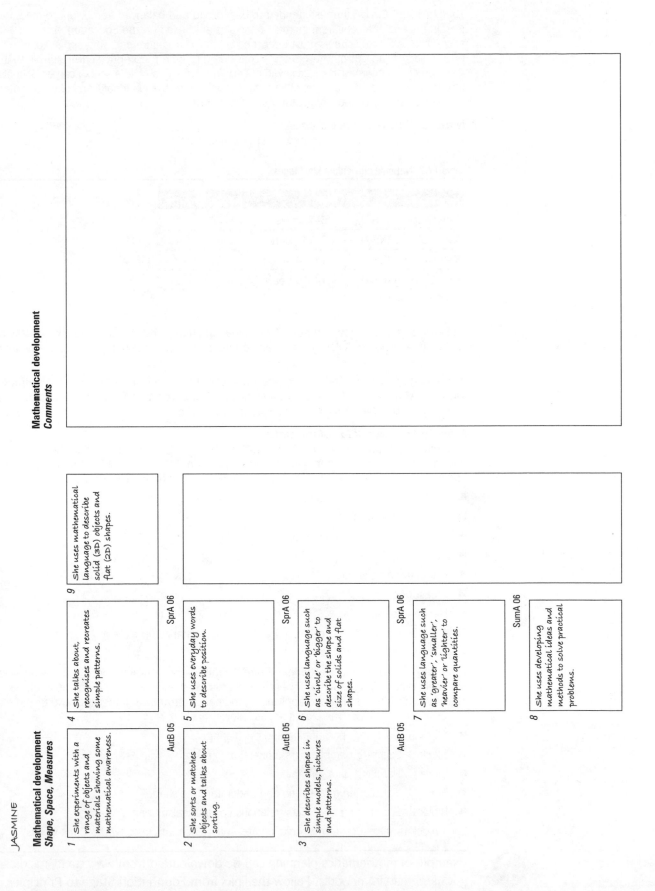

1 She experiments with a range of objects and materials showing some mathematical awareness.

AutB 05

2 She sorts or matches objects and talks about sorting.

AutB 05

3 She describes shapes in simple models, pictures and patterns.

AutB 05

4 She talks about, recognises and recreates simple patterns.

SprA 06

5 She uses everyday words to describe position.

SprA 06

6 She uses language such as 'circle' or 'bigger' to describe the shape and size of solids and flat shapes.

SprA 06

7 She uses language such as 'greater', 'smaller', 'heavier' or 'lighter' to compare quantities.

SumA 06

8 She uses developing mathematical ideas and methods to solve practical problems.

9 She uses mathematical language to describe solid (3D) objects and flat (2D) shapes.

Mathematical development
Comments

National Curriculum

The **National Curriculum** is intended to be a broad and balanced framework to meet the learning needs of all children; its main principles are based on the Education Acts of 1988 and 1996. All state schools must offer the National Curriculum and although schools in the private sector can opt out, few do. It is considered to be a prescriptive curriculum in that it gives precise outcomes to be achieved at certain stages in a child's school career. Schools are also free to provide extra areas of learning in addition to the National Curriculum to reflect the particular needs and circumstances of the setting.

National Curriculum key stages

The National Curriculum is divided into key stages (Table 17.2).

Table 17.2 National curriculum key stages

Key stage	Age	Year groups
Key Stage 1 (KS1)	5–7 years	1–2
Key Stage 2 (KS2)	7–11 years	3–6
Key Stage 3 (KS3)	11–14 years	7–9
Key Stage 4 (KS4)	14–16 years	10–11

QCA (2000), pages 74–81

The key stage that follows on from the Foundation Stage is Key Stage 1. You will usually work with children who are following this stage during placement experience in a Year 1 or Year 2 class.

At the end of each key stage, there are a number of tests known as **Standard Attainment Tasks (SATs)**, which all children must complete. The purpose of SATs is to monitor each individual child's performance as they progress through school.

Primary Framework for Mathematics

The **Primary Framework for Mathematics** sets out core learning aims for both literacy and mathematics for children in each year group, from Foundation Stage through to Year 6/7. There are seven strands to the Primary Framework for mathematics. They are:

- Using and applying mathematics
- Counting and understanding number
- Knowing and using number facts
- Calculating
- Understanding shape
- Measuring
- Handling data.

Table 17.3 sets out the core learning aims for mathematics up to Year 2.

Planning

Planning for mathematics within the Primary Framework is through organising learning into five main blocks. The structure for each year group is the same. Each block incorporates objectives from the 'Using and applying mathematics' strand, together with two or three of the other core strands. The blocks are as follows:

- Block A: Counting, partitioning and calculating
- Block B: Securing number facts, understanding shape
- Block C: Handling data and measures
- Block D: Calculating, measuring and understanding shape
- Block E: Securing number facts, relationships and calculating.

Each block is made up of three units and teaching each unit lasts two to three weeks.

Example of mathematics planning can be downloaded from www.standards.dfes.gov.uk/primaryframeworks. **Follow the links from Foundation Stage to Principles of planning.**

Table 17.3 Core learning in mathematics by year

Foundation Stage Most children learn to:			
Using and applying mathematics	**Counting and understanding number**	**Knowing and using number facts**	**Calculating**
Use developing mathematical ideas and methods to solve practical problems Match sets of objects to numerals that represent the number of objects Sort objects, making choices and justifying decisions **Talk about, recognise and recreate simple patterns** Describe solutions to practical problems, drawing on experience, talking about their own ideas, methods and choices	**Say and use number names in order in familiar contexts** Know that numbers identify how many objects are in a set **Count reliably up to 10 everyday objects** Estimate how many objects they can see and check by counting Count aloud in ones, twos, fives or tens **Use language such as 'more' or 'less' to compare two numbers** Use ordinal numbers in different contexts **Recognise numerals 1 to 9**	Observe number relationships and patterns in the environment and use these to derive facts **Find out more or one less than a number from 1 to 10** Select two groups of objects to make a given total of objects	**Begin to relate addition to combining two groups of objects and subtraction to 'taking away'** **In practical activities and discussion begin to use the vocabulary involved in adding and subtracting** Count repeated groups of the same size Share objects into equal groups and count how many in each group

Understanding shape	**Measuring**	**Handling data**
Use familiar objects and common shapes to create and recreate patterns and build models **Use language such as 'circle' or 'bigger' to describe the shape and size of solids and flat shapes** **Use everyday words to describe position**	**Use language such as 'greater', 'smaller', 'heavier' or 'lighter' to compare quantities** Use everyday language related to time; order and sequence familiar events and measure short periods of time	Sort familiar objects to identify their similarities and differences Count how many objects share a particular property, presenting results using pictures, drawings or numerals

All statements and wording in bold refer to the Early Learning Goals.

Year 1 Most children learn to:			
Using and applying mathematics	**Counting and understanding number**	**Knowing and using number facts**	**Calculating**
Solve problems involving counting, adding, subtracting, doubling or halving in the context of numbers, measures or money, for example to 'pay' and 'give change' Describe a puzzle or problem using numbers, practical materials and diagrams; use these to solve the problem and set the solution in the original context	Count reliably at least 20 objects, recognising that when rearranged the number of objects stays the same; estimate a number of objects that can be checked by counting Compare and order number, using the related vocabulary; use the equals (=) sign	**Derive and recall all pairs of numbers with a total of 10 and addition facts for total to at least 5; work out the corresponding subtraction facts** Count on or back in ones, twos, fives and tens and use this knowledge to derive the multiples of 2, 5 and 10 to the tenth multiple	Relate addition to counting on; recognise that addition can be done in any order; use practical and informal written methods to support the addition of a one-digit number or a multiple of 10 to a one-digit or two-digit number

Year 1 Most children learn to:			
Using and applying mathematics	**Counting and understanding number**	**Knowing and using number facts**	**Calculating**
Answer a question by selecting and using suitable equipment, and sorting information, shapes or objects; display results using tables and pictures Describe simple patterns and relationships involving numbers or shapes; decide whether examples satisfy given conditions Describe ways of solving puzzles and problems, explaining choices and decisions orally or using pictures	**Read and write numerals from 0 to 20, then beyond; use knowledge of place value to position these numbers on a number track and number line** Say the number that is 1 more or less than any given number, and 10 more or less for multiples of 10 Use the vocabulary of halves and quarters in context	Recall the doubles of all numbers to at least 10	Understand subtraction as 'take away' and find a 'difference' by counting up; use practical and informal written methods to support the subtraction of a one-digit number from a one-digit or two-digit number and a multiple of 10 from a two-digit number **Use the vocabulary related to addition and subtraction and symbols to describe and record addition and subtraction number sentences** Solve practical problems that involve combining groups of 2, 5 or 10, or sharing into equal groups

Understanding shape	Measuring	Handling data
Visualise and name common 2-D shapes and 3-D solids and describe their features; use them to make patterns, pictures and models Identify objects that turn about a point (e.g. scissors) or about a line (e.g. a door); recognise and make whole, half and quarter turns Visualise and use everyday language to describe the position of objects and direction and distance when moving them, for example when placing or moving objects on a game board	**Estimate, measure, weigh and compare objects, choosing and using suitable uniform non-standard or standard units and measuring instruments (e.g. a lever balance, metre stick or measuring jug)** Use vocabulary related to time; order days of the week and months; read the time to the hour and half hour	**Answer a question by recording information in lists and tables; present outcomes using practical resources, pictures, block graphs or pictograms** Use diagrams to sort objects into groups according to a given criterion; suggest a different criterion for grouping the same objects

Key objectives are in bold.

Year 2 Most children learn to:			
Using and applying mathematics	**Counting and understanding number**	**Knowing and using number facts**	**Calculating**
Solve problems involving addition, subtraction, multiplication or division in contexts of numbers, measures or pounds and pence	Read and write two-digit and three-digit numbers in figures and words: describe and extend number sequences and recognise odd and even numbers	**Derive and recall all addition and subtraction facts for each number to at least 10, all pairs with totals to 20 and all pairs of multiples of 10 with totals up to 100**	**Add or subtract mentally a one-digit number or a multiple of 10 to or from any two-digit number; use practical and informal written methods to add and subtract two-digit numbers**

Year 2			
Most children learn to:			
Using and applying mathematics	**Counting and understanding number**	**Knowing and using number facts**	**Calculating**
Identify and record the information or calculation needed to solve a puzzle or problem; carry out the steps or calculations and check the solution in the context of the problem Follow a line of enquiry; answer questions by choosing and using suitable equipment and selecting, organising and presenting information in lists, tables and simple diagrams Describe patterns and relationships involving numbers or shapes, make predictions and test these with examples Present solutions to puzzles and problems in an organised way; explain decisions, methods and results in pictorial, spoken or written form, using mathematical language and number sentences	**Count up to 100 objects by grouping them and counting in tens, fives or twos; explain what each digit in a two-digit number represents, including numbers where 0 is a place holder; partition two-digit numbers in different ways, including into multiples of 10 and 1** Order two-digit numbers and position them in a number line; use the greater than (>) and less than (<) signs Estimate a number of objects; round two-digit numbers to the nearest 10 Find one half, one quarter and three quarters of shapes and sets of objects	Understand that halving is the inverse of doubling and derive and recall doubles of all numbers to 20, and the corresponding halves Derive and recall multiplication facts for the 2, 5 and 10 times-tables and the related division facts; recognise multiples of 2, 5 and 10 Use knowledge of number facts and operations to estimate and check answers to calculations	Understand that subtraction is the inverse of addition and vice-versa; use this to derive and record related addition and subtraction number sentences Represent repeated addition and arrays as multiplication, and sharing and repeated subtraction (grouping) as division; use practical and informal written methods and related vocabulary to support multiplication and division, including calculations with remainders **Use the symbols +, −, ×, ÷ and = to record and interpret number sentences involving all four operations; calculate the value of an unknown in a number sentence (e.g. □ ÷ 2 = 6, 30 − □ =24)**

Understanding shape	**Measuring**	**Handling data**
Visualise common 2-D shapes and 3-D solids; identify shapes from pictures of them in different positions and orientations; sort, make and describe shapes, referring to their properties Identify reflective symmetry in patterns and 2-D shapes and draw lines of symmetry in shapes Follow and give instructions involving position, direction and movement Recognise and use whole, half and quarter turns, both clockwise and anticlockwise; know that a right angle represents a quarter turn	Estimate, compare and measure lengths, weights and capacities, choosing and using standard units (m, cm, kg, litre) and suitable measuring instruments Read the numbered divisions on a scale, and interpret the divisions between them (e.g. on a scale from 0 to 25 with intervals of 1 shown but only the divisions 0, 5, 10, 15 and 20 numbered); use a ruler to draw and measure lines to the nearest centimetre **Use units of time (seconds, minutes, hours, days) and know the relationships between them; read the time to the quarter hour; identify time intervals including those that cross the hour**	Answer a question by collecting and recording data in lists and tables; represent the data as block graphs or pictograms to show results; use ICT to organise and present data **Use lists, tables and diagrams to sort objects; explain choices using appropriate language, including 'not'**

Key objectives are in bold.

DfES (2006), pages 70–5

The plans provided on the DfES website all follow the same format (see the example below). The format is as follows:

- What we want the children to learn (development matters)
- Related Early Learning Goals (showing the interdependency of all six areas of learning)
- Possible contexts (contexts for the learning to take place)
- Example of adult-led activities (an example learning context with ideas for the role of the adult)
- Opportunities for children to explore and apply (learning contexts for children's spontaneous play and ideas for the role of the adult)

- Look, listen and note (examples to support observation for assessment)
- Assessment opportunities (examples to support observation for assessment)
- Related Scale Points (Foundation Stage Profile scale points that these learning contexts might support).

This is an example of mathematics planning and resourcing:

What we want the children to learn (Development matters)

(*The objectives in italics refer to Early Learning Goals*)

Mathematics objectives

- Estimate how many objects they can see and check by counting
- *Count reliably up to 10 everyday objects*

Using and applying mathematics

- *Use developing mathematical ideas and methods to solve practical problems*

Related Early Learning Goals

- Respond in a variety of ways to what they see, hear, smell, touch and feel (CD)

Possible contexts

- Use collections of rhymes, songs, storybooks and props.
- Provide a variety of objects and collections for children to sort, match and incorporate into play.
- Use clipboards inside and outside in the learning environment and encourage children's mark making of numbers of objects.
- Use washing lines to match objects, and encourage children to find collections of objects to set their own challenges.
- Engage in games and small world play throughout the day and challenge children to estimate quantities and check the number by counting, for example the number of children on the climbing frame, the number of apples in the fruit box, the number of pens in the pot.
- Develop interactive displays of objects with number cards for matching, moving and reordering.
- When tidying up, pay attention to numbers of objects, for example cutlery, construction equipment and garden tools.

Example of adult-led activity

Context: Using a storybook

Read the story with the children, for example *Handa's Surprise*. Have a basket of the fruit, count them in the basket and illustrate the story as each one is taken.

Provide opportunities for the children to retell the story, for example children telling each other from the book, using toy animals and fruit to act out the story or scan the pages of the story into interactive whiteboard software or into PowerPoint as an electronic book.

Tell the children they can use the fruit to make fruit kebabs. (There are eight types of fruits and animals in *Handa's Surprise*. Add two to reinforce counting up to 10.) Say that the kebabs can have one piece of each kind of fruit. If they don't like some of the types of fruit, they can swap them for ones they do like but they mustn't have more than the number of types of fruit available (10). Encourage their methods in problem solving to work out how many pieces of each fruit they are putting on their kebab when they are leaving some kinds out.

Welcome the children's different ways of recording their recipes for their own kebabs. Share with them how they have represented their different types of fruit and how many they had of each. Count together and see that each kebab was made up of 10 pieces of fruit.

Make a pictogram (could use '2Count' from the *2Simple Infant Video Toolbox*) to find out which was the favourite and which was the least favourite fruit.

Adult role

- Model counting in everyday experiences.
- Use a puppet to count wrongly and encourage the children to correct.

- Demonstrate counting accurately during group activities, e.g. 'How many cups do we need? 1, 2, 3 ...'
- Scaffold children's learning by helping them to count accurately in their own play.
- Participate in all areas of children's experience and model counting for a purpose, e.g. 'How many wheels are we going to need on this car?'
- Encourage children to make guesses about numbers and then check, e.g. 'Let's guess how many objects there are in this box.'

Opportunities for children to explore and apply

- In construction and small world play, provide plans for models using photographs or children's own models showing number of objects, for example 4 wheels or 10 pieces of straight track.
- Use photographs of numbers of objects and their numerals in the learning environment for children to collect and match when tidying, for example numbers of items of cutlery, cups or plates or construction tools.
- Provide clipboards inside and outside in the learning environment and model uses for shopping lists, recording measurements of, for example, sunflowers growing, turn taking and children waiting, planning picnics/parties, numbers of skips or jumps or other achievements.
- Provide a collection of counting rhymes, songs and storybooks and tapes or CD-ROMs with props. Encourage children to make their own. Model uses and encourage children to share in similar ways with each other.
- Use interactive whiteboard software to recreate stories using numbers of objects, for example 'Goldilocks and the three bears'.
- Make a wide variety of collections available for children to sort, match and incorporate into play, and to hide and find.
- Model games for them, for example dropping objects into a tin and guessing their number by listening to the sounds or asking how many of each object will fit into a matchbox.
- Use dice and domino numbers to help with the visual pattern of numbers. Children begin, for example, to see patterns of four as two twos, and six as two threes.

Adult role

- Model counting in everyday experiences.
- Use a silly puppet to count wrongly and encourage the children to correct.
- Demonstrate counting accurately.
- Scaffold children's learning by helping them to count accurately.
- Participate in all areas of children's experience and model counting for a purpose. For example; how many wheels are we going to need on this car?
- Encourage children to make guesses about numbers and then check. For example; let's guess how many objects there are in this box.

Look, listen and note

- Observe how children count an irregular arrangement of up to 10 objects. For example; as Zara dropped pennies noisily into the tin, she said 'Listen for how many.'
- Note how children count out up to six objects from a larger group, for example, when a group of children were doing a jigsaw together, they shared out the pieces and counted to check everyone has the same number.
- Notice how children represent numbers using fingers, marks on paper or pictures. For example; Kim and Edward made a number track to 10. They then added numbers to 17 when they realised they could throw the beanbag further than they had expected.

Assessment opportunities

- Encourage children to join in rhymes and songs and notice how they are able to count, for example, five little ducks, ten green bottles, five little speckled frogs, five currant buns. Use a puppet to 'speak' and get numbers wrong, encouraging children to correct the puppet.

- Use collections of objects and everyday materials to count, for example when tidying things back into containers or baskets.

Related Scale Points

NLC 5, 6, 7

www.standards.dfes.gov.uk/primaryframeworks

Link

Refer to page 168 for an example of a completed Foundation Stage profile.

See the example planning sheets in Figure 17.6.

Fig 17.6 Examples of planning sheets: (a) planning a unit in mathematics; (b) teaching and learning focus chart; (c) medium-term plan

Planning a Unit in mathematics

Unit:		Curriculum links:
Learning objectives and *Children's learning outcomes* Most children will learn to:	Vocabulary	Building on prior learning and intervention materials Check that children can already:

Teaching and learning focus	Lessons	Learning focus, teaching notes and resources	**Assessment for learning** Questions and success criteria
***Introductory** teaching to assess and review learning*	Day(s)		
***Direct** teaching of new knowledge, skills and concepts, with opportunities to practise and apply learning*	Day(s)		
***Interactive** whole class teaching*	Day(s)		
***Consolidation** and further practice*	Day(s)		
***Interim review** of achievement and progress*	Day(s)		
***Intervention** support with groups*	Day(s)		
***Enquiry**, extension enrichment work, problem solving, reasoning*	Day(s)		
***Summary** assessment of progress over the unit with children*	Day(s)		

Medium Term Plan:

Year: Term:

	Unit (Weeks)	Learning Objectives	Children's Targets	Successful criteria	Focus and use of application
1					
2					
3					
4					
5					

Notes:
-
-
-

Learning through play

Early years professionals have promoted learning through play for decades, and as described earlier in this unit, in recent years government policy groups have voiced their agreement too, although there will probably always be discrepancies in how 'play' is actually thought of and defined between the early years profession and the policy makers. As the process of curriculum and strategy development has evolved (Foundation Stage Curriculum, Birth to Three Matters, Every Child Matters, Early Years Foundation Stage, etc.), each stage emphasises (just that bit more) how play should be the basis for early learning, raising the status of a play-based curriculum.

Professional Practice

- Reflect on activities you have carried out with children, identifying which were play-based. Think about any that you identify as not being play-based, and how they could be made so another time.

Link

Refer to pages 178–183 for ideas on supporting numeracy through play.

i

- Tina Bruce and Janet Moyles are modern-day theorists whose thinking is firmly based in the value of play. Refer to books by either of them to further your understanding – see the bibliography on page 402.
- Also refer to Green (2007) page 217 for ideas on learning through play in general.

Impact of legislation/guidance on practice

As mentioned above, in recent years greater levels of guidance on practice have been drawn up by government and implemented by early years practitioners. Initially, practitioners were concerned at the structure of the curriculum guidance, and thankfully this has been reviewed and redeveloped, and is considered much more acceptable by most practitioners today. There have always been good early years settings, excellent early years settings and settings which needed to improve their provision. There have also always been settings that provided a good range of opportunities for children, but where staff did not always understand the full value of what they were providing, perhaps seeing just the main learning opportunity to be gained from an activity, without realising just how many other aspects of learning were also involved. The structure of strategies such as the Foundation Stage Curriculum has enabled more staff to develop their understanding of the value of play to a greater level. This has been beneficial to children, to the staff and to the field of early years generally.

Funded places for children, initially for 4-year-olds, and more recently for 3-year-olds, has been a massive boost to many families, enabling all parents who wish it to receive an early years placement for their child. For nurseries and other early years settings, there have however been some concerns about the impact on occupancy levels, and issues of funding not actually covering fees completely, leaving providers in a position of losing revenue for their businesses. This problem is ongoing.

The other main impact of recent legislation and practice guidance has been the more stringent inspection procedures. These have been controversial at times, and it took time for practitioners to fully value the process, but for children it has meant that, on the whole, most unacceptable provision has been identified, and guidance given on how those settings can raise their standards. In some cases low standards have meant the closure of settings which were considered not to meet standards sufficiently. There have been clearer pathways set up for concerns to be raised, and the greater level of policies and procedural paperwork, whilst adding to the workload of those who write them and need to regularly review them, has helped to support safe working practice for all.

The introduction of (initially) Early Excellence centres and, more recently, Sure Start centres around the UK has been welcomed by the majority as a move forward in providing extended care, learning and support for both children and their families, incorporating health, education and adult learning. There have, however, been concerns regarding funding and the impact some of these centres has had on other provision in the area.

activity
INDIVIDUAL WORK 17.4

P4

M2

Take an example of mathematical learning you have seen used in your placement. Describe in detail where it fits into the curriculum guidance for the age range of the children in your example. How do you consider the relevant curriculum guidance has influenced or impacted this type of learning experience?

Provide examples of how the curriculum guidance is planned and implemented within your placement setting, explaining their use and reflecting on their success.

activity
INDIVIDUAL WORK 17.5

D1

Research the National Primary Framework for Mathematics, interviewing at least two practitioners who work with it, and, using their opinions together with your own findings, reflect on the effectiveness of this framework in the development of children's numeracy and mathematical skills.

Be able to develop a range of activities that can be used to support children's understanding and use of number, shape, space and measure

Activities

Most activities involve numeracy and/or mathematical understanding in some way. This may simply be through counting with or by the adult, grouping objects or children by a specific factor, e.g. height, date of birth, or within the instruction given, e.g. get into groups of three, stand behind/in front of/opposite a partner. It may be that the planned activity involves the scribing of or demonstration of a specific number or group of numbers.

Children will only build up an understanding of number use and mathematical terminology if they are exposed to it, preferably within the context of everyday actions. This practical application of numeracy consolidates their learning and helps them develop the confidence to try to work out answers and solve mathematical problems mentally. It is therefore important that early years practitioners use a wide and varied mathematical vocabulary with all the children they work with. This means, for example, thinking about how you describe and discuss position, quantity, size and measurement, introducing new terminology whenever possible, encouraging children to think, to predict, to reflect and evaluate, and to ask themselves and others questions, e.g. How many? How far? How long? How heavy? and to make comparisons.

Link

As you read through this section, refer also to Unit 18 Supporting Children's Literacy Skills, page 255. Links to literacy within some of the same activities have been included.

Board and boxed games

Board games, such as snakes and ladders, and boxed games, such as picture lotto, all involve numeracy. Snakes and ladders involves terminology linked to position, e.g. climbing up the ladder, slithering along or down the snake, overtaking X and Y, being X places ahead, X places behind, etc. Picture lotto encourages children to count how many pictures they still need to get, who has the most pictures/least pictures/same number of pictures, etc. Both games involve the use of dice, counting or recognising the numbers of spots, etc. and picture lotto involves early matching skills.

Fig 17.7 Children learn numeracy through board games

Role play

Role play can provide children with opportunities to group and match objects, e.g. cups and saucers, knives and forks. They use practical counting skills in providing appropriate numbers of resources for however many people are sitting at the table. They develop estimating and matching skills as they dress large dolls in large clothes, and small dolls in smaller clothes, and they learn to use money and write numerals as they go shopping, play at being shopkeeper, café owner, post office worker, etc.

Role play gives children opportunities to use both verbal and written numeracy. There will be opportunities, for example, for:

- labelling and putting up notices as their role-play area becomes a shop, the post office, a bank, etc.
- writing lists and prices as they make up menus for their café, takeaway or restaurant
- noting down orders from customers, writing cheques at the bank, writing receipts at the petrol station, etc.

- writing reference numbers as they make luggage labels, tickets and boarding passes to get on their aeroplane
- using mark-making to indicate temperatures on a chart during hospital play, plotting the weight of a baby during baby clinic play.

NB This is not an exhaustive list.

i

You may find it interesting to also look at Green (2005b) – see the bibliography on page 412.

Books

Books can be both for pleasure and for information. In our modern-day world, heavily led by technology, it is important to help children value the use of books as a tool of reference. Linking books to displays and interest tables is an easy way to help children make this link. Even with the youngest toddlers and babies we use books to help children focus on a specific aspect of mathematical understanding, e.g. opposites such as big/small, short/tall, high/low, heavy/light, thick/thin, etc. We can use maps to locate places children know of or have been to, referring to direction, reference numbers, etc. This all helps to support a child's understanding of numeracy in its widest contexts and also how book use is still important in our technology-led world.

Fig 17.8 Numeracy can be enjoyed through sharing books at home too

Storytelling

Stories provide both pleasure and information. Stories can be either written or oral and can provide opportunities to count, order, describe actions and position, and will often include repetition too. Good examples include *1 Hunter* by Pat Hutchins, a fun book of lovely pictures for children to count in sequence, and also *Going on a Bear Hunt* by Michael Rosen and Helen Oxenbury. In this story (full of fun and lots of repetition), each time the children reach a new obstacle in their path, they find that they 'can't go over it, can't go under it', they have to go 'through it', and when they run from the bear, and get home they have to 'run up the stairs, down again to shut the door, and then get under the covers'.

You can probably think of many more examples.

remember

You can always develop the story further yourself with the help of the children – counting hooves, predicting and comparing size of horns, adding in fences for goats to climb over (and count), estimating distance to the meadow, etc.

Music and dance

The use of music and dance can easily support the understanding of position, orientation, grouping, sequencing and ordering. Through movement and the instructions given by the supervising adult, children will learn positional terms such as behind, next to, opposite, step forward, jump backwards. They will learn to form a circle, square, etc., to group themselves by specified numbers, to add one more on, or take one off of a line of children. Terms linked to symmetry will be learned through actions copying another child, e.g. mirroring, copying, being the same as, matching, and also terms to describe the opposite effect, e.g. different to, unlike, reverse. These are just a few examples. Again, you can probably think of others.

The use of rhythm is important too, as language is full of rhythm, and listening to and being able to identify and replicate rhythm can help general speech and language development as well as aiding numeracy skills.

Drama

Numeracy can be supported through drama as children respond to and act out stories well

case study 17.2 The Three Billy Goats Gruff drama

Class 1 had enjoyed re-enacting the timeless classic – 'The Three Billy Goats Gruff'. It was part of a focused topic on positional language. Their teacher was following the drama session up with a discussion. She began by asking the children to think about the movements they had made during the drama, e.g. across the river, over the bridge, through the meadow, etc.

activity

1 What other aspects of discussion could she introduce relevant to numeracy and mathematical development?

2 What mathematical terminology would you link to 'The Three Billy Goats Gruff'?

3 What opportunities for written numerical work could you bring to this project?

known to them, e.g. the story of the 'Three Little Pigs', 'Three Billy Goats Gruff', 'Three Bears', etc., counting to three, taking on the roles of biggest, middle-sized and smallest, speaking their 'lines' and following the story structure from its beginning, through its main sections and on to the climax. It also supports understanding of one-to-one correspondence.

Small world play

Small world play is play with resources such as farms, zoos, roadways, doll houses, etc. It is basically playing out 'life' in miniature. It is favoured mostly by children of pre-school ages who tend to speak to themselves in a monologue as they play. This gives great opportunities for mathematical thinking as children:

- name positions of objects, e.g. the car is behind the bus but in front of the tractor, the cows are standing next to each other
- labelling actions, e.g. going upstairs, moving along the road, going in, coming out, going through the tunnel
- vocalising intentions regarding positions, e.g. I am putting my car in front of, behind, on top of, underneath, beside, inside, outside
- lining objects up by size (sequencing), grouping them by colour or type
- making patterns, e.g. horse/cow/sheep, horse/cow/sheep, horse/cow/sheep.

The range of activities that you will be providing will help children learn in the areas shown in Figure 17.9.

Suggestions to ensure that children learn number names include:

- counting games and rhymes
- matching numbers of children to the written number
- grouping small objects into numbered hoops
- hopping five times, ten times, 100 times.

Suggestions for helping them learn one-to-one correspondence include:

- laying the table in the role-play area to seat a specified number of 'guests'
- matching up sets of objects, e.g. in hoops
- counting games and rhymes
- buying and selling items, 1 pence per item initially, building up as understanding develops.

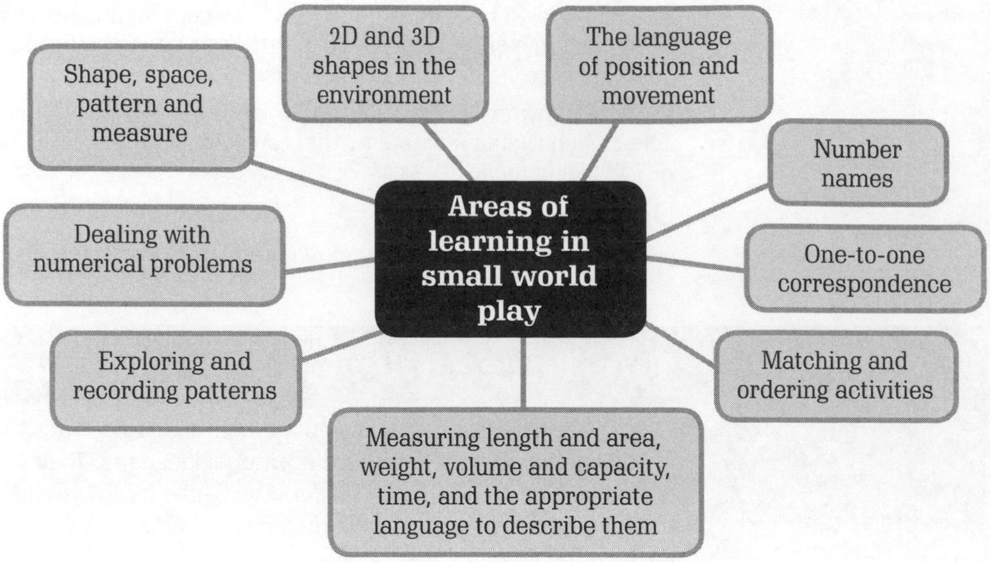

Fig 17.9 Learning opportunities in small world play

Suggestions for matching and ordering activities include:

- threading large beads in a repeated order, e.g. by colour or shape
- children sorting themselves into order of height
- making a display, setting objects out by size, e.g. a row of different-sized teddy bears
- matching socks into pairs on a washing line.

Suggestions for exploring and recording patterns include:

- making a class/group chart to show numbers of something, e.g. how many red bricks compared to blue, green or brown bricks
- grouping objects (e.g. teddy bears) into small, medium and large
- tessellating patterns using colour
- printing activities with intended outcomes.

Suggestions for numerical problems include:

- counting games, songs and rhymes, e.g. Five currant buns, five speckled frogs on a speckled log, ten green bottles
- number puzzles and games
- number lines on wall, referred to as a whole group, or individual number lines for use in counting activities, adding on and taking one away
- sharing out resources, cakes, fruit pieces, etc.

activity
INDIVIDUAL WORK 17.6

P5

M3

1 Draw up planning for two different activities to promote children's number skills. You may wish to use the example shown on page 167 as a guide. Remember to consider resources, environment, adult input and assessment opportunities, as well as stating clearly what your learning objectives are and where they fit into the relevant curriculum.

2 Carry out at least one of the activities with children in your placement, recording the outcomes clearly.

Suggestions to ensure children learn about shape, space, pattern and measure include:

- sand and water play, having a range of utensils to experiment with
- cooking activities, weighing, noting scientific changes, etc.
- play with a variety of shaped objects, e.g. exploration of a range of fruit, vegetables, seeds
- finding items around the classroom or at home that are 'longer than my pencil', 'shorter than my arm', 'same height as me', etc.

Suggestions to help children recognise 2D and 3D shapes in the environment include:

- whole-group discussions thinking of items (large or small) that are square (e.g. a window), round (e.g. a hoop), rectangular (e.g. a door) or that are a cube (e.g. a soft play block), a sphere (e.g. a football), a cylinder (e.g. a drainpipe), etc.
- home activity to identify and draw objects of a certain shape from around the home, e.g. 'What can you find that is round?'
- using shaped backgrounds to displays made with the children, e.g. a large circle of card as the background for a display of circular paintings or drawings, or pictures of round items collected by the children, consolidating their recognition of various shapes and their names
- using a 'feely bag' of 3D shapes, and asking children to find a cube, a sphere, etc. without looking.

Suggestions to help children use the language of position and movement include:

- jigsaw puzzles, from the easiest play tray puzzles through to more complex designs, for table or floor, big or small pieces. All puzzles help children to learn about shape and making sense of spaces, linking shapes to gaps, estimating and trying to position the pieces and developing the understanding of how to manoeuvre them
- dance activities involving sequences of movement (could sometimes be designed by the children), helping them to follow the required pattern
- using programmable toys, learning to control and operate them to follow a trail, and to instruct others in their movements
- playing follow the leader type games, being trains, caterpillars, etc.

Suggestions for measuring length and area, weight, volume and capacity, time, and the associated appropriate language include:

- sand play, with children filling and transporting containers, matching, comparing, weighing and measuring
- water play, with children using small containers to fill larger containers, encouraging them to estimate and predict, count and reflect
- making time lines, e.g. of people: baby/toddler/child/teenager/parent/grandparent, or of the children's usual day, e.g. getting out of bed/breakfast/getting dressed/school/lunchtime/school/teatime/storytime/bathtime/bedtime
- introducing children to terms such as volume, capacity, level, equal.

Materials, settings and environments

When developing a range of activities, it is important to take into account the resources you are providing, where the activity will be taking place within the room, and the environment

Fig 17.10 Considerations when providing an activity to support numeracy

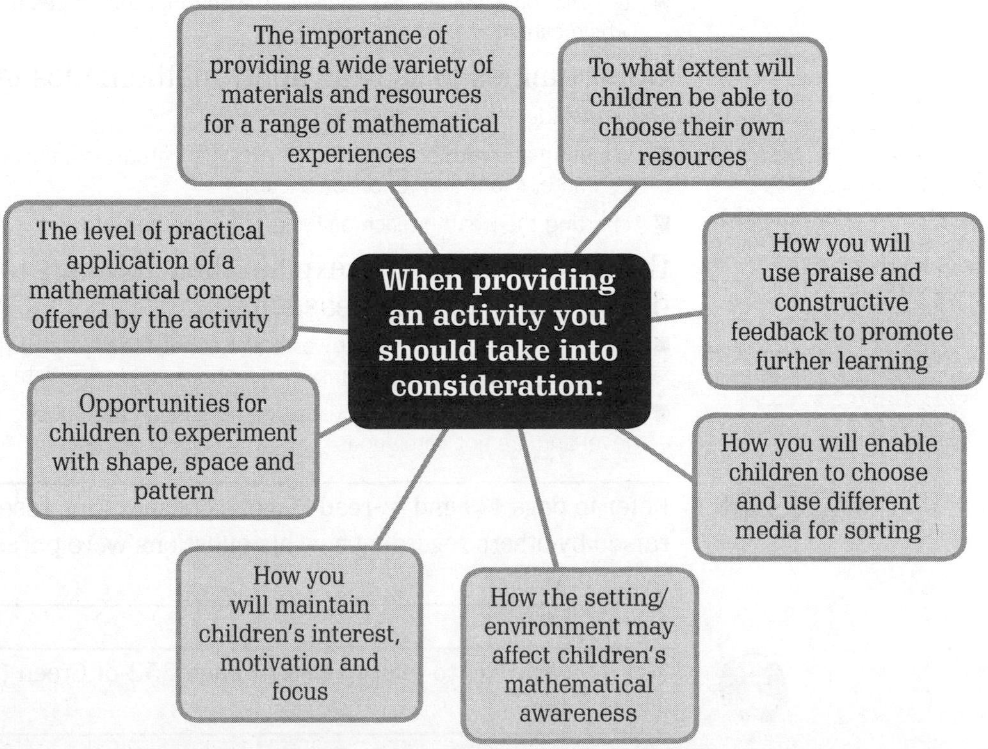
When providing an activity you should take into consideration:
The importance of providing a wide variety of materials and resources for a range of mathematical experiences
To what extent will children be able to choose their own resources
How you will use praise and constructive feedback to promote further learning
How you will enable children to choose and use different media for sorting
How the setting/ environment may affect children's mathematical awareness
How you will maintain children's interest, motivation and focus
Opportunities for children to experiment with shape, space and pattern
The level of practical application of a mathematical concept offered by the activity

in general. Each of these affects the success of an activity and getting it wrong can have a negative impact on learning. You will need to consider the points in Figure 17.10.

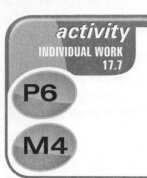

activity
INDIVIDUAL WORK 17.7

P6

M4

1 Draw up planning for two different activities to promote children's understanding of shape, space and/or measure. You may wish to use the example shown on page 167 as a guide. Remember to consider resources, environment, adult input and assessment opportunities, as well as stating clearly what your learning objectives are and where they fit into the relevant curriculum.

2 Carry out at least one of the activities with children in your placement, recording the outcomes clearly.

Providing a wide variety of materials and resources for mathematical experiences

- Ensure that there are sufficient resources and space available to provide each child with a meaningful and satisfactory experience.
- Remember that children differ in their interests, and in their learning styles. It is important to have a range of resources that support both interest and learning style.

Enable children to choose their own resources

- Ensure that resources are easily accessible, e.g. through child-friendly storage units.
- Clearly label all resources, with visual labels (illustrations of the resource) used to support the independence of younger children.

Enable children to choose and use different media for sorting

- Provide natural items such as leaves, cones, pebble and seeds, or commercial items such as compare bears, elephants, beads, counting cubes.
- Provide opportunities to sort and group small world items, e.g. zoo animals, farm animals, small vehicles.

Experiment with shape, space and pattern

This includes:

- learning to fold paper equally and then discuss shape, size, shapes within shapes, etc.
- tessellation activities, experimenting with different shapes to see which can tessellate and which cannot.

Opportunities to use and apply mathematics in practical tasks

These include:

- counting and grouping children in everyday situations, encouraging children to suggest, estimate, count and reflect on accuracy
- charting the weather each day and noting temperature.

Encourage children to explain their thinking to support the development of their reasoning

- Build children's sense of self-worth and self-esteem to give them the confidence to speak out in a group, to ask and answer questions, and to initiate ideas.
- Use careful and sensitive questioning, ensuring that questions are clear, at the appropriate level and are not ambiguous.

Link

Refer to page 139 and re-read Piaget's conservation research and the issues raised by others regarding how his questions were phrased and the impact this might have had.

i

You may also like to refer to Unit 4, page 232 of Green (2007) where self-esteem is discussed.

How the setting/environment can affect children's mathematical awareness

This includes:

- ensuring that displays make maximum use of all aspects of mathematics, e.g. use of shape, pattern, grouping and making links, highlighting opposites, contrasts and symmetry.
- the number of children in a teaching group – this will be determined by staffing, the overall class size, the range of learning styles within the class and the ability levels of the children. It will also be influenced by how much individual input each child is likely to need. Whenever practicable, work with children in small numbers, or one-to-one. Some children will be able to learn from their peers, and so a well-thought-through pairing can be a good strategy.

Link

Refer to page 140 and also to Unit 14, page 106, for information on Lev Vygotsky and his theory known as the zone of proximal development, and also Jerome Bruner's thinking on scaffolding.

How to maintain interest, motivation and focus

- Be aware that poor concentration can result from distraction, boredom and lack of confidence. Adults should ensure that children are not distracted by unsuitable seating or work surfaces which can take their attention away from a task.
- Reduce noise levels. Many children find listening to instructions and concentration hard, so it is important that unnecessary noise is kept to a minimum.
- A child who has a good understanding of the concept required for an activity, but who finds writing difficult may be 'put off' if he is set tasks that involve too much written evidence. Provide opportunities for practically-based evidence wherever possible.

How to use praise and constructive feedback to promote further learning

- Give praise and encouragement for effort. This is particularly important for those children learning English as an additional language, to build up children's self-confidence and help them avoid developing low-self-esteem.
- Give one-to-one attention whenever possible, particularly if a child is known to find concentration difficult, e.g. children with disorders such as ADD and ADHD.

Link

Refer to Unit 27, page 282 for more on ADD and ADHD.

activity
INDIVIDUAL WORK 17.8
D2

1 Reflect upon the two activities you implemented in your placement for the activities on pages 176 and 178.

2 Evaluate how effective each activity has been in meeting your learning objectives for the children.

Make clear what was successful in each case, and what could have been better, and note the changes you would make another time. If you have written feedback from your placement supervisor, include this also, and use it to support your reflection.

Hopefully, you will now have a clearer understanding of how children develop mathematical understanding and will feel able to support their learning with confidence.

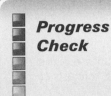

Progress Check

1 What are the four main stages of Jean Piaget's thinking regarding how children develop a sense of understanding?
2 Explain Lev Vygotsky's ZPD theory, and give an example of how you have seen this in action.
3 What are Jerome Bruner's three modes of thinking and describe the term scaffolding and its links to the work of Lev Vygotsky.
4 Explain Janet Moyles' play spiral and give an example of this in relation to mathematical understanding.
5 Give ten examples of how you use mathematical vocabulary in your day-to-day work with children.
6 Give five examples of how children can consolidate their mathematical development at home.
7 Explain how dyslexia can affect numeracy skills.
8 What is dyscalculia?
9 Explain the main areas of learning for Problem Solving, Reasoning and Numeracy within the Early Years Foundation Stage.
10 Explain the main elements of the seven strands of the primary framework for mathematics.
11 Give at least five examples of how role play supports mathematical development.
12 Explain how small world play helps a child in their mathematical development.
13 Give five examples of activities that support the understanding of one-to-one correspondence.
14 Give five examples of activities that support the understanding of matching and ordering.
15 Give five examples of activities that support the understanding of shape.

UNIT 18

Supporting Children's Literacy Skills

This unit covers the following objectives:

- Understand the development of literacy skills
- Know current national initiatives and curriculum guidance relating to the development of children's literacy skills
- Be able to implement a range of speaking and listening activities that can be used to support the development of children's skills
- Be able to implement a range of reading and writing activities that can be used to support the development of children's skills

This unit provides an overview of a variety of differing theories of how language and language use develops, with reference to some of the main theorists. It explains the usual sequence of development, setting it out in stages. It should of course always be remembered that, as with all aspects of development, each child reaches each stage in their own time. Guidance on planning and meeting additional needs is given, using a variety of activities as examples, together with references to relevant curriculum frameworks, and legislation, and the contexts within which children learn best

grading criteria

To achieve a **Pass** grade the evidence must show that the learner is able to:	To achieve a **Merit** grade the evidence must show that, in addition to the Pass criteria, the learner is able to:	To achieve a **Distinction** grade the evidence must show that, in addition to the Pass and Merit criteria, the learner is able to:
P1 Identify two different theories of language development Page 190	**M1** Compare and contrast the two theories of language development using practical examples to support or contradict the theories Page 190	
P2 Describe the sequences and stages in the development of children's reading, writing, speaking and listening skills Page 200		
P3 Identify one piece of legislation/curriculum document, and its influence on supporting children's literacy skills Page 254	**M2** Explain how the identified legislation/curriculum guidance is used in a children's setting to support the development of literacy skills Page 254	**D1** Evaluate the effectiveness of the identified legislation/curriculum guidance in promoting children's literacy skills Page 254

To achieve a **Pass** grade the evidence must show that the learner is able to:	To achieve a **Merit** grade the evidence must show that, in addition to the Pass criteria, the learner is able to:	To achieve a **Distinction** grade the evidence must show that, in addition to the Pass and Merit criteria, the learner is able to:
P4 Describe the role of the adult in developing literacy skills and meeting specific needs Page 216		
P5 Develop two activities to promote children's speaking and listening skills Page 260	**M3** Implement at least one of the planned activities to support the development of children's speaking and listening skills Page 260	**D2** Evaluate the effectiveness of the implemented activities Page 266
P6 Develop two activities to promote reading and writing skills Page 263	**M4** Implement at least one of the planned activities to support the development of children's reading and writing skills Page 263	

Understand the development of literacy skills

Theories of language development

There are various theories regarding how language develops. Some are based on the theory of innate learning and some are based more on the influences of environment and experience. Theorists specifically recognised for their thinking on language development are:

- Burrhus F. Skinner
- Noam Chomsky
- Eric Lenneberg
- Jean Piaget
- Lev Vygotsky
- Jerome Bruner.

The following theories offer some very different ideas about how language develops. As you read them, consider which you could accept and which seem less likely.

Theories of language development include:

- association theory
- behaviourist theory
- language acquisition device theory
- maturational theory
- interactionist theory.

Association theory

The theory of learning by association proposes that a child gradually builds their language by associating words with what they see. This theory works well up to a point, but does not take into account all aspects of language, e.g. those used to describe feelings or emotions.

Behaviourist theory

Theorists such as Skinner proposed that a child's language is shaped by the responses given to them by their parents or main carers (operant conditioning); the positive reinforcement of vocalisations encourages the child to repeat a specific sound over and over again. For example, Daniel is an infant of 6 months whose babbling sounds have become 'dadadada'. Daniel's mother greets this with delight and encouragement, stating that 'Dada' will be home soon.

Skinner believed that the continuous positive reinforcement of 'correct' speech sounds, and the lack of positive response to sounds or (eventually) sentence structure that is not 'correct', will mould a child's language formation. For example, if Daniel's babbling sounded like 'bibibibibi', his mother is less likely to have reinforced it, as she would not have recognised it as a 'word' and therefore would not have used it when speaking back to him.

Skinner's theory would indicate that children have to go through a trial-and-error process for every aspect of speech, but this is obviously not the case, although it is accepted that infants are encouraged by the positive reactions of adults. It does not take into account how quickly children can pick up language which clearly is not learnt simply through regular reinforcement.

Skinner's theory was challenged by many psychologists and consequently the nativist theories set out below became an inviting alternative.

Professional Practice

- **The principles of social learning theory can also be applied to language, that is, that humans repeat behaviour that they see being rewarded (refer to Albert Bandura's social learning theory experiment with Bobo dolls in 1965, Unit 14, page 111). If, for example, a child sees an older brother or sister being rewarded for speech, the younger child may try to imitate that behaviour.**

Language acquisition device (LAD) theory

Noam Chomsky (a nativist) believed in the biologically-based theory that infants are born with a predisposition for language. He suggested that infants have a language acquisition device (LAD). He considered that this LAD enabled children to absorb the language that they heard, to decode it and then develop an understanding of its rules and grammatical structure. It has been shown that children of all cultures develop language at much the same time and this gave support to the theories of Chomsky and others like him.

However, other researchers have shown that simply hearing language is not sufficient for full speech development. Children need to interact with others, to converse, in order to fully develop their spoken language skills.

It is interesting that research carried out with hearing children born to deaf parents has shown that, while a child may learn words from what they hear around them (radio, television, DVDs, and so on), they need to be actively involved in conversation in order to develop their understanding and use of grammar. In the cases of some children, speech therapy resulted in a sudden improvement in their language structure which soon brought them up to the expected level of language development for their age. This indicated that they had previously been ready to learn the grammatical rules associated with their culture, but needed the active involvement with others in order to facilitate it.

Maturational theory

Eric Lenneberg, like Chomsky, considered that as long as children were exposed to language, they would simply pick it up as their development progressed in other ways too. (This should not be confused with Gesell's maturational theory which is concerned with other aspects of maturation.) Lenneberg considered that there is a critical period in which children need to be exposed to language. He considered that it is linked to brain development and how in the earlier years there is less defined use of each side of the brain. There have been cases where brain damage has occurred to the left side of a child's brain (normally associated with language). The older the child is at the time of the accident, the less likely they are to have a full recovery. Conversely, there have also been cases where children have had extensive periods without hearing language early in life, and they have been able to develop some form of communication, even if not full speech.

Interactionist theory

The basis of the interactionist theory is that the schemas that children develop subsequently facilitate language development: children first experience and then talk about their experiences. Therefore, this theory sees language as a reflection of cognitive development.

Piaget, Vygotsky and Bruner took this interactionist approach to their thinking on language and its development.

Jean Piaget considered that cognitive development starts during what he called the sensorimotor period, and that children's language follows these sensory experiences and that their early words are often linked to symbolic play. Piaget did not place any particular significance on social interaction and its impact on language development.

Link

Refer to Unit 14, page 104 for more on the work and thinking of Jean Piaget.

Lev Vygotsky considered that language and thought initially developed separately with early language developing simply as a means of communication. He considered that gradually children internalise language to help their thinking, 'thinking aloud' at times when faced with a significant challenge. Vygotsky put considerable emphasis on the importance of social interaction in language development. This is the main difference between the thinking of Piaget and Vygotsky.

Link

Refer to Unit 14, page 106, for more on the work and thinking of Vygotsky.

Jerome Bruner considered that a child's language was very dependent on their interactions with their primary carers and other familiar adults, the adults helping the child to make sense of the vocalisations he hears around him. His thinking was referred to as a language acquisition support system (LASS).

Link

Refer to Unit 14, page 106 for more on the work and thinking of Bruner.

i

A detailed discussion of the theories of language can be found in Cullis *et al.* (1999).

activity
GROUP WORK 18.1

P1

M1

1 Work in two teams. Each team should choose a theory regarding language development to research as fully as possible.

2 Hold a debate/discussion in which each team promotes and upholds their chosen theory.

You should produce as much evidence as you can to back up your theory, and include examples from placement where practical.

Sequences and stages

Development of speaking and listening skills

Language is the main way in which humans communicate with one another. It involves facial expressions, tone of voice, body posture and expression of meaning through the use of words or symbols.

Language is:

- rule-governed – grammatical rules are present in each language (syntax)
- structured – the sound system that makes up the speech sounds (phonology)
- symbolic – words have meanings, building into phrases, and so on (semantics)
- generative – it is the basis of the sharing of knowledge (pragmatics).

Pre-requisites for language

The normal, unimpeded development of language is affected by other areas of development. For example, socially and cognitively an awareness of the need to interact as a means of communication is imperative, as are the physical abilities of vision, hearing and speech.

Children learn the basis of their culture through communication (socialisation theory) and develop understanding of themselves and how they fit within their peer and social groups (goodness of fit). As discussed above, some psychologists believe that language plays an important part in all aspects of human development, with some theorists arguing that language is the basis of learning. An important debate involves the questions:

- Is language dependent on thought?
- Or is thought dependent on language?

You may find it helpful to consider what are your first thoughts on this language v. thought debate. Do you think understanding is needed in order to develop linguistically? Or do you think that language enables understanding to develop? Come back to these questions again once you have completed this unit.

Stages of language development

As with every aspect of development, children develop language at differing rates within what is considered to be the 'normal' range. This process of language development can be divided into ten basic stages:

1 Non-verbal communication/expression
2 Speech-like noises
3 Controlling sounds, using mouth and tongue
4 Imitating sounds
5 First words
6 Development of vocabulary (50 words is usual at 2 years)
7 Putting words together to form simple phrases and sentences
8 Use of grammar
9 Use of meaning
10 Using language to develop other skills, e.g. early literacy.

These ten stages can be linked to approximate ages as shown in Table 18.1.

Table 18.1 The stages of language development

Age	Understanding	No. of words	Type of words	Average length of sentence
3 months	Soothed by sound	0	Cooing and gurgling	0
6 months	Responds to voice tones	0	Babble	0
1 year	Knows own name and a few others	1	Noun (naming word)	1 word
18 months	Understands simple commands	6–20	Nouns +	1 word
2 years	Understands much more than they can say	50+	Verbs and pronouns (action + name)	1–2 word phrases
2½ years	Enjoys simple and familiar stories	200+	Pronouns I, me, you; Questions what, where	2–3 word phrases
3 years	Carries out complex commands	500–1,000	Plurals; Verbs in present tense; Questions who	3–4 word phrases
4 years	Listens to long stories	1,000–1,500	Verbs in past tense; Questions why, where, how	4–5 word phrases
5 years	Developing the ability to reason	1,500–2,000	Complex sentences with adult forms of grammar	5–6 word phrases

Professional Practice

- As you move through the various placements that will make up your professional practice experience, observe and note the differences in speech intonation, questioning and grammar of children at different ages and stages.

The development of speech sounds in the English language

Until around 7 or 8 months, the babblings of babies is universal. From this age onwards their speech sounds begin to take on the speech sounds of the languages that surround them, i.e. their heritage language. This section describes the usual pattern in spoken English. You will see how complex it can be to articulate clearly, and will hopefully build on your understanding of how difficult some children find it, and why that might be.

Speech sounds are made up of consonants, vowels, syllables and words.

Consonants

Consonants are 'closed' sounds. This means that, for a consonant sound to be produced, the airflow is obstructed by parts of the mouth coming into contact with each other or almost contacting, e.g.

- Try saying the word book. To pronounce the b in book, the lips need to come into contact.
- To pronounce the s in the word sand, the tip of the tongue touches the ridge just behind the top front teeth.

There are five main types of consonants:

- plosives
- nasals
- fricatives
- affricates
- approximants.

Table 18.2 shows the development of consonants in the English language, and Table 18.3 gives examples of how the obstructions are made.

Table 18.2 The approximate sequential development of consonants in the English language

At 2 years	*m, n, p, b, t, d, w*
At 2½ years	*k, g, ng* (as in *sing*), *h*
2½–3 years	*f, s, l, y*
3½–4 years	*v, z, ch, j, sh*
4½ years onwards	*th* (as in *thin*), *th* (as in *the*), *r*
Double consonants such as *sp*, *tr* and *fl*, and also the sounds *r* and *th*, can develop as late as 6½ years in some children.	

Table 18.3 English consonant sounds 'at a glance'

	Bilabial	Labio-dental	Dental	Alveolar	Post-alveolar	Palatal	Velar	Glottal
Plosive	*p, b*			*t, d*			*c/k, g*	
Nasal	*m*			*n*			*ng*	
Fricative		*f, v*	*th, th*	*s, z*	*sh, zh*			*h*
Affricate					*ch, j*			
Approximant	*w*			*l*	*r*	*y*		

Professional Practice

- How we pronounce sounds is quite complex. It is, however, a useful exercise for early years workers to explore their own pronunciation to gain a better understanding of how the parts of the mouth work together and how each sound is subsequently produced. This helps with understanding the difficulties faced by some children in developing their speech sounds.

Plosives
Plosives are produced by a complete obstruction of the airflow at some position in the mouth, e.g. the lips coming together. Air builds up behind the temporary obstruction and when the obstruction is removed (e.g. the lips part) the air rushes out (a plosive).

Plosives can be voiceless (produced without the involvement of the vocal cords) or voiced (involving the vibration of the vocal cords). They occur in pairs:

- first pair: p, b – the two lips come together to form a complete obstruction. These are known as bilabial plosives (two lips). Try pronouncing them.
- second pair: t, d – these involve the tip of the tongue contacting the gum ridge (alveolar ridge) just behind the top front teeth. (Run your tongue over your alveolar ridge to identify where it is.) These are known as alveolar plosives. Try pronouncing them.
- third pair: c/k, g (as in goat) – the back of the roof of the mouth is known as the soft palate (velum). Velar plosives are sounded when the tongue is in contact with the soft palate.

Try pronouncing these three consonant sounds.

Nasals
When a plosive sound is made, the soft palate is raised so that it touches the back of the throat and stops air from escaping through the nose. Nasals are similar in that there is a complete obstruction of air flow in the mouth, but the air pressure does not build up. It is allowed to escape through the nose by lowering the soft palate.

There are three nasals:

- m is a bilabial nasal where the sound is formed at the front of the mouth, with the lips coming together
- n is an alveolar nasal, where the obstruction is between the back of the tongue and the soft palate
- ng (as in sing) is a velar nasal. This sound never appears at the beginning of a word in English.

Try pronouncing these nasal consonants.

Fricatives
These sounds are formed by the narrowing of the mouth passage by any two of the articulators (lips, teeth, tongue, roof of mouth) coming into near contact. The air is forced through a narrow gap creating a friction sound, hence the name, fricative consonant. Each of these sounds can be prolonged by first taking a deep breath.

There are four pairs of fricatives:

- first pair: f, v – these are articulated with slight contact between the bottom lip and the top front teeth. They are known as labio-dental fricatives.
- second pair: th (as in thin), th (as in that) – these fricatives involve the tongue nearly contacting the top front teeth. The sounds are quite hard for young children to pronounce and they often use alternatives, e.g. f instead of th and/or v instead of th.
- third pair: s, z – these are formed when the tongue is almost in contact with the alveolar ridge. They are known as alveolar fricatives.
- fourth pair: sh, zh (as 'sounded' in the middle of the word measure) – these post-alveolar fricatives are formed further back in the mouth when the middle of the tongue comes into contact with the roof of the mouth, just behind the alveolar ridge. The zh sound is never found at the beginning of a word in English.

The final fricative is h. It is a glottal fricative. It is made deep down in the throat (the glottis). This sound is never found at the end of a word in English.

Try pronouncing these fricative consonants.

Affricates
The affricates are the sounds that combine both a complete obstruction with a partial obstruction. They start with a complete obstruction formed by the tip of the tongue contacting the alveolar ridge, but then the air is released slowly with friction, behind the alveolar ridge. No air is released in an explosive way.

These sounds are j and ch. They are post-alveolar affricates. Try pronouncing them.

Approximants

The term 'approximant' is used for the sound made when the mouth passage is not completely obstructed, as it is with the plosives and the nasals, nor is it restricted so that friction is developed. Two articulators (tongue, teeth, etc.) approximate closely together.

The approximants are:

- w, formed by the two lips approximating closely (bi-labial approximant)
- l, made by the tongue approximating to the alveolar ridge (alveolar approximant)
- r, sounded by the tongue being behind the alveolar ridge (post-alveolar approximant)
- y, articulated with the middle of the tongue approximating closely to the palate (palatal approximant).

Try pronouncing these approximants.

Link

Refer to Table 18.3 to help consolidate your understanding.

Vowels

The basic vowel sounds are a, e, i, o and u, but there are other vowel sounds too. These include the double sounds such as ee, oo, and so on. Vowels are 'open' sounds. There is no obstruction to the airflow during pronunciation and each sound differs according to the position of the mouth. For example:

- If the lips are spread widely, the sound ee is produced.
- If the lips are rounded, the sound oo is produced.
- Vowels can be long sounds as in the word more. They can also be short sounds as in the word pack.
- There are simple vowels such as o as in pot, u as in put, a as in pat. They are simple because once the mouth is set in position it does not need to alter in order to produce the sound.
- There are also more complex vowel sounds such as oy as in boy and ow as in cow. With these sounds, you need to change the mouth and/or tongue position for the full sound to be made.
- All vowels in English are 'voiced'. This means that they involve the vibration of the vocal cords.

Syllables

Speech sounds combine together to form syllables. A syllable is made up of a combination of consonants (c) and at least one vowel (v). There can be up to three consonants before a vowel and up to four consonants after a vowel in the English language.

Examples of syllables:

- be = cv (1 consonant and 1 vowel)
- and = vcc (1 vowel and 2 consonants), and so on
- plot = ccvc
- strip = cccvc
- tempts = cvcccc.

The more consonants in a syllable, the harder it will be for a child to pronounce, because it requires a greater ability to co-ordinate the articulators.

Words

Syllables, in turn, combine together to form words. Some words have just one syllable, e.g. cat, dog and hen. These are called monosyllabic words. All other words have more than one syllable and are known as polysyllabic words.

Even in adulthood, some people have difficulty in pronouncing some polysyllabic words. For example, common difficulties are found in pronouncing:

- laboratory (often mispronounced as labroratrory)
- certificates (often mispronounced as cerstificates).

There may be words you find difficult, or stumble over on occasions? Think why this might be. Also, which words have you noticed other adults having difficulty with and how complex are the syllable combinations of these words?

Disordered or delayed speech

Many children have phases of unclear speech, but they do not all need to be seen by a speech therapist.

Dysfluency

Many temporary disorders are due to the child hastening to say something and stumbling over it in their eagerness and excitement. This common occurrence is known as **dysfluency**.

Hesitation occurs as a child tries to express themselves. This type of dysfluency is often associated with their attempt to use a more complex language structure. Speech therapists refer to this as normal developmental dysfluency as it does not usually need professional intervention.

When conversing with a dysfluent child, it is important to give them time and attention to minimise the effect of the dysfluency.

Professional Practice

The following checklist should be helpful.

- Do speak steadily and clearly yourself.
- Do give the dysfluent child your full attention.
- Do avoid interrupting the child whenever possible.
- Do focus on what they are saying, and try to ignore the dysfluency.
- Do not ask the child to repeat it or to start again.
- Do not tell the child to 'take a deep breath' before they speak.
- Do not tell the child to slow down.
- Do not ask the child to 'think it through' before they speak.
- Do not allow discussion of their dysfluency in their presence.

If a child's dysfluency continues for more than a short period of time, or if the parents or the child appear to be worried by the dysfluency, a referral to a speech therapist will usually be made. The British Stammering Association has drawn up the following guidelines to help with decision-making regarding referrals. A referral is made if the child has dysfluent speech and one or more of the following factors are present:

- a family history of stammering or speech or language problems
- the child is finding learning to talk difficult in any way
- the child shows signs of frustration or is upset by his speaking
- the child is struggling when talking
- the child is in a dual language situation and is stammering in her first language
- there is parental concern or uneasiness
- the child's general behaviour is causing concern.

Source: Mukherji & O'Dea (2000)

Elision

The term **elision** refers to when a child regularly misses out part of a speech sound altogether. It is a common occurrence, particularly with the second consonant of a cluster of two, e.g.

- the st in the word postman would become pos'man
- the pt in the word slept would become slep'.

In young children this is part of the maturational development of speech patterns. In older children and adults it is usually more likely to be habit!

Language disorders and speech therapy

Concerns regarding language development include:

- lack of communication with parents and carers in early weeks
- significant feeding difficulties (speech therapists are often involved at this early stage)
- lack of vocalisation from 3 months onwards
- no babbling from 8–9 months onwards

- lack of verbal responses to play
- vocalisation completely out of line with the developmental 'norms'.

When expressing themselves, language disordered children may:

- have difficulty in finding appropriate words
- display word-order confusion
- have difficulty in giving explanations
- use confused grammar
- omit grammatical word endings
- use confused sounds within individual words.

Language disorder can therefore affect other aspects of a child's learning and development.

Fig 18.1 Language disorder

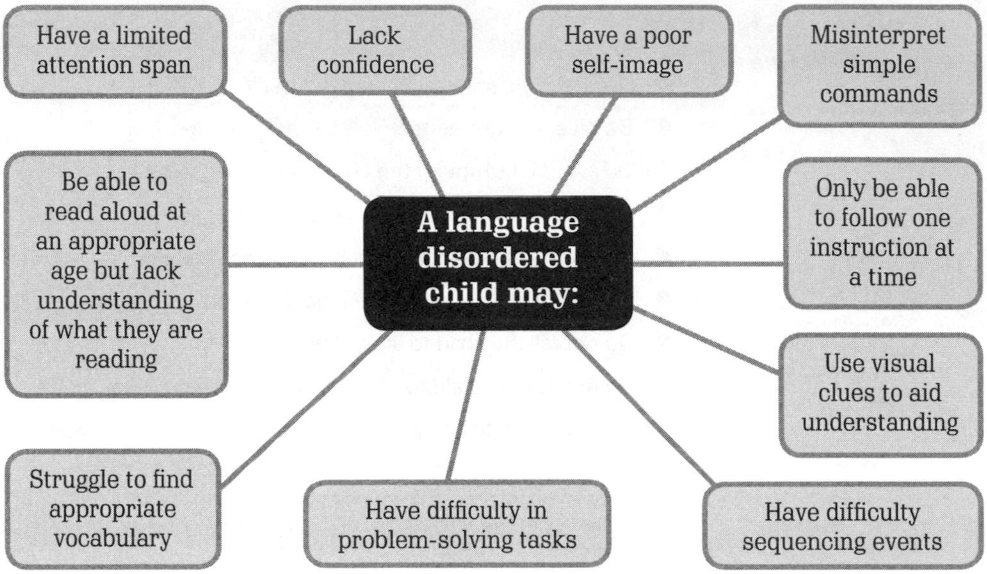
A language disordered child may:
Have a limited attention span
Lack confidence
Have a poor self-image
Misinterpret simple commands
Be able to read aloud at an appropriate age but lack understanding of what they are reading
Only be able to follow one instruction at a time
Use visual clues to aid understanding
Struggle to find appropriate vocabulary
Have difficulty in problem-solving tasks
Have difficulty sequencing events

Additional factors that can affect language include medical problems such as glue-ear. This is a condition of the middle ear in which sticky mucus is formed which is unable to drain away through the eustachian tubes in the normal way. If severe and left untreated, it can lead to permanent hearing loss.

A cleft lip and palate is another medical and physical problem that can affect speech. A child born with one or both of these physical conditions will automatically be referred to a speech therapist, to ensure that the most appropriate feeding positions are established from birth.

A useful source of further reading to extend your understanding of language development is Mukherji & O'Dea (2000).

Language delay
As with language disorder, any significant delay in language developing along the expected 'norms' is monitored, and a referral made to a speech therapist as appropriate. There are environmental, medical, social, cultural and genetic factors that can affect language development, as summarised in Figure 18.2.

Language as a means of communication
Language is essential to humans in order to communicate our needs, express our feelings and extend our experiences beyond our own environment by interacting with others. These interactions enable us to enhance our thinking and learn new skills. Spoken language is our most important means of communication. It is enhanced by facial expression, tone of voice and body language. Communication is an important aspect of early years professionalism.

Development of listening skills

If a child does not listen, he will miss out on a range of communication opportunities. Good listening skills ensure that messages are understood and their meanings are clear. Children

Fig 18.2 Factors contributing to language delay

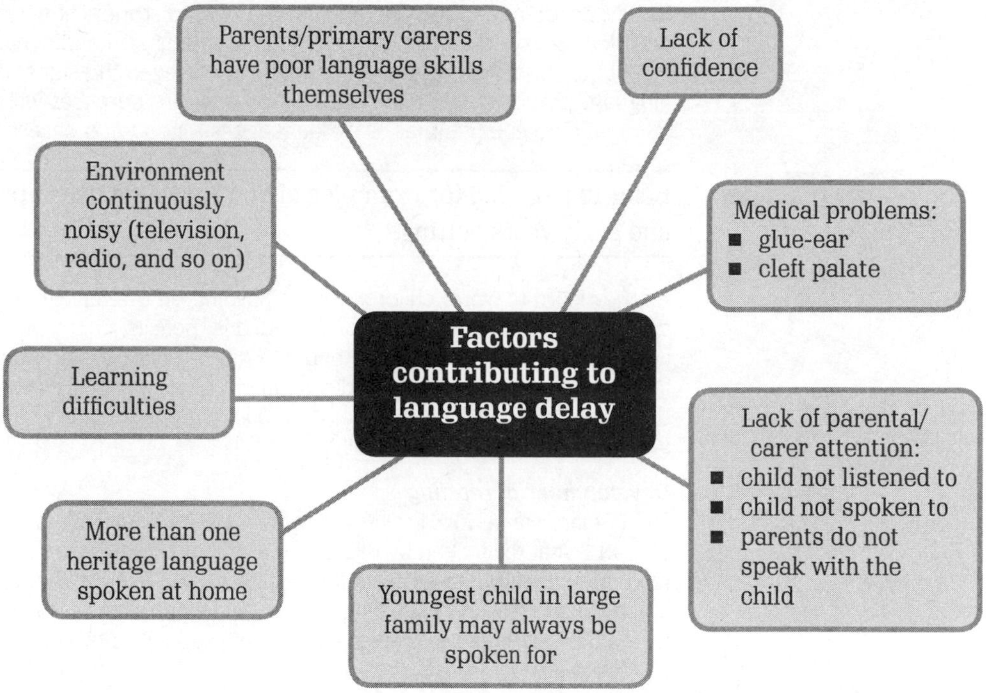

are more likely to develop good listening skills if they are listened to by significant adults and these adults are good listening role models for them. Palmer & Corbett (2003) state that a good listener:

- looks at the speaker
- tries to keep still
- concentrates on what the speaker is saying
- thinks about what the speaker says
- asks questions if it is not clear
- values what the speaker has to say
- tries to remember what the speaker has said.

Children need a good foundation in listening to enable them to discriminate sounds, a vital part of phonic work. If you look at the aims of the Foundation Stage Curriculum for communication, language and literacy you will see that it includes:

- 'enjoy listening to and using spoken and written language, and readily turn to it in their play and learning
- sustain attentive listening, responding to what they have heard by relevant comments, questions or actions
- listen with enjoyment, and respond to stories, songs and other music, rhymes and poems and make up their own songs, rhymes and poems
- hear and say initial and final sounds in words, and short vowel sounds within words
- link sounds to letters, naming and sounding the letters of the alphabet
- use their phonic knowledge to write simple regular words and make phonetically plausible attempts at more complex words.'

Source: QCA (2000)

Refer also to Green (2007), Units 1 and 3.

Development of reading and writing skills

As children learn to read, they will be using the experiences they have already had of rhyme, letter recognition, alliteration and phonic sounds. It is an accepted fact that children who are introduced to and surrounded by language in all its forms from birth, are likely to be earlier, better and more interested readers at an earlier age than those children who have limited exposure to language or the written word at a later date.

Ideally, children will have an early introduction to stories, finger rhymes, picture books, and singing, together with opportunities for discussion and conversation, and looking at alphabets. Also, having their awareness raised regarding signs, labels and the use of written language by adults for both practical and pleasure purposes will again help them build an automatic acceptance that using language is a good and necessary part of their life.

Link

Refer to page 255 for examples of how language use is promoted in the classroom and early years setting.

As they learn to write, children will be building on the mark-making skills they would have developed through the use of paint, crayons, pencils, charcoal, etc. Exposure to these media is needed for them to develop their fine motor skills, and an appropriate tripod grasp needed for concise pencil control. The development of controlled movements of the arm and shoulder through twirling streamers or ribbons, painting on easels or covered wall surfaces, and arm gestures linked to music, will all be helpful.

Development of reading

The Primary Framework for Literacy uses the term 'searchlights' to explain how children learn to read. What they mean by this is that a child uses four main 'pathways' of learning as they read through any written material, constantly cross-referring between each 'searchlight' to gain and build on their understanding. Understanding of phonics is needed initially in early reading, followed by letter and word recognition, both supported by context and general knowledge.

Fig 18.3 Knowledge and support provided by these 'searchlights'

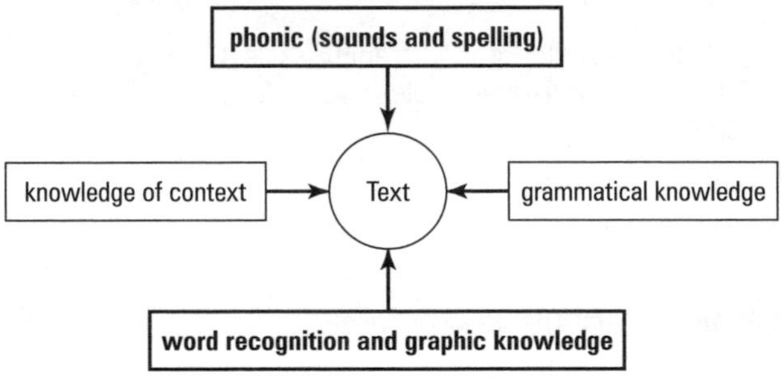

Children need to understand letter sounds and how they combine together to form blended sounds. As with all areas of learning it is important that the learning styles of all children are taken into account, having a balance of each style. Learning styles include:

- visual learners, who like uncluttered learning environments which do not easily distract them. They enjoy visual images to support them and are often creative learners who have a good imagination.
- auditory learners, who tend to have good memories, so will be able to cope with references back to previous learning. They learn well through discussion, can think well and benefit from the use of questioning.
- **kinaesthetic learners**, who like to be active. They will benefit from practical tasks, and hands-on learning opportunities where they learn through trial and error. They can be easily distracted so benefit from a focused learning environment.

Development of mark-making

The formation of letters follows on from the pencil control of mark-making and drawing. The illustration below shows how this process usually takes place. As with all development, it tends to be sequential and children follow the same sequential process, but at their own individual pace.

i

You may find it useful to refer to Palmer & Corbett (2003) for easy-to-follow guidance on supporting the development of literacy skills.

Link

Refer also to page 226 for an overview of the Early Learning Goals for Communication, Language and Literacy and the Core Learning Aims of the Primary Framework for Literacy for Reception, Year 1 and Year 2.

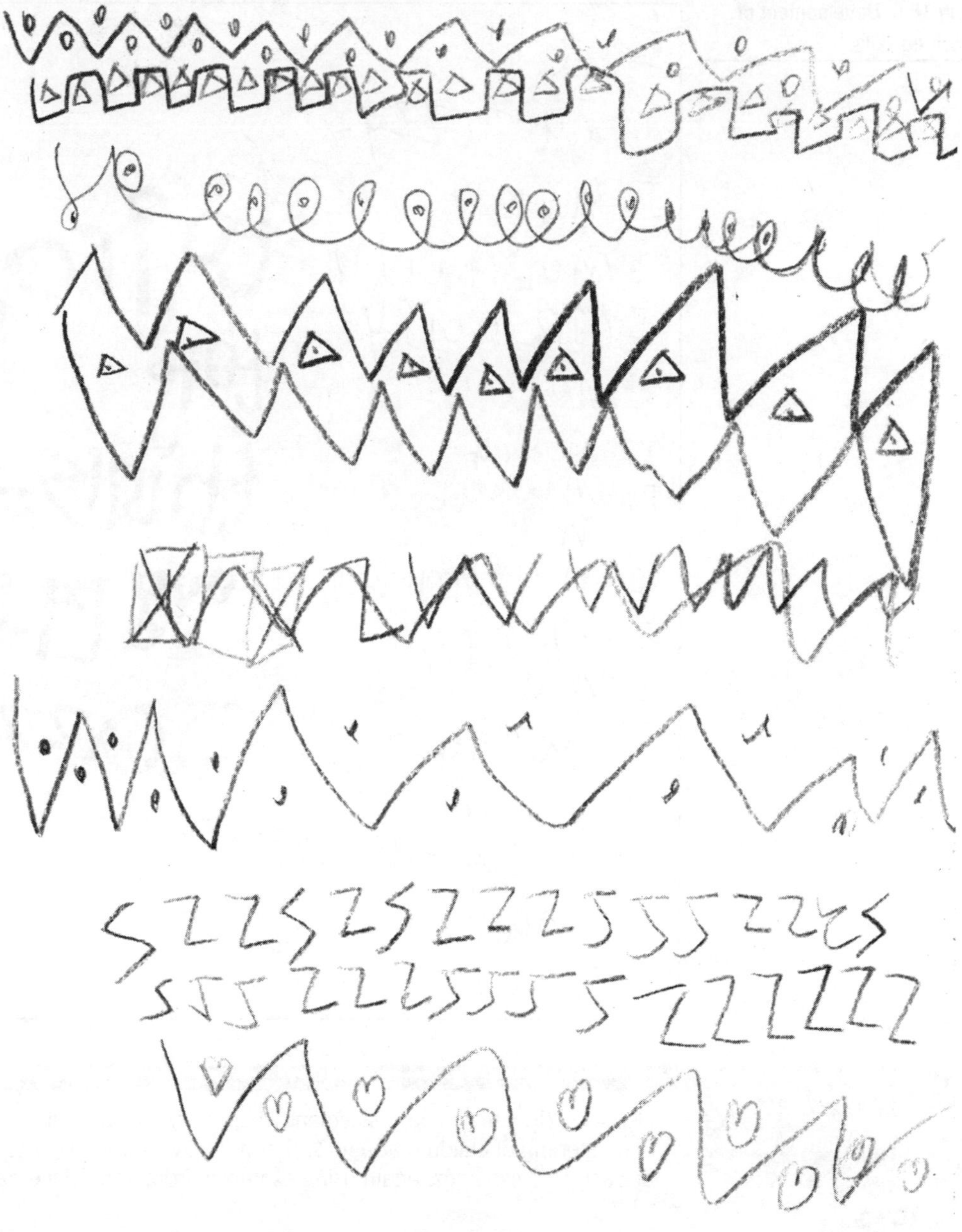

Fig 18.4 Early pattern practice helps develop letter formation

Fine motor development required for writing

Young children need to have opportunities to develop their fine motor skills through the use of resources such as:

- malleable materials: sand, water, clay
- puzzles
- construction and model making with junk, etc.
- threading activities, sewing and weaving
- pencils, crayons, pens, paint
- dressing-up clothes
- domestic skills such as dressing and undressing, teeth cleaning, using cutlery.

Access to these everyday play and domestic opportunities sees children move from having the clumsy primitive grasp of the youngest toddler as she crayons for the first time, through to developing the careful handling of pens and pencils and the desired neat script of the older child, as illustrated below. Their fine skills are developed through the actions needed for each activity, e.g. squeezing, rolling, grasping, pummelling, kneading, threading, careful positioning, manoeuvring, connecting, fixing, stacking, holding, and also the manipulation of knives, forks, zips, buttons, toggles, Velcro, hooks, sleeves, gloves, scarves, hats, shawls, etc.

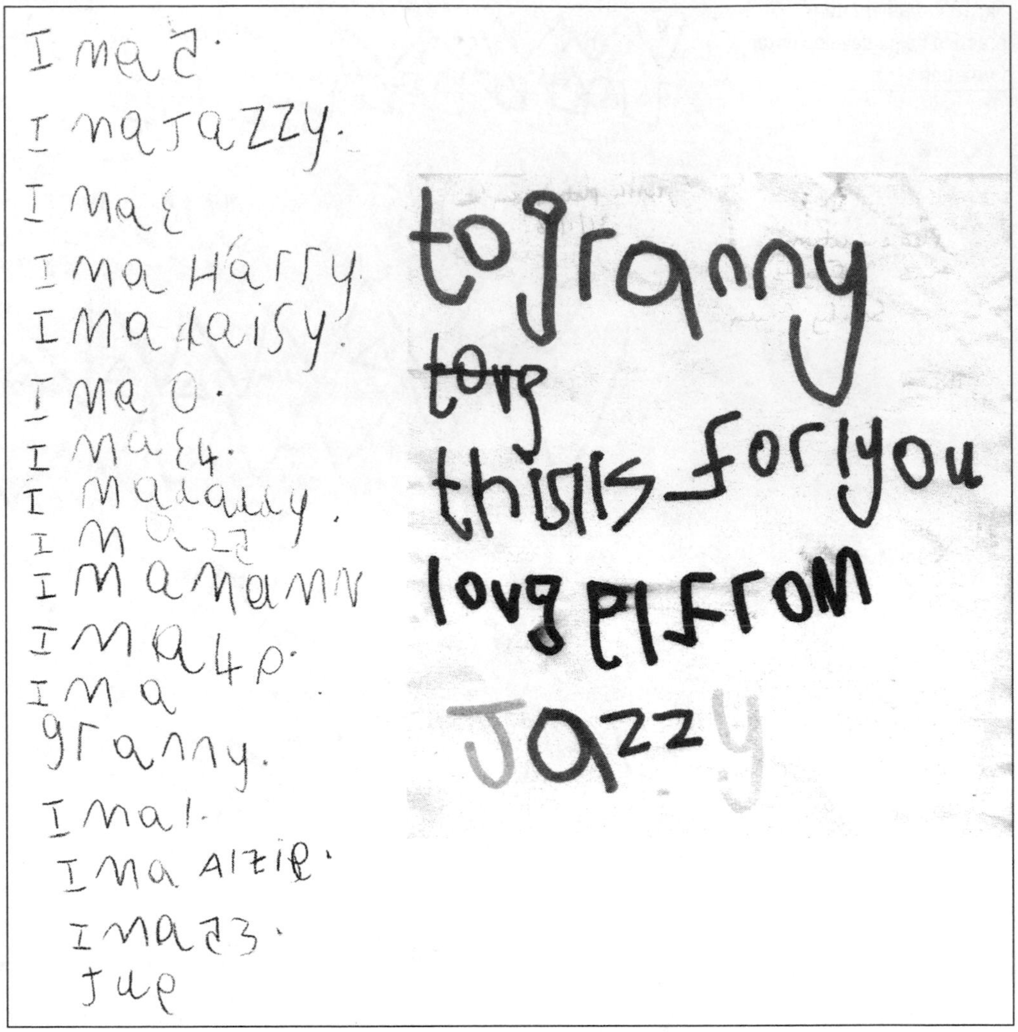

Fig 18.5 Development of writing skills

activity
INDIVIDUAL WORK 18.2
P2

Using children from your placement where possible, describe the stages of reading, writing and listening of children at age 3, 5 and 7. Give some ideas to support further development at each of these ages, again using examples from your placement where possible.

Methods for assessing literacy skills and development

Assessment can be both formative and summative.

- Formative assessment is assessment *for* learning (AfL).
- Summative assessment is the assessment *of* learning (AoL).

Assessment is a key part of the learning process as it provides information and feedback for teachers and early years practitioners to enable them to provide the most appropriate learning opportunities for the children in their care.

Assessment of learning (AoL)

This form of assessment is a snapshot of where a child has reached at a specific point in time. Examples include where the child has reached at the point of transfer from:

- early years setting to primary school
- one year group to another
- one key stage to another.

Assessment for learning (AfL)

This form of assessment should inform the next stage of learning, i.e. activities should be built on the outcomes of assessment, continually helping the child to develop a skill further and further.

Regarding the Primary Framework for Literacy, the Assessment Reform Group identified five key factors that improve learning through assessment:

- providing effective feedback to children
- actively involving children in their own learning
- adjusting teaching to take account of the results of assessment
- recognising the profound influence assessment has on the motivation and self-esteem of children, both of which are crucial to learning
- considering the need for children to be able to assess themselves and to understand how to improve.

The Assessment Reform Group also identified seven key characteristics which were evident in schools where AfL was effective in promoting learning and in raising standards of attainment. Table 18.4 illustrates the linkage between these seven characteristics and the key areas of development identified for schools.

Table 18.4 How the seven key characteristics link to the key areas of development for schools

Key characteristics of AfL	Key areas of development for schools
AfL is embedded in a view of learning and teaching of which it is an essential part.	■ Conditions for learning ■ Designing opportunities for learning ■ Day-to-day assessment strategies
AfL involves sharing learning goals with learners.	■ Using curricular targets ■ Designing opportunities for learning ■ Feedback on learning
AfL aims to help learners to know and to recognise the standards for which they are aiming.	■ Using curricular targets ■ Formative use of summative assessment
AfL involves learners in peer- and self-assessment.	■ Feedback on learning ■ Day-to-day assessment strategies ■ Formative use of summative assessment
AfL provides feedback which leads to learners recognising their next steps and how to take them.	■ Feedback on learning ■ How ICT can be used to support AfL
AfL is underpinned by the confidence that every learner can improve.	■ Conditions for learning ■ Feedback on learning
AfL involves both learner and teacher reviewing and reflecting on assessment data.	■ Feedback on learning ■ Involving parents and carers ■ Formative use of summative assessment data ■ How ICT can be used to support AfL

Based on materials from the Primary National Strategy website

Assessing the Foundation Stage

Assessment of learning will be recorded through the use of the newly developed Early Years Foundation Stage Profile. There is an example on p.202 which has been taken from the assessment profile of a child who moved through the Foundation Stage Curriculum, before the EYFS. Although headings may differ, it will give you an idea of how an assessment profile might be set out. Many practitioners will use the optional booklet developed by the DfES. Others will develop their own. As practitioners are only just starting to work with the new EYFS (which is not mandatory until September 2008) there are no completed profiles as yet available. The following material refers to the original assessment profile.

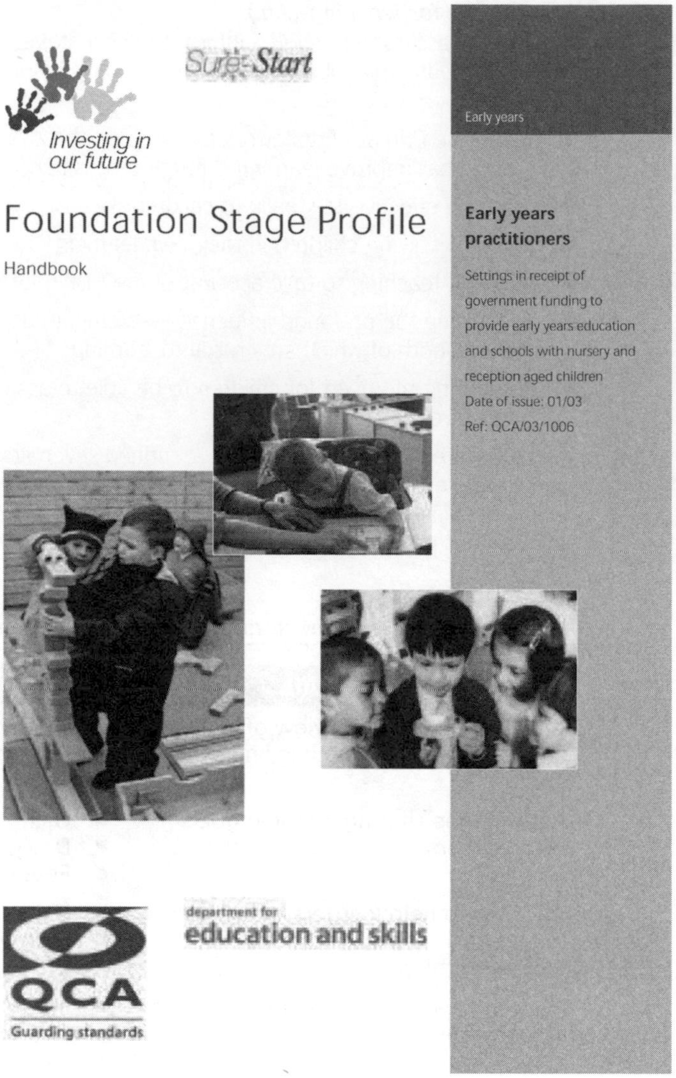

Sure Start
Investing in our future
Foundation Stage Profile
Handbook
Early years
Early years practitioners
Settings in receipt of government funding to provide early years education and schools with nursery and reception aged children
Date of issue: 01/03
Ref: QCA/03/1006
QCA
Guarding standards
department for
education and skills

Fig 18.6 Foundation Stage Profile Handbook

The most recent version of the Foundation Stage Profile Handbook can be downloaded at www.qca.org.uk.

The six areas of learning are set out as 13 assessment scales, shown in italics in the following list:

- Personal, social and emotional development
  - *dispositions and attitudes*
  - *social development*
  - *emotional development*
- Communication, language and literacy
  - *language for communication and thinking*
  - *linking sounds and letters*
  - *reading*
  - *writing*
- Mathematical development
  - *numbers as labels and for counting*
  - *calculating*
  - *shape, space and measure*

- *Knowledge and understanding of the world*
- *Physical development*
- *Creative development.*

Each assessment scale has nine assessment points:

- Points 1–3 of each assessment scale are based mostly on the stepping stones in the curriculum guidance file. It is usual for children to achieve points 1 to 3 before they achieve any of the Early Learning Goals (points 4 to 8).
- Points 4–8 have been taken form the Early Learning Goals and are approximately in the order of difficulty, based on early research trials. Most children will achieve in this order, but, as with all development, there will always be children whose development differs from the 'norm'.
- Point 9 in each assessment scale describes a child who is consistently working beyond the expected level of the Early Learning Goals, demonstrating a greater degree of both breadth and depth in their learning.

As the teacher or practitioner builds up a child's profile, it will be clear at which stage in the academic year each point in the assessment scale has been reached by the simple process of circling the appropriate dot to indicate autumn, spring or summer term.

Link

An example of a completed assessment profile is given on page 208.

Assessing and recording literacy skills

This section describes the four assessment scales for communication, language and literacy.

Language for communication and thinking (LCT)

The first three points of assessment for *Language for communication and thinking* are:

- listens and responds
- initiates communication with others, displaying greater confidence in more informal contexts
- talks activities through, reflecting on and modifying actions.

The *Foundation Stage Profile Handbook* explains how to approach assessments of each point in the assessment scale:

1 *Listens and responds* – At this stage, interaction with others is characterised mainly by the child's listening and responding to what others say through words and/or gestures. S/he rarely initiates talk. Assessment should be made on the basis of the child's achievement in her/his preferred language. For some children, this may be a recognised sign language or Picture Exchange Communication symbol system.

2 *Initiates communication with others, displaying greater confidence in more informal contexts* – The child talks and listens with emerging self-confidence in informal contexts, for example role play or snack-time. S/he responds willingly but is less likely to instigate talk during more adult-led group activities such as story-time. Again, assessment should be based on achievement in the child's preferred language.

3 *Talks activities through, reflecting on and modifying actions* – The child reveals her/his thinking through speech or other forms of communication. As the child reflects, s/he may modify actions or solve problems.

Assessments of scale points 4 to 9 should be in English (or BSL or sign-supported English), reflecting the child's emerging competence in the language. These are:

- listens with enjoyment to stories, songs, rhymes and poems, sustains attentive listening and responds with relevant comments, questions or actions
- uses language to imagine and recreate roles and experiences
- interacts with others in a variety of contexts, negotiating plans and activities and taking turns in conversations
- uses talk to organise, sequence and clarify thinking, ideas, feelings and events, exploring the meanings and sounds of new words
- speaks clearly with confidence and control, showing awareness of the listener.

The *Foundation Stage Profile Handbook* explains how to approach assessments of each point in the assessment scale:

4 *Listens with enjoyment to stories, songs, rhymes and poems, sustains attentive listening and responds with relevant comments, questions or actions* – The child listens attentively and with enjoyment, to stories, rhymes, etc, which s/he is able to recall in increasing detail, for example by sequencing pictures or cards. When listening to suggestions or explanations, s/he responds appropriately through actions or comments, or by asking relevant questions.

5 *Uses language to imagine and recreate roles and experiences* – During a range of activities, for example role-play, the child uses language to imagine, act out or develop experiences.

6 *Interacts with others in a variety of contexts, negotiating plans and activities and taking turns in conversations* – The child interacts with others, taking account of what they say and using language to negotiate plans and activities.

7 *Uses talk to organise, sequence and clarify thinking, ideas, feelings and events, exploring the meanings and sounds of new words* – The child often uses language rather than action to rehearse and reflect on experiences and to clarify ideas and feelings. S/he may talk to her/himself or others through challenging activities.

8 *Speaks clearly with confidence and control, showing awareness of the listener* – The child speaks clearly and with confidence in familiar groups, and also with people other than those who are well known to him or her. There is awareness of the listener, for example by the child's use of conventions such as greetings and courtesies, or by her/his inclusion of some detail when offering accounts or explanations.

By this stage, the child has achieved all the Early Learning Goals for language for communication and thinking. In addition, the child:

9 *Talks and listens confidently and with control, consistently showing awareness of the listener by including relevant detail. Uses language to work out and clarify ideas, showing control of a range of appropriate vocabulary* – The child talks and listens very confidently in a wide range of situations, sometimes adapting her/his vocabulary and tone of voice to the particular situation. S/he uses appropriate vocabulary in explaining ideas clearly. S/he shows an awareness of the needs of the listener by including relevant details, for example when describing events or activities that took place when the listener was not present.

Source: Based on QCA (2003)

Linking sounds and letters (LSL)
The first three points of assessment for *Linking sounds and letters* are:

- joins in with rhyming and rhythmic activities
- shows an awareness of rhyme and alliteration
- links some sounds to letters.

1 *Joins in with rhyming and rhythmic activities* – The child takes an active part in singing and rhyming activities, joining in with some of the words and following the rhythm.

2 *Shows an awareness of rhyme and alliteration* – The child is increasingly aware of rhyme in songs and poems. S/he sometimes distinguishes one sound from another or notices when words begin with the same sound.

3 *Links some sounds to letters* – The child hears some sounds and links them to specific letters, for example the letters in her/his name, and is able to recognise them.

Assessments of scale points 4–9 should be in English (or BSL or sign-supported English), reflecting the child's emerging competence in the language:

- links sounds to letters, naming and sounding letters of the alphabet
- hears and says initial and final sounds in words

- hears and says short vowel sounds within words
- uses phonic knowledge to read simple regular words
- attempts to read more complex words, using phonic knowledge.

4 *Links sounds to letters, naming and sounding letters of the alphabet* – Across the range of activities, the child is able to name and sound letters of the alphabet, and can recognise all or almost all of them.

5 *Hears and says initial and final sounds in words* – When sounding out words, the child distinguishes and says initial and final sounds.

6 *Hears and says short vowel sounds within words* – The child identifies some short vowel sounds, mainly in simple words with a consonant-vowel-consonant (CVC) pattern, e.g. hat, dog, pen.

7 *Uses phonic knowledge to read simple regular words* – The child uses her/his emerging phonic knowledge to read a range of simple words, particularly consonant-vowel-consonant (CVC) words, some of which are unfamiliar.

8 *Attempts to read more complex words, using phonic knowledge* – S/he attempts to read more complex words, sometimes with adult support.

By this stage, the child has achieved all the early learning goals for language for communication and thinking. In addition, the child:

9 *Uses knowledge of letters, sounds and words when reading and writing independently* – In her/his independent reading and writing, the child uses a range of strategies when tackling unfamiliar words, including fluent and appropriate use of phonic knowledge.

Source: Based on QCA (2003)

Reading (R)
The first three points of assessment for *Reading* are:

- is developing an interest in books
- knows that print conveys meaning
- recognises a few familiar words.

1 *Is developing an interest in books* – The child takes part in book-sharing activities, listening to stories with interest or choosing to look at books in the book area. S/he handles books appropriately, turning pages and looking at pictures.

2 *Knows that print conveys meaning* – The child can distinguish between pictures and print and recognises that information can be relayed in the form of print.

3 *Recognises a few familiar words* – The child recognises some familiar words, for example her/his own name and common words in the environment.

Assessments of scale points 4–9 should be in English (or BSL or sign-supported English), reflecting the child's emerging competence in the language:

- knows that, in English, print is read from left to right and top to bottom
- shows an understanding of the elements of stories, such as main character, sequence of events and openings
- reads a range of familiar and common words and simple sentences independently
- retells narratives in the correct sequence, drawing on language patterns of stories
- shows an understanding of how information can be found in non-fiction texts to answer questions about where, who, why and how.

4 *Knows that, in English, print is read from left to right and top to bottom* – The child follows print, for example when listening to taped stories or pretending to read, usually by pointing with a finger, from left to right and from top to bottom of the page.

5 *Shows an understanding of the elements of stories, such as main character, sequence of events and openings* – When discussing a familiar story, the child identifies the main characters and sequence of events. S/he understands that these elements are common to most stories. Stories that s/he knows very well are used as a basis for further development, for example through the child's imaginative play.

6 *Reads a range of familiar and common words and simple sentences independently* – With encouragement, the child gains meaning from simple story texts, making some use of a range of cues, including knowledge of the story or context, what makes sense grammatically and word/letter recognition. S/he reads at least 20 common words in a range of contexts.

7 *Retells narratives in the correct sequence, drawing on language patterns of stories* – The child retells the main points or events of a simple narrative in the correct sequence, using linking language. Particular language patterns, such as 'Once upon a time' or '"Not I," said the cat' (*The Little Red Hen*), are remembered and used.

8 *Shows an understanding of how information can be found in non-fiction texts to answer questions about where, who, why and how* – The child distinguishes fiction and non-fiction texts. S/he is developing an understanding of how to find information in non-fiction texts, for example by using the contents page.

By this stage, the child has achieved all the early learning goals for language for communication and thinking. In addition, the child:

9 *Reads books of own choice with some fluency and accuracy* – The child uses a range of strategies to read simple texts independently with fluency and understanding. Examples of suitable books are *Hold Tight Bear!*, *Not Now Bernard*, *Titch* or *Nandy's Bedtime*. S/he may need adult help when tackling an unfamiliar or more complex text.

Source: Based on QCA (2003)

Writing (W)
The first three points of assessment for *Writing* are:

- experiments with mark-making, sometimes ascribing meanings to the marks
- uses clearly identifiable letters to communicate meaning
- represents some sounds correctly in writing.

1 *Experiments with mark-making, sometimes ascribing meanings to the marks* – The child makes marks, choosing from a variety of markers such as brushes, pens and pencils, and observing the effect of moving the marker across a surface. S/he may not always ascribe a meaning to those marks, although there is a general awareness of the writing process.

2 *Uses clearly identifiable letters to communicate meaning* – The letters which the child produces, for example in a role-play context, may be from her/his own name. S/he assigns a meaning to what has been written. There is often no sound/symbol match at this stage.

3 *Represents some sounds correctly in writing* – The child's attempts at writing words include some appropriate letters, usually in the initial position.

Assessments of scale points 4–9 should be in English (or BSL or sign-supported English), reflecting the child's emerging competence in the language:

- writes own name and other words from memory
- holds a pencil and uses it effectively to form recognisable letters, most of which are correctly formed
- attempts writing for a variety of purposes, using features of different forms
- using phonic knowledge to write simple regular words and make phonetically plausible attempts at more complex words
- begins to form captions and simple sentences, sometimes using punctuation.

4 *Writes own name and other words from memory* – The child writes at least her/his first name, as well as some other words. These may be key words currently featured in literacy session and/or words that are important to her/him, such as 'mum', 'dad', 'cat' and perhaps the names of other family members.

5 *Holds a pencil and uses it effectively to form recognisable letters, most of which are correctly formed* – The child's writing consists of recognisable letters. When assessing this criterion, the practitioner should observe the child while engaged in a writing activity, to establish that the child is holding a pencil effectively and that letters are generally correctly formed, for example by the use of an anti-clockwise movement and the retracing of vertical lines when appropriate.

6 *Attempts writing for a variety of purposes, using features of different forms* – Often in a role-play context, the child attempts writing for a range of purposes, for example writing a shopping list, a doctor's prescription, instructions for playing a game or a letter to Father Christmas. S/he may also write stories. Features of different forms, such as lists or labels, are evident.

7 *Uses phonic knowledge to write simple regular words and make phonetically plausible attempts at more complex words* – The child's efforts are phonetically plausible when s/he writes simple regular words and particularly when s/he attempts to write more complex words, sometimes with support.

8 *Begins to form captions and simple sentences, sometimes using punctuation* – The child attempts to write simple sentences, sometimes using capital letters and full stops. S/he may need adult support.

By this stage, the child has achieved all the early learning goals for language for communication and thinking. In addition, the child:
Source: Based on QCA (2003)

9 *Communicates meaning through phrases and simple sentences with some consistency in punctuation sentences* – The child attempts writing in a variety of forms using an appropriate range of vocabulary. The text is readable, as words are either spelt correctly or are phonetically plausible. Letters are reasonably consistent in size and spacing between words is generally consistent. What is written makes sense and there is some consistency in the use of capital letters and full stops.

See the example of a completed assessment profile in Figure 18.7.

Changes to the assessment process will be found on the following website: www.standards.dfes.gov.uk/eyfs/. Your placement supervisor may also be able to show you an example.

Fig 18.7 An example of a completed assessment profile for the old foundation stage

JASMINE

Communication, language and literacy
Language for communication and thinking

1 She listens and responds.
Entry

2 She initiates communication with others, displaying greater confidence in more informal contexts.
SprA 06

3 She talks activities through, reflecting on and modifying actions.
SprA 06

4 She listens with enjoyment to stories, songs, rhymes and poems, sustains attentive listening and responds with relevant comments, questions or actions.
SumA 06

5 She uses language to imagine and recreate roles and experiences.
AutA 06

6 She interacts with others in a variety of contexts, negotiating plans and activities and taking turns in conversation.
SumA 06

7 She uses talk to organise sequence and clarify thinking, ideas, feelings and events, exploring the meanings and sounds of new words.
SumA 06

8 She speaks clearly with confidence and control, showing awareness of the listener.

9 She talks and listens confidently and with control, consistently showing awareness of the listener by including relevant detail. uses language to work out and clarify ideas, showing control of a range of appropriate vocabulary.

Communication, language and literacy
Linking sounds and letters

1 She joins in with rhyming and rhythmic activities.
Entry

2 She shows an awareness of rhyme and alliteration.
EndFSP

3 She links some sounds to letters.
SprA 06

4 She links sounds to letters, naming and sounding letters of the alphabet.
SumA 06

5 She hears and says initial and final sounds in words.
EndFSP

6 She hears and says short vowel sounds within words.
EndFSP

7 She uses phonic knowledge to read simple regular words.
EndFSP

8 She attempts to read more complex words, using phonic knowledge.

9 She uses knowledge of letters, sounds and words when reading and writing independently.

Fig 18.7 An example of a completed assessment profile for the olld foundation stage

JASMINE

Communication, language and literacy
Reading

1 She is developing an interest in books.
Entry

2 She knows that print conveys meaning.
SprA 06

3 She recognises familiar words.
EndFSP

4 She knows that in English, print is read from left to right and top to bottom.
SprA 06

5 She shows an understanding of the elements of stories, such as main character, sequence of events and openings.
SumA 06

6 She reads a range of familiar and common words and simple sentences independently.

7 She retells narratives in the correct sequence, drawing on language patterns of stories.
SumA 06

8 She shows an understanding of how information can be found in non-fiction texts to answer questions about where, who, why and how.

9 She reads books of her own choice with some fluency and accuracy.

Communication, language and literacy
Reading

1 She experiments with mark-marking, sometimes ascribing meaning to the marks.
Entry

2 She uses some clearly identifiable letters to communicate meaning.
SprA 06

3 She represents some sounds correctly in writing.
SumA 06

4 She writes her own name and other words from memory.
SprA 06

5 She holds a pencil and uses it effectively to form recognisable letters, most of which are correctly formed.
SumA 06

6 She attempts writing for a variety of purposes, using features of different forms.
SumA 06

7 She uses phonic knowledge to write simple regular words and make phonetically plausible attempts at more complex words.

8 She begins to form captions and simple sentences, sometimes using punctuation.

9 She communicates meaning through phrases and simple sentences with some consistency in punctuating sentences.

Fig 18.8 An example of how an assessment can be made

QCA (2003), pages 70–1

Example of an assessment opportunity

The example in Figure 18.8 is typical of how many practitioners set out their planning.

Focus: sharing and recreating a poem, rhyme or song

Key scale points:	Links to other areas of learning:
Communication, language and literacy: ***LCT 4*** Listens with enjoyment to stories, songs, rhymes and poems, sustains attentive listening and responds with relevant comments, questions or actions. ***LCT 5*** Uses language to imagine and recreate roles and experiences. ***LCT 6*** Interacts with others in a variety of contexts, negotiating plans and activities and taking turns in conversation. ***LCT 7*** Uses talk to organise, sequence and clarify thinking, ideas, feelings and events, exploring the meanings and sounds of new words. ***LCT 8*** Speaks clearly with confidence and control, showing awareness of the listener.	Personal, social and emotional development: ***DA 7, DA 8, SD 4, SD 9*** Communication, language and literacy: ***LSL 1, LSL 2, R 4, R 6, R 7***

Resources:

- poster or big book of a well-known poem, nursery rhyme or song, which is familiar to children
- glove and/or finger puppet/s

Introducing the activity to the children:

Look at the rhyme together. The children may want to comment on the illustrations or what the poem/rhyme is about. Share the poem with the group, encouraging them to join with the repetitive and rhyming phrases. Discuss the poem with the children, allowing them to relate it to their own experiences. Encourage them to talk about how the poem makes them feel, or about how the characters in the poem feel (eg how Humpty Dumpty felt after his fall. What would the children want to give him to make him feel better?).

Encourage children to act out aspects of the poem or rhyme, for example using finger puppets. Suggest that they work as a group and decide among themselves how to do this. They may wish to 'perform' their work to you or to another group of children. Discuss how the children could use the poem to make their own version, substituting words, rhymes, or characters. Collect ideas from the group about a different version. Help the children to subsequently organise their ideas and develop their ideas with the practitioner as the scribe.

State the learning objective/intention to the children just before they begin the activity and remind them of it as necessary as they carry out the activity

Let's see how well you can act out the rhyme with the finger puppets or make up your own version

Assessment opportunities:

Communication, language and literacy

- Does the child remember previously sharing the poem? Does s/he focus on the poem, even if not joining in? Does s/he join in with spoken words or actions depicting the rhyme or respond to the rhythm as the rhyme is spoken? Does the child offer comments/opinions about the poem, relating to their own experiences, or the illustrations? Does s/he use language to recreate aspects of the poem? Does/she use some of the language of the poem when acting it out in a small group? Does the child interact and negotiate when planning the retelling of the poem, or helping to create a new version? ***LCT 4, 5, 6, 7, 8***
- Does s/he follow the words on the poster when sharing the rhyme? Does s/he retell the narrative in the correct sequence? ***R 4, 6, 7***

Personal, social and emotional development

- Does s/he contribute during the group discussion, or when acting out the poem together?
- Does s/he sustain concentration over the period? ***DA 7,8***

Fig 18.8 An example of how an assessment can be made

QCA (2003), pages 70–1

Case Study:

Curriculum context:

The nursery rhyme 'Mary had a little lamb'.

How the activity was introduced and the success criteria made clear:

First, we talked about rhyming words, and pairs of words that do/do not rhyme. I told the children that we were going to read the (Mary had a little lamb) rhyme out loud together. After this part of the activity, I asked them if they could change the ending of the rhyme.

Brief outline of adapted activity:

- Children identified words that do and do not rhyme.
- I held up a big book of nursery rhymes and we discussed the picture – some of the children guessed that the nursery rhyme was Mary had a little lamb.
- All the children joined in with saying the rhyme out loud.
- The children discussed their pets and how they would have felt if they had followed the children.
- We also discussed the word 'rule' and its meaning, and why there are rules.
- We acted out the rhyme as a group, with children taking different roles.
- Finally we discussed how to make our own version of the rhyme.

Observations – what the children said and did:

Amber: from the illustrations, thought the nursery rhyme was 'Little Bo Peep'. Said she would feel happy if her rabbit had followed her like the lamb in the rhyme.

Carly: thought the rhyme was 'Baa baa black sheep'. She said that 'rule' means (in this context) 'no pets allowed in school' ***(SD 6)***. She enthusiastically offered ideas on how to act out the poem using finger puppets ***(LCT 5, 6)***. Suggested replacing 'lamb' and 'fleece' with 'dog' and 'fur' ***(LCT 5)***.

Jordan: immediately recited the poem to everyone when he saw the illustration ***(LCT 4)***. Said that he feels happy when his cat follows him into the garden. Commented that there are rules 'So children don't get hurt' ***(SD 6)***. Used his puppet to say 'hello' to the other children's puppets ***(LCT 5)***. He took the lead in clarifying ideas on how to act out the poem ***(LCT 7)***.

Jemina: followed the words of the rhyme in the book with her finger as it was read out loud ***(R 4)***. She was happy to negotiate ideas when acting out/developing an alternative version of the poem ***(LCT 6)***.

Laurence: managed to concentrate while reciting poem but attention wavered and went off topic when discussing it.

remember

Assessment helps practitioners ensure that every aspect of the relevant curriculum is being covered. Using observations and assessments to inform planning helps guarantee that a child's needs are being identified and that strategies to support those needs and help children achieve a planned goal are included in future sessions or activities.

The role of the adult

The role of the adult in planning and implementing opportunities to develop reading and writing skills is summarised in Figure 18.9.

Observation and assessment

Using a range of observation methods, individual children's progress should be followed and recorded according to the setting's procedural practice. This helps identify any specific areas of need, the areas of literacy in which they are less able (if any) and also their preferred learning style. In early years settings this will usually be carried out by a child's key worker, using the benchmarks of the appropriate curriculum or guidance structure, e.g. Birth to Three Matters, Foundation Stage Curriculum or, from September 2008, the Early Years Foundation Stage. In school this would usually be the class teacher, but could also be carried out by the classroom assistant, with assessment linked to the Primary National Strategy and National Curriculum as appropriate.

Fig 18.9 The role of the adult

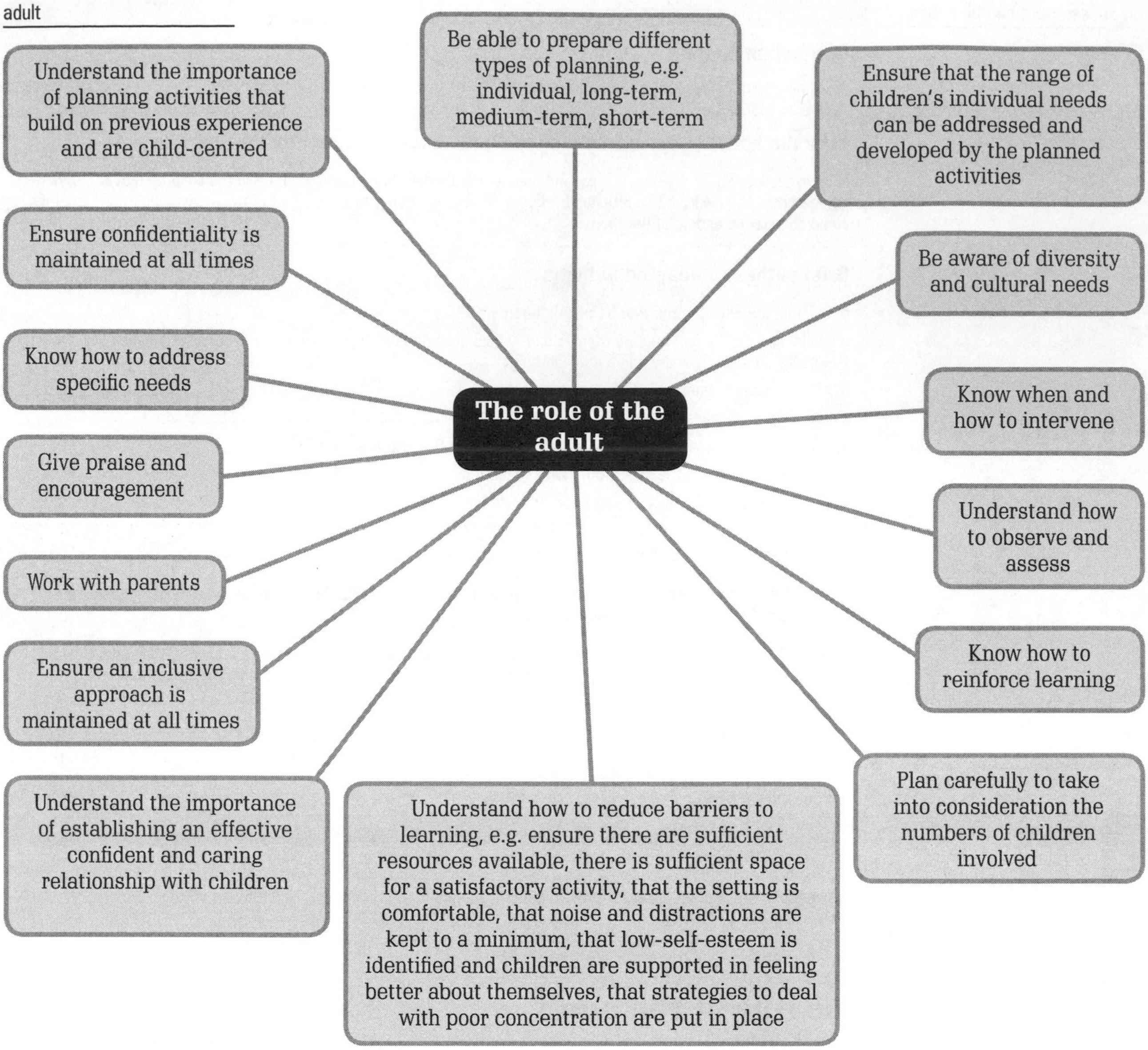

Reinforcement

Some children will develop the understanding of how letters are linked to individual speech sounds (grapheme–phoneme) quite quickly and be ready to sound out word blends (e.g. d/o/g). The explanation of how vowels and consonants are articulated on pages 186–188 demonstrates how difficult this can be for some children and how the greater number of consonants in a word, the more complex the spoken or written format becomes.

It is usual for most children (without any noticeable speech difficulty) to be able to pronounce complex words long before they can write them, although they may make attempts (part of emergent writing).

Reinforcement is about repeating elements of learning to help consolidate them for the child or group. Children need a:

> 'broad and rich language curriculum that takes full account of developing the four independent strands of language – speaking, listening, reading and writing – and enlarging children's stock of words.'
>
> Source: DfES (2006)

remember It is important that a group of children are not simply taught through one learning style.

Sometimes a different approach will be needed for different children according to preferred learning styles. Additional practice is appropriate for some children. For most children, taking a contextualised approach works best.

Praise and encouragement

As with all activities, praise and encouragement work wonders. Children need to know that they have adult approval and will continue to work to achieve this further.

Link Refer to Unit 14, page 110, to remind yourself about positive reinforcement.

Working with parents

At times, children will need extra practice in order to maintain progress, or to reach their potential. In schools teachers have limited time to spend with each child on an individual basis and if a child takes a little more time than others to grasp a concept, or to consolidate new learning, time spent with the child on these skills outside of the classroom can be invaluable. Having 'homework' is now commonplace and most children enjoy sharing these experiences with their family. Good links with parents enables active encouragement of reading at home, using either schemed readers or library books, and also word tins/lists, etc. for parents to help encourage, reinforce and be actively involved with their development.

The importance of planning activities that build on previous experience and are child-centred

case study 18.1

Stella and Max

Max learns best by doing. He is easily distracted from tasks and his key worker, Stella, tries to find as many hands-on opportunities as she can for him. Max has recently been building with construction materials. He is very proud of what he has achieved. Stella has made a set of labels for the block shapes he has been using and the colours in the construction kit. She is now helping him to match them to his building.

activity

1 What else could Stella do to support Max?

2 Is this child-centred learning do you think?

The more opportunities built on children's current interests, the more successful learning will be for many children, especially those who are kinaesthetic learners.

Professional Practice

- There needs to be a planned curriculum and day for children of all ages, as this provides both stability and structure. However, teachers and early years practitioners should also, whenever possible, take up spontaneous learning opportunities. These 'triggers' will often be initiated by the arrival of an object of interest, a sudden downfall of snow or hailstones, the return of a child or adult from somewhere special, e.g. hospital, holiday, etc. Such opportunities offer rich learning opportunities that may be lost if relegated to a planned 'slot' at a later date.

Numbers of children involved

The number of children in any one teaching group will be determined by staffing, the overall class size, the range of learning styles within the class and the ability levels of the children. It will also be influenced by how much individual input each child is likely to need. If you know that a child or group of children are likely to need a higher level of adult guidance or support than 'average', you should whenever practicable work with these children in smaller numbers, or one-to-one. Some children will be able to learn from their peers, and so a well thought through pairing can be a good strategy.

Link Refer to page 190 and also to Unit 14, page 106, for information on Lev Vygotsky and his theory known as the zone of proximal development, and also Jerome Bruner's thinking on scaffolding.

The range of needs to be addressed and developed by the activities

Some children will be considered 'able' in some aspects of literacy, but struggle with other areas. These are important aspects to take into account. For example, a child who has a good vocabulary and tries to use it in his writing, but who finds letter formation slow and difficult, can be 'put off' if he is set tasks that are too challenging for him to undertake with some degree of success. Have a look at the following case study.

case study 18.2

Bryn

Bryn is 6 years old. He uses a range of vocabulary to describe and discuss all that interests him or happens around him, asking relevant questions and listening carefully to the answers. He is a confident speaker, both one-to-one and in a group. However, Bryn finds writing difficult. He has a clumsy pencil grip and writing is a slow and laborious process. Bryn gets frustrated during written activities and his extensive knowledge and understanding of many different subjects is not evidenced by his writing.

activity

1 What activities could you devise for Bryn to help him improve his pencil skills?
2 What would you encourage Bryn to do to build on his fine motor skills in general?
3 How else could Bryn's knowledge and understanding be evidenced?
4 What might be the outcome of an assessment purely based on Bryn's writing?

Awareness of diversity and cultural need

Some children will be learning English as an additional language. It will be important in helping them understand and consolidate their learning to introduce and embed language within appropriate contexts. The use of both two-dimensional and three-dimensional visual images will be helpful, showing children an artefact or picture of the object you are talking to them about, e.g. having a selection of brushes when discussing personal care, emphasising each name as they are being demonstrated: toothbrush, hairbrush, clothes brush. This helps to introduce the word brush, and shows how the same word is used in each action, i.e. 'brush' is the action word, and 'hair, tooth and clothes' are the nouns.

When asking questions, again an action to accompany your words may be helpful, e.g.

- pointing to the garden whilst asking, 'Do you want to go outside?'
- making a drinking motion with your hand whilst asking, 'Do you want a drink?'
- dabbing your eyes and pointing to the child to ask, 'Are you feeling upset?'
- making an 'open book' action with your hands and pointing back and forth between the child and yourself to indicate, 'Would you like to share a story with me?'

Children will need to have plenty of opportunities to listen to the new language they are learning being spoken. Examples include group talking times (Circle Time is ideal), listening to taped stories, songs and rhymes, etc. These will all help familiarise the child with the language sounds. It is important to speak clearly and as normally as possible.

It will also be important to show that a child's heritage language is valued by the setting, also benefiting English-speaking children as they are introduced to a range of different writing styles and letter formations. Most schools and early years settings have greetings signs or welcome posters in a range of languages, but there is so much more that can be done.

Having a selection of dual language books readily available can be invaluable. Practitioners can read to the group using the English, whilst showing the other language alongside. This helps the child understand that their heritage language is valued by the setting. It will also encourage non-English speaking parents to sit and read them with their own child (and others too), enabling all the children to listen to, and appreciate the differences in their language. This helps the whole family feel valued and part of the school or early years setting community, and also helps reinforce the message that learning both their heritage language and English is a good thing.

Professional Practice

- Whenever possible, it can be helpful if early years practitioners and teachers learn a few words in each heritage language represented within their group or class.
- Many parents will be very willing to transcribe greetings, messages, etc. for labelling and display use. They often just need to be asked.
- Where possible, include artefacts from a child's culture in relevant play situations, e.g. chappati pan, chopsticks, sari, shalwah kameez.

remember

Many languages do not follow the left to right convention, as found in written English.

Children who are learning more than one language at a time are generally slower in their language development in general. It should be recognised that some children will be learning more than one dialect at home, so learning English may well be a third language for them.

Activities to encourage left to right actions will help children to understand the writing conventions of written English before they are ready to read or write themselves. Pencil skills, weaving, sewing, etc. can all help reinforce this action.

Children learning English as an additional language will build up their skills gradually. They normally understand far more than they can speak in the earliest weeks and months, and they will normally be able to speak far more than they can read or write as time moves on. In this way, language development follows the same sequential pathway as for any child learning their heritage language. You have probably found the same if you have tried to learn another language in the past.

Types of planning – individual, long-term, medium-term, short-term

Planning for the long term provides practitioners with a broad overview of the main themes they wish to cover. This type of planning is not usually followed rigidly, it is flexible according to need and circumstance. Written long-term plans are useful as a basis for all staff to refer back to, reminding them of how the period of time (e.g. an academic or calendar year) is intended to be approached.

Early years settings

In early years settings, long-term plans ensure that all six areas of learning in the Early Years Foundation Stage (EYFS) are given sufficient attention, both in allocated time and in regularity, in order for children to have meaningful learning experiences and for them to make progress appropriately.

Short-term planning is more likely to focus on day-to-day planning, or weekly plans. These should be taking into account the observations and informal assessments made of children and use them to inform the next stage of short-term planning.

Medium-term planning is used by some, but not all practitioners. It provides a secure link between the long-term and the short-term plans, e.g.

- Long-term planning may cover a whole school year, term by term, or season by season.
- Medium-term planning may be linked to each of the terms or seasons within the planning year, setting out topics to be covered over short periods of time.
- Short-term plans will be the weekly and daily planning, breaking down each topic even further, often specifying resources, timings, etc.

Schools

Regarding the long-term planning of the Primary Framework for Literacy, schools will be working with three major themes, made up from clusters of objectives from the framework. These main themes are:

- Narrative – narrative, plays and play scripts
- Non-fiction
- Poetry.

Each of the main themes will be divided up into unit blocks, and each unit will last two weeks, three weeks or four weeks.

Link Refer to page 246 for the 12 strands of the Primary Framework for Literacy.

The framework is available on line at www.standards.dfes.gov.uk/primaryframework.

Professional Practice

- There is no hard and fast rule regarding planning, but each school or early years setting will have their preferred 'in-house' method. Be sure to check the requirements of each setting where you are on placement, or in which you work.

Importance of establishing an effective, confident and caring relationship with children

Building up relationships with children and their families is a fundamental part of the role of every teacher and early years practitioner. If an adult has a secure and positive relationship with a child, then it is likely that the child will feel able to ask questions, express their worries, and feel able to 'try' without fearing making mistakes. An adult who upholds confidentiality and is known to do this will receive the trust of parents. This effective relationship enables practitioners to have a better understanding of:

- when and how to intervene in the learning of each individual child
- the inclusive needs of individual children
- how they can address each child's specific needs.

It will also enable them to raise concerns with parents about a child's progress, knowing that the parent will usually trust them and their judgement and be willing to explore options and take advice from other professionals, knowing that it will be carried out within a framework of confidence and professionalism.

Reducing barriers to learning

For optimum progress in language and literacy development, it is important that any identified barriers are removed or reduced. Examples include:

- ensuring that there are sufficient resources and space available to provide each child with a meaningful and satisfactory experience
- ensuring that children are not distracted by unsuitable seating or work surfaces, causing discomfort or taking their attention away from where it is meant to be
- reducing noise levels. Many children find listening hard, so it is important that unnecessary noise is kept to a minimum. Having an 'only one person to speak at a time' rule will help children to keep focused
- giving praise and encouragement for effort. This is particularly important for those children learning English as an additional language, to build up children's self-confidence and help them avoid developing low self-esteem
- giving one-to-one attention whenever possible, particularly if a child is known to find concentration difficult, e.g. children with disorders such as ADD and ADHD.

remember

Poor concentration can result from distraction, boredom and lack of confidence. The points noted above will help.

Link

Refer to Unit 27, page 282, for more on ADD and ADHD.

activity
INDIVIDUAL WORK 18.3
P4

Using Figure 18.9 (p. 206) as a starting point, give a range of examples of how you personally have been involved in supporting the development of literacy skills with children during your placement experience. Remember to include examples from each of the age ranges you have worked with, and each type of setting you have experienced, e.g. nursery, school, childminder, etc.

Specific needs

Meeting children's individual learning needs

In order to meet the individual needs of a child, practitioners need to understand the main problems associated with conditions and disorders they are likely to come across, and where they can obtain information on less common disorders, should they need to support a child who has them. Commonly heard terms linked to additional needs include:

- developmental delay
- congenital conditions and illness, e.g. hearing and sight loss
- dysphasia
- dyslexia
- dyspraxia
- dysgraphia

Developmental delay

Developmental delay can be due to a variety of reasons. Some children will develop slowly due to being born prematurely. These infants may have delayed development for the first few years, with most eventually catching up with their peers.

Some children who have a chronic illness may also suffer delayed development. Many will miss out on schooling, or will regularly be tired, due either to their illness or the effect of medication. Time with friends can also be limited which can impact on children's social development.

Development can be delayed due to sensory disabilities, physical difficulties and genetically inherited disorders and also through social and environmental factors, such as passive smoking and/or either alcohol or drug intake whilst still in the womb. Poverty, passive smoking, neglect, abuse and a lack of secure attachments can also impact on development.

Link

Refer to Unit 14, page 114, and Unit 27, page 268, for more on this.

You may also like to refer to Unit 5, page 237, of Green (2007) for more on the impact of abuse.

Congenital conditions and illness

If a child is born with a condition already present, it is referred to as being congenital. These conditions are mostly identified at birth, e.g. Down's syndrome and some forms of cerebral palsy. Some are identified within the first few weeks, e.g. blindness or vision impairment, profound deafness or hearing loss, as reactions by the infant differ to what is expected of them. Others are identified through specific testing, e.g. the distraction hearing test carried out at around 8 months, and the otoacoustic emissions test (that has mostly taken over from the distraction hearing test), which is carried out before an infant reaches 4 weeks old. Children with congenital problems can be helped to reach their full potential through a carefully planned programme of activities designed to stimulate and compensate for any known sensory loss.

Children who are blind or are visually impaired can be helped by:

- tactile experiences to help them develop understanding through touch
- an environment that enriches all their senses
- a rich spoken environment, with adults talking to them throughout each activity, domestic routine or experience, naming, describing, explaining, etc.
- rhymes and songs, musical boxes, musical instruments and listening to music
- listening to stories, both orally and through tapes/CDs, enjoying repetition and familiarity, and learning to predict, to anticipate, to understand the process of stories told either orally or through auditory media
- input from Portage workers in the earliest years.

Children who are deaf or have a hearing impairment can be helped by:

- a rich visual environment which encourages them to look carefully and with pleasure
- an environment that enriches all of their senses

- an environment where written text is used widely, labelling items all around them, helping them make links between spoken (or signed) words and printed text
- learning sign language or a signing system such as Makaton
- the use of puppets, dolls and small world play to help them re-enact stories for themselves
- books of all types, picture books in both colour and black and white, stories with pictures alongside as cues, illustrated alphabet books, etc.
- input from Portage workers in the earliest years.

Dysphasia

Dysphasia is the term used to describe a child who has difficulty in expressing their thoughts in words. Another term, **aphasia**, describes the child who is unable to express their thoughts in words.

Children with dysphasia can be helped by:

- opportunities to express themselves through painting and drawing
- opportunities to use a range of creative resources
- modelling of actions and expressions by adults working alongside them
- the use of alternative communication systems
- patience and plenty of time allowed for their communications to take place
- an environment with minimum distractions to help them concentrate
- input from a speech therapist.

Dyslexia

Dyslexia is a neurological disorder caused by a slight impairment to sensory pathways. It affects reading, both its fluency and its accuracy. It can also affect writing and spelling. Children who are dyslexic have normal levels of intelligence. Their difficulties with reading, writing, etc. often appear as an inconsistency to a child who is otherwise bright, inquisitive and able. Dyslexia is a lifelong disorder, but children can be taught strategies to help them deal with it and overcome any limitations it may have posed to people in the past.

Children with dyslexia can be helped by:

- patience and plenty of time to complete work and activities
- visual or oral clues alongside written text where appropriate
- one-to-one guidance from practitioners on developing organisational skills
- an environment with minimal distractions to help concentration
- the use of coloured overlays, usually in yellow, which help them in reading written text
- opportunities to use alternative ways to express themselves
- opportunities to listen to story tapes ether alone or in a group
- specific emphasis on phonetic work
- specific work on sequencing
- input from an educational psychologist.

Dyspraxia

Dyspraxia is a sensory disorder affecting the organisation of movement skills. Children tend to be clumsy and unco-ordinated, and this impacts on their use of mark-making materials, books and generally in their play and learning. In the earliest months and years, it can affect feeding and the usually expected motor development milestones of walking, etc. As children get older, it affects communication, both their own, and their understanding and responses to communication from others. Children with dyspraxia tend to be easily excited, particularly in noisy environments.

Children with dyspraxia can be helped by:

- a calm environment with minimum noise
- one-to-one guidance by their key worker or classroom assistant
- a very structured approach to each task or activity
- patience and plenty of time given to them

- input from an occupational therapist
- input from a physiotherapist
- input from a speech therapist
- input from an educational psychologist.

Dysgraphia

Dysgraphia is often linked to dyslexia or dyspraxia. It is a difficulty in controlling a pen or pencil sufficiently to allow the individual to write correctly. It can cause difficulties in letter formation, consistency of letter size and shape.

Children with dysgraphia can be helped by:

- the use of pencil grips to help them develop a good tripod grasp
- opportunities to use alternative means of expressing themselves
- sensory boards and shapes to help letter formation and writing in lines
- specific work on visual memory skills
- specific work on fine motor skills development
- input from an occupational therapist.

Dealing with difficulties in ways which do not undermine the child's confidence

Every child needs to feel good about themselves in order to achieve their potential. A child's difficulty or disability should not overshadow who they are as an individual. It is important to see them as a child first and foremost, and as a child with X, Y or Z as an additional need, after. Sometimes adults make assumptions about a child's ability, based on what they can or cannot do in another aspect of their learning. This can be dangerous. In making an assumption, rather than observing and assessing ability, you may plan inappropriately for a child's needs, either providing him with challenges that are too great, potentially knocking his confidence as he struggles to cope, to keep up with peers or to achieve, or conversely, assuming that a child will not be able to do something so leave them under-challenged, unstimulated and bored, potentially leading to an unmotivated child who lacks enthusiasm for new experiences.

The manner in which children are paired up or grouped for tasks can help or hinder progress. This is linked to levels of challenge, but also issues of personality, age, learning styles and interests.

Professional Practice

- Sometimes simple aids can help a child, e.g. rubber pencil grips will help a child position their fingers and thumb correctly, gradually helping them to favour this grip automatically.

When and how to access help

A child may benefit from an assessment by another professional if their progress slows down and seems to stop, if they are making only minimal progress despite already having a programme of learning specifically set up for them by current staff, or if they are working at a level considerably below that of their peers. The Special Educational Needs Co-ordinator (SENCO) is always the first port of call. It is their role to make appropriate contacts, and, along with parents, help develop a programme of intervention for any child who needs it.

Link

Refer to Unit 27, page 320, for more information on meeting additional needs and the role of SENCOs.

Know current national initiatives and curriculum guidance relating to the development of children's literacy skills

There is a range of relevant legislation and curriculum guidance to support the development of children's literacy skills either directly or indirectly. This includes:

- Children Act 1989 and 2004
- Continuing the learning journey 2005
- Childcare Act 2006
- Warnock Report 1978
- Code of Practice 2001
- Every Child Matters: Change for Children
- Birth to Three Matters – Will be completely replaced by EYFS in September 2008
- Foundation Stage Curriculum – Will be completely replaced by EYFS in September 2008
- Primary Framework for Literacy and Mathematics
- Early Years Foundation Stage (EYFS) – Mandatory from September 2008.

Legislation

Children Act 1989 and 2004

The Children Act 1989 and its update of 2004 legislates for the all-round health, development and safe living of young children. It sets out minimum requirements for staffing numbers, staffing qualifications, the state of and resources within the care and learning environment, and how children's needs should be met. The regulatory body Ofsted oversees the maintenance of standards of both care and learning, and has the powers to act if these standards are not met. Ofsted inspection teams ensure that all areas of care, stimulation and learning, as set out by the Birth to Three Matters strategy and the Foundation Stage Curriculum, are fully met. Communication, language and literacy are significant aspects of each of these.

Childcare Act 2006

The Childcare Act 2006 includes specific updates on the Children Act 2004. It asks for local authorities and their local partners to reduce inequalities for young children in their areas by providing an integrated service for children and their families, part of the ethos of Sure Start. Each local area should have sufficient provision for care and learning for all the children aged 3 and 4 of parents who wish to take it up. A free minimum amount of provision for all 3- and 4-year-olds is set out.

Section 12 of the Act highlights the newly extended age range (now up to age 20 years) for which parents have a right to obtain information for their child. This includes language skills and the use of advocates and interpreters where appropriate.

Sections 39–48 of the Act introduce the Early Years Foundation Stage (EYFS), and explain how it builds on the Birth to Three Matters, Foundation Stage Curriculum, and the National Standards for Day Care and Childminding. It explains how the new EYFS will support an integrated provision for children from birth through to 5 years, and makes reference to the adjusted Ofsted Childcare Register standards.

Warnock Report 1978

In 1978 Mary Warnock headed the first enquiry for almost 90 years into the 'education of handicapped children and young people'. The focus of the enquiry was on the children's rights to an education, whatever their disability, and the importance of seeing the child as a child first and foremost, and as a child with a disability second.

The report concluded that although around 20 per cent of children might have a special educational need (SEN), either ongoing or temporary, many of this group of children could be successfully educated in a mainstream setting. It concluded that it was inappropriate to place all children with a SEN in a 'special' school or unit. Each child's needs would be assessed individually in conjunction with the child's parents.

Much of the 'old' terminology (e.g. remedial, sub-normal) was discontinued following the Warnock Report, with terms such as 'mild', 'moderate' or 'severe' learning difficulties, and 'children with specific learning difficulties' being the favoured terms. It proposed that labelling should be avoided whenever possible and also that children should not be categorised as either having or not having a handicap or disability as this causes an unnecessary division.

The term 'specific learning difficulties' would often be used to describe the needs of children with conditions such as dyslexia, dysgraphia, visual or auditory loss. These children have an identified specific need that can be targeted specifically with appropriate strategies. The report recommended that relevant resources and equipment should be included in the classrooms for children with specific learning difficulties, e.g. hearing aids, tactile learning materials.

The term special educational need (SEN) came into use following the report along with the five-stage process of assessment.

The report also highlighted the importance of early years provision for all children, again whenever practical, within a mainstream setting.

There have been many more legislative papers and acts since the Warnock Report in 1978. Each paper has attempted to build on the foundations of Mary Warnock and her enquiry team.

Link

You may find it of interest to research further using the internet. Also, refer to Unit 27, page 320, for more on supporting the additional needs of children.

Code of Practice 2001

The Code of Practice 2001 responded to the Education Act 1996, providing teachers, teaching assistants and all other early years practitioners with practical guidance on how to meet the needs of children considered to have a SEN. Regarding the support and development of literacy skills, the following paragraphs (summarised below) of the Code of Practice are particularly relevant.

Statements for children under two

- 4.48 It is rare for a child under the age of 2 to be given a statement, but Portage and/or specific peripatetic services should be made available for children identified as being blind or deaf, or having either a visual or auditory impairment.

Moving to primary school

- 4.54, 4.55 The needs of a child who enters school, having had a considerable level of support (e.g. from Portage or similar), but without a statement should be carefully considered, in both the context of their current learning and in the wider context of the home environment and circumstances to establish if their difficulty is linked to any family issue. A record of their progress and needs should be passed on to the school, with agreement of their parents. The school will then be alerted to potential support needs for that child.

Communication and interaction

- 7.55, 7.56, 7.57 These paragraphs raise the point that children with SENs are more able in some areas than in others, and that their communication needs may be 'both diverse and complex'. It states that children may require some or all of the following:
  - flexible teaching arrangements
  - help in acquiring, comprehending and using language
  - help in articulation
  - help in acquiring literacy skills
  - help in using augmentative and alternative means of communication
  - help to use different means of communication confidently and competently for a range of purposes, including formal situations
  - help in organising and coordinating oral and written language
  - support to compensate for the impact of a communication difficulty or learning in English as an additional language
  - help in expressing, comprehending and using their own language, where English is not the first language.

Children may be supported through School Action Plus, or if acceptable progress has not been made following receipt of this support over a period of time, statutory assessment will be considered.

Refer to www.everychildmatters.gov.uk for information on:

- Early Years Action
- Early Years Action Plus
- School Action
- School Action Plus.

Cognition and learning

- 7.58, 7.59 This section refers to severe and profound difficulties, and also to specific learning difficulties such as dyslexia. It states that these children may require:
  - flexible teaching arrangements
  - help with processing language, memory and reasoning skills
  - help and support in acquiring literacy skills
  - help in organising and coordinating spoken and written word to aid cognition
  - help with sequencing and organisational skills
  - help with problem solving and developing concepts
  - programmes to aid improvement of fine and motor competencies
  - support in the use of technical terms and abstract ideas
  - help in understanding ideas, concepts and experiences when information cannot be gained through first-hand sensory or physical experiences.

Speech and language therapy

- 8.49, 8.50, 8.51, 8.52, 8.53 Speech and language is considered to be so fundamental to learning that 'addressing speech and language impairment should normally be recorded as educational provision unless there are exceptional reasons for not doing so.'

Speech and language support is usually provided through NHS support. Some children will receive regular support either one-to-one or in a small group from a speech therapist. In some cases it is felt appropriate for a child's teacher to 'deliver a regular and discreet programme of intervention under the guidance and supervision of a speech and language therapist.' And occasionally children will receive language support as an integral part of their day. This too will be supported and monitored regularly by a speech and language therapist.

LEA support services

- 10.7 The Code of Practice describes how local education authorities (LEAs) can provide advice on teaching techniques, classroom management and appropriate resources and materials. Also direct teaching or practical support for teachers, specialist teaching assistants and specialist help.

Source: Based on DfES Special Educational Needs Code of Practice 2001

Link

You may wish to read through the Code of Practice in more detail. Most college libraries will have a copy.

Curriculum guidance

Curriculum guidance and frameworks to support all-round health, education and well-being are provided for both before and throughout compulsory schooling. All children attending any care or education setting that meets the criteria to receive government funding, will be supported through government strategy or curriculum guidelines. At present these frameworks include:

- Birth to Three Matters – Will be completely replaced by EYFS in September 2008
- Foundation Stage Curriculum – Will be completely replaced by EYFS in September 2008
- Early Years Foundation Stage (EYFS) – Mandatory from September 2008
- National Curriculum.

The strategies for England are set out below, together with website links for each separate home country within the UK.

Each geographical area of the UK has its own home country curriculum and strategy for care and learning. The following websites may be of interest:

- England – www.dfes.gov.uk
- Wales – www.learning.wales.gov.uk for the Cwricwlwm Cymreig
- Scotland – www.scotland.gov.uk
- Northern Ireland – www.ccea.org.uk for the Northern Ireland Curriculum for Communication, language and literacy.

Continuing the learning journey (2005)

This was a package of inset training materials to support practitioners in successfully helping children make the transition between the foundation stage and key stage 1.

The package aimed to:

- 'Establish an understanding of the principles of the foundation stage
- Show how these principles can be used to ensure an effective transition into key stage 1
- Promote continuity in learning by ensuring that year 1 teachers are aware of children's achievements and can implement the next stage in their learning
- Show how information from the foundation stage profile can be used to support school development.'

Source: www.qca.org.uk

Professional Practice

- Continuous Professional Development (CPD) is important to all teachers and practitioners. There are many inset packages and training sessions available. The example above is just one example. There will be others within your local area, and also within each setting you work within. Undertaking CPD throughout your career will keep you up to date with new thinking and ensure that your practice remains appropriate and meets the needs of all the children you work with.

Birth to Three Matters (2003)

Although this framework will be replaced by the EYFS by September 2008, this summary will help you understand how aspects of the curriculum frameworks have developed. Refer to EYFS overview on p.155. The Birth to Three Matters framework was not intended to be a formal curriculum as such but was designed as a framework for effective practice that would inform work with the under-3s. There has long been an increasing awareness of the importance of the first three years of life for development and this has been supported by neurological research studies. The framework was designed to inform the practice of anyone working with the under-3s regardless of the nature of the setting and it had four main aspects:

- a strong child
- a skilful communicator
- a competent learner and
- a healthy child.

Each aspect was further broken down into key components that inform the delivery of care and early learning. These are:

- A strong child
  - Me, myself and I
  - Being acknowledged and affirmed
  - Developing self assurance
  - A sense of belonging
- A skilful communicator
  - Being together
  - Finding a voice

  - Listening and responding
  - Making meaning
- A competent learner
  - Making connections
  - Being imaginative
  - Being creative
  - Representing
- A healthy child
  - Emotional well-being
  - Growing and developing
  - Keeping safe
  - Healthy choices.

These aspects and components were to be used to inform and structure innovative and imaginative care for the very youngest children. Babies are 'born to learn' and benefit from a rich, stimulating and emotionally supportive environment. Most provision for them was to be found within baby units or separate baby rooms. There is some evidence to suggest that they benefit from time spent with older babies and young children, but they also need a discrete and appropriate environment where there is a high ratio of qualified staff. The different aspects and components of the Birth to Three Matters framework could be used to inform daily care activities as well as more structured learning opportunities. It could be used equally by practitioners in day nurseries, family homes, children's centres and by childminders.

The aspect of 'a skilful communicator' was clearly the most directly relevant aspect of the strategy in the development of children's literacy skills, but the general well-being of the whole child also contributes.

A useful series of books to refer to is Harpley & Roberts (2006).

Foundation Stage Curriculum

Although this framework will be replaced by the EYFS by September 2008, this summary will help you understand how aspects of the curriculum frameworks have developed. Refer to EYFS overview on p.155. The early years curriculum is one part of a range of connected strategies for children's services and was based on six main areas of learning:

- personal, social and emotional development
- communication, language and literacy
- mathematical development
- knowledge and understanding of the world
- physical development
- creative development.

Environments that implemented the Foundation Stage Curriculum successfully centred their practice on play and the holistic development of the individual child. Each of the areas of learning has Early Learning Goals that are measurable, but it also values everything a child does in the setting as the curriculum included 'everything children do, see, hear or feel in their setting, both planned and unplanned' (QCA, cited in Drake, 2001).

All settings offering the Foundation Stage Curriculum and achieving satisfactory inspection outcomes from Ofsted received funding for their 4-year-olds and 3-year-olds from a finance source known as the Nursery Education Grant.

The Foundation Stage Curriculum was offered from the age of 3, until the child began to follow the National Curriculum. The Principles of the Foundation Stage Curriculum were:

'supporting, fostering, promoting and developing children's:

- Personal, social and emotional well-being: in particular by supporting the transition to and between settings, promoting an inclusive ethos and providing opportunities for each child to become a valued member of that group and community so that a strong self-image and self-esteem are promoted;
- Positive attitudes and dispositions towards their learning: in particular an enthusiasm for knowledge and learning and a confidence in their ability to be successful learners;

- Social skills: in particular by providing opportunities that enable them to learn how to co-operate and work harmoniously alongside and with each other and to listen to each other;
- Attention skills and persistence: in particular the capacity to concentrate on their own play or on group tasks;
- Language and communication: with opportunities for all children to talk and communicate in a widening range of situations, to respond to adults and to each other, to practise and extend the range of vocabulary and communication skills they use and to listen carefully;
- Reading and writing: with opportunities for all children to explore, enjoy, learn about and use words and text in a broad range of context and to experience a rich variety of books;
- Mathematics: with opportunities for all children to develop their understanding of number, measurement, pattern, shape and space by providing a broad range of contexts in which they can explore, enjoy, learn, practise and talk about them;
- Knowledge and understanding of the world: with opportunities for all children to solve problems, make decisions, experiment, predict, plan and question in a variety of contexts, and to explore and find out about their environment and people and places that have significance in their lives:
- Physical development: with opportunities for all children to develop and practise their fine and gross motor skills and to increase their understanding of how the body works and what they need to do to be healthy and safe;
- Creative development: with opportunities for all children to explore and share thoughts, ideas and feelings through a variety of art, design and technology, music, movement, dance and imaginative and role-play activities.'

Source: QCA (2000), pages 8–9

Early Years Foundation Stage (EYFS)

The EYFS principles which guide the work of all practitioners are grouped into four distinct but complementary themes:

A Unique Child recognises that every child is a competent learner from birth who can be resilient, capably, confident and self-assures. The commitments are focused around development; inclusion; safety; and health and well-being.

Positive Relationships describes how children learn to be strong and independent from a base of loving and secure relationships with parents and/or a key person. The commitments are focused around respect; partnership with parents; supporting learning; and the role of the key person.

Enabling environments explains that the environment plays a key role in supporting and extending children's development and learning. The commitments are focused around observation, assessment and planning; support for every child; the learning environment; and the wider context – transitions, continuity, and multi-agency working.

Learning and Development recognises that children develop and learn in different ways and at different rates, and that all areas of learning and development are equally important and inter-connected.

Within Learning and Development there are six areas of learning covered by the early learning goals and educational programmes. These are:

- Personal, social and Emotional Development
- Communication, Language and Literacy
- Problem Solving, Reasoning and Numeracy
- Knowledge and Understanding of the World
- Physical Development
- Creative Development

Each of these areas must be delivered within a broad range of contexts, through planned purposeful play, with a balance of adult-led and child-initiated activities.

Read through the following pages to help you understand the guidance for Communication, Language and Literacy.

Language for Communication

	Development matters	Look, listen and note	Effective practice	Planning and resourcing
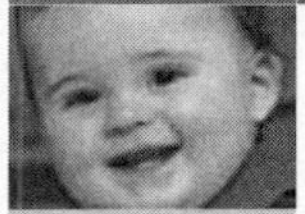 Birth-11 months	■ Communicate in a variety of ways including crying, gurgling, babbling and squealing. ■ Make sounds with their voices in social interaction.	■ Response to your communication, for example movement, attentiveness to the speaker, and sounds from the home language and English for a child learning more than one language. ■ The different ways babies communicate – such as gurgling when happy.	■ Being physically close, making eye contact, using touch or voice all provide ideal opportunities for early 'conversations' between adults and babies, and between one baby and another. ■ Find out from parents how they like to communicate with their baby, noting especially the chosen language. ■ Learn and use key words in the home languages of babies in the setting. ■ Share stories, songs and rhymes from all cultures and in babies' home languages.	■ Display photographs showing the signs that tell us how young babies communicate. ■ Provide tapes and tape recorders so that parents can record familiar, comforting sounds, such as lullabies in home languages. Use these to help babies settle if they are tired or distressed. ■ Share favourite stories as babies are settling to sleep, or at other quiet times.
 8-20 months	■ Take pleasure in making and listening to a wide variety of sounds. ■ Create personal words as they begin to develop language.	■ The sounds babies enjoy making and listening to. ■ The signs or words babies use, noting any words in home languages, to communicate what they want, like or dislike. ■ Babies' developing vocabulary in their mother tongue, as well as English, noting which words are in English and which are in the home language. Note in which circumstances the different languages are used.	■ Try to 'tune in' to the different messages young babies are attempting to convey. ■ Find out from parents greetings used in English and in languages other than English; encourage staff, parents and children to become familiar with them. ■ Recognise and value the importance of all languages spoken and written by parents, staff and children.	■ Communicate with parents to exchange and update information about babies' personal words. ■ Display lists of words from different home languages, and invite parents and other adults to contribute. Include languages such as Romany and Creole, since seeing their languages reflected in the setting will encourage all parents to feel involved and valued.

00012-2007BKT-EN
© Crown copyright 2007

Communication, Language and Literacy

Language for Communication

	Development matters	Look, listen and note	Effective practice	Planning and resourcing
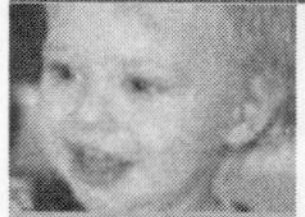 16-26 months	■ Use single-word and two-word utterances to convey simple and more complex messages. ■ Understand simple sentences.	■ The meanings young children generate in their language through the creative ways in which they use words. ■ Young children's use of their first language, with peers and adults, and how children with several languages may use their home language in some circumstances, perhaps when they are very enthusiastic or excited about something, and English in others.	■ Recognise young children's competence and appreciate their efforts when they show their understanding of new words and phrases. ■ Sensitively demonstrate pronunciation and ordering of words in response to what children say, rather than correcting them. ■ Accept and praise words and phrases in home languages, saying English alternatives and encouraging their use. ■ Plan to talk through and comment on some activities to highlight specific vocabulary or language structures, for example, "You've caught the ball. I've caught the ball. Nasima's caught the ball". This approach is helpful in encouraging all children's developing language skills.	■ Allow time to follow young children's lead and have fun together while talking about actions such as going up, down or jumping. ■ Encourage parents whose children are learning English as an additional language to continue to encourage use of the first language at home. ■ Provide books with repetitive stories and phrases to read aloud to children to support specific vocabulary or language structures.
 22-36 months	■ Learn new words very rapidly and are able to use them in communicating about matters which interest them.	■ How children begin to use words to question and negotiate. ■ Features of adult/child interaction, remembering these are culturally determined, and that conventions for interaction vary, both within and across speech communities.		■ Display pictures and photographs showing familiar events, objects and activities and talk about them with the children. ■ Provide activities which help children to learn to distinguish differences in sounds, word patterns and rhythms.

00012-2007BKT-EN
© Crown copyright 2007

Language for Communication

	Development matters	Look, listen and note	Effective practice	Planning and resourcing
 22-36 months			■ Talk about things which interest young children and listen and respond to their ideas and questions. For children learning English as an additional language, value non-verbal communications and those offered in home languages. Respond by adding to words, gesture, objects and other visual cues to support two-way understanding.	
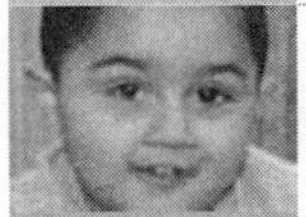 30-50 months	■ Use simple statements and questions often linked to gestures. ■ Use intonation, rhythm and phrasing to make their meaning clear to others. ■ Join in with repeated refrains and anticipate key events and phrases in rhymes and stories. ■ Listen to stories with increasing attention and recall. ■ Describe main story settings, events and principal characters. ■ Listen to others in one-to-one or small groups when conversation interests them. ■ Respond to simple instructions. ■ Question why things happen and give explanations. ■ Use vocabulary focused on objects and people that are of particular importance to them.	■ The gestures and body language children use. ■ Children's responses to stories and information books you read with them. ■ How children act out rhymes and stories. ■ Instances of children recalling and recounting their own experiences and sharing them with others. ■ How children take account of what others say during one-to-one conversations. ■ Children's understanding of instructions and the questions they ask. ■ The range and variety of words that children use.	■ Talk with children to make links between their gestures and words, for example, "Your face does look cross. Has something upset you?". ■ Support children in using a variety of communication strategies, including signing, where appropriate. ■ Listen to children and take account of what they say in your responses to them. ■ Choose stories with repeated refrains, dances and action songs involving looking and pointing, and songs that require replies and turn-taking such as 'Tommy Thumb'.	■ Encourage children to express their needs and feelings in words. ■ Provide opportunities for children whose home language is other than English, to use that language. ■ Find out from parents how children make themselves understood at home; confirm which is their preferred language. ■ Set up a listening area where children can enjoy rhymes and stories. ■ Introduce 'rhyme time' bags containing books to take home and involve parents in rhymes and singing games. Ask parents to record regional variations of songs and rhymes in other languages.

00012-2007BKT-EN
© Crown copyright 2007

Language for Communication

	Development matters	Look, listen and note	Effective practice	Planning and resourcing
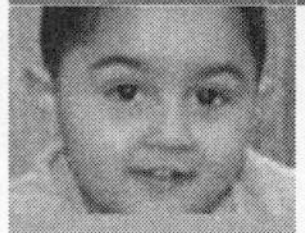 30-50 months	■ Begin to experiment with language describing possession. ■ Build up vocabulary that reflects the breadth of their experiences. ■ Begin to use more complex sentences. ■ Use a widening range of words to express or elaborate on ideas.	■ How children are beginning to develop and expand on what they say, for example, "Come in, it's time for dinner. You'll get hungry if you stay out there". ■ Children's developing use of a preferred language and whether this has changed since, for example, attending the current setting.	■ Share rhymes, books and stories from many cultures, sometimes using languages other than English, particularly where children are learning English as an additional language. ■ Give children clear directions and help them to deal with those involving more than one action, for example, "Put the cars away, please, then come and wash your hands and get ready for lunch". ■ When introducing a new activity, use mime and gesture to support language development. Showing children a photograph of an activity such as handwashing helps to reinforce understanding. ■ Provide practical experiences that encourage children to ask and respond to questions, for example, explaining pulleys or wet and dry sand. ■ Introduce new words in the context of play and activities. ■ Show interest in the words children use to communicate and describe their experiences. ■ Help children expand on what they say, introducing and reinforcing the use of more complex sentences.	■ Introduce, alongside books, story props, such as pictures, puppets and objects, to encourage children to retell stories and to think about how the characters feel. ■ Help children to build their vocabulary by extending the range of their experiences. ■ Ensure that all practitioners use correct grammar.

00012-2007BKT-EN
© Crown copyright 2007

Language for Communication

	Development matters	Look, listen and note	Effective practice	Planning and resourcing
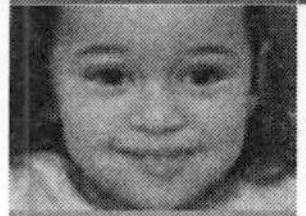 40-60+ months	■ Have confidence to speak to others about their own wants and interests. ■ Use talk to gain attention and sometimes use action rather than talk to demonstrate or explain to others. ■ Initiate conversation, attend to and take account of what others say. ■ Extend vocabulary, especially by grouping and naming. ■ Use vocabulary and forms of speech that are increasingly influenced by their experience of books. ■ Link statements and stick to a main theme or intention. ■ Consistently develop a simple story, explanation or line of questioning. ■ Use language for an increasing range of purposes. ■ Use simple grammatical structures.	■ Children's readiness to engage in conversation. ■ Children's awareness of conventions, such as taking turns to talk. ■ How children link statements to develop stories and explanations. ■ The purposes for which children use talk, for example, to gain attention or to resolve disagreements. ■ How children concentrate on what others say and their responses to what they have heard. ■ Rhymes and songs children know by heart. ■ Children's made-up songs. ■ Children's growing vocabulary. ■ The occasions when children speak clearly and confidently and show awareness of the listener.	■ Encourage conversation with others and demonstrate appropriate conventions: turn-taking, waiting until someone else has finished, listening to others and using expressions such as "please", "thank you" and "can I…?". At the same time, respond sensitively to social conventions used at home. ■ Show children how to use language for negotiating, by saying "May I…?", "Would it be all right…?", "I think that…" and "Will you…?" in your interactions with them. ■ Model language appropriate for different audiences, for example, a visitor. ■ Encourage children to predict possible endings to stories and events. ■ Encourage children to experiment with words and sounds, for example, in nonsense rhymes.	■ Give time for children to initiate discussions from shared experiences and have conversations with each other. ■ Give thinking time for children to decide what they want to say and how they will say it. ■ Set up collaborative tasks, for example, construction, food activities or story-making through role-play. Help children to talk about and plan how they will begin, what parts each will play and what materials they will need. ■ Provide opportunities for talking for a wide range of purposes, for example, to present ideas to others as descriptions, explanations, instructions or justifications, and to discuss and plan individual or shared activities. ■ Foster children's enjoyment of spoken and written language by providing interesting and stimulating play opportunities. ■ Provide word banks and writing resources for both indoor and outdoor play. ■ Resource role-play areas with listening and writing equipment and provide easy access to word banks.
Early learning goals	■ **Interact with others, negotiating plans and activities and taking turns in conversation.** ■ **Enjoy listening to and using spoken and written language, and readily turn to it in their play and learning.**			

Communication, Language and Literacy

© Crown copyright 2007

Language for Communication

	Development matters	Look, listen and note	Effective practice	Planning and resourcing
 40-60+ months Early learning goals	■ **Sustain attentive listening, responding to what they have heard with relevant comments, questions or actions.** ■ **Listen with enjoyment, and respond to stories, songs and other music, rhymes and poems and make up their own stories, songs, rhymes and poems.** ■ **Extend their vocabulary, exploring the meanings and sounds of new words.** ■ **Speak clearly and audibly with confidence and control and show awareness of the listener.**		■ Encourage children to sort, group and sequence events in their play, using words such as: first, last, next, before, after, all, most, some, each, every. ■ Encourage language play, for example, through stories such as 'Goldilocks and the Three Bears' and action songs that require intonation. ■ Value children's contributions and use them to inform and shape the direction of discussions.	■ Provide opportunities for children to participate in meaningful speaking and listening activities. For example, taking models that they have made to show children in another class and explaining how they were made.

00012-2007BKT-EN
© Crown copyright 2007

Language for Thinking

	Development matters	Look, listen and note	Effective practice	Planning and resourcing
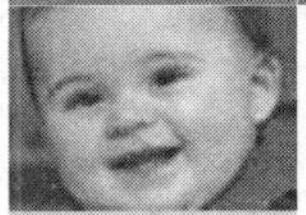 Birth-11 months	■ Are intrigued by novelty and events and actions around them.	■ How babies listen to, concentrate on or gaze intently at things that catch their interest.	■ Interpret and give meaning to the things young babies show interest in.	■ Provide resources that stimulate babies' interests such as a shiny bell, a book or a mirror.
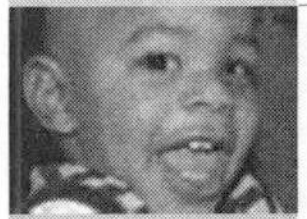 8-20 months	■ Understand simple meanings conveyed in speech. ■ Respond to the different things said to them when in a familiar context with a special person.	■ The ways in which babies show you they have understood.	■ Talk to babies about what you are doing, so they will link words with actions, for example, preparing lunch.	■ Create an environment which invites responses from babies and adults, for example, touching, smiling, smelling, feeling, listening, exploring, describing and sharing.
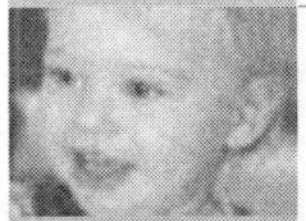 16-26 months	■ Are able to respond to simple requests and grasp meaning from context.	■ The ways in which young children respond to adults and other children and the circumstances in which this takes place.	■ Be aware that young children's understanding is much greater than their ability to express their thoughts and ideas.	■ Plan play activities and provide resources which encourage young children to engage in symbolic play, for example, putting a 'baby' to bed and talking to it appropriately.
 22-36 months	■ Use action, sometimes with limited talk, that is largely concerned with the 'here and now'. ■ Use language as a powerful means of widening contacts, sharing feelings, experiences and thoughts.	■ Situations where children use actions and some talk to support and think about what they are doing. ■ How children show what they understand, by what they do and say, for example, actions, questions, new words and the rhythms and intonations they use.	■ Use talk to describe what children are doing by providing a running commentary: "Oh, I can see what you are doing, you have to put the milk in the cup first". ■ Provide opportunities for children to talk with other children and adults about what they see, hear, think and feel. ■ Encourage children to learn one another's names and to pronounce them correctly. Ensure all staff can pronounce the names of children, parents and other staff members.	■ Include things which excite young children's curiosity, such as hats, bubbles, shells, story books, seeds and snails. ■ Provide activities, such as cooking, where talk is used to anticipate or initiate what children will be doing, for example, "We need some eggs. Let's see if we can find some in here". ■ Plan to encourage correct use of language by telling repetitive stories, and playing games which involve repetition of words or phrases.

Communication, Language and Literacy

Communication, Language and Literacy

Language for Thinking

	Development matters	Look, listen and note	Effective practice	Planning and resourcing
 30-50 months	■ Talk activities through, reflecting on and modifying what they are doing. ■ Use talk to give new meanings to objects and actions, treating them as symbols for other things. ■ Use talk to connect ideas, explain what is happening and anticipate what might happen next. ■ Use talk, actions and objects to recall and relive past experiences.	■ How children use talk to think through and revise what they are doing. For example, following a farm visit, Fiona talks as she rearranges toy farm animals, "Put baby sheep here… oh no… no mummy… that sheep has lost its mum". ■ How children use talk to connect ideas and explain things.	■ Prompt children's thinking and discussion through involvement in their play. ■ Talk to children about what they have been doing and help them to reflect upon and explain events, for example, "You told me this model was going to be a tractor. What's this lever for?".	■ Set up shared experiences that children can reflect upon, for example, visits, cooking, or stories that can be re-enacted. ■ Help children to predict and order events coherently, by providing props and materials that encourage children to re-enact, using talk and action.
 40-60+ months	■ Begin to use talk instead of action to rehearse, reorder and reflect on past experience, linking significant events from own experience and from stories, paying attention to how events lead into one another. ■ Begin to make patterns in their experience through linking cause and effect, sequencing, ordering and grouping. ■ Begin to use talk to pretend imaginary situations.	■ How children use talk to reflect upon, clarify, sequence and think about present and past experiences, ideas and feelings. ■ How children link one thing to another to explain and anticipate things. For example, "We won't play out today because it's too windy… you might get blown away". ■ Ways in which children use language in their pretend and imaginary play. ■ For children speaking languages other than English, note which language is dominant, as well as their use of gesture and intonation to convey meaning.	■ Ask children to think in advance about how they will accomplish a task. Talk through and sequence the stages together. ■ Use stories from books to focus children's attention on predictions and explanations, for example, "Why did the boat tip over?". ■ Help children to identify patterns, for example, what generally happens to 'good' and 'wicked' characters at the end of stories; to draw conclusions, "The sky has gone dark. It must be going to rain"; to explain effect, "It sank because it was too heavy"; to predict, "It might not grow in there if it is too dark" and to speculate, "What if the bridge falls down?".	■ Set up displays that remind children of what they have experienced, using objects, artefacts, photographs and books. ■ Provide for, initiate and join in imaginative play and role-play, encouraging children to talk about what is happening and to act out the scenarios in character.
Early learning goals	■ **Use language to imagine and recreate roles and experiences.** ■ **Use talk to organise, sequence and clarify thinking, ideas, feelings and events.**			

00012-2007BKT-EN
© Crown copyright 2007

Language for Thinking

	Development matters	Look, listen and note	Effective practice	Planning and resourcing
 40-60+ months			■ Take an interest in what and how children think and not just what they know.	

00012-2007BKT-EN
© Crown copyright 2007

Communication, Language and Literacy

Linking Sounds and Letters

	Development matters	Look, listen and note	Effective practice	Planning and resourcing
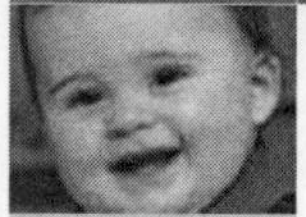 Birth-11 months	■ Listen to, distinguish and respond to intonations and the sounds of voices.	■ The sounds and signs babies make.	■ Encourage playfulness, turn-taking and responses, including peek-a-boo and rhymes.	■ Plan times when you can sing with young babies, encouraging them to join in exploration of their fingers and toes.
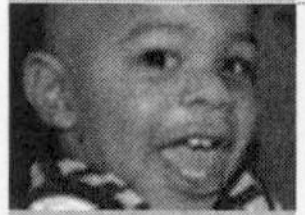 8-20 months	■ Enjoy babbling and increasingly experiment with using sounds and words to represent objects around them.	■ The wide variety of sounds and words a baby produces.	■ Share the fun of discovery and value babies' attempts at words, for example, by picking up a doll in response to "baba".	■ Find out from parents the words that children use for things which are important to them, such as "dodie" for dummy, remembering to extend this question to home languages. Explain that strong foundations in a home language support the development of English.
 16-26 months	■ Listen to and enjoy rhythmic patterns in rhymes and stories.	■ Young children's responses to music, rhymes and stories.	■ Encourage young children to explore and imitate sound. Talk about the different sounds they hear, such as a tractor's "chug chug" while sharing a book .	■ Collect resources that children can listen to and learn to distinguish between. These may include noises in the street, and games that involve guessing which object makes a particular sound.
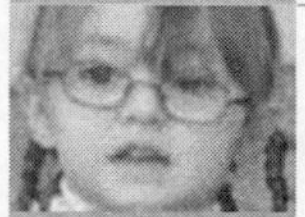 22-36 months	■ Distinguish one sound from another. ■ Show interest in play with sounds, songs and rhymes. ■ Repeat words or phrases from familiar stories.	■ The words, phrases and sounds children like to say or sing. ■ The languages they understand and use.	■ Encourage repetition, rhythm and rhyme by using tone and intonation as you tell, recite or sing stories, poems and rhymes from books. ■ Use rhymes from a variety of cultures and ask parents to share their favourites from their home languages.	■ Use puppets and other props to encourage listening and responding when singing a familiar song or reading from a story book.

00012-2007BKT-EN
© Crown copyright 2007

Linking Sounds and Letters

	Development matters	Look, listen and note	Effective practice	Planning and resourcing
 22-36 months			■ Be aware of the needs of children learning English as an additional language.	
 30-50 months	■ Enjoy rhyming and rhythmic activities. ■ Show awareness of rhyme and alliteration. ■ Recognise rhythm in spoken words.	■ The rhymes and rhythms that children enjoy, recite and create in words and music, for example, tapping out the rhythms of their names.	■ When singing or saying rhymes, talk about the similarities in the rhyming words. Make up alternative endings and encourage children to supply the last word of the second line, for example, 'Hickory Dickory boot, The mouse ran down the...'.	■ When making up alliterative jingles, draw attention to the similarities in sounds at the beginning of words and emphasise the initial sound, for example, "mmmmummy", "shshshshadow", "K-K-K-K-Katy".
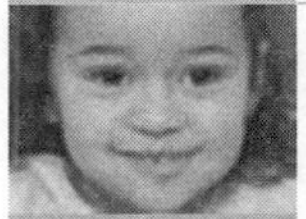 40-60+ months Early learning goals	■ Continue a rhyming string. ■ Hear and say the initial sound in words and know which letters represent some of the sounds. ■ **Hear and say sounds in words in the order in which they occur.** ■ **Link sounds to letters, naming and sounding the letters of the alphabet.** ■ **Use their phonic knowledge to write simple regular words and make phonetically plausible attempts at more complex words.**	■ Children's alternative versions of favourite rhymes that draw upon their phonic knowledge. ■ Children's knowledge of initial sounds at the beginning of words, short vowel sounds within words and endings of words. For example, Ranjit notices the letters in his name whenever he sees them, such as 'j' at the beginning of jam. ■ How children link sounds to letters and begin to use this knowledge to write words, for example, "Pz cn I hv a d" (Please can I have a drink).	■ Talk to children about the letters that represent the sounds they hear at the beginning of their own names and other familiar words. Incorporate these in games. ■ Demonstrate writing so that children can see spelling in action. Encourage them to apply their own grapheme-phoneme knowledge to what they read and write. ■ When children are ready (usually by the age of five) provide systematic regular phonics sessions. These should be multi-sensory in order to capture their interests, sustain motivation and reinforce learning.	■ Ensure that role-play areas encourage writing of signs with a real purpose, for example, a pet shop. ■ Plan fun activities and games that help children create rhyming strings of real and imaginary words, for example, Maddie, daddy, baddie, laddie.

© Crown copyright 2007

Linking Sounds and Letters

	Development matters	Look, listen and note	Effective practice	Planning and resourcing
 40-60+ months		■ Children's confidence in blending and segmenting and in using grapheme-phoneme knowledge to read and spell regular consonant-vowel-consonant (CVC) words, including consonant digraphs and long vowels. ■ The ways in which children use their phonic knowledge and the number of grapheme-phoneme correspondences used for reading and writing in a variety of contexts. ■ How children read simple words by sounding out and blending the phonemes all through the word from left to right.		■ When practitioners judge that children are ready to begin a programme of systematic phonic work they should refer to the guidance on the EYFS CD-ROM, which can be found in areas of Learning and Development: Communication, Language and Literacy: Early Reading. This will support practitioners working in the EYFS and beyond to start teaching the phonic knowledge and skills children need to be able to recognise words and read them with fluency by the end of KS1. Practitioners need to make principled professional judgements as to when individual children are ready to start such work. For most children this will be by the age of five.

00012-2007BKT-EN
© Crown copyright 2007

Reading

	Development matters	Look, listen and note	Effective practice	Planning and resourcing
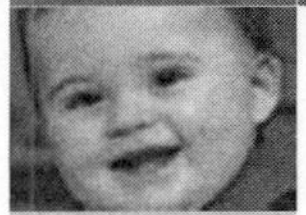 Birth-11 months	■ Listen to familiar sounds, words, or finger plays.	■ Responses that tell you a young baby is listening.	■ Use finger play, rhymes and familiar songs from home to support young babies' enjoyment.	■ Collect a range of board books, cloth books and stories to share with young babies.
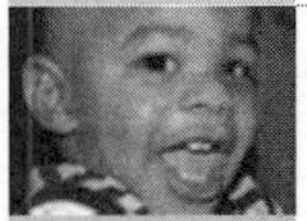 8-20 months	■ Respond to words and interactive rhymes, such as 'Clap Hands'.	■ How babies' responses develop as they learn to anticipate and join in with finger and word play.	■ Tell, as well as read, stories, looking at and interacting with young babies. ■ Let children handle books and draw their attention to pictures.	■ Discover from parents the copying games that their babies enjoy, and use these as the basis for your play.
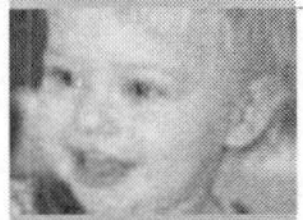 16-26 months	■ Show interest in stories, songs and rhymes.	■ Children's responses to picture books and stories you read with them.	■ Use different voices to tell stories and encourage young children to join in wherever possible.	■ Provide CDs and tapes of rhymes, stories, sounds and spoken words.
 22-36 months	■ Have some favourite stories, rhymes, songs, poems or jingles.	■ Children's favourite stories, rhymes, songs, poems or jingles.	■ Find opportunities to tell and read stories to children, using puppets, soft toys, or real objects as props.	■ Provide stories, pictures and puppets which allow children to experience and talk about how characters feel. ■ Provide dual language books to raise awareness of different scripts. Try to match dual language books to languages spoken by families in the setting. Remember not all languages have written forms and not all families are literate either in English, or in a different home language.

00012-2007BKT-EN
© Crown copyright 2007

Reading

	Development matters	Look, listen and note	Effective practice	Planning and resourcing
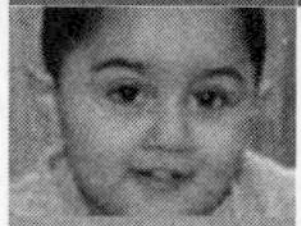 30-50 months	■ Listen to and join in with stories and poems, one-to-one and also in small groups. ■ Begin to be aware of the way stories are structured. ■ Suggest how the story might end. ■ Show interest in illustrations and print in books and print in the environment. ■ Handle books carefully. ■ Know information can be relayed in the form of print. ■ Hold books the correct way up and turn pages. ■ Understand the concept of a word.	■ The stories and poems children choose and know how to follow. For example, retelling a story, using words and phrases from a well-known story. ■ Children's familiarity with the way books work. For example, turning the pages and telling the story using the pictures and using phrases such as "Once upon a time". ■ Children's references to and understanding of how print works. For example, asking what a word says or what instructions mean. ■ Children's recognition of their names, or letters or words, in scripts other than English.	■ Encourage children to use the stories they hear in their play. ■ Discuss with children the characters in books being read. Encourage them to predict outcomes, to think of alternative endings and to compare plots and the feelings of characters with their own experiences. ■ Focus on meaningful print such as a child's name, words on a cereal packet or a book title, in order to discuss similarities and differences between symbols. ■ Help children to understand what a word is by using names and labels and by pointing out words in the environment and in books. ■ Read stories that children already know, pausing at intervals to encourage them to 'read' the next word.	■ Create an attractive book area where children and adults can enjoy books together. ■ Provide some simple poetry, song, fiction and non-fiction books. Include books containing photographs of the children that can be read by adults and that children can begin to 'read' by themselves. ■ Create an environment rich in print where children can learn about words, for example, using names and labels. ■ Introduce children to books and other materials that provide information or instructions. Carry out activities using instructions, such as reading a recipe to make a cake. ■ Ensure access to stories for all children by using a range of visual cues and story props. ■ Plan to include home language and bilingual story sessions by involving qualified bilingual adults, as well as enlisting the help of parents.

00012-2007BKT-EN
© Crown copyright 2007

Reading

	Development matters	Look, listen and note	Effective practice	Planning and resourcing
 30-50 months				■ When practitioners judge that children are ready to begin a programme of systematic phonic work they should refer to the guidance on the EYFS CD-ROM which can be found in areas of Learning and Development: Communication, Language and Literacy: Early Reading. This will support practitioners working in the EYFS and beyond to start teaching the phonic knowledge and skills children need to be able to recognise words and read them with fluency by the end of KS1. Practitioners need to make principled professional judgements as to when individual children are ready to start such work. For most children this will be by the age of five.
 40-60+ months Early learning goals	■ Enjoy an increasing range of books. ■ Know that information can be retrieved from books and computers. ■ **Explore and experiment with sounds, words and texts.** ■ **Retell narratives in the correct sequence, drawing on language patterns of stories.**	■ Children's book choices. ■ Children's understanding about how information is kept in different places and can be retrieved. ■ Children's understanding of the elements of stories, for example, Mehmet refers to the 'beginning' and 'end' of a story. He says, "I don't like that ending. I think he should've run away and been happy ever after".	■ Create imaginary words to describe, for example, monsters or other strong characters in stories and poems. ■ Discuss and model ways of finding out information from non-fiction texts. ■ Explain to parents the importance of reading to children, ask about favourite books, and offer book loans.	■ Encourage children to add to their first-hand experience of the world through the use of books, other texts and information, and information and communication technology (ICT). ■ Provide story boards and props which encourage children to talk about the sequence of events and characters in a story.

00012-2007BKT-EN
© Crown copyright 2007

Communication, Language and Literacy

Reading

	Development matters	Look, listen and note	Effective practice	Planning and resourcing
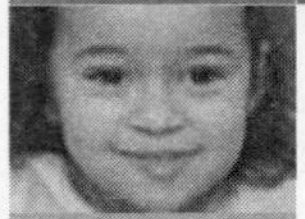 40-60+ months Early learning goals	■ **Read a range of familiar and common words and simple sentences independently.** ■ **Know that print carries meaning and, in English, is read from left to right and top to bottom.** ■ **Show an understanding of the elements of stories, such as main character, sequence of events and openings, and how information can be found in non-fiction texts to answer questions about where, who, why and how.**	■ How children use non-fiction books. ■ The favourite books, songs and rhymes children turn to, to be re-read and enjoyed. ■ The phonic skills children use in decoding text. ■ The strategies that children use to read. ■ The words that children recognise, such as their name and signs such as 'open'. ■ The confidence with which children use their developing phonic knowledge.	■ Help children to identify the main events in a story and to enact stories, as the basis for further imaginative play. ■ Make story boxes with the children. Practitioners should maximise the opportunities that these reading activities present to reinforce and apply children's developing phonic knowledge and skills, particularly once they have started a programme of systematic phonic work which will enable children to recognise words and read them for meaning. For example, demonstrate using phonics as the prime approach to decode words while children can see the text, for example, using big books. ■ Encourage children to recall words they see frequently, such as 'welcome', their own and friends' names, 'open' and 'bus stop'. ■ Play word bingo to develop children's grapheme correspondence, so that they can rapidly decode words.	■ Provide story sacks and boxes for use in the setting and at home. ■ Provide varied texts and encourage children to use their phonics knowledge to recognise words. ■ Provide some simple texts which children can decode to give them confidence and to practise their developing skills. ■ Provide picture books, books with flaps or hidden words, books with accompanying CDs or tapes, and story sacks.

© Crown copyright 2007

Writing

	Development matters	Look, listen and note	Effective practice	Planning and resourcing
 Birth-11 months	■ Move arms and legs and increasingly use them to reach for, grasp and manipulate things.	■ The random marks young babies make in food.	■ Talk about the random marks young babies make, showing them that you value what they do.	■ Provide gloop (cornflour and water) in small trays so babies can enjoy making marks in it.
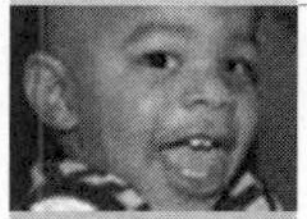 8-20 months	■ Begin to make marks.	■ Babies' interest in marks, for example, the marks they make when they rub a rusk round the tray of a feeding chair.	■ Talk to babies about the patterns and marks they make.	■ Encourage babies to make marks in paint or with thick crayons.
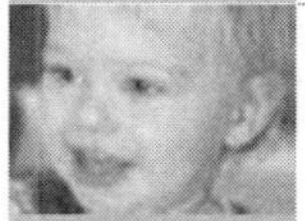 16-26 months	■ Examine the marks they and others make.	■ Marks young children make when given a crayon, a brush or other tools.	■ Discuss with young children what marks represent.	■ Give young children, who are keen to represent the same experience repeatedly, a range of mark-making materials.
 22-36 months	■ Distinguish between the different marks they make.	■ What children tell you about the marks they make.	■ Draw attention to marks, signs and symbols in the environment and talk about what they represent. Ensure this involves recognition of English and other relevant scripts.	■ Provide materials which reflect a cultural spread, so that children see symbols and marks with which they are familiar, for example, Chinese script on a fabric shopping bag.
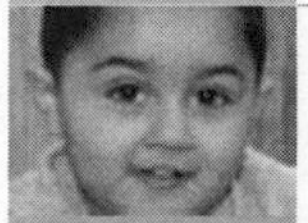 30-50 months	■ Sometimes give meaning to marks as they draw and paint. ■ Ascribe meanings to marks that they see in different places.	■ The marks children make and the meanings that they give to them, such as when a child covers a whole piece of paper and says, "I'm writing".	■ Make books with children of activities they have been doing, using photographs of them as illustrations. ■ Write poems and short stories with children, scribing for them. ■ Support children in recognising and writing their own names.	■ Provide activities during which children will experiment with writing, for example, leaving a message. ■ Include opportunities for writing during role-play and other activities.

Communication, Language and Literacy

00012-2007BKT-EN
© Crown copyright 2007

Writing

	Development matters	Look, listen and note	Effective practice	Planning and resourcing
 30-50 months			■ Encourage the children to use their phonic knowledge when writing consonant-vowel-consonant (CVC) words.	
 40-60+ months Early learning goals	■ Begin to break the flow of speech into words. ■ Use writing as a means of recording and communicating. ■ **Use their phonic knowledge to write simple regular words and make phonetically plausible attempts at more complex words.** ■ **Attempt writing for different purposes, using features of different forms such as lists, stories and instructions.** ■ **Write their own names and other things such as labels and captions, and begin to form simple sentences, sometimes using punctuation.**	■ How children use writing to record things or to communicate, for example, Marcus writes "Marcus, fz (Faraz) and tm (Tommy)" on a drawing of himself and his two friends playing together. ■ Instances of writing for different purposes such as labelling the contents on the outside of a box. ■ How children make use of phonic knowledge as they attempt to write words and simple sentences, for example, "I went to see fiyuwercs and hat to pc by the hut" (I went to see fireworks and had to park by the hut).	■ Act as a scribe for children. After they say a sentence, repeat the first part of it, say each word as you write, and include some punctuation. ■ Encourage children to use their ability to hear the sounds at the beginning of words and then in the order in which they occur through words in their writing. ■ Play games that encourage children to link sounds to letters and then write the letters and words. ■ Encourage children to re-read their writing as they write.	■ Provide materials and opportunities for children to use writing in their play, and create purposes for independent and group writing. ■ Plan occasions where you can involve children in organising writing, for example, putting recipe instructions in the right order. ■ Provide word banks and other resources for segmenting and blending to support children to use their phonic knowledge.

00012-2007BKT-EN
© Crown copyright 2007

Handwriting

	Development matters	Look, listen and note	Effective practice	Planning and resourcing
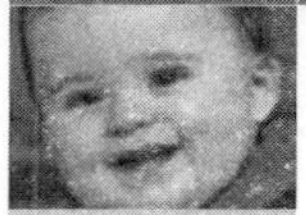 Birth-11 months	■ Play with own fingers and toes and focus on objects around them.	■ How young babies fix their gaze on objects or on their own feet or fists.	■ Place young babies where they can focus on and grasp toys, and wriggle and roll freely.	■ Provide a variety of toys that encourage young babies to reach and grasp, for example, a baby gym.
 8-20 months	■ Begin to bring together hand and eye movements to fix on and make contact with objects.	■ The movements and sounds babies make as they explore materials such as musical instruments, paint, dough, glue and the space around them.	■ Describe the movements young babies make as they move round and round, or ride a push-along toy in a straight line.	■ Plan a range of activities that encourage large and fine motor skills, such as throwing and kicking balls, riding push-along toys, feeding the guinea pigs.
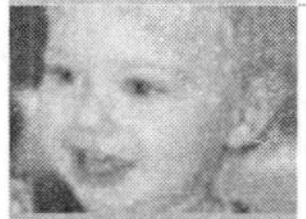 16-26 months	■ Make random marks with their fingers and some tools.	■ The different ways young children make marks, for example, in dough or clay.	■ Help young children to develop their manipulative skills by engaging them in activities such as tearing (paper), scribbling, rolling and printing.	■ Provide resources for finger-painting and play with soapy water, to interest young children who are not yet able to hold a brush or felt pen to make marks.
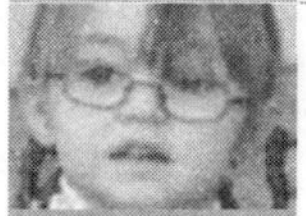 22-36 months	■ Begin to show some control in their use of tools and equipment.	■ Ways in which children begin to develop fine motor skills, for example, the way they use their fingers when trying to do up buttons, pull up a zip, pour a drink or use a watering can.	■ Encourage children to handle and manipulate a variety of media and implements, for example, clay, finger-paint, spoons, brushes and shells.	■ Vary the range of tools and equipment located with familiar activities, for example, put small scoops, rakes or sticks with the sand.
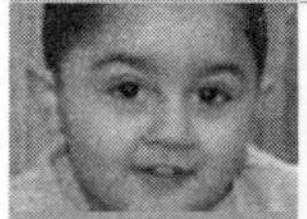 30-50 months	■ Use one-handed tools and equipment. ■ Draw lines and circles using gross motor movements. ■ Manipulate objects with increasing control.	■ The way children control equipment and materials. ■ The marks children like to make.	■ Provide activities that give children the opportunity and motivation to practise manipulative skills, for example, cooking and playing instruments.	■ Provide opportunities for large shoulder movements, for example, swirling ribbons in the air, batting balls suspended on rope and painting. ■ Encourage children to make shapes like circles and zig-zags in the air and in their play, for example, with sand and water and brushes.

00012-2007BKT-EN
© Crown copyright 2007

Communication, Language and Literacy

Handwriting

	Development matters	Look, listen and note	Effective practice	Planning and resourcing
 40-60+ months Early learning goals	■ Begin to use anticlockwise movement and retrace vertical lines. ■ Begin to form recognisable letters. ■ **Use a pencil and hold it effectively to form recognisable letters, most of which are correctly formed.**	■ Children's dexterity in using a range of tools in their play and writing. ■ Children's formation of recognisable letters.	■ Teach children to form letters correctly, for example, when they label their paintings. ■ Encourage children to practise letter shapes as they paint, draw and record, and as they write, for example, their names, the names of their friends and family, or captions. ■ Continue writing practice in imaginative contexts, joining some letters, if appropriate, for example, at, it, on.	■ Provide a variety of writing tools and paper, indoors and outdoors. ■ Give children practice in forming letters correctly, for example, labelling their work, making cards and writing notices. ■ Provide opportunities to write meaningfully, for example, by placing notepads by phones or having appointment cards in the role-play doctor's surgery.

00012-2007BKT-EN © Crown copyright 2007

- Further details of the EYFS can be downloaded at www.standards.dfes.gov.uk/eyfs/. Information is likely to continue to be updated on the website up to and after its full implementation.
- In Wales there will also be changes, with the new Foundation Phase curriculum also being put into place in 2008. Details of the Foundation Phase can be found at www.wales.gov.uk.

National Curriculum

The National Curriculum is intended to be a broad and balanced framework to meet the learning needs of all children; its main principles are based on the Education Acts of 1988 and 1996. All state schools must offer the National Curriculum and although schools in the private sector can opt out, few do. It is considered to be a prescriptive curriculum in that it gives precise outcomes to be achieved at certain stages in a child's school career. Schools are also free to provide extra areas of learning in addition to the National Curriculum to reflect the particular needs and circumstances of the setting.

National Curriculum key stages

The National Curriculum is divided into key stages.

Link

Table 17.2 on page 170 shows the National Curriculum key stages.

The key stage that follows on from the Foundation Stage is Key Stage 1. You will usually work with children who are following this stage during placement experience in a Year 1 or Year 2 class.

At the end of each key stage, there are a number of tests known as Standard Attainment Tasks (SATs), which all children must complete. The purpose of SATS is to monitor each individual child's performance as they progress through school.

Primary Framework for Literacy

The Primary Framework for Literacy sets out core learning aims for both literacy and numeracy for children in each year group, from Foundation Stage through to Year 6/7. There are 12 strands for literacy. They are:

- *Speak and listen for a wide range of purposes in different contexts*

1 **Speaking**
  - Speak competently and creatively for different purposes and audiences, reflecting on impact and response
  - Explore, develop and sustain ideas through talk

2 **Listening and responding**
  - Understand, recall and respond to speakers' implicit and explicit meanings
  - Explain and comment on speakers' use of language, including vocabulary, grammar and non-verbal features

3 **Group discussion and interaction**
  - Take different roles in groups to develop thinking and complete tasks
  - Participate in conversations, making appropriate contributions building on others' suggestions and responses

4 **Drama**
  - Use dramatic techniques, including work in role to explore ideas and texts
  - Create, share and evaluate ideas and understand through drama

- *Read and write for a range of purposes on paper and on screen*

5 **Word recognition: decoding (reading) and encoding (spelling)**
  - Read fluently and automatically by using phonic knowledge of grapheme-phoneme correspondences and the skills of blending as their prime approach for decoding unfamiliar words, and thereby:
  - build up a store of words that are instantly recognised and understood on sight
  - segment words into their constituent phonemes and understand that spelling is the reverse of blending phonemes into words for reading

6 **Word structure and spelling**
  - Learn that segmenting words into their constituent phonemes for spelling is the reverse of blending phonemes into words for reading
  - Spell words accurately by combining the use of grapheme-phoneme correspondence knowledge as the prime approach, and also morphological knowledge and etymological information
  - Use a range of approaches to learn and spell irregular words

7 **Understanding and interpreting texts**
  - Retrieve, select and describe information, events or ideas
  - Deduce, infer and interpret information, events or ideas
  - Use syntax, context, word structures and origins to develop their understanding of word meanings
  - Identify and comment on the structure and organisation of texts
  - Explain and comment on writers' use of language, including vocabulary, grammatical and literary features

8 **Engaging with and responding to texts**
  - Read independently and creatively for purpose, pleasure and learning
  - Respond imaginatively, using different strategies to engage with texts
  - Evaluate writers' purposes and viewpoints, and the overall effect of the text on the reader

9 **Creating and shaping texts**
  - Write independently and creatively for purpose, pleasure and learning
  - Use and adapt a range of forms, suited to different purposes and readers
  - Make stylistic choices, including vocabulary, literary features and viewpoints or voice
  - Use structural and presentational features for meaning and impact

10 **Text structure and organisation**
  - Organise ideas into coherent structure including layout, sections and paragraphs
  - Write cohesive paragraphs linking sentences within and between them

11 **Sentence structure and punctuation**
  - Vary and adapt sentence structure for meaning and effect
  - Use a range of punctuation correctly to support meaning and emphasis
  - Convey meaning through grammatically accurate and correctly punctuated sentences

12 **Presentation**
  - Develop a clear and fluent joined handwriting style
  - Use keyboard skills and ICT tools confidently to compose and present work

Table 18.5 shows the core learning aims for each strand for literacy up to Year 2.

Table 18.5 Core learning in literacy by year

Foundation stage Most children learn to:					
1. Speaking	**2. Listening and responding**	**3. Group discussion and interaction**	**4. Drama**	**5. Word recognition: decoding (reading) and encoding (spelling)**	**6. Word structure and spelling**
Enjoy listening to and using spoken and written language and readily turn to it in play and learning Use talk to organise, sequence and clarify thinking, ideas, feelings and events Use language to imagine and recreate roles and experiences Speak clearly and audibly with confidence and control and show awareness of the listener Extend their vocabulary, exploring the meanings and sounds of new words	**Listen with enjoyment and respond to stories, songs and other music, rhymes and poems and make up their own stories, songs, rhymes and poems** **Sustain attentive listening, responding to what they have heard by relevant comments, questions or actions** **Extend their vocabulary, exploring the meanings and sounds of new words**	**Interact with others, negotiating plans and activities and taking turns in conversation** **Use talk to organise, sequence and clarify thinking, ideas, feelings and events**	**Use language to imagine and recreate roles and experiences**	**Explore and experiment with sounds, words and texts** **Link sounds to letters, naming and sounding the letters of the alphabet** **Use a pencil and hold it effectively to form recognisable letters, most of which are formed correctly** **Hear and say sounds in words in the order in which they occur[1]** Read simple words by sounding out and blending the phonemes all through the word from left to right Recognise common digraphs Read some high frequency words **Use phonic knowledge to write simple regular words and make phonetically plausible attempts at more complex words** **Read a range of familiar and common words and simple sentences independently** Read texts compatible with their phonic knowledge and skills Read and write one grapheme for each of the 44 phonemes	**Use phonic knowledge to write simple regular words and make phonetically plausible attempts at more complex words**

7. Understanding and interpreting texts	**8. Engaging with and responding to texts**	**9. Creating and shaping texts**	**10. Text structure and organisation**	**11. Sentence structure and punctuation**	**12. Presentation**
Know that print carries meaning and, in English, is read from left to right and top to bottom Extend their vocabulary, exploring the meanings and sounds of new words Show an understanding of the elements of stories, such as main character, sequence of events, and openings and how information can be found in non fiction texts to answer questions about where, who, why and how	Listen with enjoyment to stories, songs, rhymes and poems, sustain attentive listening and respond with relevant comments, questions or actions Show an understanding of the elements of stories, such as main character, sequence of events, and openings and how information can be found in non-fiction texts to answer questions about where, who, why and how	Attempt writing for various purposes, using features of different forms such as lists, stories and instructions	Attempt writing for various purposes, using features of different forms such as lists, stories and instructions	Write their own names and other things such as labels and captions and begin to form simple sentences sometimes using punctuation	Use a pencil and hold it effectively to form recognisable letters, most of which are correctly formed

7. Understanding and interpreting texts	8. Engaging with and responding to texts	9. Creating and shaping texts	10. Text structure and organisation	11. Sentence structure and punctuation	12. Presentation
Retell narratives in the correct sequence, drawing on the language patterns of stories	Use language to imagine and recreate roles and experiences				

Foundation Stage objectives in bold refer to the Early Learning Goals.

Throughout this document, the specific objectives identified for the Foundation Stage are dependent upon the outcomes of the consultation on the EYFS.

[1] The wording of this objective may change depending upon the outcomes of the consultation on changes to the Early Learning Goals pending parliamentary approval.

Year 1 Most children learn to:					
1. Speaking	**2. Listening and responding**	**3. Group discussion and interaction**	**4. Drama**	**5. Word recognition: decoding (reading) and encoding (spelling)**	**6. Word structure and spelling**
Tell stories and describe incidents from their own experience in an audible voice Retell stories, ordering events using story language Interpret a text by reading aloud with some variety in pace and emphasis Experiment with and build new stores of words to communicate in different contexts	Listen with sustained concentration, building new stores of words in different contexts Listen to and follow instructions accurately, asking for help and clarification if necessary Listen to tapes or video and express views about how a story or information has been presented	Take turns to speak, listen to others' suggestions and talk about what they are going to do Ask and answer questions, make relevant contributions, offer suggestions and take turns Explain their views to others in a small group, decide how to report the group's views to the class	Explore familiar themes and characters through improvisation and role-play Act out their own and well-known stories, using voices for characters Discuss why they like a performance	Recognise and use alternative ways of pronouncing the graphemes already taught, for example, that the grapheme 'g' is pronounced differently in 'get' and 'gem'; the grapheme 'ow' is pronounced differently in 'how' and 'show' Recognise and use alternative ways of spelling the phonemes already taught, for example that the /ae/ sound can be spelt with 'ai', 'ay' or 'a-e'; that the /ee/ sound can also be spelt as 'ea' and 'e'; and begin to know which words contain which spelling alternatives Identify the constituent parts of two-syllable and three-syllable words to support the application of phonic knowledge and skills Recognise automatically an increasing number of familiar high frequency words Apply phonic knowledge and skills as the prime approach to reading and spelling unfamiliar words that are not completely decodable Read more challenging texts which can be decoded using their acquired phonic knowledge and skills, along with automatic recognition of high frequency words	Spell new words using phonics as the prime approach Segment sounds into their constituent phonemes in order to spell them correctly Recognise and use alternative ways of spelling the graphemes already taught, for example that the /ae/ sound can be spelt with 'ai', 'ay' or 'a-e'; that the /ee/ sound can also be spelt as 'ea' and 'e'; and begin to know which words contain which spelling alternatives

Year 1 Most children learn to:					
1. Speaking	**2. Listening and responding**	**3. Group discussion and interaction**	**4. Drama**	**5. Word recognition: decoding (reading) and encoding (spelling)**	**6. Word structure and spelling**
				Read and spell phonically decodable two-syllable and three-syllable words	Use knowledge of common inflections in spelling, such as plurals, *-ly*, *-er* Read and spell phonically decodable two-syllable and three-syllable words
7. Understanding and interpreting texts	**8. Engaging with and responding to texts**	**9. Creating and shaping texts**	**10. Text structure and organisation**	**11. Sentence structure and punctuation**	**12. Presentation**
Identify the main events and characters in stories, and find specific information in simple texts Use syntax and context when reading for meaning Make predictions showing an understanding of ideas, events and characters Recognise the main elements that shape different texts Explore the effect of patterns of language and repeated words and phrases	Select books for personal reading and give reasons for choices Visualise and comment on events, characters and ideas, making imaginative links to their own experiences Distinguish fiction and non-fiction texts and the different purposes for reading them	Independently choose what to write about, plan and follow it through Use key features of narrative in their own writing Convey information and ideas in simple non-narrative forms Find and use new and interesting words and phrases, including story language Create short simple texts on paper and on screen that combine words with images (and sounds)	Write chronological and non-chronological texts using simple structures Group written sentences together in chunks of meaning or subject	Compose and write simple sentences independently to communicate meaning Use capital letters and full stops when punctuating simple sentences	Write most letters, correctly formed and orientated, using a comfortable and efficient pencil grip Write with space between words accurately Use the space bar and keyboard to type their name and simple texts

Foundation Stage objectives in bold refer to the Early Learning Goals.
Throughout this document, the specific objectives identified for the Foundation Stage are dependent upon the outcomes of the consultation on the EYFS.

Year 2 Most children learn to:					
1. Speaking	**2. Listening and responding**	**3. Group discussion and interaction**	**4. Drama**	**5. Word recognition: decoding (reading) and encoding (spelling)**	**6. Word structure and spelling**
Speak with clarity and use appropriate intonation when reading and reciting texts Tell real and imagined stories using the conventions of familiar story language Explain ideas and processes using imaginative and adventurous vocabulary and non-verbal gestures to support communication	Listen to others in class, ask relevant questions and follow instructions Listen to talk by an adult, remember some specific points and identify what they have learned Respond to presentations by describing characters, repeating some highlight and commenting constructively	Ensure that everyone contributes, allocate tasks, and consider alternatives and reach agreement Work effectively in groups by ensuring that each group member takes a turn challenging, supporting and moving on Listen to each other's views and preferences, agree the next steps to take and identify contributions by each group member	Adopt appropriate roles in small or large groups and consider alternative courses of action Present part of traditional stories, their own stories or work drawn from different parts of the curriculum for members of their own class Consider how mood and atmosphere are created in live or recorded performance	Read independently and with increasing fluency longer and less familiar texts Spell with increasing accuracy and confidence, drawing on word recognition and knowledge of word structure, and spelling patterns Know how to tackle unfamiliar words that are not completely decodable Read and spell less common alternative graphemes including trigraphs Read high and medium frequency words independently and automatically	Spell with increasing accuracy and confidence, drawing on word recognition and knowledge of word structure, and spelling patterns including common inflections and use of double letters Read and spell less common alternative graphemes including trigraphs

7. Understanding and interpreting texts	**8. Engaging with and responding to texts**	**9. Creating and shaping texts**	**10. Text structure and organisation**	**11. Sentence structure and punctuation**	**12. Presentation**
Draw together ideas and information from across a whole text, using simple signposts in the text Give some reasons why things happen or characters change Explain organisational features of texts, including alphabetical order, layout, diagrams, captions, hyperlinks and bullet points Use syntax and context to build their store of vocabulary when reading for meaning Explore how particular words are used, including words and expressions with similar meanings	Read whole books on their own, choosing and justifying selections Engage with books through exploring and enacting interpretations Explain their reactions to texts, commenting on important aspects	Draw on knowledge and experience of texts in deciding and planning what and how to write Sustain form in narrative, including use of person and time Maintain consistency in non-narrative, including purpose and tense Make adventurous word and language choices appropriate to the style and purpose of the text Select from different presentational features to suit particular writing purposes on paper and on screen	Use planning to establish clear sections for writing Use appropriate language to make sections hang together	Write simple and compound sentences and begin to use subordination in relation to time and reason Compose sentences using tense consistently (present and past) Use question marks, and use commas to separate items in a list	Write legibly, using upper and lower case letters appropriately within words, and observing correct spacing within and between words Form and use the four basic handwriting joins Wordprocess short narrative and non-narrative texts

Foundation Stage objectives in bold refer to the Early Learning Goals.

Throughout this document, the specific objectives identified for the Foundation Stage are dependent upon the outcomes of the consultation on the EYFS.

DfES (2006), pages 22–7

Possible structure of a literacy teaching session

In past years, schools were asked to use a framework known as the Literacy Hour. This was initially set up as a specific time slot allotted each day to focus on literacy skills. The aim of this approach was to raise the standards of literacy everywhere, focusing on the earliest age groups, reducing the numbers of children leaving school with limited reading and/or writing skills. The time-bound structure lacked the flexibility needed by teachers and learners and the guidance for teaching literacy has been changed. The term Literacy Hour has now been abandoned, along with its set timings but the basic teaching elements remain. For example, a teacher may use the following structure to a literacy session:

- whole-class work, e.g. shared text work – a balance of reading and writing
- whole-class work, e.g. focused word work or sentence work
- group and independent work, e.g. independent reading, writing or word work, enabling the teacher to work with specific ability groups on guided text work (reading or writing)
- whole-class time, e.g. reviewing, reflecting, consolidating teaching points, and presenting work covered in the lesson.

Source: Based on material from www.standards.dfes.gov.uk

Shared text work

During this stage of a literacy teaching session the teacher may use written material relevant to all children. This would often be a 'big book'. This stage is likely to involve:

- shared reading as a whole class at Key Stage 1, focusing on comprehension and on specific text features such as word-building, spelling, punctuation and layout of the text for a purpose. This provides a specific context for applying and teaching the use of reading cues to check for meaning, and word level skills
- combining shared writing with shared reading to help children develop an understanding of grammar, sentence construction and punctuation.

At Key Stage 2 shared reading extends reading skills and is a context for teaching and reinforcing grammar, punctuation and use of vocabulary.

Shared reading:

- helps children to work with texts that are beyond their independent reading levels, giving them access to richer and more complex texts than they would be able to access alone, building confidence and building on skills
- provides opportunities for children to learn, apply and reinforce skills with careful teacher guidance.

Ideally, shared reading and writing will be linked, e.g. firstly, through the introduction of a text, secondly through shared reading work, and finally by using the text as a frame or stimulus for writing.

Focused word work

This section needs to provide regular and focused work on the awareness and use of phonics and spelling, using the relevant word-level objectives. These objectives can be practised through shared reading, but also need to be specifically taught through structured activities. At Key Stage 2 children should be working on sentence-level objectives.

Group and independent work

This section of a session could have two complementary purposes:

- to enable the teacher to teach at least one group each session, differentiated by ability, for a sustained period through 'guided' reading or writing
- to enable other children to work independently – individually, in pairs or in groups – without recourse to the teacher.

It is an important part of this section of a session for children to learn not to interrupt the teacher.

Guided reading

The aim is for children to become independent readers. Usually children will be in small groups of around the same ability. They will use the same (carefully selected) text and the teacher will focus on independent reading, rather than modelling reading for the child. At Key Stage 1 the teacher usually introduces the text and the general context of the story. They also point out any key words. The children then read the text with the teacher assessing and supporting them individually. At Key Stage 2 silent reading is gradually and increasingly encouraged, with progress assessed through questioning and discussion.

Guided writing

The aim is for children to become independent writers. The work covered here will often be linked to whole-class shared writing sessions, again working towards specific objectives.

Whole-class work

The final stage of this style of session would bring the class back together to:

- enable the teacher to re-emphasise points, clear up misunderstandings and develop new teaching points
- enable children to reflect upon what they have learned and clarify their thinking
- enable children to revise and practise newly learned skills
- provide feedback, encouragement and constructive criticism
- enable children to present and talk about key issues, and for the teacher to monitor and assess the work of some of the children.

Source: Based on material at www.standards.dfes.gov.uk

You can access a copy of these word-level and sentence-level objectives at www.standards.dfes.gov.uk by following the links to Primary Framework, then Literacy and then Objectives. Alternatively, you could ask the class teacher at your placement, if you are in a school, if you can look at their copy.

Learning through play

Early years professionals have promoted learning through play for decades, and in recent years, government policy groups have voiced their agreement too, although there will probably always be discrepancies in how 'play' is actually thought of and defined between the early years profession and the policy makers. As the process of curriculum and strategy development has evolved (Foundation Stage Curriculum, Birth to Three Matters, Every Child Matters, Early Years Foundation Stage, etc.), each stage emphasises (just that bit more) how play should be the basis for early learning, raising the status of a play-based curriculum.

Professional Practice

- Reflect on activities you have carried out with children, identifying which were play-based. Any that you identify as not being play-based, think through whether they could be made so another time.

Link

Refer to pages 255 and 261 for ideas on supporting literacy through play.

- Tina Bruce and Janet Moyles are modern-day theorists whose thinking is firmly based in the value of play. Refer to material by either of them to further your understanding. Details can be found in the Bibliography on page 412.
- Also, refer to Green (2007) page 223 for ideas on learning through play in general.

Impact of legislation/guidance on practice

As mentioned above, in recent years greater levels of guidance on practice have been drawn up by government and implemented by early years practitioners. Initially, practitioners were concerned at the structure of the curriculum guidance, and thankfully this has been reviewed and redeveloped, and is considered much more acceptable by most practitioners today. There have always been good early years settings, excellent early years settings and settings which needed to improve their provision. There have also always been settings that provided a good range of opportunities for children, but where staff did not always understand the full value of what they were providing, perhaps seeing just the main learning opportunity to be gained from an activity, without realising just how many other aspects of learning were also involved. The structure of strategies such as the Foundation Stage Curriculum has enabled more staff to develop their understanding of the value of play to a greater level. This has been beneficial to children, to the staff and to the field of early years generally.

Funded places for children, initially for 4-year-olds and more recently for 3-year-olds, has been a massive boost to many families, enabling all families who wish it to receive an early years placement for their child. For nurseries and other early years settings, there have however been some concerns about the impact on occupancy levels, and issues of funding not actually covering fees completely, leaving providers in a position of losing revenue for their businesses. This problem is ongoing.

The other main impact of recent legislation and practice guidance has been the more stringent inspection procedures. These have been controversial at times, and it took time for practitioners to fully value the process, but for children it has meant that, on the whole, most unacceptable provision has been identified, and guidance given on how those settings can raise their standards. In some cases low standards have meant the closure of settings which were considered not to meet standards sufficiently. There have been clearer pathways set up for concerns to be raised, and the greater level of policies and procedural paperwork, whilst adding to the workload of those who write them and need to regularly review them, has helped to support safe working practice for all.

The introduction of (initially) Early Excellence centres, and more recently Sure Start centres around the country has been welcomed by the majority as a move forward in providing extended care, learning and support for both children and their families, incorporating health, education and adult learning. There have, however, been concerns regarding funding and the impact some of these centres have had on other provision in the area.

activity
INDIVIDUAL WORK 18.4

P3

M2

1. Choose either a piece of legislation linked to literacy, or a curriculum document linked to your current setting.
2. Produce a poster setting out the main aims for literacy support and include examples of how this is supported within your current placement.

activity
GROUP WORK 18.5

D1

1. Discuss as a group how a piece of legislation or curriculum document promotes and supports children's literacy development, evaluating its effectiveness.
2. Write a report on its effectiveness, giving examples from each of your placements to support your thinking.

Be able to implement a range of speaking and listening activities that can be used to support the development of children's skills

Activities

Professional Practice

- Language involves communicating, thinking, linking sounds to letters, reading and writing. These separate but inter-connected aspects of learning should be kept in mind when planning. Think about them as you read through the following section.

Every activity will involve language in some way. This may simply be through the adult reading a story or using written instructions on how to do something. It may be that the planned activity involves writing or reading or using a reference source such as a book or information website. Children will only build up a wide vocabulary if they are exposed to one, so it is important that you use a wide and varied vocabulary with all the children you work with. This means thinking about how you describe and discuss something, introducing alternative names for objects, using a range of descriptive terms, encouraging children to think, to describe, to ask questions: Why? What if? When? How?

Board and boxed games

Board games, such as snakes and ladders, and boxed games, such as picture lotto, all involve verbal interaction. Snakes and ladders involves terminology linked to position, e.g. climbing up the ladder, slithering along or down the snake, overtaking X and Y, being X places ahead or X places behind. Picture lotto involves the use of description, and the skill of matching words to pictures, e.g. Who has the red car? Who has the teddy with the hat?

Link

Refer also to Unit 17, page 178, for ideas to promote number skills too throughout each of the following activity areas.

Role play

Role play can involve the child acting out a role, dressing up, being another person, acting out a scenario either imaginary, from previous experience, or something that may be about to happen, or they are worried might happen.

In role-play situations, most children will naturally speak within their role, taking on the language of mummy, daddy, baby, shopkeeper, ticket collector, etc. They will use expression and intonation, often mimicking what they have heard at home. They may express concerns, worries and anxiety. Observation, together with sensitive adult input can help alleviate these fears and anxieties by using books, discussion, etc. at another time to help them work through how they are feeling. These instances show how important having language skills is to a child being able to make themselves understood and communicate their needs, either directly or indirectly.

At times undesirable expressions may be used. These can be left to pass unless it is regular, excessive or causing distress to others, but modelling more appropriate language will be helpful. If, however, what a child says or intimates ever causes you concern regarding their safety or well-being, you should speak to your placement supervisor, who will know what (if any) action to take.

In role play children will draw on both their own personal experiences, and those that they have seen on television, heard about in stories, and discussed with others either formally or informally.

Role play gives children opportunities to use both verbal and written language. There will be opportunities, for example, for:

- inviting others to play, and joining in play on request or invitation from others
- using appropriate questions and responses when 'shopping' or in other role-play situations
- using verbal social conventions within context

- labelling and putting up notices as their role-play area becomes a shop, the post office, a bank, etc.
- writing lists as they make up menus for their café, takeaway or restaurant
- noting down orders from customers, writing cheques at the bank, writing receipts at the petrol station, etc.
- writing to others as they make party invitations, send letters, Christmas or birthday cards
- writing names as they make luggage labels, tickets and boarding passes to get on their aeroplane
- using mark-making to indicate temperatures on a chart during hospital play, plotting the weight of a baby during baby clinic play
- reading newspapers during 'at home' play, magazines at the hairdressers, holiday brochures at the travel agents.

The list can be endless.

You may find it interesting to look at Green (2005b).

Books

Books can be both for pleasure and for information. In our modern-day world, heavily led by technology, it is important to help children value the use of books as a tool of reference. Linking books to displays and interest tables is an easy way to help children make this link. Using books to help children follow up an idea, an experience or an opportunity will again encourage the habit of book use. Examples include:

- using books at the centre of a discussion, or to start off a new topic
- looking at books on birds to support work on flight/feathers/bird feeding
- using maps to help place children's holiday locations
- looking at books on the body following a visit from a doctor, or following a child's stay in hospital for an operation, talking through experiences and discussing 'people who help us' where appropriate.

Reference books can be used to support all areas of the curriculum. This also applies to stories.

Storytelling

Stories provide both pleasure and information. Stories can be either written or oral, and can provide either imaginary events or descriptions of real life, past or present. Children love stories. They usually feel comfortable with them as there is a familiar structure to them. They have a beginning, and a clear end, with usually an interesting and perhaps exciting or funny middle. The way the story starts helps children to know and predict what might come next, e.g.

- Once upon a time ...
- When Jake went to hospital, he ...
- In the woods, near the stream ...

Each of these beginnings provide the child with a clue as to where the story is set, and what sort of story it is likely to be.

Stories support the development of language and literacy through:

- the introduction of new vocabulary, when and how to use it
- supporting understanding of sentence structure
- supporting children's own initial attempts at constructing stories
- description and alliteration
- the links they can give to current topics and the overall curriculum
- the introduction of alternative cultures, religions and the associated language structures, greetings and social gestures
- helping children find pleasure through listening and concentration, forming good habits for life in general.

Props and story sacks

Using props alongside storytelling can bring an extra dimension to the story, can extend learning and also help children to maintain focus. Fidgety children can be stilled by the encouragement to hold a shell, refer to a puppet or doll, take part in placing a picture on a storyboard, etc. Props can be almost anything linked to the story being told. Storyboards can either be produced along the way, with a group of children, or used as a ready prepared prop. They can easily be made, using simple illustrations, backed with Velcro or something similar, and placed on a textured board or cloth.

Fig 18.10 Examples of home-made storyboards I have used in nurseries since the early 1970s. They are still enjoyed today

Professional Practice

- Children love stories with repetition and these opportunities to join in regularly during a story give encouragement to quieter children to contribute verbally, and encouragement to all children to listen carefully, anticipating the next opportunity to join in the 'chant', etc.

Story sacks as a concept have been around for many years. They are in essence a collection of related props and, as with the storyboards, they can be home-made or commercial. As a commercial idea they were set up by Neil Griffiths in the 1990s. A typical story sack includes an illustrated story book, an information book to help extend learning, puppets or toys linked to the story, a recorded version of the story and some associated props, e.g. a simple game and relevant artefacts. The age group the story sack is aimed at is clearly indicated, and there are always instructions for parents on how to use the story sack with their children.

The use of story sacks extends story time and encourages language use through discussion, repetition and the exploration of the accompanying props and artefacts.

- Neil Griffiths provides training in developing story sacks and many schools and early years settings have benefited from this, going on to produce their own library of story sacks.
- You may find it interesting to look at Green (2006). School-made story sacks are featured on page 66.

Music and dance

The use of music and dance helps introduce vocabulary linked to movement and expression in a fun way. Through imitation initially, children will learn terms such as glide, soar, fly, hover, etc. as they move to appropriate music. They will learn the terms stomp, march, thump, flatten, etc. as they move around as giants, and the terms roar, screech, howl and groan as they play at being monsters. There are many other examples that could be used here. You can probably think of more.

Similarly, terms linked to position and direction will be learned as children are asked to move to the right, step forward, jump backwards, face a partner. Terms linked to symmetry can be learned through actions copying another child, e.g. mirroring, copying, same as, matching, and also terms to describe the opposite effect, e.g. different to, unlike, reverse.

Once again, you can probably think of many more examples to add to the above.

The use of rhythm is important, as language is full of rhythm, and listening to and being able to identify and replicate rhythm can also help general speech and language development.

Drama

Language and literacy is supported through drama as children reflect on stories well known to them, e.g. the story of the three little pigs, taking on various roles, speaking their 'lines' and following the story structure from its beginning, through its main sections and processes, and on to the climax with the big bad wolf. Re-enacting stories is part of the literacy strategy. It encourages children to listen, to speak and make links with the written word. It can also help develop discussion skills.

case study 18.3 The Three Little Pigs drama

Class 2 had enjoyed re-enacting the timeless classic, 'The Three Little Pigs'. It was part of a project on homes and buildings. Their teacher was following the drama session up with a discussion about houses. She began by asking the children what sort of building they lived in.

activity

1. What other aspects of discussion could she introduce?
2. What examples can you think of to extend children's vocabulary linked to 'The Three Little Pigs'?
3. What writing opportunities could you bring to the project? How would you set them up?

Opportunities to share a drama experience as a whole group can be helpful, especially for less confident children, encouraging them to take part, share verbal exchanges and experiences with others, reinforcing for themselves a sequential process. Other examples could be working as a team to be a large wave in the sea, a huge snake moving around the room, a volcano exploding.

You may find it of interest to refer to Boulton & Ackroyd (2004). There are three books in the series full of great ideas.

Story tapes

A range of well known and much loved stories, both classic and contemporary, is now available on tapes and CDs. Listening to tapes or CDs will never replace the importance of an adult reading to a child, but they do make an excellent alternative and additional source of exposing children to language and literature. Encouraging children to listen to a story in this way in the home is a far more focused experience for them than passively watching television or a DVD, and encouraging parents to consider this can also be beneficial to children.

Because story tapes are usually read by professionals, often practising actors, the use of tone, expression and emphasis is usually extremely good, helping to build on children's understanding of language use.

Professional Practice

- Parents who are not fluent readers themselves will also benefit from the experience of sharing a story with their child in this way.

Making tapes

Making tapes with or for children can be great fun. Popular examples would be to record a range of commonly heard sounds. Children will be using auditory discrimination as they listen and identify what they hear. Examples could include:

- household sounds: running water, toilet flushing, door bell ringing, the telephone, a broom sweeping, the spraying from a polish tin, etc.
- street sounds: dog barking, car horn, bus doors closing, siren from an emergency vehicle, birds fluttering, etc.
- a walk in the park or woods: the wind in the trees, birds singing, frogs croaking, walking on crunchy leaves, etc.

You could also help children make a recording of them each saying hello, playing it back and identifying each other's voices, or take it in turns to tell a story, a little bit at a time. Children love to hear their own voices, and again this focuses their listening and helps them discriminate sounds.

Circle time

Circle time is a regular time slot in a class or group where either specific topics are discussed, perhaps linked to the PSHE Citizenship strand of the National Curriculum, or where there is simply time for the whole group to gather, to listen to each other's news and ideas and perhaps discuss plans for something specific. Only one person is allowed to speak at any one time, and it is usual with young children for the speaker to hold something special, e.g. a large shell, a teddy or a beautiful artefact of some kind. This reminds the group who they should be focusing on. The 'only one person to speak at a time' rule helps teach the louder and more outgoing children to listen to others, building on their listening skills, their concentration and their social skills, and encourages the quieter, less confident children to feel more able to speak within a group setting, helping them build on their confidence and self-esteem. This also gives them opportunities to express themselves, and put forward ideas that they might otherwise not feel able to contribute.

Small world play

Small world play is play with resources such as farms, zoos, roadways, doll houses, etc. It is basically playing out 'life' in miniature. It is favoured mostly by children of pre-school ages who tend to speak to themselves in a monologue as they play. This gives great opportunities for:

- naming objects, e.g. car, bus, tractor, lorry, table, basin, lamp, cow, horse, bear, lion
- labelling actions, e.g. going upstairs, moving along the road, going in, coming out, going through the tunnel
- vocalising understanding of positions, e.g. in front of, behind, on top of, underneath, beside, inside, outside
- vocalising social greetings and pleasantries as they play, e.g. hello, goodbye, thank you, excuse me.

Materials and sources

Other opportunities to support the development of language and literacy include:

- using puppets, hand puppets, paper puppets, pop-up puppets, etc., also, life-size puppets and persona dolls
- using rhymes and finger rhymes, easily filling any short time gaps with a rhyme to reinforce current learning aims
- giving children instructions and directions, and asking them to do the same for each other. This can be either indoors or outside, involving the children moving physically, or controlling programmable toys, using computer programmes, etc.
- setting up discussion tables and displays, planning with the children what is needed, where objects can be collected from, etc.
- the labelling of any relevant objects or places, notices, signposts and posters. These all reinforce the meaning of printed text and teach the convention (in English) of reading from left to right, and from top to bottom
- making books with children. This helps introduce them to the construct of a book, e.g. its title page, the introduction, the main body of text, the conclusion
- using stories in the development of listening and comprehension skills, encouraging the skills of recall and summary
- spoken language in any shape or form. Any adult working with children can help their language development simply by conversing with them. If a child is listened to, they will also learn to listen to others
- reading poetry. Language is often set out at its best within poetry, so regularly enjoying poems with children can help them to learn about both timing, rhyme and vocabulary, and also develop an appreciation of the expression and emotions often found within the poem
- using tape recorders and listening centres. These encourage children to focus on listening to something specific, without the distractions of surrounding noise (dulled by the wearing of headphones). They offer opportunities for extension work for children working at the higher levels, focused time for easily distracted children, helping them to keep 'on task' whilst freeing up their teacher to work with others and as a source of pleasure for all
- using dual language books. It is important that there are appropriate resources for those children for whom English is an additional language. This includes the use of dual language labelling and notices, and also books wherever possible.

remember

Some children live in homes where being heard is a challenge above the noise of a busy household. This tends to make them feel they need to shout and talk over others, in order to be heard. Knowing that they will be listened to will help them learn to wait their turn without anxiety.

Good sources of dual language books can be found at:
www.mantralingua.com
www.milet.com.

activity
INDIVIDUAL WORK 18.6

P5

M3

1 Choose a role play scenario and develop two different activities that would support the development of children's speaking and listening skills. Give consideration to the numbers of children to be involved, the type and number of resources needed, the environment in which the activity would be taking place and your role as the supervising adult.

2 Carry out one of the activity ideas you have developed in your current placement.

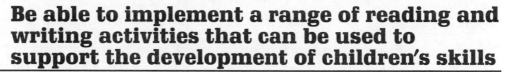

Be able to implement a range of reading and writing activities that can be used to support the development of children's skills

Contexts for reading and comprehension skills

It is important to consider how the context in which children learn affects the learning process. This was referred to on page 242 where a suggested structure for a literacy session was set out, explaining how children benefit from shared and guided opportunities in both reading and writing. It should be remembered that children need:

- shared reading experiences to learn to work with texts that alone they would not be ready to manage
- opportunities to read aloud and alone
- opportunities to read for pleasure, enjoying a wide variety of books of differing styles
- reading to be linked to other activities, to learn how it is used and contextualised within the world they live in
- to listen to and discuss stories and rhymes on a one-to-one, small group or whole-class basis. This helps consolidate learning and helps them progress further
- to learn about cues and conventions, e.g. phonics, graphic and contextual cues, the structure of a text and the organisation of texts. Each of these aspects are supported through listening to stories, reading with an adult following the text together, using books for reference and knowing where to look to find what they need, e.g. index, contents list. Rhymes and repetition are also of benefit, as are games involving the sounds of letters, syllables, etc.

Link

Refer to page 191 to remind yourself of the order in which articulation usually occurs, and how vocalising is partially influenced by a child's physical ability.

Writing forms

Children need to want to write, to have a purpose for writing, and understand the breadth of purposes that written communication can be used for. They need to be able to practise letter formation freely. They need opportunities for letter formation, word development and the use and meaning of punctuation from an early age, building on each aspect as they move through school. Active involvement of children in labelling their own work, making choices about greetings and messages when creating 'products' for special occasions, developing signs and indicators within the learning environment and in giving titles to display work, will increase their ownership of the written word. Also, group and individual opportunities to develop composition work incorporating various forms and genres should be built into planning, taking on children's own ideas as well as those proposed by the adult.

Activities

Figure 18.11 lists activities which help to support reading and writing.

The text that follows gives brief examples of how each activity helps support reading and writing. These are just a few to get you started. You will be able to think of many more.

Link

As you read this section, refer to pages 255–260, and also to Unit 17 for further ideas.

Role play supports the development of reading and writing as children:

- write shopping lists
- take down messages
- 'read' newspapers and magazines.

Sand play supports the development of reading and writing as children:

- develop fine motor skills whilst filling and pouring
- learn to control implements
- use fingers to make patterns and letter shapes.

Fig 18.11 Activities to support reading and writing

Painting supports the development of reading and writing as children:

- develop arm and hand control through brush use
- enjoy early mark-making experiences
- create an expression with paint.

Story sacks support the development of reading and writing as children:

- make links between what they hear and the written word
- listen to tapes and CDs
- join in repetition and story format, using the provided props.

Printmaking supports the development of reading and writing as children:

- make patterns
- learn to work from left to right
- plan, implement and reflect on what they produce.

Patterns support the development of reading and writing as children:

- learn about shape, size and structure
- learn to discriminate and group by function
- identify and learn about order.

Story telling supports the development of reading and writing as children:

- develop an understanding of story order; beginning, middle, conclusion
- find enjoyment in the experience, wanting more
- experience a variety of story types and genres.

Poetry supports the development of reading and writing as children:

- learn about pattern and rhyme
- identify and enjoy repetition
- experience sounds, and links between similar sounds in a fun way.

Music supports the development of reading and writing as children:

- respond to rhythm
- follow patterns during movement sessions
- observe written music and how it is formed from left to right.

Drama supports the development of reading and writing as children:

- take on roles, responding to the process of familiar stories
- maintain interest in books to support further experiences
- use gesture and develop body control.

Use of technology supports the development of reading and writing as children:

- develop the skills they will need to use online sources of reference for the future
- practise early design and creativity through computer games
- develop keyboard skills alongside early letter recognition.

Writing for different audiences support the development of reading and writing as children:

- recognise how important written communication is in the world
- try out different forms of writing, expression and structure
- experience the practical application of writing as they use references.

Group and individual books support the development of reading and writing as children:

- experience stories in different formats
- learn alongside others, sometimes supported by those at a more advanced level
- learn to share reading times with parents, siblings and friends, as well as teachers and other practitioners.

Cutting and sticking supports the development of reading and writing as children:

- explore their own creativity
- impose order and pattern on their work
- develop fine motor skills as they use small utensils.

fig 18.12 Sharing a story at home with family

activity
INDIVIDUAL WORK 18.7

P6

M4

1. Choose two activities, one involving a book or story, and one of your choice from those set out above. Develop them so they would support the development of children's reading and writing skills. Give consideration to the numbers of children to be involved, the type and number of resources needed, the environment in which the activity would be taking place, and your role as the supervising adult.
2. Carry out one of the activity ideas you have developed in your current placement.

Materials, settings and environments

Importance of providing a wide variety of materials and resources for reading and stimuli for writing

Children need to learn that books are good, useful, and play a vital part in life and learning. They need to be inspired by what they see, read and refer to. Adults should regularly review the books on offer in their nursery, pre-school or classroom. Settings should be providing books that:

- are fun
- are visually appealing
- are appropriate to the children's level of understanding and concentration span
- are factual
- are fictional
- are used for reference
- offer repetition and the chance to join in with familiar refrains
- introduce children to poetry and rhymes
- introduce children to new experiences
- help children learn about fears and emotions and how to deal with them
- portray positive images regarding gender and ability
- portray a range of cultures and heritage in positive ways
- show both similarities and differences between cultures, celebrating those differences
- are in more than one language, ideally having a representation of all languages spoken within the setting.

For younger children, books need to:

- be durable
- be easy to handle
- be (mostly, but not exclusively) presented in clear, bold text
- be inviting to look at
- have clear pictures
- offer satisfaction
- be short, with an easy to follow content.

For older children, books need to:

- include both classic and contemporary language use
- stretch concentration spans
- relate to interests and potential risks
- extend learning of health issues, personal safety and care.

Early years settings should be providing free-writing areas at all times. There should be mark-making and writing opportunities alongside all role play, and adults should take all opportunities, planned or spontaneous, to encourage the writing of written records, reflective comments, etc.

Professional Practice

- **As you move from placement to placement, note the different ways in which children are encouraged to write for both practical purposes and for pleasure. Note the differing stimuli teachers and other practitioners use, e.g. stories, festive occasions, stormy weather, etc.**

Enabling children to choose own reading materials and appropriate writing forms for particular contexts

Having easy access to reading materials will encourage children to choose to read during free-learning sessions, or as time-fillers at the end of a session. In early years settings books would normally be set out in book boxes, on shelves and tables, racks or storage units. These need to be secure and unable to close or fall.

Fig 18.13 Learning about the pleasure of books

Having a comfortable and inviting book area will encourage children to enjoy a quiet time curled up with a book, perhaps alongside a friend or as a shared experience with an adult.

The labels, notices, posters and signs around the setting will illustrate different writing forms for children. Providing them with relevant materials to choose freely will help them start to develop an understanding of writing contexts.

How setting/environment may affect children's reading performance and comprehension

remember A child's learning style can be helped or hindered by the environment in which their learning takes place.

Throughout your studies for this qualification, there will have been many references to the importance of providing a suitable environment for children, both in their care and in their learning. Regarding literacy development, the more that language is used around children, in all its forms, the greater their respect for it will be developed and consolidated. A child who is provided with an exciting range of books to choose from, appropriate to their level of ability and to their current interests, will be most likely to develop a love of language and literature for the future.

Link

Refer to page 198 where issues of learning styles (visual, auditory and kinaesthetic) are discussed.

activity
INDIVIDUAL WORK 18.8
D2

1 Reflect upon the two activities you carried out on pages 250 and 253. How well did each activity support the children's learning?
2 Make clear whether your learning objectives for the children had been met and how you have been able to evidence this.
3 Explain what you would do differently another time and why, and provide any written feedback given to you by your placement supervisor. Reflect on their comments and include a written response.
4 Evaluate the resources to support literacy at your placement in general, and explain their availability to the children, both through free access and through adult-led activities.

Progress Check

1 Name the main theorists associated with language development.
2 Explain at least three theories regarding how language develops and state which theorist agrees with each theory.
3 What is syntax?
4 What is phonology?
5 What are semantics?
6 Describe the ten basic stages of language development and what is needed for successful language to develop.
7 What is dyslexia?
8 What is dysgraphia?
9 Explain the main areas of learning for communication, language and literacy development within the Early Years Foundation Stage.
10 Explain the main elements of the 12 strands of the Primary Framework for Literacy.
11 Give examples of how you can help children develop good listening skills.
12 Explain what is meant by visual learners, auditory learners and kinaesthetic learners.
13 Give at least five examples of activities that can help develop the fine motor skills needed for writing.
14 Explain how role play supports the development of literacy skills.
15 Explain how storytelling helps support the development of literacy skills.

UNIT 27

Meeting Additional Requirements for Children's Care, Learning and Development

This unit covers the following objectives:

- Understand factors that may lead to children having additional requirements
- Understand the impact of legislation, regulations and codes of practice on provision for children with additional requirements
- Understand inclusive practice and how to support children with additional requirements

During the last 20 years or so there has been a shift in attitude towards the education of children with special educational (or additional) needs or disabilities. It is common for these children to be educated in mainstream settings. This is known as inclusion. There has also been a dramatic increase in the number of children who have been diagnosed with conditions such as attention deficit hyperactivity disorder, autistic spectrum disorder and dyslexia and associated learning difficulties. It is therefore essential for anyone working in a pre-school or school environment to have knowledge about additional needs, the principle of inclusive education and the strategies that can be implemented to support the education of these children.

This unit will give you an overview of some of the conditions that you may encounter in your setting. It will examine the shift in attitude towards the education of children with additional needs and the legislation and codes of practice which have been put into place to address this. You will also learn about strategies that can be used to ensure that children with additional needs are able to access the curriculum and you will consider the importance of working in partnership with parents and other agency workers.

grading criteria

To achieve a **Pass** grade the evidence must show that the learner is able to:	To achieve a **Merit** grade the evidence must show that, in addition to the Pass criteria, the learner is able to:	To achieve a **Distinction** grade the evidence must show that, in addition to the Pass and Merit criteria, the learner is able to:
P1 Describe six factors that may lead to children having additional needs page 280		
P2 Describe the role of legislation, regulations and codes of practice in the provision of services for children with additional needs page 293	**M1** Explain how legislation, regulations and codes of practice help to promote the provision of services for children with additional needs page 293	

To achieve a **Pass** grade the evidence must show that the learner is able to:	To achieve a **Merit** grade the evidence must show that, in addition to the Pass criteria, the learner is able to:	To achieve a **Distinction** grade the evidence must show that, in addition to the Pass and Merit criteria, the learner is able to:
P3 Describe models of disability and how these may impact upon children and their families page 296	**M2** Compare two models of disability in terms of how these may impact upon children and their families page 296	**D1** Evaluate two models of disability in terms of explaining the concept of disability page 297
P4 Use examples to describe positive working practices that support children with additional needs page 303	**M3** Explain the role of positive working practices in supporting inclusion in a children's setting page 303	
P5 Describe two policies in a children's setting that promote inclusive practice page 309	**M4** Explain how the policies help to promote inclusion in the setting page 309	
P6 Describe one example of multidisciplinary working in supporting children with additional needs and their families page 312	**M5** Explain how the example of multidisciplinary working supports children with additional needs and their families page 312	**D2** Evaluate a range of strategies for supporting children with additional needs and promoting inclusion page 312
P7 Describe the role of partnerships with parents in supporting children with additional needs and their families page 314		

Understand factors that may lead to children having additional requirements

Additional needs

There are many reasons why a child may have additional needs.

- Some conditions are genetic, some may be hereditary (that is inherited), some are congenital (being present at birth), while other conditions are due to environmental conditions. Examples of environmental conditions include prescription and illegal drugs taken during pregnancy, excess alcohol taken during pregnancy and antenatal conditions such as pregnancy-related hypertension.
- Accidents causing head injury and illness such as meningitis and rubella can give rise to additional needs such as cognitive difficulties and sensory impairment.
- There are conditions for which there is no known cause or where the cause is due to a combination of factors, e.g. autistic spectrum disorder.

Some additional needs are primarily physical, e.g. cystic fibrosis, others are primarily mental difficulties e.g. autistic spectrum disorder. There are some specific learning difficulties such as dyslexia and there are additional needs that are primarily behavioural such as attention deficit disorder.

Professional Practice

- Many children will have a combination of physical, mental, learning and behavioural needs. In some cases frustration caused as a result of one of the first three areas of need may give rise to behavioural issues. For example, if a child's additional needs have not been recognised or addressed, they may feel anger and frustration particularly if they are unable to communicate their needs.

The following are some examples of additional needs.

Genetic factors

Down's syndrome

Down's **syndrome** is a genetic condition (i.e. something you are born with, which is present in the baby from the moment of conception) caused by the presence of an extra chromosome. Chromsomes are tiny particles, which are present in every cell in every tissue in our bodies and they carry the 'blueprint' for all the characteristics we inherit. This blueprint is carried in the form of a coded message in a chemical substance called DNA. There are 23 pairs of chromosomes in each cell, hence 46 altogether. One of each pair comes from the father, one from the mother.

In 1959, a French geneticist, Professor Jerome Lejeune, discovered that Down's syndrome was caused by the presence of an extra copy of chromosome 21, making 47 chromosomes in all. The name 'Down' comes from the English doctor, John Langdon Down, who first described the syndrome in 1866.

Every day in the UK between one and two babies are born with Down's syndrome which means that one baby in every 1000 has the condition. The causes of the presence of extra number 21 chromosome is not yet known and it can come from either the mother or the father.

- The most common type of Down's Syndrome, Standard Trisomy 21 (about 94 per cent of all people with Down's syndrome fall into this group) occurs because of an unusual cell division which has produced either an egg or a sperm with 24 chromosomes instead of 23. When this egg or sperm fuses with an ordinary egg or sperm, the first cell of the developing baby has 47 chromosomes instead of 46 and all that baby's cells will have 47 chromosomes. There is no way of predicting whether a person is more or less likely to make eggs or sperm with 24 chromosomes. Babies born to older mothers have a higher chance of having Down's syndrome but it is not known why.
- The Translocation type of Down's syndrome occurs in about 3 per cent of babies with Down's syndrome. Part of the number 21 chromosome becomes attached to another chromosome so that both parts of the new large chromosome move together as one. In about half of the people who have Translocation Down's syndrome, the translocation is a one-off occurrence and does not mean that it will happen again in any future pregnancies, but in the other half the chance of having another child with Down's syndrome is quite high because one parent, though having a normal balanced chromosomal make-up, has one of the number 21s 'stuck on' to another chromosome.
- Mosaicism is the third type of Down's syndrome with about 2–3 per cent of people with Down's syndrome falling into this category. In this type, the cells with the extra 21 chromosome are mixed with other 'normal' cells and therefore only a certain percentage of the cells are affected.

Summary

- It is an easily identifiable syndrome at birth.
- Children have distinct facial features which include an upward slant to eyes.
- Congenital heart disease is present in many cases.
- Respiratory and ear infections are a common feature, sometimes leading to deafness.
- Intellectual development is slow, but can reach the lower levels of normal in some children.
- Life expectancy is usually to around middle age, but occasionally people with Down's syndrome may live longer.

Fig 27.1 Child with Down's syndrome

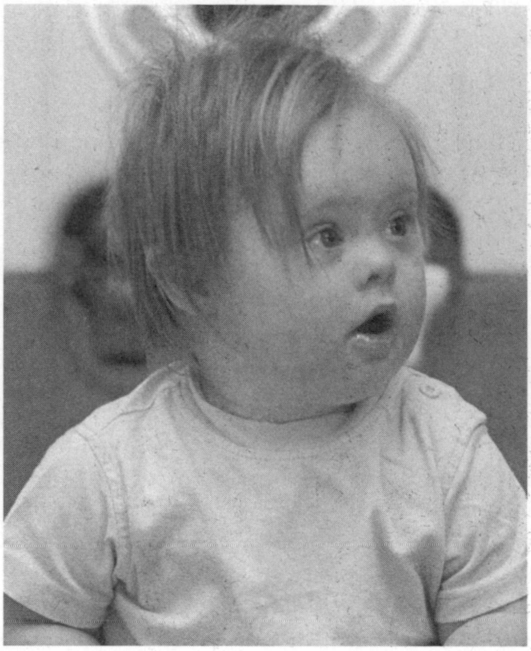

William's syndrome

William's syndrome is a rare disorder and, like Down's syndrome, it is caused by an abnormality of chromosomes. There is no cure for the syndrome and there is a wide variation in ability between individuals with the condition.

It is a non-hereditary syndrome which occurs at random and can affect brain development in varying degrees, combined with some physical effects or physical problems. These include lack of co-ordination, slight muscle weakness, possible heart defects and occasional kidney damage. Hypercalcaemia (a high calcium level) is often discovered in infancy and normal development generally delayed. The incidence is approximately 1 in 25,000 but the figure is rising as awareness of the syndrome increases. Diagnosis is not easy as the effects of the syndrome vary considerably, but there are certain indications that William's syndrome may be present, such as:

Fig 27.2 Children with William's syndrome

- Facial features – all the children have a facial similarity sometimes referred to as 'elfin' features. They include a wide mouth with large, slack bottom lip, a nose turned up at the tip with flattened bridge, slightly 'bulgy' cheeks, irregular teeth widely spaced, sometimes a squint.
- Early problems – these can include low birth weight, often being 'late for dates', slow weight gain and sometimes weight loss, below average growth, very slow feeding, restless sleeping and irritability, sometimes a hernia, a squint and excessive vomiting leading to dehydration and constipation. A raised calcium level is found in some babies.
- Heart problems – all children with William's syndrome appear to have a slight narrowing of the aorta above the valve, in many cases insignificant, but occasionally leading to more serious heart defects.
- Psychological – this includes hyperactivity in early years, extreme uninhibited behaviour, excessive talking in an inappropriate and 'adult' manner, over-friendliness with strangers, compulsion to talk to adults while being unable to make friends with peers, obsessional interest in certain things, e.g. cars, trains, vacuum cleaners, wheels and so on, fear of heights, open stairs, uneven surfaces.
- Emotional immaturity – this is exhibited by over-reaction to events and exaggerated displays of fear, excitement, sadness, happiness, etc.
- Hypersensitivity to noise – about 90 per cent of children with William's syndrome show great distress on hearing loud sudden noises such as guns firing, balloons bursting, Christmas crackers, fireworks, etc.

Cystic fibrosis

Cystic fibrosis is the UK's most common life-threatening inherited disease. It is caused by a single faulty gene that controls the movement of salt in the body. It affects over 7500 people in the UK and over 2 million people carry the faulty gene that causes it. For a baby to be born with cystic fibrosis, both parents must be carriers of the faulty gene. There is currently no cure for cystic fibrosis.

Summary

- The most commonly found inherited disorder in the UK.
- A sticky mucus is produced in many of the infant's organs.
- Obstruction of the bowel is often found soon after birth.
- The lungs and pancreas are particularly affected.
- A high calorie diet is recommended.
- An enzyme supplement is given shortly before each meal to help with the absorption of nutrients.

Fig 27.3 A child undergoing percussion therapy

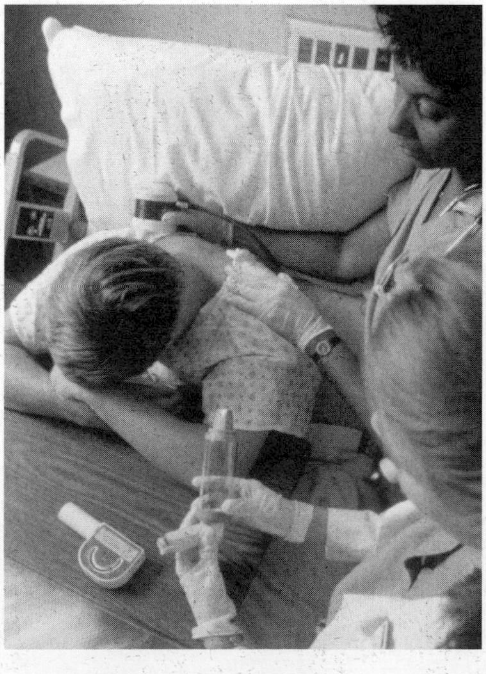

Fig 27.4 The lungs of a person with cystic fibrosis

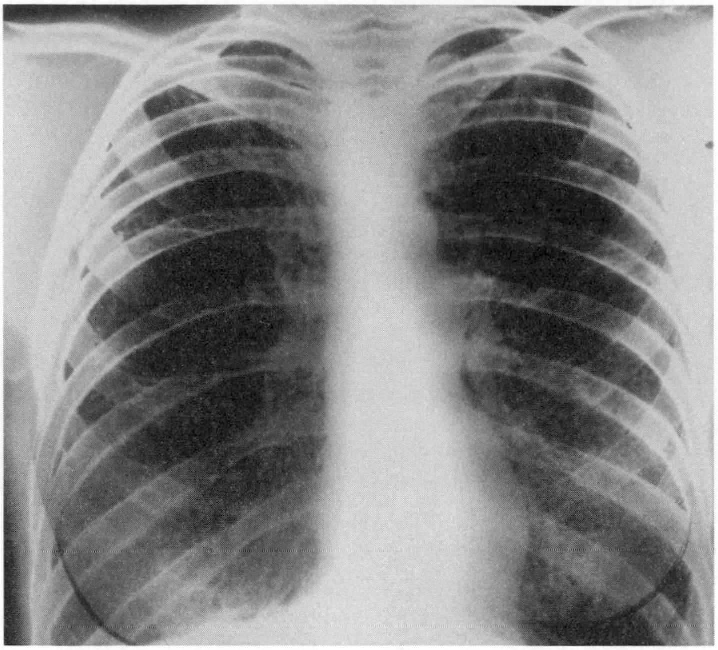

- Lung problems are the most serious aspect.
- Physiotherapy (percussion therapy – this is physiotherapy of the chest to loosen secretion blocking the lungs) is needed regularly throughout the day to keep the lungs clear.
- Life span is often around 20 years, depending on severity, but this is increasing with improved treatments.

Sickle-cell anaemia

Sickle-cell anaemia is an inherited genetic condition in which there is an abnormality of haemoglobin, the oxygen-carrying protein found in red blood cells.

People with sickle-cell anaemia have a type of haemoglobin known as sickle haemoglobin which is different from normal haemoglobin. Normal blood cells can bend and flex easily, and so travel around the blood vessels easily. When sickle haemoglobin gives up its oxygen to the tissues, it sticks together to form long rods inside the red blood cells, making these cells rigid and sickle shaped. They are then less able to squeeze through small blood vessels. These small blood vessels easily become blocked, preventing oxygen from getting through and causing severe pain and damage to organs. Blockage of a blood vessel causes an attack known as a crisis. This is more likely to happen when the person is stressed by another illness, exhaustion, cold, dehydration and other problems. Organs such as the liver, kidney, lungs, heart and spleen become damaged, causing severe pain, especially in the bones. The red blood cells also break up, easily leading to anaemia.

There is no cure for sickle-cell anaemia, but the frequency and severity of crises and their complications can be reduced by prompt recognition and treatment.

Fig 27.5 Normal blood cells and sickle-cell blood cells

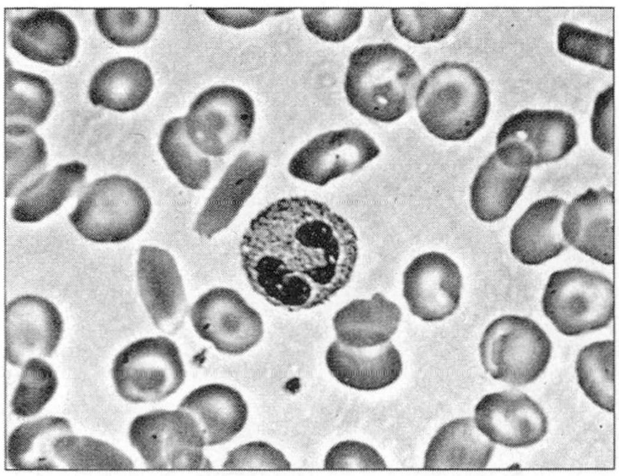

Summary

- It is a lifelong condition.
- It is seen in people of Mediterranean countries, African-Caribbean people and in some Asian and Middle Eastern people.
- The first signs are seen at about 6 months old with swelling of bones on hands and feet.
- It involves the abnormality of the oxygen-carrying substance in red blood cells.
- The shape of the cells becomes changed (sickle-shaped) and causes severe pain.
- Anaemia is a common and ongoing problem.
- Problems with an enlarged spleen can occur.
- Bone infections and enuresis (bed-wetting) are common problems.

Duchenne muscular dystrophy

Duchenne muscular dystrophy is a genetic disorder caused by an error in the dystrophic gene. The condition causes progressive muscle weakness as the muscle cells break down and die. About 100 boys are born in the UK each year with the disorder which was named after the doctor who first studied the condition in the 1800s.

Summary

- Only boys are affected by this condition.
- The first signs are seen at around 18 months old.
- A delay in walking is common.
- Falls become increasingly noticeable.
- Child will have difficulty in running or climbing due to weakening in the pelvic and leg muscles.
- Muscles become increasingly contracted (tight and restrictive).
- This is a progressive condition and boys often need to use a wheelchair by the age of 10 to 12 years.
- Chest infections are serious.
- A limited life span usually results from respiratory or heart failure.

Fragile X syndrome

Fragile X syndrome is the most common known cause of inherited learning disability. As it is a genetically inherited condition, when one child in a family is diagnosed with Fragile X there are enormous implications for the parents and siblings and other relatives. Both men and women are carriers of the syndrome and it occurs in all populations and ethnic groups.

First seen under the microscope in 1969, Fragile X was not associated with the particular problems of delayed development and behavioural difficulties until 1977. The condition is transmitted on the X chromosome, one of the chains of genetic material which determines inherited characteristics. Under a microscope a Fragile X chromosome has an abnormal appearance at the tip which looks as if it is breaking off but not quite separated. The X chromosome is one of a pair, which decides a child's sex. A boy has one X and one Y chromosome, while a girl has two X chromosomes. If a girl has one 'fragile' X she also has a 'good' one and it seems that the 'good' chromosome can compensate to a degree for the effects of the 'fragile' one. In this way girls may unknowingly carry and pass Fragile X to the next generation.

Summary

- It most frequently (and more severely) affects boys.
- Girls mostly have a normal level of intelligence.
- Boys' intellectual levels can change from severe to just below normal.
- A long thin face is a usual physical feature.
- Large ears and a prominent forehead are common in boys.
- Life expectancy is normal.

Haemophilia

Haemophilia is a blood condition in which an essential clotting factor is either partly or completely missing. This causes a person with haemophilia to bleed for longer than normal. The main problem is not cuts and grazes but internal bleeding into joints, muscles and soft tissues. Haemophilia is a lifelong inherited genetic condition which affects females as carriers and males who inherit the condition. Almost a third of new diagnoses are where there is no previous family history. It appears worldwide and occurs in all racial groups.

Summary

- Almost exclusively boys are affected.
- It is a bleeding disorder.
- Severe internal bleeding occurs at the slightest knock or injury.
- Swelling of joints and bones at the site of injury.
- Deformity and pain are common.
- Minor surgery (e.g. dental surgery) can be problematic without special procedures to restrict the blood loss.
- Sufferers are particularly susceptible to being infected with hepatitis B and need to be immunised against it.
- Pain killers containing asprin should not be given as they affect the blood clotting process.

Thalassaemia

Thalassaemia is a hereditary blood condition. The disorder is a form of anaemia that requires specialist care and management. People who are of Asian, Mediterranean, Middle Eastern and African origins are most at risk of thalassaemia. Caucasian people are also affected but this is less common.

Summary

- It is a lifelong condition.
- There are two different types of the condition – alpha and beta.
- The first signs are seen between 3 and 6 months.
- Symptoms include anaemia, lack of interest in feeding and vomiting after feeds.
- Jaundice is common due to a faster breakdown of the red blood cells.
- Enlarged liver and spleen are often a problem.
- Diabetes can also occur.
- Life expectancy can be shorter in individuals severely affected by the condition.

Other genetic conditions

Examples of some other conditions that you may encounter are:

- Batten's disease
- Phenylketonuria (PKU)
- Marfan syndrome
- Osteogenesis imperfecta (brittle bones)
- Angelman's syndrome
- Achondroplasia
- Prader-Willi syndrome
- Usher's syndrome.

Batten's disease

Batten's disease is an inherited disorder of the nervous system that is usually first noticed in childhood. Early symptoms are problems with vision or seizures. In some cases the early signs are subtle, taking the form of personality and behaviour changes, slow learning, clumsiness or stumbling. Symptoms vary with each child and the early symptoms can be confusing and not easily recognised even by doctors. As well as visual impairment which often progresses to complete blindness and seizures, there will be a loss of communication skills, loss of fine and gross motor skills, abnormal body movements and a general progressive deterioration.

Boys and girls are equally affected and it usually results in death by the age of around 10 years.

Phenylketonuria (PKU)

PKU is a rare biochemical abnormality which is inherited by a child from both parents. At birth, the baby appears to be quite normal but the condition will be discovered before the age of 1 month by a **screening** blood test which is taken from all babies born in the UK.

A positive blood test shows that there is too much of a substance called phenylalanine in the baby's blood.

Before early screening and treatment became available and high levels of phenylalanine were allowed to continue in the blood, the normal growth and development of the baby's brain was affected and, in some cases, the children became severely mentally abnormal. Phenylalanine is a natural part of all protein foods and is essential in any normal diet. In PKU, the aim of treatment is to stop the build-up of phenylalanine by following a special diet. When the diet is monitored carefully, it allows the baby's brain to grow and develop so that a normal lifestyle, apart from the dietary restrictions, can be expected.

Marfan syndrome

Marfan syndrome is an inherited disorder of connective tissue which affects many organ systems including eyes, heart and blood vessels. A gene for Marfan syndrome has been located on chromosome 15.

A person with Marfan syndrome will usually be characteristically tall and slim with lax joints. The range of complications caused by Marfan syndrome and their severity varies considerably between individuals.

Fig 27.6 A child with Marfan syndrome

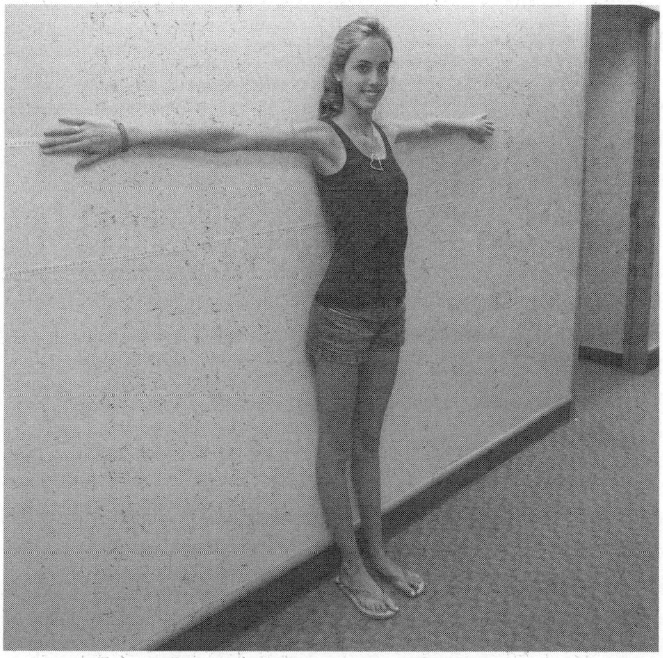

Osteogenesis Imperfecta (brittle bones)

Osteogenesis imperfecta, also known as brittle bone disease, is a large group of conditions characterised by fragility of the bones present from childhood. The most common cause is inherited defects of collagen, the protein responsible for the strength of the bone. The severity of the condition may vary. Some affected individuals may have multiple fractures while in others it may be difficult to diagnose. There are four varieties of osteogenesis imperfecta, with Type 2 being the most serious as severe fractures cause infants to be stillborn or die in the first few weeks of life. Types 1 and 4 are milder conditions where the child has good stature and relatively few fractures. Associated problems may include lax joints, fragile teeth, excessive sweating and easy bruising. Additionally temporary brittle bone disease may cause fractures in the first year of life and improve later. Fractures in childhood may also be caused by rickets due to vitamin D deficiency.

Angelman's syndrome

This is a congenital chromosome disorder first described in 1965 by Harry Angelman, an English doctor. In 70 per cent of cases, it is inherited from the mother with similar genetic changes on the chromosome 15 of paternal origin which produces Prader-Willi syndrome.

Angelman's syndrome is not evident at birth but becomes obvious as the child matures. Characteristics include microcephaly (small head circumference). Difficult feeding can be a problem due to poor brain development and so difficulties in sucking. Developmental delay leading to severe learning disability occurs over the early years. Speech is affected, with expressive speech less developed than receptive language. Walking is late and there is a jerky gait in the early years which may produce deformities in joints which may need correction at a later date. Arm movements are also jerky and stereotyped and together with the unusual gait and hand flapping have given rise to the term 'happy puppet'. Seizures are common during infancy and childhood. There are characteristic facial features with children tending to have large mouths with widely spaced teeth and protruding tongues.

Prader-Willi syndrome

Prader-Willi syndrome (PWS) is caused by an abnormality on chromosome 15. Features of the condition are

- hypotonia – weak muscle tone and floppiness at birth
- hypoganadism – immature development of sexual organs and other sexual characteristics
- obesity caused by excessive appetite and over-eating and a decreased calorific requirement owing to low energy expenditure level
- central nervous system and endocrine gland dysfunction causing varying degrees of learning disability
- short stature
- somnolence and poor emotional and social development.

Many people with PWS also exhibit characteristic facial and other physical features including almond-shaped eyes, a narrow forehead, a down-turned mouth with a triangular shaped upper lip and small hands and feet. People with PWS have poor large-muscle strength, often coupled with poor co-ordination and balance. Muscle tone can be improved with appropriate therapy and exercise.

Achondroplasia

Achondroplasia is the most common form of disproportionate short stature, or short-limbed dwarfism, a developmental disorder in which bone tissue does not develop properly in the long bones of the arms and legs. The condition affects about 1 in 25,000 individuals of all ethnic groups.

Affected individuals reach a maximum height of about four feet. The head may be larger than normal with a prominent forehead and nose. There is no cure for achondroplasia, but growth hormone can help to achieve moderate growth in some children and surgery can be used in some cases to increase leg length by up to 30 cm. It is sometimes necessary to test children for hydrocephalus and, if necessary, to drain fluid and relieve pressure on the brain. Surgery can also be used to prevent spinal compression.

Children affected with achondroplasia frequently have delayed motor milestones, otitis media and bowing of the knees. Most individuals are of normal intelligence and are able to lead independent and productive lives but because of their short stature a number of psycho-social problems can arise.

Usher's syndrome

Usher's syndrome is inherited genetically and usually parents are unaware that they have an Usher gene because they would need two of the mutated genes in order to show signs of the Usher syndrome.

Usher's syndrome is the most common condition that involves both hearing and vision problems. The major symptoms of Usher's syndrome are hearing impairment and retinitis pigmentosa, an eye disorder that causes a person's vision to worsen over time. Some people with Usher's syndrome also have balance problems. The severity of the symptoms depends on the type of Usher's syndrome a child has. People with Type 1 are profoundly deaf from birth and have severe balance problems and most will use sign language as their primary means of communication. Because of their balance problems they are slow to sit without support and rarely learn to walk before 18 months. These children usually begin to develop vision problems by the time they are 10 and these tend to progress rapidly until the individual is completely blind. Individuals with Type 2 are born with moderate to severe hearing impairment and normal balance. Most can benefit from hearing aids and perform well in mainstream classrooms. Visual problems develop more slowly than in children with Type 1 but when an individual's vision deteriorates to blindness his or her ability to lip read is lost. Children with Type 3 have normal hearing and normal to near normal balance. Hearing worsens over time and usually they become deaf by mid-to-late adulthood and by mid-adulthood the individual is usually blind.

Developmental factors

Autistic spectrum disorder

Although it was first identified in 1943 (by an Austrian, Leo Kanner), autism is still a relatively little known disability. People with autism are not physically disabled in the same way that a person with cerebral palsy may be. Due to its invisible nature, it can be much harder to create awareness and understanding of the condition.

Autism is a lifelong developmental disability that affects the way a person communicates and relates to people around them. People with autism often have accompanying learning disabilities, but everyone with the condition shares a difficulty in making sense of the world. Similarly someone with a disability such as Down's syndrome or a sensory impairment can also have autism. The term autistic spectrum disorder is now used to encompass those who may be very intellectually able but nevertheless still have aspects of the 'triad of impairment' (see below) and those who may have no speech and multiple learning difficulties.

The exact causes of autism are still not known but research shows that genetic factors are important. It is also evident from research that autism may be associated with a variety of conditions affecting brain development which occur before, during or very soon after birth.

Boys are affected more commonly than girls by about 4:1. Autism may also co-exist with a number of other conditions, e.g. attention deficit hyperactivity disorder, obsessive compulsive disorder and oppositional defiance disorder.

Children will not usually be diagnosed until the age of 2–3 years. In order to be diagnosed with autistic spectrum a child has to be affected in each of the three areas which comprise the triad of impairment:

- language impairment
- social impairment
- impaired imagination.

Language impairment (verbal and non-verbal communication)
This includes:

- poor understanding and use of facial expressions, body language, etc.
- problems with semantics – meaning of words
- problems with syntax – sentence construction, e.g. questions, difficulty with who, what, why, when
- poor pragmatics – sense of audience, e.g. people without autism know when it is appropriate to say something to one person but not another – the child with autism does not make this distinction
- poor conversation skills – often the child with autism will talk incessantly about their particular interest but not engage in a conversation and not recognise when the other person is bored
- difficulties in understanding sarcasm, irony and metaphor
- echolalia – copying what has just been said; it can sometimes be 'delayed echolalia'
- poor inferential thinking (being able to infer meaning).

Some children with autism are non-verbal and may never acquire speech.

Social impairment
This includes:

- difficulties associated with impaired language
- a range of behaviours from 'withdrawn' to 'active but odd'
- difficulties understanding the minds of other people
- poor understanding of other people's knowledge
- difficulties predicting other people's behaviour
- difficulties in recognising and understanding feelings and emotions
- lack of understanding of social conventions
- poor attention span.

Impaired imagination

This includes:

- rigidity of thought and lack of imagination
- ritualistic behaviours
- reliance on routines
- inability to cope with change
- problems with generalisation
- extreme delay or absence of 'pretend play'
- substituted repetitive behaviours or special interests
- obsessions
- attention difficulties.

Asperger's syndrome

Children with Asperger's syndrome form part of the autistic spectrum.

The syndrome is named after Hans Asperger who recognised the characteristics in a group of adults in 1944. Children with Asperger's syndrome are sometimes referred to as 'high-functioning' autistic children due to their verbal skills and often in-depth knowledge about particular subjects and aptitudes in subjects such as mathematics, science and computer science.

Summary

- There is a lack of interaction (or appropriate interaction) with others.
- Children tend not to form relationships. However, unlike children with more severe autism, children with Asperger's syndrome want to make friends. They do not know how to.
- Facial expressions tend to be inappropriate.
- Body language tends to be stiff.
- Communication 'cues' are missing.
- Children with Asperger's syndrome tend to become obsessed with a specific interest.
- Routines can become obsessive and crucial to maintaining normality, with even slight changes causing great distress.
- Some individuals have a good level of intellectual ability.
- Some individuals are able to live independently and hold down regular employment but the more severely affected individuals need sheltered living facilities.

Dyspraxia

Summary

- A neurological disorder where messages are not transmitted in the brain in the normal way.
- An impairment or immaturity of the organisation of movement.
- In most cases there is no known cause.
- Associated problems of language, perception and thought:
  - Speech and language – speech may be immature or unintelligible in early years. Language may be impaired or late to develop.
  - Perception and thought – poor understanding of the messages conveyed by senses. Difficulty in relating to those messages. Spatial perception is poor and children will tend to bump into objects and people.
- Dyspraxia may also be known as the Clumsy child syndrome, Developmental co-ordination disorder, minimal brain dysfunction, motor learning difficulty or perceptuo-motor dysfunction.
- Physical activities are hard to learn, difficult to retain and generalise and children are hesitant and awkward in performance.
- Symptoms and severity of the condition vary enormously.
- Up to 10 per cent of the population may show symptoms of dyspraxia and 2 per cent are severely affected. Of those diagnosed, 80 per cent are male.

- Many people go through life with the condition undiagnosed and may cope reasonably well – mainly by avoiding situations which they find difficult or by developing coping strategies, e.g. writing lists to overcome poor short-term memory.

Dyslexia

Dyslexia is a specific learning difficulty that mainly affects reading and spelling. It is a congenital (being so from birth) *and* developmental condition. The causes are not yet known, but dyslexia tends to run in families and there is growing evidence that there are several genes that contribute to a genetic risk of dyslexia and that there are differences between the functioning of the left brain hemisphere in dyslexics and normal readers. Research into the role of the cerebellum is also helping to explain why a number of people with dyslexia also have difficulties in areas other than literacy – such as balance, motor co-ordination and speed of processing – areas which are heavily influenced by the cerebellum.

Summary

- Dyslexia is characterised by difficulties in processing word-sounds and by weaknesses in short-term verbal memory.
- Its effects may be seen in spoken language as well as written language.
- Dyslexia is lifelong, but its effects can be minimised by targeted literacy intervention, technological support and adaptations to ways of working and learning.
- Dyslexia is not related to intelligence, race or social background.
- Dyslexia varies in severity and often occurs alongside other specific learning difficulties, such as dyspraxia and/or attention deficit disorder, resulting in variations in the degree and nature of strengths and weaknesses.
- Many dyslexic people have difficulties with short-term memory, sequencing and organisation.

Cerebral palsy

Cerebral palsy is a condition which affects movement, posture and co-ordination. These problems may be seen at or around the time of birth and may not become obvious until early childhood when developmental milestones are not being met.

Cerebral palsy has several different causes, including

- an infection in the mother during the first weeks of a baby's development inside the mother, e.g. rubella (German measles) or a cytomegalovirus
- a difficult or pre-term birth perhaps because the baby fails to breathe properly
- cerebral bleed (haematoma) which may occur in pre-term babies
- bleeding into cavities inside the brain (intraventricular haemorrhage) which may occur in pre-term babies
- the baby's brain being formed abnormally, for no apparent reason
- a genetic disorder which can be inherited, even if both parents are completely healthy.

As cerebral palsy is a wide-ranging condition and can affect people in many different ways, care will depend on the individual needs of the child. Some children have cerebral palsy so mildly that its effects are barely noticeable, while others may be extremely affected and require help with many or all aspects of daily life.

In the UK, about 1500 babies are born with or develop cerebral palsy each year. It can affect boys and girls, and people from all races and social backgrounds.

Cerebral palsy jumbles messages between the brain and the muscles. There are three types of cerebral palsy, depending on which messages are affected:

- spastic cerebral palsy
- athetoid cerebral palsy
- ataxic cerebral palsy.

Many people with cerebral palsy have a combination of two or more types.

Spastic cerebral palsy

'Spastic' means 'stiff'. People with this kind of cerebral palsy find it very difficult to control some or all of their muscles and look stiff. Their muscles tend to be tight and weak, and they often hold their arms, legs or head in certain characteristic ways. Spastic cerebral palsy is usually caused when nerve cells in the outer layer of the brain, called the cortex, do not work properly.

- Hemiplegia is where either the left or the right half of the body is affected by spastic cerebral palsy, but the other half functions normally.
- Diplegia is where both legs are affected but the arms are normal, or only slightly affected.
- Quadriplegia is where both legs and both arms are affected.

Athetoid cerebral palsy

People with this kind of cerebral palsy have muscles which change rapidly from floppy to tense. Their arms and legs move a lot, in a way that they cannot control. Their speech may be hard to understand because they have difficulty controlling their tongue, breathing and vocal cords. Athetoid cerebral palsy is the result of the middle part of the brain, known as the basal ganglia, not working properly.

Ataxic cerebral palsy

People with this kind of cerebral palsy find it very difficult to balance. If they learn to walk, they will probably be very unsteady. They are also likely to have shaky hand movements and jerky speech.

Ataxic cerebral palsy is the result of the cerebellum, at the base of the brain, not working properly.

Link

See Figure 12.12 on page 54 for a diagram of the brain.

Summary

- If a child has cerebral palsy, part of the child's brain either is not working properly or has not developed normally. The affected area is usually one of the parts which control the muscles and certain body movements.
- It can occur before birth, due to infection or placental problems.
- It can occur at birth, following a difficult delivery.
- It can occur immediately after birth, due to head injury or infection.
- The condition is not reversible.
- It does not change in its severity.
- It affects physical movement and limb control.
- Speech is often difficult to understand.
- Intellectual ability is unaffected.
- Physiotherapy and speech therapy are usually offered.

activity
INDIVIDUAL WORK 27.1
P1

Using the information in this section and by referring to Units 3 and 35 and resources in your library, complete a chart like the one below describing at least six factors that may lead to children having additional needs. Give examples of the additional needs.

Description of factors that may lead to children having additional needs	Examples of conditions caused by this factor

Link

Development is covered in Unit 35, pages 332–351.

See also Unit 3, Promoting Children's Development, in Green (2007).

Spina bifida

Summary

- A failure in the development of the neural tube during pregnancy leads to defects in one or more areas of the vertebrae (the bones in the spine).
- Women are advised to increase their intake of folic acid before and during the first months of pregnancy to help prevent neural tube defects occurring.
- Minor type (spina bifida occulata) is identified as a dimple or tuft of hair on the lower area of the spine where the vertebrae is not completely joined.
- A slightly more serious version (myelomeningocele) causes the spinal cord and the meninges (the tissue lining the spinal cord) to push through the gap in the vertebrae. With myelomeningocele, infection is common due to the membrane breaking and the individual will be paralysed from the affected part of the vertebrae downwards.
- Bowel and bladder problems are common.
- Hydrocephalus (water on the brain) is a commonly found additional problem.
- Mobility support is needed.
- Support in the management of both bowel and bladder is needed.
- Varying degrees of learning difficulty are found in individuals with hydrocephalus.

Environmental factors

Some additional needs are the result of **environmental factors**. These include illnesses such as meningitis and rubella.

Meningitis

Meningitis and meningococcal septicaemia are serious diseases that can affect anyone at any time. Complications can happen with any type of meningitis but are more common after bacterial meningitis. Recovery from viral meningitis can be very slow but is normally complete. However sufferers can still get headaches, tiredness, depression, memory loss and concentration problems.

Following meningitis, some babies and young children may experience learning difficulties and behavioural problems. Fortunately, many of these sort themselves out on their own. Some of the short-term effects which may be experienced include general tiredness, persistent headaches, clumsiness, giddiness and sore or stiff joints. However, some effects are permanent.

- Memory problems are a common result of brain damage because many parts of the brain are concerned with storing and processing different kinds of information. The effect of memory loss can vary. Many people experience short-term memory loss, or find it hard to concentrate following meningitis.
- Hearing loss is the most common after-effect of meningitis and can range from mild degrees of hearing loss through to profound deafness in one or both ears.
- Damage to the inner ear can also result in balance problems and tinnitus.
- Meningitis can damage the nerve responsible for sight (optic nerve), resulting in partial loss of vision or blindness in one or both eyes.
- Severe brain damage is not common and the level of damage to the areas of the brain may not be clear early on and it may take some time for health professionals and families to understand the full implications.
- Epilepsy can happen in a small number of people. It is not always immediately obvious. Occasionally, children and adults who have recovered from meningitis go on to develop epilepsy, which needs long-term medication.
- Emotional difficulties may arise even if there has been a good physical recovery and young children can often experience nightmares, bedwetting, clinginess and temper tantrums.

Rubella

Rubella (German measles) is a mild disease caused by a virus found in the noses and throats of infected people. Rubella is serious if caught by a pregnant woman as it can cause damage to her unborn child who is then said to have congenital rubella syndrome. The baby's organs can be seriously damaged in the early stages of pregnancy. Some of the common effects include impairments to the:

- ears – a child may have hearing loss in one or both ears due to damage to the inner ear, which links the ears to the brain
- eyes – babies may be born with cataracts in one or both eyes; others may have heart problems from birth and require hospital treatment
- heart – rubella can affect the heart in many ways and children may require hospital treatment
- brain – rubella can also affect a child's brain and nervous system. Difficulties can vary from mild to severe.

Congenital rubella syndrome is one of the most common causes of congenital deafblindness (someone born with combined hearing and sight difficulties).

The health of the pregnant woman

The health of a woman is an important factor in pregnancy. There are many lifestyle factors relating to the emotional well-being of a woman during pregnancy, e.g. maintaining a healthy diet and regular exercise are known to be beneficial to the health of the woman and baby. Also important are regular antenatal care and screening.

There are also factors associated with risk to the health of the mother and baby, e.g. drug and alcohol abuse (**foetal alcohol syndrome**). Maternal smoking can influence the health of a baby and may result in a low-birthweight baby. Drug abuse by the mother, particularly cocaine, is a cause of prematurity.

Premature births

Babies born before 37 weeks' gestation are considered premature and may be at risk of complications due to their low birthweight and the immaturity of their body systems. The lungs, digestive system and nervous system (including the brain) are under-developed in premature babies, and are particularly vulnerable to complications. Bronchopulmonary dysplasia (BPD), sometimes called chronic lung disease, may develop as a consequence of prematurity and progressive lung inflammation. BPD is one of the most common chronic lung diseases in children along with asthma and cystic fibrosis. Most infants fully recover from BPD and have few long-term health problems as a result but it can be a serious condition requiring intensive medical care.

About half of babies born at 25 weeks will have learning difficulties and/or problems with their eyesight and hearing. Extremely premature babies may also have problems with growth and are more likely to develop asthma.

Accidents

Children may acquire additional needs as a result of an accident. A head injury can result in similar problems to the brain injury caused through an illness such as meningitis, for example. These may include memory loss, difficulties with concentration, personality disorders and depression. Depending on the location of the injury within the brain, there may be difficulties with speech and/or movement.

Injury or disease to a person's nervous system can affect the ability to move a particular part of the body. This reduced motor ability is called paralysis. Paraplegia is paralysis of both legs *or* both arms and quadriplegia, sometimes called tetraplegia, is paralysis of both legs and arms.

Other factors

Attention deficit hyperactivity disorder

Attention deficit hyperactivity disorder (ADHD) is a medical diagnosis given to children who have developmental, behavioural and cognitive difficulties compared with their peers. It is normally used to describe children who have three main kinds of problem:

- difficulty in paying attention and concentrating
- impulsive behaviour
- over-active behaviour (hyperactivity).

A diagnosis is only correctly made when there are problems in these areas over and above those found in the peer group and in more than one setting. It is known that genetic factors are important in ADHD but as yet it is not known which genes are involved. Environment also plays a part.

As they are over-active and impulsive, children with ADHD often find it difficult to fit in at school and may have problems getting on with other children.

Some children have significant problems in concentration and attention, but are not necessarily overactive or impulsive. They are sometimes described as having attention deficit disorder (ADD) and are frequently overlooked because they may be quiet and dreamy rather than disruptive.

ADHD is not related to intelligence. Children with all levels of ability can have ADHD, but unless the condition is recognised and treated, children may not reach their potential as the characteristics of the disorder mean that learning becomes more difficult.

Hearing impairment

There are two types of hearing loss:

- conductive hearing loss which affects the middle ear and is the most common and temporary
- sensori-neural loss in which the inner ear or auditory nerve is affected and this is generally considered to be irreversible.

A conductive loss is anything which interferes with the conduction of sound from the outer ear to the inner ear. The most common cause is otitis media, often associated with infection of the upper respiratory tract. The middle ear and eustachian tube become blocked with fluid or mucus, the eardrum becomes rigid and sound is not conducted normally. If the fluid becomes infected, this may cause the ear drum to perforate. Glue ear is a term used to describe chronic otitis media. About 20 per cent of children under 8 suffer from middle ear problems causing conductive hearing loss.

Sensori-neural deafness can be caused by hereditary factors or induced by drugs, disease or trauma. About two children in every 1000 will be affected by a sensori-neural loss. The inner ear or auditory nerve is affected, generally considered to be irreversible.

The effects of a hearing loss include poor listening skills, delayed speech, delayed language development, poor social and emotional development and delay in literacy and other formal areas of the curriculum.

Visual impairment

Children with impaired vision can range from those with a minimal loss of vision to those who have no useful vision for educational purposes. Most children with a visual impairment have enough residual vision to use visual methods in learning. Very few are completely blind. For educational purposes, children are defined as 'educationally blind' if their main method of learning is through tactile material, e.g. Braille.

As 80 per cent of learning is through the visual sense, it is vital that practitioners working with a child with a vision problem ensure that the child is making the best possible use of their vision so that there is no interference in the learning process.

Professional Practice

- **A child's vision may vary from day to day.**
- **A child with impaired vision may need more time to complete the task and may get more tired.**
- **The child should be encouraged to take responsibility for their own learning.**

Tourette's syndrome

This syndrome is named after Dr George Gilles de la Tourette, the French neurologist who first reported it in literature in 1885.

Tourette's syndrome is a recognised medical condition which is often inherited. Although there are treatments, there is no cure. It is both a movement disorder and a neurological condition and affects all aspects of life – education, relationships and employability. It sometimes occurs with other conditions, e.g. attention deficit disorder (ADD) or attention deficit hyperactivity disorder (ADHD) and obsessive compulsive disorder (OCD).

While the cause of Tourette's syndrome has not yet been established, it involves the abnormal processing of the neurotransmitters called dopamine and serotonin. The condition is three to four times more likely in boys.

Symptoms of Tourette's syndrome are tics (repeated movements and speech). They usually start in childhood at around the age of 7 and persist throughout life although they may decrease towards the end of adolescence. Types of tics include:

- movement – this may include eye-blinking, head jerking, shoulder shrugging and facial grimacing; it may also include jumping, touching people and things, smelling and twirling
- sound – throat clearing, yelping and other noises, sniffing and tongue clicking. It may also include uttering words or phrases out of context, coprolalia (saying unacceptable words) and echolalia (repeating a sound, word or phrase just heard).

Sometimes hitting and biting oneself may be symptoms present in some individuals.

Mental illness

Between 10 and 20 per cent of children and young people have a mental health problem, and a small percentage will have a severe mental illness. People with mental illnesses or disorders may experience a wide range of symptoms which can vary in their severity. Examples of mental illness include anxiety disorders, bipolar disorder, depression, eating disorders and schizophrenia.

With more local education authorities including children with special educational needs in mainstream schooling the likelihood is that you will encounter one of the above disorders. However there are many others, and some quite rare conditions, that you may be presented with and will need to know how to deal with. The support groups or organisations for individual conditions such as the Williams Syndrome Foundation are an invaluable source of information.

www.williams-syndrome.org.uk

Impact of additional needs

Professionals must be aware of the likely impact of having a child with special educational needs in the family. When a child is born with a disability, parents may experience the same sorts of emotions that a bereaved person goes through:

- shock
- disbelief
- anger
- sorrow
- feeling of numbness.

Although most parents come to terms with the fact that they have to reassess their expectations regarding their child's future, this will take time and varies within each family. In some cases the child may be adopted if the family feel that they cannot cope.

Whatever decisions are made and depending on the nature and the severity of the child's disability, there are likely to be substantial changes to the lifestyle of the family. Possible implications could include:

- 24-hour care necessitating both parents giving up their jobs – in less extreme cases, one parent may find that they cannot continue working, e.g because there are many hospital appointments to keep
- financial problems – travel expenses for hospital appointments, clothing expenses, extra washing, specialist equipment and adaptations to the home can also contribute to financial hardship
- additional stress on the marriage or partnership (although sometimes families are brought closer together) – the time devoted to the care of a child with a disability will be taken from other aspects of life, e.g. visiting friends, social life and spending time with each other
- physical stresses – parents may suffer from disturbed sleep if the child is uncomfortable, in pain or has a poor sleep pattern as a result of the disability. The extra demands of a disabled child in addition to usual commitments, such as work, household tasks and other family commitments, may take their toll physically. Depending on the disability, the child

may need to continue to require to be lifted as he gets older and heavier. Similarly parents may still be required to perform personal care for the child

- a negative impact on siblings – it is important that their needs are not overlooked and that they are able to enjoy their childhood and not spend too much time in the role of additional carer. On the positive side, many families report that siblings of the child with a disability often grow up with a sensitive nature and may choose to enter one of the 'caring' professions

It can be difficult for siblings to have their friends visit the family home, either because the parent is immersed in the care of the child with a disability or because in some cases embarrassment is caused to the sibling by the behaviour of their brother or sister or the medical condition

- bullying – some children are bullied because they have a sibling with a disability. This is often when the disability is not visible and is misunderstood. Sometimes the child with the disability is bullied and the sibling may feel protective of their brother or sister
- difficulties with 'normal' family activities, e.g. going on outings or holidays
- isolation – many parents feel very isolated. The emphasis in the western world is laid heavily on fitness and beauty. There is still a strong tendency to stigmatise and to reject those who do not fit in with our norms. A great deal of this is tied up with fears for our own health and fitness and the way in which society handles its guilt.

case study 27.1

Hannah

Hannah works at a pre-school setting and her supervisor has told her that a new child called Luca is due to join the group. Luca has cystic fibrosis. Hannah speaks to her supervisor and decides that she needs to do some research on cystic fibrosis, so that she has a good idea of Luca's needs and the implications for the setting. To help her, the supervisor gives Hannah the pro forma in Fig 27.7 to fill out.

Fig 27.7

Name of condition: **Description of condition:**
Care needs of the child: *(include environmental issues)*
Educational needs of the child:

activity

Write a report for your setting manager using the above form, information from Activity 27.1 and information from your library to help you.

Link

See pages 321–330 for the care and educational needs for the conditions described above.

Understand the impact of legislation, regulations and codes of practice on provision for children with additional requirements

Legislation and regulations

The inclusion of children with special educational needs in mainstream schools is a result of a change in society's attitudes towards people who have additional needs or disabilities. The law has tended to reflect society's view of children with special educational needs, and for centuries anyone with a noticeable disability was either ignored, tolerated, shut away or offered charity. In Victorian times, so-called 'mentally defective' children who were in need of care were placed in workhouses or infirmaries such as the 'Asylum for Idiots' in London.

Education Act 1870

This Act (also known as Forster's Act) introduced state education. Some special schools were established for deaf and blind children. In 1892 Leicester had a special class for selected 'feeble-minded' pupils and in the same year the London Board established a special school for physically and mentally deficient children.

Education Act 1944

This was the first piece of legislation to outline provision for children with what we now call 'special educational needs'. Children were assessed by a School Medical Officer and placed in one of 11 categories of need:

- deaf
- partially deaf
- epileptic
- delicate
- blind
- physically handicapped
- partially sighted
- speech disordered
- diabetic
- maladjusted
- educationally subnormal.

Each category of 'handicap' had its own special school to which pupils who had been assessed were expected to go for specialist treatment and care, often against their parents' wishes.

Children who did not fit in any of these categories were considered to be unable to benefit from education. They were generally placed in hospitals or Junior Training Centres run by the health authority. These would be children who we would now consider to have severe learning difficulties or profound and multiple learning difficulties.

From 1970 the local education authority as opposed to the health authority decided on the appropriate school placement for children. Thus the emphasis moved from the medical model of disability to the social model of disability.

Link

Models of disability are discussed on page 294.

Warnock Report 1978

One of the key defining statements of the Warnock Report of 1978 was that children with special educational needs are not a distinct and separate group. They are on a continuum from the very academically able (these children may also be placed on the special educational needs register if a school has one) to the child with complex and multiple additional needs. In fact it was claimed that as many as 20 per cent of children may have special educational needs at any one time and that some of these needs may be temporary in nature.

The report also suggested that:

- each child's needs are unique and so it is inappropriate to attempt to place children in categories
- problems in learning do not lie solely within the child and therefore **assessment** should be carried out within a child's familiar settings and by a range of different people
- children learn from the example of others and so pupils with special educational needs should be educated, as far as is practicable, with 'non-handicapped peers' (the language reflects the date it was written)
- parents have a key role to play in the assessment of their child and should be fully involved throughout the process.

Just as the very academically able child will need more challenging tasks in the classroom in order to stimulate and extend their learning, so the child with special educational needs will require some form of **differentiation** in order that he is able to access the curriculum.

The Warnock Report informed the 1981 Education Act.

Education Act 1981

The 1981 Education Act gave local education authorities (LEAs) the responsibility for identifying pupils with special educational needs (SENs) and for arranging a multi-professional assessment involving the parents, the school, the educational psychologist and the school medical officer. Children with special educational needs who met specific criteria were eligible for a Statement of Special Educational Needs. This is a document which is drawn up describing in some detail their educational needs and the provision that should be made to meet those needs.

Link

The assessment procedure and the Statement of Special Education Needs are discussed on page 315.

Since the implementation of the 1981 Act, the number of children with special educational needs (sometimes the term 'additional needs' is now preferred) attending mainstream school has increased significantly. It is estimated that approximately 70–80 per cent of children with Down's syndrome, for example, now begin their schooling in a mainstream primary school, with 20–25 per cent completing their education in mainstream settings. In order to meet the needs of the individual child, a teaching assistant is often employed to support the child and allow him/her to access the curriculum. The number of teaching assistants employed in schools has almost trebled in the past decade and continues to increase. It is essential that all staff working with children with special educational needs are aware of the implications of those needs so that the child receives the best possible education in a safe and secure environment.

Mental Health Act 1983

This Act governs the admission of people to psychiatric hospital against their will, their rights while detained, discharge from hospital and aftercare. The Act applies to England and Wales. Scotland and Ireland are covered by the Mental Health (Scotland) Act 1984 and the Mental Health (Northern Ireland) Order 1986.

For more information, go to www.mind.org.uk.

Education Reform Act 1988

This Act introduced the National Curriculum in schools into UK schools and all children were expected to study the range of subjects under its umbrella.

The Children Act 1989

The Children Act 1989 in its Code of Practice: Collaboration and Co-operation on Statutory

Assessment states that when an LEA proposes to make a statutory assessment it must seek advice from the relevant social services department (SSD). Following notification, the SSD should:

- inform the LEA of any relevant information which it may have about the family or child
- consider combined assessment of a child 'in need' under the Children Act and with special educational needs under the 1993 Act
- provide relevant information if the child is receiving social services provision
- give the LEA information about the child's care plan if the child is 'looked after' by the local authority
- ensure relevant information is provided if the child is in the care of the local authority and the local authority has parental responsibility
- give appropriate advice if the child is subject to child protection procedures.

In the revision of the 1993 Code of Practice (2002) a multidisciplinary approach was also emphasised and again in the 2004 Government Strategy for Special Educational Needs, Removing Barriers to Achievement.

Link

- Removing Barriers to Achievement is discussed on page 291.
- Multidisciplinary working is discussed on page 309.

Education Act 1993

This Act defined special educational needs as follows:

> 'A child has special educational needs if he or she has a learning difficulty which calls for special educational provision to be made for him or her. A child has a learning difficulty if he or she:
>
> a) has significantly greater difficulty in learning than the majority of children of the same age;
>
> b) has a disability which either prevents or hinders the child from making use of educational facilities of a kind provided for children of the same age in schools within the area of the local education authority;
>
> c) is under five and falls within the definition at (a) or (b) above or would do if special educational provision was not made for the child.'

The definition includes children with physical disabilities, cognitive disability and specific learning difficulties such as dyslexia.

The 1993 Education Act stated that schools should have a Special Educational Needs Co-ordinator (SENCO) and a SEN policy. They were also required to have a register of all children identified as having SEN. Although this is no longer mandatory, many schools continue with the practice. Under the 2002 Code of Practice pre-schools and nurseries also have to have a SENCO and a special educational needs policy.

Link

The role of the SENCO is discussed on page 320.

Disability Discrimination Act 1995

This gave people with disabilities rights in the areas of employment, buying and renting a property, access to goods, facilities and services. It allows the government to establish standards on minimum access for new taxis, trains and buses.

Education Act 1996

Section 316 of this Act contained four caveats (exceptions to the rule) about the placement of children with SEN in mainstream schools. These caveats allowed the LEA to refuse a child for a mainstream placement only when four conditions applied:

- that it was not an efficient use of the LEA's resources
- when it was not in the best interests of other children
- when it was not the parental choice
- when it was felt not to be in the best interests of the child.

The Act also established that children with special educational needs could have modifications made to the National Curriculum.

Look at these websites to find out about the following:

- Human Rights Act 1998 – www.yourrights.org.uk
- Data Protection Act 1998 – www.legislation.hmso.gov.acts1998/19980029.htm
- Carers and Disabled Children's Act 2000 – www.carers.gov.uk
- White Paper, Valuing People: A new strategy for learning disabilities for the 21st century, 2001 – www.dh.gov.uk/en/policy

Special Needs and Disability Act 2001 (SENDA)

This Act made major changes to Section 316 of the 1996 Education Act. The caveats have been removed except the second caveat – efficient education of other children. Those lobbying for the inclusion of SEN children in mainstream schooling were concerned that the remaining caveat could be used by less committed or cash-strapped authorities to divert children from mainstream provision. A further concern was the possible assumption that disabled children are more disruptive and so undermine the inclusionist intent of the legislation.

SENDA requires schools to anticipate that they will be educating a child with special educational needs and they will need to show in their strategic planning that they have considered this. There are two main duties on schools which came into effect in September 2002:

- not to treat disabled pupils less favourably for a reason that relates to their disability
- to make reasonable adjustments to ensure that disabled pupils are not at a substantial disadvantage.

The new duties cover every aspect of the life of the school including:

- teaching and learning
- after-school clubs
- excursions
- organisation of the school
- what happens in the dinner queue
- timetabling
- use of classroom support
- homework
- anti-bullying policies
- admissions
- exclusions.

Fig 27.8

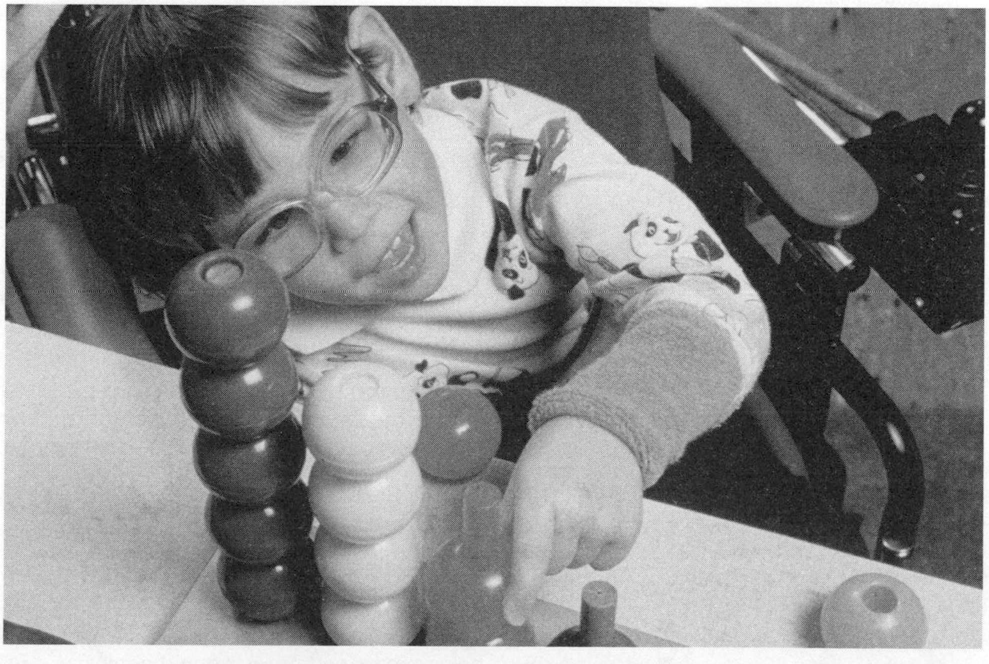

The Act introduced an important requirement for strategic planning to increase the accessibility of the school and the curriculum. The plan has to anticipate the potential needs of pupils to ensure the school's accessibility. These anticipatory duties will encourage schools to plan for inclusion in a more systematic way.

However, the cost implications may be considerable, e.g. installing a lift. Some local authorities have designated a school within a cluster of schools where more money has been devolved in order to adapt the environment as necessary, purchase specialist equipment (e.g. low-level ovens in a secondary school Food Technology room at the correct height for pupils who may use a wheelchair). Bath and North East Somerset LEA, for example, is aware that some of its older schools are not easily accessible for physically disabled children or their parents. While it is working towards making all schools more accessible, it is meeting the immediate needs of disabled children by ensuring that there is one fully accessible primary school in each area and one secondary school in each of the three main urban areas of the authority.

Link

Inclusion is discussed further on page 297.

Birth to Three Matters 2002

The Birth to Three Matters framework published by Sure Start acknowledges the contribution made to the development of very young children by the adults who care for them. It recognises that:

- young babies are primed to be social beings and they crave close attachments with a special person
- warm, mutual affirmative relationships give babies the courage to express their feelings
- when young children have a close relationship with a warm and responsive adult, they explore from a safe place to which they can return
- as children learn to do things for themselves, they gain confidence, knowing that the adult is close by, ready to support and help if needed.

However, poverty and other factors which affect family life and create stress for parents can also impact on children. Some factors that appear to be linked to a risk of poor development and lower achievement include chronic illness, mental and physical disabilities. These could be biological, e.g. genetic disorders, or exposure in the womb to the ill effects of infectious diseases, drugs or alcohol; or related to temperament, for example, irritable and difficult to soothe babies may put the parent–child relationship at risk and leave some children vulnerable to higher rates of anxiety later in life. Other factors may include impaired parenting, which could be through a number of factors including mental illness, and social disadvantage, which can encompass family poverty, lack of access to medical care, racism and minority status, and exposure to community violence.

If children experience three or more risk factors, both parent and child may become overwhelmed and risk accumulates, especially where no intervention is available. The length of time a child is exposed to risk factors decreases the likelihood of becoming resilient, especially in cases where other life changes such as substitute care (e.g. fostering or care from the local authority) occurs. Young children will find it difficult to cope if their parents cannot support them and they may become passive or be unable to react other than in an inflexible way because they are so used to trying to deal with stress.

The major factors that foster resilience include good health, positive disposition, a positive self-concept, good social skills, a balance between independence and interdependence and good relationships with other children.

Protective factors associated with the family include strong attachment relationships, competent parents who model competence for the child, household rules and parental monitoring, stable relationships between parents and high levels of parental education.

Factors associated with the community include access to health care, adequate housing, supportive adults outside the family, consistent parental employment and low level of poverty, family participation in a religious community and neighbourhood stability.

Every Child Matters 2003

Initiatives such as Social and Emotional Aspects of Learning (SEAL) have been introduced into schools as a direct result of the five outcomes from the 2003 Green Paper, Every Child Matters. These are:

- being healthy – enjoying good physical and mental health and living a healthy lifestyle
- staying safe – being protected from harm and neglect

- enjoying and achieving – getting the most out of life and developing the skills for adulthood
- making a positive contribution – being involved with the community and society and not engaging in anti-social or offending behaviour
- economic well-being – not being prevented by economic disadvantage from achieving their full potential in life.

Link Social and Emotional Aspects of Learning (SEAL) is discussed on page 302.

Every Child Matters was written in response to the inquiry into the death of Victoria Climbie.

See Unit 5, Protecting Children in Green (2007), page 264.

A range of measures was subsequently introduced to reform and improve children's care, such as the creation of Sure Start Children's Centres in each of the 20 per cent most deprived neighbourhoods, combining nursery education, family support, employment advice, childcare and health services on one site.

Other initiatives include:

- promoting full service extended schools which are open beyond school hours to provide breakfast clubs and after-school clubs and childcare and which have health and social care support services on site
- increasing investment in child and adolescent mental health services
- importantly for children with additional needs, improving speech and language therapy where the intention is to train professionals in settings, supported by specialist staff.

Early intervention and effective protection are key elements of the Every Child Matters framework. In order to ensure that children receive services at the outset of problems, the document proposes to improve information-sharing between agencies, develop a common assessment framework, introduce a lead professional and develop on-the-spot service delivery by encouraging professionals to work in multidisciplinary teams based in and around schools and children's centres.

To support local integration, the government has created a Minister for Children, Young People and Families in the Department for Education and Skills to co-ordinate policies across government.

You can download Every Child Matters online at www.dfes.gov.uk/everychildmatters.

A children and young people's version of Every Child Matters is also available.

Children Act 2004

This Act provides the legal underpinning for the Every Child Matters: Change for Children programme. A series of documents have been published which provide guidance under the Act to support local authorities and their partners in implementing new statutory duties.

Removing Barriers to Achievement 2004

In 2004 the UK government issued its SEN strategy, known as Removing Barriers to Achievement, in response to the Audit Commission's report, *Special Educational Needs – a mainstream issue* (2002). This report highlighted a number of continuing challenges:

- Too many children wait too long to have their needs met.
- Children who should be able to be taught in mainstream settings are sometimes turned away and many staff feel ill-equipped to meet the wide range of pupil needs in today's classrooms.
- Many special schools feel uncertain of their future role.
- Families face unacceptable variations in the level of support available from their school, local authority or local health services.

The key areas that are the focus of Removing Barriers to Achievement link in with reform of children's services as set out by Every Child Matters. They are:

- early intervention – to ensure that children who have learning difficulties receive the help they need as soon as possible and that parents of children with special educational needs and disabilities have access to suitable childcare
- removing barriers to learning – by embedding inclusive practice in every school and early years setting
- raising expectations and achievement – by developing teachers' skills and strategies for meeting the needs of children with SEN and focusing on the progress made by children
- delivering improvements in partnership – taking a hands-on approach to improvement so that parents can be confident that their child will get the education they need.

Mental Capacity Act 2005

In relation to health and social care, this Act aims to better support people who are unable to consent to proposals by NHS bodies or local authorities for:

- serious medical treatment
- a stay of more than 28 days in hospital or 8 weeks in a care home
- a change in a person's accommodation to another hospital for more than 28 days or more than 8 weeks in a care home
- a change in or to provide residential accommodation for more than 8 weeks.

Disability Discrimination Act 2005

This builds on and extends earlier disability discrimination legislation, principally the Disability Discrimination Act 1995. The Act extends the DDA to cover people who have some forms of cancer, HIV/AIDS and multiple sclerosis. It places a duty on the public sector to promote equality of opportunity for disabled people and to eliminate discrimination. This duty is anticipatory, meaning that public authorities will have to review all their policies, practices, procedures and services to ensure that they do not discriminate against disabled people and ensure that all their services are planned with disabled people's needs fully considered in advance. The duty covers schools as well.

To read the text of any Act of Parliament, go to the website of the Office of Public Sector Information: www.opsi.gov.uk/acts.

Childcare Act 2006

To download a summary of the Childcare Act 2006 go to www.surestart.gov.uk/resources/general.

Conventions

European Convention on Human Rights and Fundamental Freedoms 1950

This was adopted under the auspices of the Council of Europe in 1950 to protect human rights and fundamental freedoms. The Convention established the European Court of Human Rights and any person who feels their rights have been violated under the Convention by a state party can take a case to the Court. The decisions of the Court are legally binding and the Court has the power to award damages.

UN Convention on the Rights of the Child 1989

The **UN Convention on the Rights of the Child** (UNCRC) was adopted by the United Nations General Assembly on 20 November 1989. The Convention has been ratified by 191 out of 193 countries making it a global bill of rights. A 'child' is defined as every human being under the age of 18.

The Convention consists of 54 articles. The key provisions of the Convention are that:

- all rights apply to all children without exception or discrimination of any kind
- the best interests of the child must be a primary consideration in all actions concerning children
- countries have an obligation to ensure as much as possible every child's survival and development
- children's views must be taken into account in all matters affecting them.

Guidance

Special Educational Needs Code of Practice 2001

The SEN Code of Practice provides practical advice to LEAs, maintained schools, early education settings and others on carrying out their statutory duties to identify, assess and make provision for children's special educational needs. The Education Act of 1993 required a Code of Practice and this Code replaces the 1994 Code of Practice. It includes new rights and duties introduced by the SEN and Disability Act 2001. These include:

- a stronger right for children with SEN to be educated at a mainstream school
- new duties on LEAs to arrange for parents of children with SEN to be provided with services offering advice and information and a means of resolving disputes
- a new duty on schools and relevant nursery education providers to tell parents when they are making special educational provision for their child
- a new right for schools and relevant nursery education providers to request statutory assessment of a child.

There are separate chapters on provision in the early years, primary and secondary phases and new chapters on:

- working in partnership with parents
- pupil participation
- working in partnership with other agencies.

i The SEN Code of Practice can be downloaded from www.dfes.gov.uk.

Children's Workforce Development Council (CWDC)

The CWDC aims to improve the lives of children and young people, their families and carers by ensuring that all people working with them have the best possible training, qualifications, support and advice. It also helps children and young people's organisations and services to work together more effectively so that the child is at the centre of all services.

i Visit the website of CWDC at www.childrensworkforce.org.uk.

activity
INDIVIDUAL WORK 27.2

P2

M1

1 Describe how legislation, regulations and codes of practice have improved the provision of services for children with additional needs, giving examples such as Every Child Matters.

2 Talk to professionals at your placement asking them how legislation, regulations and codes of practice have impacted on their provision for children with additional needs giving at least two examples, such as Every Child Matters.

Understand inclusive practice and how to support children having additional requirements

Disability and dependency as social constructs

In the UK, people with an additional need are often referred to as having a disability. This term has largely replaced the term 'handicap' which is thought to provoke the image of someone begging for support – having a cap in their hand to collect money. In the UK this term would be associated with the medical model or charitable model (see below), however the term handicap is still used widely in the USA.

remember It is important to our society that people with disabilities are included in every aspect of life.

The Disability Discrimination Act defines a disabled person as someone who has a physical or mental impairment that has a substantial and long-term adverse effect on his or her ability to carry out normal day-to-day activities.

The World Health Organisation defines impairment as any loss or abnormality of psychological, physiological or anatomical structure or function.

It is a disabled person's right to access services, resources and information available to non-disabled people. Service providers must ensure that they meet all people's access requirements and that provision is not offered as a 'favour' or to help them.

Models of disability

There are two main models of disability:

- the medical model
- the social model.

Medical model

It was believed that the person with the disability was in need of treatment and that the disability was the defining aspect of that person.

Sometimes called the 'individual model', the emphasis in the medical model is placed on what a person with a disability cannot do (compared to 'normality') as opposed to what they can do. The medical model sees the disabled person as the problem. They need to be adapted to fit in with the world as it is and if this is not possible then they need to have specialised treatment (in the form of education, housing, etc.). The emphasis is on dependence and usually the impairment is focused on rather than the needs of the person.

With this model the power to change things for disabled people appears to lie with the medical and associated professions with the aim of curing or 'normalising' the disabled person. Disabled people's lives are often handed over to the professionals in this model. Their decisions affect finding work and suitable work environments, accessing leisure and entertainment facilities, using private and public transport, obtaining suitable housing, and their personal, family and social life.

Medical model views are often reinforced in the media. Many disabled people internalise negative views of themselves and develop feelings of low self-esteem and under-achievement. The medical model, plus the built environment and social attitudes it creates, lead to a cycle of dependency and exclusion which is difficult to break.

Increasingly today the medical model is being rejected. Many people feel that expecting disabled people to adapt to existing circumstances or, if this is not possible, caring for them in specialised institutions, is wrong.

Fig 27.9 The medical model: disabled people as passive receivers of services aimed at cure or management

Social model

It is believed that it is society that is disabling the person with a disability and that the solution is to eliminate discrimination as opposed to finding a cure or providing treatment. This is not to deny the very necessary role of medical science in keeping many disabled people alive and reducing their pain and discomfort, but it argues that disabled people should not be reduced to just their impairments.

The social model starts from the standpoint that all disabled adults and children have the right to belong to and be valued in their local community. The social model approach suggests disabled people's disadvantage is due to institutional discrimination, that the discrimination against disabled people is socially created and that they are subjected to a common oppression by the non-disabled world. Most people have not been brought up to accept all people as they are – to value difference. Barriers and discrimination develop through fear, ignorance and **prejudice** and these attitudes can disable some people. Social model thinking has important implications for the education system.

Link
See inclusion on page 297.

Fig 27.10 The social model: disabled people working towards equality with supporters

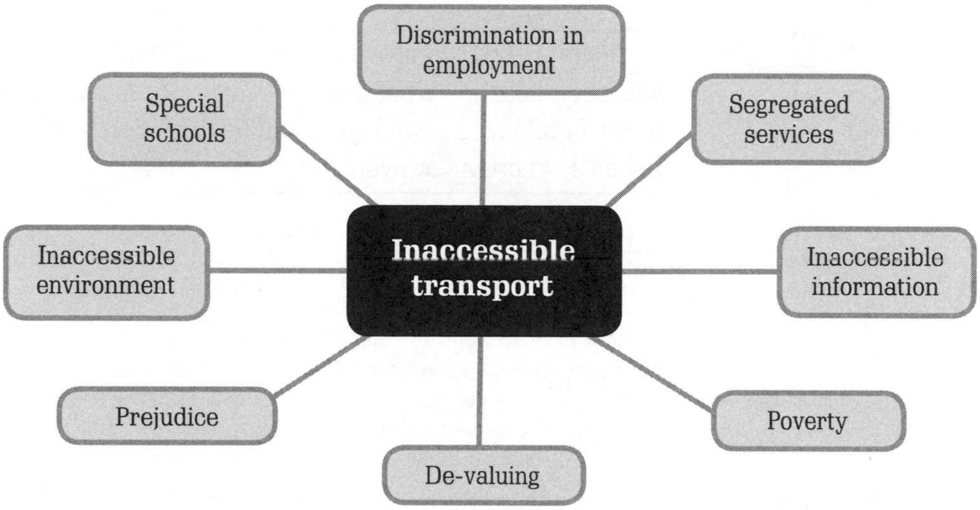

Sometimes a 'charitable model' is also included in the models of disability. This is similar to the medical model and is used to promote an image of disability that will encourage people to raise money for research into various disabilities. Unfortunately it often portrays a rather negative impression of disability.

Fig 27.11 Which of these is an example of the medical model and which the social model? Explain why.

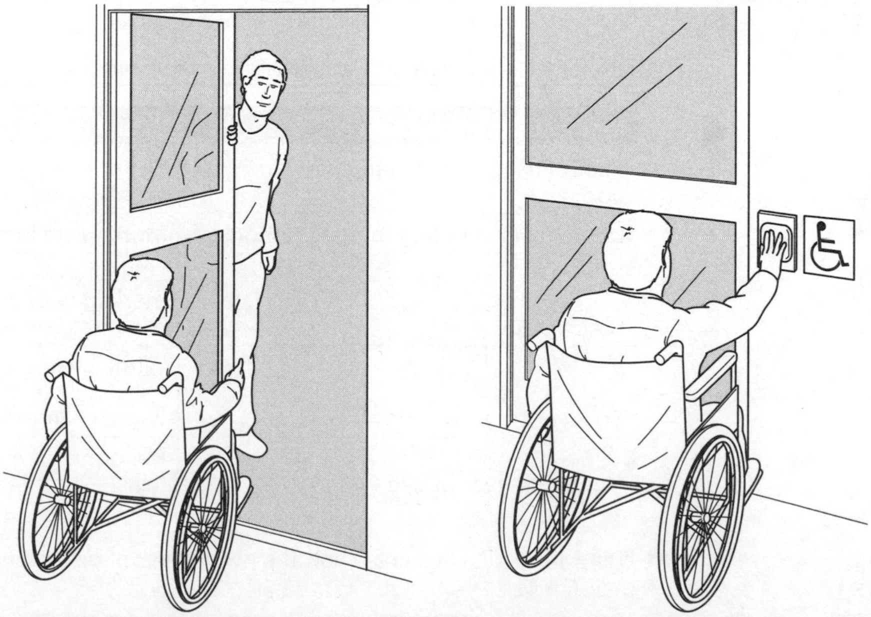

Normalisation

Normalisation involves the acceptance of people with disabilities, offering them the same conditions that are offered to other citizens. There are a few misconceptions about the principle of normalisation:

- Normalisation means making people 'normal' – forcing them to conform to societal norms.
- Normalisation supports placing people into the community or into schools without support.

Normalisation has been blamed for the closure of services (such as institutions) leading to a lack of support for children and adults with disabilities. However support services which facilitate normal life opportunities such as special educational services, housing support, employment support and advocacy are not incompatible with normalisation.

Holistic approach

A **holistic approach** means taking into consideration all aspects of a person and not just concentrating on one area, e.g. a physical difficulty. It takes into account somebody's mental and social conditions as well recognising that an additional need rarely exists in isolation. Following a holistic approach has an impact on services that are providing support. It will recognise that there are services which can support the family, e.g. with financial considerations or respite care, as well as the child.

Link

Look again at the categories used in the 1944 Education Act (page 286). Was this approach holistic? What problems might there have been when deciding where to place a child who nowadays would be diagnosed with autistic spectrum disorder, Usher's syndrome or dyspraxia?

Impact on services provided

It is essential that services, such as the health service, education and social services, work together to support a child with a disability and their family. The child is at the centre and services need to work together in order to enable the child and the family to access the support necessary to lead as independent and fulfilling a life as possible. Communication between services is therefore essential. A statementing review meeting or an IEP review meeting, where all the agencies working with the child are invited to meet with the child and their parents/carers to review progress and set new targets, is an example of co-operative multidisciplinary working.

Link

IEPs are discussed on page 316 and Statements of Special Educational Needs on page 318.

activity
INDIVIDUAL WORK 27.3

P3

M2

1 Use the examples in Table 27.1 to help you describe the two main models of disability and how they impact on children and their families.

Table 27.1 Medical model problems and social model solutions

Medical model problem	Social model solution
Painful hands, unable to open jars, doors	Better designed lids, availability of levers, automatic doors
Difficulty in standing for long periods	More seats in public places
Stairs/steps	Lifts or ramps, edge of steps/stairs marked with contrasting strip to provide greater visual definition
Toilets	Wheelchair users need extra room and hand rails to enable easy transfer from wheelchair to lavatory
Unable to hear or see	Recognition and use of sign language, Braille/raised letters

2 Using Table 27.1, compare how the two models of disability may impact on children and their families.

activity
INDIVIDUAL WORK 27.4

D1

Polly is an 8-year-old pupil at Springbank Primary School. She has a slight vision impairment which has health and safety implications when playing games and for physical education lessons. At her previous school, it was not thought safe for her to play netball with her classmates and she spent the lesson passing the ball back and forth to the teaching assistant assigned to her and aiming at a net away from the netball court.

Once at Springbank, the class teacher discussed with Polly, with input from the LEA's Sensory Impairment Team, how she could be more effectively included in the netball lesson. It was decided that court lines and the goal posts and nets should be painted in fluorescent paint, a brighter coloured ball should be used and that the children should wear fluorescent strips. It was also suggested that when the ball was to be thrown to Polly her name was called out first so that she could anticipate the throw.

With these measures in place Polly was able to participate in and enjoy the netball sessions.

Using the example of Polly to help you, evaluate two models of disability explaining the concept of disability in each case.

Positive working practices

Integrated/inclusive practice

The term **inclusion** is a relatively recent one in relation to the education of children with SEN. Under the Warnock report which informed the 1981 Education Act, the term integration was used. Three different sorts of integration were described:

- locational integration, e.g. when there is a unit for children with additional needs such as autistic spectrum disorder located alongside a mainstream school
- social integration, e.g. where the pupils with additional needs join the mainstream children for playtimes, lunch, after-school clubs and activities
- functional integration, which takes integration a step further. This is where the children with additional needs are educated alongside the mainstream children. In some cases, this is the same as inclusion but implicit in inclusion is that services are put into place in order that the inclusion of the child can be successful.

The Centre for Studies on Inclusive Education (CSIE) states that:

> 'Inclusive education means disabled children and young people learning together in ordinary pre-school provision, schools, colleges and universities, with appropriate networks of support. Inclusion means enabling pupils to participate in the life and work of mainstream institutions to the best of their abilities, whatever their needs.'

For inclusion to be effective, LEAs and ordinary schools have to adapt their approach to:

- the curriculum
- teaching support
- funding mechanisms
- the built environment.

Some schools include a child with SEN completely in the mainstream environment for every aspect of the day. This may be with the support of a teaching assistant. Generally speaking, the younger the child, the easier it is to do this.

case study 27.2

Sunshine Pre-School

Jamie, a 3-year-old boy with Down's syndrome, will be attending Sunshine Pre-School in September. In discussion with Jamie's parents, you have discovered that, in common with most children with Down's syndrome, Jamie was late meeting the developmental milestones (e.g. he was late in developing the gross motor skills such as crawling and walking). He also has delayed language acquisition and communicates mostly by using gestures and vocalisations. He has a few single words and his Portage tutor has been using Makaton signing with him. Jamie is a friendly child, but his social skills are those of a much younger child. He has difficulty sharing toys and he can sometimes be overly boisterous with other children, which upsets them. Jamie has a tendency towards temper tantrums if he is not able to do as he wishes. His Portage tutor uses positive reinforcement and praise to which Jamie responds well. Jamie is toilet-trained but is sometimes unreliable, especially when he becomes excited.

activity

1 Would you need to make any special preparations before Jamie started Sunshine Pre-School? For example, would you consult with any professionals that have been working with Jamie?

2 Would you need to make any special arrangements or adaptations to the environment to take account of Jamie's special educational needs?

3 Would you or your colleagues require any specific support in order to meet Jamie's special educational needs, e.g. in the form of resources or personnel?

4 Would you require any additional parental involvement over and above that which would be expected from other parents? If so, what form might this take and what would be its purpose?

5 How difficult would it be for you to include Jamie in your setting? What are the advantages and disadvantages for Jamie and the other children of his being included in the setting?

Link

- Portage is discussed on page 306.
- Makaton is discussed in Unit 35, page 403.

Other schools may have a unit attached to them where the child may be educated part of the time. Examples of specialist units are:

- hearing or vision units
- units for children who have a physical disability
- units for children with behavioural, emotional and social difficulties (BESD)
- units for children on the autistic spectrum.

These units are staffed by experienced personnel who are able to share their knowledge and expertise with the mainstream class teachers and teaching assistants so that the child receives the best possible education and support in accessing the curriculum. The child may spend part of his/her time in the unit and part in the mainstream classroom.

Other mainstream schools have a relationship with the local special school. This may take the form of the child spending part of the week in the special school and part of the week in the mainstream school. Often a teaching assistant from the special school will support the child in the mainstream setting, giving some continuity and security for the child.

A considerable number of children with special educational needs who are educated in mainstream schools may be withdrawn from the classroom for one-to-one support or small group work. Sometimes this support is given in the classroom and sometimes children are taken outside the classroom to another area to work.

In some areas of the UK, local authorities have closed many of the special schools, e.g. Nottingham and the London borough of Newham have very few special schools left. The money they have saved by doing this has been devolved into mainstream schools and the expertise of the staff from the special schools is shared with the mainstream schools.

When the UK government issued the Green Paper in 1997 (Special Educational Needs) many people were concerned that they were planning to shut down all special schools and parents would lose the right to choose a special school over a mainstream placement for their child with a disability. In practice this has not happened (although since that date 93 special schools have closed) and the government continue to pledge that there will continue to be special schools alongside mainstream schools as they recognise that some children with particular special educational needs or complex or profound disabilities may be better served in a special school.

In response to the Education and Skills Committee's report on special educational needs (July 2006) which was critical of government policy, accusing it of being confused, Lord Adonis, the minister responsible for special educational needs and disability, stated:

> 'Special schools have closed over the years. But new special schools have opened and provision in mainstream schools has developed to cater for a wider range of needs. ... inclusion is about the quality of a child's experience and providing access to a high quality education which enables them to make progress in their learning and participate fully in the activities of their school and community. We want local authorities and schools to work together to build provision in mainstream schools so that over time a mainstream place is a viable option for all parents who wish their children to be taught in mainstream school. But at the same time we see a vital and continuing role for special schools as part of an inclusive education system, meeting children's needs directly and working in much closer partnership with mainstream schools to build expertise throughout the system.'

Promoting children's rights, equal opportunities and challenging discrimination

The legislation that you have read about in the previous section has been instrumental in promoting children's rights, e.g. the Children's Acts of 1989 and 2004, promoting equal opportunities and anti-discriminatory practice regarding children with additional needs, e.g. the Special Needs and Disability Act 2001. They are concerned with challenging attitudes towards discrimination as are disability groups such as the Disability Foundation, a registered charity which promotes the lives of all disabled people and their families by supporting them in their desire to live an independent lifestyle.

In the last 30 years, disabled people have campaigned for and won a human-rights-based approach to disability and it is beginning to be accepted that disability discrimination, prejudice, negative attitudes and stereotypes are not acceptable. The disability movement has advocated a different way of looking at disability known as the social model. Recent legislation has adopted the social model of disability, the emphasis being on needs-led assessment.

Link

The social model is discussed on page 295.

Child-centred planning, empowerment and enabling

Child-centred planning is at the heart of the SEN Code of Practice and Every Child Matters. These policies, and changing attitudes towards disability in society, are empowering to the person with a disability and their families. Positive reinforcement, whether by making changes in the environment to facilitate independence or by allowing someone with a learning disability to achieve success by differentiating the curriculum, is enabling.

Link

Look again at Figure 27.11 and note which one is enabling to the person in the wheelchair.

- Disability Foundation – www.the-disability-foundation.org.uk
- Disability Rights Commission – www.drc.org.uk

Stereotyping and labelling

All professionals working with children with additional needs must be aware of the effect of **stereotyping** and labelling.

One of the ways in which self-esteem can be damaged in children with special educational needs is by the thoughtless use of language, both by professionals and by other children. Use of correct terminology and positive language when working with children with special education needs is very important. For example, the word 'spastic' is often used as a derogatory term. It is in fact a form of cerebral palsy where movements are jerky or involuntary. The Spastics Society is now known as Scope, which is a more positive term.

In order to develop a positive attitude towards the capabilities of children with special educational needs we need to ensure that the language we use in describing the child is also positive. As mentioned previously, terms such as 'handicapped' are unacceptable as they suggest a dependency on others. Neither should children be described according to their condition, e.g. 'the Down's child'. Using the phrase 'a child with Down's syndrome', for example, demonstrates that the child is a person first and foremost and the fact that they have Down's syndrome is secondary.

Some children with special educational needs will receive a diagnosis soon after birth, e.g. a child with Down's syndrome. For other children, the diagnosis may come much later. Some children with cerebral palsy, for example, may not be diagnosed until they have failed to meet the physical milestones, others with autistic spectrum disorder may not be diagnosed until later still. If a child has Classic or Kanner's autism this may well be recognised by professionals at the pre-school years especially when a child begins to attend a mother and toddler group or pre-school group, where the differences between the child's behaviour and that of his peers may become apparent. A child with Asperger's syndrome may not be diagnosed until school age. This is often because they will have language acquisition which initially may mask the other problems and it is not until they are seen to have difficulties in the triad of impairment that professional help may be sought.

Link The triad of impairment is described on page 277.

Some children with specific learning difficulties may never be diagnosed during their time at school. This includes children with dyslexia which was relatively unknown until recent years. Undiagnosed conditions can cause a child and his parents significant distress. There are significant numbers of adults who have not achieved academically at school and have been labelled as 'stupid' and sometimes educated in a remedial stream because they have undiagnosed dyslexia and so have not received the necessary support and understanding.

If labelling equals diagnosis of a condition, this can be beneficial in terms of the child receiving the necessary input from educational and health services and the family receiving benefits in terms of financial support and services such as respite care. Sometimes families actively welcome a diagnosis as this allows them to access support groups and to be able to explain a child's condition and behaviour to others. This may be particularly the case with the so-called 'invisible disabilities' such as autistic spectrum disorder and ADHD where parents may have blamed themselves for the child's lack of ability to conform. In fact in the 1960s one of the believed causes of autism was 'Cold Mother syndrome'. It is possible that this was due to the difficulty some parents may have had with interacting with their autistic child, but this would have been a result of the condition and not a cause.

On the negative side, if a child is given a label or diagnosis, this can sometimes lead professionals and others to stereotype the child, sometimes making assumptions about the child's capabilities which may deny them opportunities. In accordance with the Special Needs and Disability Act 2001, whenever possible the child should be given the opportunity to partake in an activity even if it has to be significantly differentiated. If this is not possible, then an acceptable alternative needs to be considered which should also be offered to all other children.

case study 27.3

Terminology

You are the leader of a pre-school and are inducting three new members of staff. You want to ensure that they use appropriate terminology when referring to disability and have set them the following activity:

Consider the following terms and put them into one of the three categories below:

wheelchair bound
the disabled
people with disabilities
disabled person
cripple
invalid
integrated
spastic
handicapped
people with learning difficulties
spina bifida
independent
sufferer
special
mental patient
mongoloid
retarded

Positive	Negative	Neutral

If you have put a term in the negative column, try to think of a more acceptable term.

activity

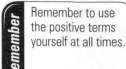

1 Complete this activity yourself. Add any other terms you can think of.
2 Explain why it is important to use the correct terminology when speaking to both parents and other professionals.

remember

Remember to use the positive terms yourself at all times.

Building self-esteem, confidence and positive self-image

Self-esteem is raised as the child experiences success. Low self-esteem can be regarded as an invisible disability. Many children with special educational needs have low self-esteem and this prevents them from reaching their potential. Other children may not have a special educational need but their low self-esteem also prevents them from reaching their potential. Self-esteem is not visible. It may be easy to spot some children with low self-esteem, e.g. they may find it difficult to accept praise and may screw up their work or scribble over it if you say what a good piece of work it is.

Professional Practice

- It is better to say *what* it is about the work that you like. For example, instead of saying that a piece of art work is good, comment on the fact that you like the colours that they have used.

Children with low self-esteem present in different ways and some may appear very confident.

In 1943 the psychologist Abraham Maslow constructed a hierarchy of needs ascending from the basic biological needs at the bottom to the more complex psychological motives that only become important after the basic needs have been satisfied. He recognised that after the requirements necessary for survival, self-esteem was necessary for a fulfilled life.

Link Remind yourself about Maslow's hierarchy of needs, Unit 14, page 109.

Do you notice any similarities between Maslow's hierarchy of needs and the five outcomes from Every Child Matters (page 280)? If so, can you think why?

Self-esteem is formed when self-image and ideal self are closely matched.

- Self-image is the picture we hold of ourselves which includes ideas about our appearance, intelligence, physical skills and about our place in society. The attitude of those important to us, i.e. significant others – usually parents or carers, later teachers, colleagues and employers – helps us to form our internal picture of ourselves. We may be valued, accepted and affirmed or rejected and criticised.
- Ideal self is formed by our perceptions of the way we are seen by other people and is the picture we have in our heads of how we would like to be.

If self-image is good and ideal self is a realistic and attainable goal, then self-esteem is high. However, if there is a conflict between self-image and ideal self and the gulf between the two is too wide, then self-esteem is low.

Self-esteem may alter throughout one's life according to circumstances, but is closely linked to how one was perceived by the adults most important to the young child. In the early years these will be parents and carers, extended family and pre-school workers. Later teachers and teaching assistants play a major role in creating an environment where self-esteem can be nurtured. As children become older, their peers play a very significant part in sustaining self-esteem. Being accepted by children of their own age becomes increasingly important in maintaining a good sense of self.

Settings can do a great deal to promote good self-esteem in their pupils. Recognising that everyone is different and has different strengths is key. Strategies used by schools and pre-schools settings include circle time and circle of friends.

Circle time

Circle time, through co-operative activities and discussion, allows the whole class group to participate as partners in the process of developing responsibility for their own behaviour and learning. It ensures that each child experiences success and, used on a regular basis, it promotes a feeling of equal value and group identity.

Circle time operates within an agreed framework of guidelines, e.g. participants take turns to speak, listen and bring their concerns or ideas to the circle. The structures and techniques within circle time teach individuals to communicate more clearly, directly and honestly with each other. By learning to express their feelings in a clear way, they are learning to develop positive relationships and therefore learn that they do not have to resort to aggressive, manipulative or withdrawn behaviour in order to have their needs met.

The strategies involved for children include co-operative games, pairs work, rounds, drama strategies, puppet play, etc., each strategy appropriate to the emotional and intellectual level of the group and chosen to highlight various issues and to help children focus on their current problems or concerns. They are designed to allow children to fully explore their feelings and anxieties and to find suitable solutions. All members share the responsibility for promoting positive behaviour and the activities foster feelings of trust, integrity and group identity. It has been found that circle time can help children build friendships, and that it can create trust, promote personal and collective responsibility, promote better behaviour, enhance social skills and support the inclusion of children with special educational needs within the class.

Circle of friends

Circle of friends is a strategy sometimes used with children with social and emotional difficulties whereby a group of peers are trained to support them in behaving appropriately in the school setting.

See Maines & Robinson (1998) for more about circle of friends.

Social and Emotional Aspects of Learning (SEAL)

Many schools now recognise the importance of emotional literacy and the SEAL project is used in some settings. This is a curriculum resource produced by the Department for Education and Skills to help primary schools develop children's social, emotional and behavioural skills. It covers children's difficulties in understanding and managing their feelings, working co-operatively in groups, motivating themselves and demonstrating resilience in the face of setbacks.

SEAL aims to develop the underpinning qualities and skills that help promote positive behaviour and effective learning, focusing on five social and emotional aspects of learning:

- self-awareness
- managing feelings
- motivation
- empathy
- social skills.

It is important to focus on these aspects of learning because they underlie almost every aspect of our lives, enable us to be effective learners, enable us to get on with other people and enable us to be responsible citizens. They have an impact on academic achievement, personal responsibility, tolerance of difference and self-esteem.

However, there are some children for whom raising self-esteem is very difficult. These include children with Attachment Disorder.

Attachment is about infants ensuring their needs are met through forming close bonds with important adults. This starts with the basic physical needs for food, shelter and safety but extends higher up Maslow's hierarchy. Newly born infants seem to be predisposed to initiate communication and control adults to respond to their needs. When their needs are consistently met, they abandon control in favour of communication. By about 18 months their internal working model seems to be established. An important part of this is the position on the trust–mistrust spectrum which is largely informed by our experience of having our needs consistently met or not. The internal working model is fixed and very slow to change (if at all) solely through a change of environment. The child whose needs have not been consistently met believes they are responsible for ensuring that they are. This has many implications for their behaviour. For example, when faced with an unfamiliar person or situation, the securely attached child looks to a trusted adult for a signal (usually non-verbal) that it is safe. The insecurely attached child sees it as her role to check it out which frequently results in excessive and inappropriate friendliness to new people.

Link

See Unit 14, page 114 for attachment theory, and page 109 for Maslow's hierarchy of needs.

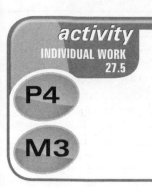

activity
INDIVIDUAL WORK 27.5
P4
M3

1 From your workplace, give five examples of positive working practices that are supporting children with additional needs.
2 Give three examples of positive working practices used in your workplace. Explain how these practices support the inclusion of children with additional needs.

Alternative communication methods

In order that children can be successfully included under the social model of disability, it is essential that steps are taken to enable them to be able to communicate effectively. In some cases, this may mean a child learning a sign language, e.g. British sign language (BSL), if they are profoundly deaf, or Makaton sign language, which can be a useful method of communication for children with Down's syndrome, whose speech is delayed as a result of their disability. It is essential that as many people in contact with the child as possible learn to use the sign language if inclusion is to be successful.

Sign language is a visual means of communicating using gestures, facial expressions and body language. BSL, which is the most common form of sign language in the UK, has its own grammatical structure and syntax. As a language, it is not dependent on nor is it strongly related to spoken English. BSL is the preferred language of 50,000–70,000 people in the UK and was recognised as a minority language in 2003.

Makaton was developed in the 1930s to help people with learning disabilities to communicate. It is now widely used with a variety of children with communication difficulties. Makaton uses speech, gesture, facial expression, eye contact and body language. It is a language programme based on a selected list of everyday words, such as daddy, door, fall and in.

- BSL – www.british-sign.co.uk
- Makaton – www.makaton.org

Link

See Unit 35, page 403 for examples of BSL and Makaton.

Children who are educationally blind will need to learn Braille. Many of the children's texts used in school are now available in Braille. It is a tactile code used instead of print for reading and writing for people who have little useful vision. Each Braille character or 'cell' is made up of a combination of six raised dots, a bit like the dots on a domino. Moon is an alternative tactile method of learning to read and write. As the characters are fairly large and over half the letters bear a strong resemblance to the print equivalent, Moon has been found particularly suitable for those who have lost their sight later in life or for people who may have a less keen sense of touch. It is an appropriate method for children with additional physical and/or learning disabilities, who can acquire some literacy skills through using Moon.

Fig 27.12 An example of Moon

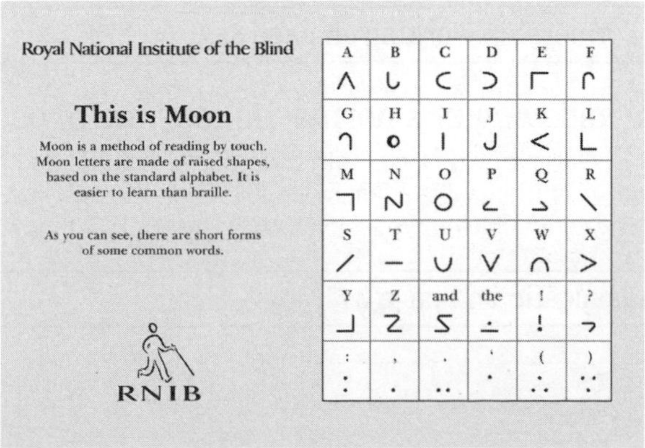
Royal National Institute of the Blind
This is Moon
Moon is a method of reading by touch. Moon letters are made of raised shapes, based on the standard alphabet. It is easier to learn than braille.
As you can see, there are short forms of some common words.
RNIB
A B C D E F
G H I J K L
M N O P Q R
S T U V W X
Y Z and the ! ?
: , . ' ( )

Link See Unit 35, page 403 for an example of Braille.

Coping strategies

A range of coping strategies can be devised and used in schools and elsewhere in order to facilitate inclusion. Examples include support given by a mobility officer to a visually impaired child enabling him to navigate his way around his environment and advice on making an area more accessible to the hearing impaired child, e.g. insulating areas to avoid echoes, etc.

Link See also page 320.

There are many types of technology that are available to enable children with special educational needs to access the curriculum more easily. Examples could be software that connects words with pictures, touch-screen computers, joysticks and tracker balls, easy-to-use keyboards, text-to-speech software, Braille-translation software.

A useful website is the British Educational Communications and Technology Agency (BECTA) – www.becta.org.uk.

Advocacy

Advocacy means to speak up for someone. There are groups of people who may need more help than others and this is particularly the case for people with learning disabilities and their families. Advocacy is about making change because people are being listened to. It means that people can make their own choices in life with the chance to be as independent as possible. An advocate acts on behalf of people with learning disabilities or on behalf of parents who may be overwhelmed, e.g. by the process of assessment of special educational needs, and require information on their rights. The advocate can clarify information and empower the parents to make informed choices.

Useful websites include:

- British Institute of Learning Disabilities – www.bild.org.uk, follow the link to Advocacy
- Advisory Centre for Education (ACE) – www.cafamily.org.uk. This is an independent advice centre for parents offering information about state education in England and Wales for 5–16-year-olds. It offers free telephone advice on many subjects like exclusion from school, bullying and SEN.
- Contact a Family – www.cafamily.org.uk. Contact a Family provides advice, information and support to families with disabled children across the UK.
- Parents for Inclusion – www.parentsforinclusion.org. This is a national charity which works to enable disabled children to learn, make friends and have a voice in ordinary school and throughout life.
- Independent Panel for Special Education Advice (IPSEA) – www.ipsea.org.uk. IPSEA has independent experts who will give free advice about a child's special educational needs.

Link See also Partnership working on page 312.

Cultural and religious norms, beliefs and expectations

It is essential that in any dealings with children the cultural and religious norms and the beliefs and expectations of the family are followed. The best way of ensuring that this happens is by communicating effectively with the family.

Link See Communication on page 314.

Policies that promote inclusion

Early years settings and schools will have a number of **policies** that promote the inclusion of children with additional needs into the setting (Fig 27.14).

Fig 27.13 Policies that promote inclusion

There are also Ofsted requirements that have to be met regarding the inclusion of children with additional needs.

See the Ofsted website: www.ofsted.gov.uk.

Your inclusion policy will most likely discuss strategies to enable the child with additional needs to access the curriculum such as:

- differentiation of the curriculum and activities
- access and safety within the physical environment.

Differentiation of the curriculum and activities

The term 'differentiation' is used to describe the various strategies teachers and other professionals use to enable pupils with diverse learning characteristics to participate in the mainstream programme. The purpose of differentiation in teaching practices and in the curriculum design is to ensure that all children maximise their potential and receive a curriculum through which they can experience success. The Special Educational Needs Code of Practice 1994 states: 'Differentiation of class work within a common curriculum framework will help the school to meet the learning needs of all children.'

Approaches to differentiation include:

- outcome – pupils are given the same task and content but the teacher assesses the outcome according to each pupil's level of ability
- delivery of task – the learning outcomes are the same but the delivery is different, e.g. one child may need to practise phonic awareness while another may need to concentrate on 'Look and Say'
- pace or extension – this allows for different speeds. Supplementary and extension work can be given to pupils who work at a faster pace
- level of work – pupils can be set work according to their ability. Some children may need an individual programme
- recording – the recording of a response can be varied, e.g. written, verbal, pictorial representation, scribing, use of computer
- resources – the content of the lesson is the same but additional resources may be used with some pupils in order to allow them to access the learning. In some cases, children may need concrete objects to help them in a task after the majority of the class are thinking abstractly, e.g. number blocks for numeracy (remind yourself of Piaget stages of development in Unit 14)
- support – some individual pupils or groups of pupils may need support in the form of a teaching assistant or a specialist teacher or health professional
- specialist techniques and strategies – these can include additional support programmes such as a multisensory programme that may be used with dyslexic children.

case study 27.4

Danny

Danny is a pupil at an infant school. He has a teaching assistant employed to support him throughout the day and in particular during the less structured times, such as playtimes and lunch times.

Danny has poor organisational skills and difficulties with paying attention and listening to instructions. The staff have made him a visual timetable so that he can see what he will be doing at different times of the day.

When the class are asked to sit on the carpet so that the teacher can introduce the literacy session, Danny has a small cushion to sit on otherwise he tends to fall into other children and annoys them. His teaching assistant sits nearby. She unobtrusively uses non-verbal signs and gestures to encourage Danny to attend to what the teacher is saying.

When the class return to their tables for guided reading, Danny is given a book with enlarged text as he has a vision impairment which means that he cannot see small print. His teaching assistant follows the words using a ruler as his eyes tend to jump up and down on the page. The pupils are then asked to write a few lines about what they have read. Danny is not yet able to do this and is asked to draw a picture instead.

activity

1 Identify the forms of differentiation that are being used in order to include Danny in the mainstream classroom.

2 Compile a list of resources or strategies that may be useful for the following children with special educational needs:

a) a child on the autistic spectrum who has difficulties with verbal communication

b) a child with dyspraxia who has difficulties with handwriting

c) a child with dyslexia who has difficulty with remembering instructions.

Portage

A pre-school child with special educational needs may be able to access support services such as the **Portage** service. It originated in Wisconsin in the USA in the early 1970s to meet the needs of young children living in rural communities (the area was called Portage). It is a non-statutory service provided by local authorities. It is a home-visiting service where a trained professional works with the child in the home, differentiating the task to meet the need of the individual child. The activity may be from one of the following areas:

- social skills
- self-help
- motor skills
- cognitive skills
- language skills
- infant stimulation.

There is also a guide to early movement skills for younger or more profoundly delayed children.

Crucially, the Portage worker works with and empowers the parent or carer in the care and education of their child. Parents and children receive regular (usually weekly) home visits from their Portage worker. Initially the child's development is observed and recorded under the areas listed above. Looking at the skills a child has acquired, plus emerging skills (those they are beginning to demonstrate), the Portage worker and parents decide on teaching objectives. Each skill is broken down into small steps via a series of linked activities to stimulate the child's development. Teaching programmes are specifically designed to meet the needs of the individual child. Portage emphasises the positive and builds on what the children can already do. Progress is recorded on a chart or in a diary and in this way a family can build a shared record of their child's involvement with Portage. This will be checked at the next meeting.

Fig 27.14 Portage checklist

Portage Checklist

Age Levels: 0–1 (1–14); 1–2 (15–24); 2–3 (25–40); 3–4 (41–64); 4–5 (65–86); 5–6 (87–108)

CARD	BEHAVIOUR	ENTRY BEHAVIOUR	DATE ACHIEVED	COMMENTS
1	Removes cloth from face, that obscures vision		/ /	
2	Looks for objects that have been removed from direct line of vision		/ /	
3	Removes object from open container by reaching into container		/ /	
4	Places object in container in imitation		/ /	
5	Places object in container on verbal command		/ /	
6	Shakes a sound-making toy on a string		/ /	
7	Puts 3 objects into a container, empties container		/ /	
8	Transfers object from one hand to the other to pick up another object		/ /	
9	Drops and picks up toy		/ /	
10	Finds object hidden under container		/ /	
11	Pushes 3 blocks train style		/ /	
12	Removes circle from form board		/ /	
13	Places round peg in pegboard on request		/ /	
14	Performs simple gestures on request		/ /	
15	Individually takes out 6 objects from container		/ /	
16	Points to one body part, e.g. nose		/ /	
17	Stacks 3 blocks on request		/ /	
18	Matches like objects		/ /	
19	Scribbles		/ /	
20	Points to self when asked 'Where's (name)?'		/ /	
21	Places 5 round pegs in pegboard on request		/ /	
22	Matches objects with picture of same object		/ /	
23	Points to named picture		/ /	
24	Turns pages of book 2–3 at a time to find named picture		/ /	
25	Finds specific book on request		/ /	
26	Completes 3 piece formboard		/ /	
27	Names common pictures		/ /	
28	Draws a vertical line in imitation		/ /	
29	Draws a horizontal line in imitation		/ /	
30	Copies a circle		/ /	
31	Matches textures		/ /	
32	Points to big and little on request		/ /	
33	Draws (+) in imitation		/ /	
34	Matches 3 colours		/ /	
35	Places objects in, on and under on request		/ /	
36	Names objects that make sounds		/ /	
37	Puts together 4 part nesting toy		/ /	
38	Names actions		/ /	
39	Matches geometric form with picture of shape		/ /	
40	Stacks 5 or more rings on a peg in order		/ /	
41	Names big and little objects		/ /	
42	Points to 10 body parts on verbal command		/ /	
43	Points to boy and girl on verbal command		/ /	
44	Tells if object is heavy or light		/ /	
45	Puts together 2 parts of shape to make whole		/ /	
46	Tells what happened next in simple, repetitive story		/ /	
47	Repeats finger plays with words and action		/ /	
48	Matches 1 to 1 (3 or more objects)		/ /	
49	Points to long and short objects		/ /	
50	Tells which objects go together		/ /	
51	Counts to 3 in imitation		/ /	
52	Arranges objects into categories		/ /	
53	Draws a V stroke in imitation		/ /	
54	Draws a diagonal line from corner to corner of 10cm square of paper		/ /	

Fig 27.14 Portage checklist

CARD	BEHAVIOUR	ENTRY BEHAVIOUR	DATE ACHIEVED	COMMENTS
55	Counts to 10 objects in imitation		/ /	
56	Builds a bridge with 3 blocks in imitation		/ /	
57	Matches sequence or pattern of blocks or beads		/ /	
58	Copies series of connected V strokes VVVVVVVVVVV		/ /	
59	Adds leg and/or arm to incomplete man		/ /	
60	Completes 6 piece puzzle without trial and error		/ /	
61	Names objects as same and different		/ /	
62	Draws a square in imitation		/ /	
63	Names 3 colours on request		/ /	
64	Names 3 shapes □△○		/ /	
65	Picks up specified number of objects on request (1–5)		/ /	
66	Names 5 textures		/ /	
67	Copies triangle on request		/ /	
68	Recalls 4 objects seen in a picture		/ /	
69	Names time of day associated with activities		/ /	
70	Repeats familiar rhymes		/ /	
71	Tells whether object is heavy or light (less than 500g difference)		/ /	
72	Tells what's missing when 1 object is removed from a group of 3		/ /	
73	Names 8 colours		/ /	
74	Names penny, 5p and 10p		/ /	
75	Matches symbols (letters and numerals)		/ /	
76	Tells colour of named objects		/ /	
77	Retells 5 main facts from story heard 3 times		/ /	
78	Draws a man (head, trunk, 4 limbs)		/ /	
79	Sings 5 lines of song		/ /	
80	Builds pyramid of 10 blocks in imitation		/ /	
81	Names long and short		/ /	
82	Places objects behind, beside, next to		/ /	
83	Matches equal sets to sample 1 to 10 objects		/ /	
84	Names or points to missing part of pictured object		/ /	
85	Counts by rote 1 to 20		/ /	
86	Names first, middle and last position		/ /	
87	Counts up to 20 items and tells how many		/ /	
88	Names 10 numerals		/ /	
89	Names left and right on self		/ /	
90	Says letters of alphabet in order		/ /	
91	Prints own first name		/ /	
92	Names 5 letters of alphabet		/ /	
93	Arranges objects in sequence of width and length		/ /	
94	Names capital letters of alphabet		/ /	
95	Puts numerals 1 to 10 in proper sequence		/ /	
96	Names position of objects first, second, third		/ /	
97	Names lower case letters of alphabet		/ /	
98	Matches capital to lower case letters of alphabet		/ /	
99	Points to named numerals 1 to 25		/ /	
100	Copies diamond shape		/ /	
101	Completes simple maze		/ /	
102	Names days of week on order		/ /	
103	Can add and subtract combinations to 3		/ /	
104	Tells month and day of birthday		/ /	
105	Sight reads 10 printed words		/ /	
106	Predicts what happens next		/ /	
107	Points to half and whole objects		/ /	
108	Counts by rote 1 to 100		/ /	

Some Portage services now offer a different service for very young children with special educational needs where emotional support for the parents/carers may be the primary aim of the contact. The Portage worker may be able to access further support for the family in the form of professional contacts and advice from specialist support groups. The Portage worker may also work with any pre-school group or school that the child will attend or be attending so that there is a smooth transition. They may work closely with teaching assistants in schools if the child is going to be supported in this way.

Fundamental to Portage support are the principles that:

- all children and parents should be valued for their unique qualities
- parents play a key role in supporting their young child's development
- services for families are most useful when they support everyday living and are delivered in a child's natural environment
- building on abilities and strengths, rather than focusing on difficulties, best supports children's learning and enjoyment.

case study 27.5

Portage activities

You are a Portage home tutor and have been visiting Lily, a 4-year-old child with global developmental delay. She is able to eat blended food but is fed by her mother. Although her fine motor skills are delayed, you feel that she is now ready to learn to feed herself using a spoon.

activity

1. Break the task of using a spoon into six achievable steps so that Lily is experiencing success.
2. Why is the Portage model a good example of ensuring that a child with a disability experiences some measure of success? How can this be empowering for the parents/carers?

Access and safety within the physical environment

In order to promote independence and to enable a child with additional needs to access the environment safely, considerations have to be made with regard to the **physical environment**. Under the Special Educational Needs and Disability Discrimination Act 2001, there is an anticipatory duty to ensure that buildings are accessible, e.g. with the addition of ramps for children using wheelchairs. In some cases lifts may need to be installed. Safety is very important, and for the visually impaired child keeping corridors and aisles free of clutter is essential. For some children who have personal care requirements there should be separate toileting and changing facilities with a shower.

activity
INDIVIDUAL WORK
27.6

P5

M4

1. List the policies in your setting that are designed to promote inclusive practice. Describe two of them in detail.
2. Using two examples of policies from your setting, explain how they are promoting inclusion in the setting.

Professional Practice

- Always remember to gain the permission of the placement supervisor when using policies from your workplace.

Multidisciplinary working

Integrated services

Good collaborative working between the different agencies, e.g. education, health and social services, is continually highlighted in educational legislation as being essential for meeting the needs of the child with special educational needs.

It is not uncommon now for health professionals, amongst others, to train school personnel in areas such as the use of feeding mechanisms, catheters, exercise regimes, and so on, as well as in strategies to support learning, such as a speech and language programme. Similarly the special needs team from an LEA may spend as much time informing and demonstrating strategies to teaching staff and teaching assistants as working with the individual child.

To ensure that a child with a physical disability is in receipt of appropriate equipment, such as seating, the input of a physiotherapist and/or occupational therapist may be sought. Organisations such as Scope are invaluable at supporting children in mainstream and special schools, offering advice on physical needs and requirements, as well as educational advice for children with cerebral palsy and other physical conditions. Local authorities will have a team of specialist teachers working for example with children with sensory impairment and will offer advice on a range of strategies to facilitate inclusion, such as mobility training for children with a vision impairment. Other specialists will include teachers with an expertise in language, dyslexia, attention hyperactivity disorder, behavioural, emotional and social difficulties, and autistic spectrum disorder.

If a child with a communication disorder is to be successfully included in mainstream schooling, then their preferred method of communication will need to be learnt by members of staff and their peers if the child is to feel fully included. This could involve a speech and language therapist teaching Makaton signing, for example. If a teaching assistant is to be working with a child who is going to be using Braille, then advice from specialist staff will need to be sought in order that the child can be supported and materials prepared.

Opportunity playgroups exist for children with special educational needs and their siblings. Multi-agency professionals such as social workers and speech and language therapists offer their services to the playgroup which can be very helpful to parents who may have to make several trips a week to access the different services required by their child. Parents not only have the support of the staff but also have the opportunity to meet other parents of children with a range of special educational needs. This can be helpful not only for sharing experiences but for emotional support as well. It can be difficult for some parents to talk about their needs with others if they do not have a child with special educational needs.

Roles of key workers

Fig 27.15 Some of the key workers who may be involved in multi-agency working

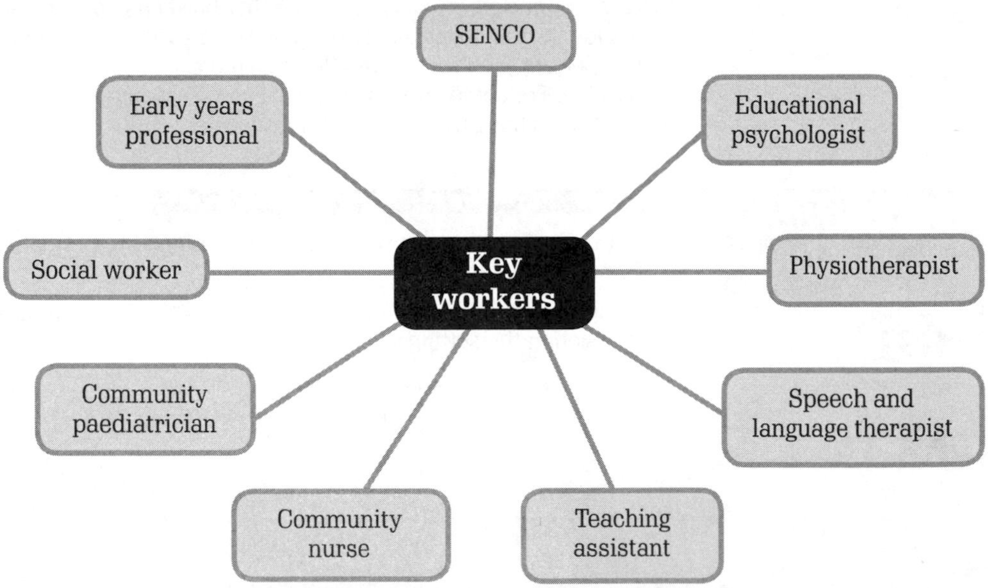

Link

See page 320 for the role of the SENCO.

Educational psychologist

These are trained and experienced teachers with additional qualifications in educational psychology. They assess children who have learning and/or behavioural difficulties, advise teachers and parents on strategies to support the children and prepare educational assessments for children requiring a Statement of Special Educational Needs.

Link

See page 318 for more about Statements of Special Educational Needs.

Physiotherapist

Physiotherapists may work in health centres, hospitals and schools. Their role is to assess children's motor skills and provide exercise and activities to improve any difficulties with movement, positioning or balancing difficulties.

Sometimes they will demonstrate exercises to a teaching assistant (if working in a school), who will then carry them out on a regular basis with the child, or to parents and carers, e.g. exercises to help breathing and coughing in children with cystic fibrosis.

Speech and language therapist

These workers are concerned with all aspects of communication, assessing children's hearing, speech and language. Individual programmes of activities and exercises to help children acquire language and use speech are designed so that parents, carers and teaching assistants can continue the programme at home or in school. Speech and language therapists are based either in the community, in hospital clinics or in schools. Children with disabilites such as Down's syndrome, cerebral palsy, hearing impairment, a stammer, cleft lip/palate are amongst those who can be helped by speech therapy.

Social worker

Social workers are usually employed by local authorities but sometimes by voluntary organisations. Their duties with regard to children with additional needs and their families include advising on accessing resources, benefits and services to which children and parents are entitled and acting as an advocate to enable them to obtain these services.

Social workers are involved in assessment for day care and respite care, and have statutory child protection duties towards children with special educational needs. They are also responsible for the quality of care for those looked after in residential care homes.

Community nurse

These nurses help and support children in their own homes who require nursing care. They assess the child's needs and identify the nursing and equipment that babies and children with additional needs may require, liaising and co-ordinating care with the hospital and primary health care team.

Community paediatrician

Paediatricians are doctors specialising in the diagnosis of children's illness, disorders and special needs and the provision of medical care. If working in the community, they will be members of the community child health service and they will be involved in multidisciplinary assessments of children with special needs.

Teaching assistant

These are sometimes called learning support assistants or classroom assistants. They may be employed to support the classroom teacher in the education and management of a whole class group or they may be assigned to a particular child, who will often be in receipt of a Statement of Special Educational Needs.

Teaching assistants may enable a child with SEN to access the mainstream curriculum by means of differentiation of the curriculum and assisting in the implementation of IEP targets.

Link

Statements of Special Educational Needs are discussed on page 318.

- Differentiation is discussed on page 305.
- IEPs are discussed on page 316.

Early years professional

Early years professionals may work with children in day nurseries, nursery classes, Foundation Stage classrooms in schools and children's centres.

Respite care

Some families may be able to access respite care for their child with a disability and this can enable them to spend time with their other children. This is usually offered by local authorities. Some authorities also offer short-term regular breaks to children and young people with learning difficulties. The service offers an environment where children can feel relaxed and have their individual needs met and where they may have opportunities for outings and play activities which their families may find difficult to provide. Another example of this type of service is offered by Shared Care Network, a national organisation which provides family-based short breaks for disabled children. The organisation represents over 300 local schemes which link disabled children with people in the community who provide regular short-term care.

activity
INDIVIDUAL WORK 27.7
P6
M5

1 Peter is a 4-year-old child who attends your pre-school. The early years SENCO is concerned that he will struggle when he begins at the local primary school in September. He has the following difficulties:

- His fine motor skills are not well developed. He tends to eat with his fingers and he makes no attempt to dress himself.
- He was late walking and is unable to jump with two feet together. He runs with an awkward gait.
- He is rather clumsy and tends to annoy other children by taking away their toys without asking.
- His expressive language is poor and he has difficulty making himself understood.
- His attention span is poor.

The SENCO is keen that an assessment is done so that, if appropriate, Peter can start primary school with a Statement of Special Educational Needs.

Which professionals do you think should take part in the assessment of Peter? (Look back to roles.) Describe the roles of three of these professionals.

2 As the early years SENCO at the pre-school mentioned above, you have to explain to Peter's parents why you are putting into motion a multidisciplinary assessment.

Explain how multidisciplinary working can support children with additional needs and their families.

activity
INDIVIDUAL WORK 27.8
D2

Looking at a range of strategies for supporting children with additional needs (examples could included differentiation of work, adaptations of buildings, support of a teaching assistant), evaluate them in terms of promoting inclusion, giving examples of children with a range of additional needs.

Partnership working

Statutory and voluntary support

Educational legislation stresses the involvement of parents in the decisions surrounding their child's educational needs. When a child is being assessed for a Statement of Special Educational Needs, parents are asked to submit a report which is considered alongside the reports of the professionals involved. Parents are able to appeal if they are in disagreement with sections of the statement, e.g. the named school. Under the 1988 Education Act, open enrolment gave parents greater choice of schools. The rights for parents of children with SEN were increased under the 1993 Act so they are able to choose the school named on the Statement of Special Educational Needs and have access to an Independent Tribunal. LEAs have to supply advocates for parents if required in order to support them through the process. Parents are invited to IEP (individual education plan) review meetings and are asked to contribute to their child's IEP targets.

There are national standards for local SEN Parent Partnership services. An important part of the role of the Parent Partnership is to support disadvantaged families and those who may have learning difficulties and disabilities themselves. Access to the Special Educational Needs and Disability Tribunal (SENDIST) is open to all parents. SENDIST aims to provide an accessible, supportive and helpful service to parents of children with SEN. It is an independent body that hears appeals against decisions made by local authorities on SEN assessments and statements.

Independent parental supporters can also help families through the procedures involved in dealing with a child's special educational needs. They work under the guidance and supervision of the local Parent Partnership service and are usually trained volunteers. Also available is the Advisory Centre for Education (ACE) which is an independent advice centre for parents, offering information about state education in England and Wales for 5–16-year-olds. It offers free telephone advice on many subjects like exclusion from school, bullying and special educational needs. The Independent Panel for Special Education Advice (IPSEA) has independent experts who will give free advice on a child's special educational needs including advice on appealing to the Special Educational Needs and Disability Tribunal, representation when needed, and second professional opinions. Parents for Inclusion is a national charity which works to enable disabled children to learn, make friends and be included in mainstream schooling and in their lives.

- Advisory Centre for Education (ACE) – www.cafamily.org.uk
- Parents for Inclusion – www.parentsforinclusion.org
- Independent Panel for Special Education Advice (IPSEA) – www.ipsea.org.uk

Building relationships between parents and professionals

It is very important that you involve parents from the start and at every stage during the child's time at your setting. Parents are the people with the most knowledge of their child and should always be consulted. If a child has a rare special educational need, the parents have often sought out information and have more knowledge about the condition than the GP who may never have come across the disability before.

Most parents will have anxieties about their child attending a nursery or pre-schools setting but for the parent of a child with special educational needs the anxieties can be much greater. Many parents of children with special educational needs may never have left the child with another carer before and they need to be reassured that you know as much as possible about how to care for and communicate with their child.

Supporting parents/carers/families

Ways in which families of children with additional needs can be supported include the following:

- support groups and programmes
- financial support.

Support groups and programmes

Support groups such as disability-specific groups can be a lifeline for parents, particularly if the learning disability is a rare one. Parents can find groups through Contact a Family (CAF) which publishes a directory of support groups. Organisations such as the Opportunity Groups can be invaluable as can telephone support such as that provided by Parentline Plus.

Sure Start is a government initiative for all children, parents and communities and brings together free early education and better childcare. The project has particular commitments to children with disabilities. Professionals work with the family to define the nature of the child's needs and the impact on the family. They look at the support needed and agree the type of equipment, medical care, therapy, information and practical advice that may be required. Sure Start Children's Centres also have support workers who visit families at home, and families can receive regular visits through the Home Start programmes.

Home Start is a family support charity. It has a network of over 15,000 trained volunteers who support thousands of parents who may be struggling due to postnatal illness, disability, bereavement, the illness of a parent or child, or social isolation.

Parent Partnership services provide information, advice and support for parents of disabled children and young people and aim to support parents in making informed decisions about their child's education. This can be particularly beneficial during the assessment process. They can provide training to guide families through the SEN procedures and processes.

Early Support is a central government programme which aims to improve the delivery of services to disabled children under 3 and their families. It offers a range of information for families in partnership with education, health and social services, voluntary organisations and the service users themselves (the children and their families). Early Support has also developed a range of disability-specific leaflets containing information about disabilities including sensory impairment, autism, rare conditions and speech and language difficulties. It also has a booklet which covers the situation where no diagnosis has yet been made but where a child often needs support services. In addition there is an Early Support Family Pack which informs parents about services which can support them. There are links to other support agencies such as the Disabled Living Foundation which has several fact sheets detailing mobility, daily living and play equipment for children.

Financial support

Sometimes parents are able to claim benefits such as:

- Disability Living Allowance (DLA) – a tax-free benefit for children and adults who need help with personal care or have walking difficulties because they are physically or mentally disabled
- Carer's Allowance – a benefit to help people who look after someone who is disabled.

Families may also be able to access financial assistance through the Family Fund, a charity which helps families of disabled and seriously ill children under the age of 16.

Grants are sometimes available for adaptations to be made to the home.

Useful websites include:

- National Parent Partnerships Network – www.parentpartnership.org.uk
- Sure Start – www.surestart.gov.uk
- Home Start – www.home-start.org.uk
- Parentline Plus – www.parentlineplus.org.uk
- Early Support – www.earlysupport.org.uk
- Disabled Living Foundation – www.dlf.org.uk

activity
INDIVIDUAL WORK 27.9
P7

Find out from your placement how parents are involved in the care and education of their child and how these strategies support children with additional needs and their families. An example could be the placement conducting home visits before the child commences pre-school.

Effective communication

Regular communication between all the agencies working with a child with additional needs and the family is essential to ensure that parents are involved and know what is happening for their child. This prevents misunderstandings arising and unnecessary worrying. A home visit, for example by a staff member from a pre-school, may be appropriate or an invitation to meet socially with other parents in the setting. This can be especially helpful if the parents or main carers are not the people who deliver and collect the child to and from the setting.

A home-link book can be an invaluable source of information both for parents and professionals and a source of reassurance for the parent that the setting is doing everything in its power to include the child and meet their needs.

Link

See Unit 14, Figure 14.9, page 135, for an example of a home-link book.

case study 27.6

Jonny

Jonny is a 4-year-old child with cerebral palsy who attends your mainstream pre-school setting on a part-time basis. He also has a placement at the local Opportunity Group where he receives regular physiotherapy and speech and language input. He also has weekly visits from a Portage tutor.

activity

Describe how a home-link book could be an important form of communication between yourself, Jonny's family and the other professionals involved in Jonny's care and education.

Other forms of communication include letters, meetings, reviews and telephone calls. It is important that professionals avoid professional jargon (e.g. educational terms used by teachers) when communicating with parents as this may have the effect of disempowering the parents.

You should remember that parents/carers are the people who know the child best. Their opinions and advice should be sought as appropriate. You need to be empathic and appreciate that the family may be experiencing a number of difficulties relating to having a child with additional needs.

Link See page 284 for the impact on the family of having a child with additional needs.

remember Be as positive as possible when talking to parents of a child with SEN. A negative comment can be very difficult to deal with.

While it is important to be realistic about a child's potential and abilities, it is also very important to be as positive as possible. When giving feedback on a child's progress, begin with a positive step that has been made. The effect of constant negative feedback is extremely damaging and can have a negative impact on the relationship between the parent/carer and the child, with the adults possibly feeling that they are in a hopeless situation.

The way in which the news is broken to the parents that their child has a disability can have a lasting impact on the way in which families deal with it so it is very important that professionals deal with this in a sensitive and tactful manner.

case study 27.7

The needs of parents/carers

You are working as a nursery nurse at an Opportunity Playgroup. The leader of the group has asked you to prepare a booklet that identifies and analyses the likely range of needs and feelings of parents/carers of a child with special educational needs.

activity

In your planning, you will need to:

- consider the impact and implications that a child's disability can have on both the child's and family's lives
- demonstrate your empathic skills towards parents/carers
- identify the professionals and agencies that will work with parents and the role that they may play
- include factual information about a range of special educational needs including physical, sensory, cognition and learning difficulties and communication and interaction special needs. Consider the impact and implications of each of these on a child's life.

Produce the booklet.

Assessment and review

Assessment process

An early years worker in a pre-school setting or class teacher in a primary school may identify a child as having additional needs through informal and formal observations and assessed work. If they are concerned, they will involve the SENCO and a differentiated programme can be put into place. This stage is known as School Action or Early Years Action. This may include the setting up of an individual education plan (IEP). The child and their parents/carers should be involved at every stage of the assessment process.

Refer to www.everychildmatters.gov.uk for information on:
- Early Years Action
- Early Years Action Plus
- School Action
- School Action Plus.

Individual education plans

Many children with special education needs will require an individual education plan (IEP) or a pupil inclusion plan (PIP).

This sets out how the objectives are to be differentiated and who is to be responsible for ensuring that they are implemented. This will be implemented by the Special Educational Needs Co-ordinator (SENCO) with input from the class teacher, teaching assistants, parents and the child at the School Action or Early Years Action stage of assessment.

Link
- See page 295 where differentiation is discussed.
- The role of the SENCO is described on page 320.

IEPs should:
- raise achievement for pupils with SEN
- be seen as working documents
- use a simple format
- detail provision *additional to* or *different from* those generally available for all pupils
- be jargon free
- be comprehensible to all staff and parents
- be distributed to all staff as necessary
- promote effective planning
- help pupils monitor their own progress
- result in good planning and intervention by staff
- result in the achievement of specified learning goals for pupils with SEN.

It is essential that the objective or targets are SMART:
- **S**pecific (they say exactly what you mean)
- **M**easurable (you can prove that you've reached them)
- **A**chievable (you can reach them in the time allowed)
- **R**ealistic (they are about the action you can take)
- **T**ime-related (they have deadlines).

With a SMART target, the child is more likely to succeed at the task and the feeling of success will encourage the child to continue with the task and then attempt the next one.

IEPs should be reviewed at least every six months. The SENCO co-ordinates the review meeting and invites everyone who has been working with the child including the child and their parents.

case study 27.8

Sam

Sam is in Year 1 and has attention deficit hyperactivity disorder (ADHD). He has difficulty sitting on the carpet for the introduction to the literacy session which lasts for 10 minutes. As the teaching assistant assigned to supporting Sam, you have been asked to explain the reasons for giving Sam an IEP.

activity

1 Explain what an IEP is and why it should be viewed as a positive document.
2 Write an IEP target for Sam ensuring that it is SMART.

Fig 27.16 An example of an IEP

IEP 2 – TARGET ACTION PLAN School:

Pupil:	Year:	SEN Stage:	IEP No:	Plan Date:	Review By Date:

The function of this plan is to record a limited number of specific targets and strategies to address the pupil's identified special educational needs. Most pupils will need a Target Action Plan, exceptions being where there are no learning or behavioural difficulties and the only issue is one of access. This Plan is likely to need regular review.

Target number	**Targets** *(A clearly stated, realistic learning or behavioural outcome)*	**Strategies** *(What will be done that is different from normal class routines – special activities and resources)*	**Roles and responsibilities** *(Which school staff will do what, when, and how often. Backup from parents)*
1	*The pupil will be able to:*		
2	*The pupil will be able to:*		
3	*The pupil will be able to:*		
4	*The pupil will be able to:*		

Signed	SENCO	Teacher/Tutor/Head of Year	Parent/Carer	Student	Support Agency

REVIEW OF TARGET ACTION PLAN

Date:	Persons attending:	
IEP Number:		

Target number	**Achieved** *(Yes/No)*	**Comments on Strategies employed** *(What worked well, what could be improved?)*	**Comments on roles and responsibilities** *(Were they carried out as planned? Efficiency and effectiveness?)*
1			
2			
3			
4			

Other comments *(from all persons present at the review including pupil and outside agencies)*	

Next step (circle): New IEP at same Stage / Move to Lower Stage / Move to higher Stage / Other ______________________

If it is thought that a child requires further support and expertise in addition to that which the school can offer, School Action Plus or Early Years Action is put into place. This is where the school draws on professionals from outside the school such as speech and language therapists. In some cases it will be considered desirable that the child is in receipt of a Statement of Special Educational Needs.

Statement of Special Educational Needs

In order to obtain a Statement for a child already in school, a statutory assessment needs to be carried out. This is where all the professionals involved in working with the child are required to write a report on the needs of the child. A panel of professionals headed by an educational psychologist will consider the evidence and decide whether or not to issue a Statement of Special Educational Needs. This is a legal document and has to be reviewed with parents at least once a year. Schools will then receive funding for the child which they can choose to use in a variety of ways, e.g. by employing a teaching assistant to support the child in a mainstream setting.

The LEA will usually inform parents and schools whether they are going to issue a statement within 12 weeks of beginning the assessment.

All children who attend special schools are in receipt of a Statement of Special Educational Needs.

The Statement of Special Educational Needs is divided into six parts:

- Part 1: Introduction
- Part 2: Special educational needs
- Part 3: Special educational provision
- Part 4: Placement
- Part 5: Non-educational needs
- Part 6: Non-educational provision.

At the time of the Warnock Report (1978), it was estimated that around 2 per cent of children would be in need of a Statement of Special Educational Needs. This continues to be the case, but LEAs differ in their criteria for issuing Statements. The process of issuing a Statement is costly and so some authorities believe the money can be better spent devolving money directly to schools for use with children with special educational needs. Therefore the percentage of children in receipt of a Statement will vary from area to area and does not necessarily reflect the number of children with significant disabilities but may be a reflection of the LEA's policy on issuing Statements.

The Statement must be reviewed at least annually, checking the child's progress and making sure that the Statement continues to meet their needs.

Parents have a right of appeal to the Special Educational Needs and Disability Tribunal (SENDIST) against Parts 2, 3 and 4 of the Statement.

Another key aspect of educational legislation is that of early identification of needs. This is highlighted in the revised Code of Practice and the Removing Barriers to Achievement (2004) document.

Link

See page 291 for Removing Barriers to Achievement.

The earlier a special educational need is identified, the sooner the necessary resources can be put into place and the child can begin to access the curriculum. In some cases, this may mean that appropriate professionals such as paediatricians or educational psychologists can be accessed in order to make a diagnosis. In other cases, there will be no diagnosis of need but strategies to support the child can be put into place.

If a need has been identified, this can alleviate any guilt that a parent may be feeling that their child is not developing like other children. If a diagnosis is made, then parents are able to access the appropriate support group, e.g. the National Autistic Society for children on the autistic spectrum or Sense for children with sensory disabilities.

If a child needs additional help with their learning the pre-school or nursery may put them on a programme called Early Years Action. The teachers or SENCO will discuss the needs of the child with the parent or carer, assess their needs and decide what help should be given. An IEP may then be used to set out short-term targets for the child's learning. If the child is not making progress under Early Years Action, then the SENCO or teacher may discuss obtaining extra help from, e.g. a specialist teacher or therapist such as a speech and language therapist. This is known as Early Years Action Plus. External specialists may start by making an assessment of what is needed and they may advise on the IEP targets and sometimes teach or support the child directly. If the child needs a large amount of help or extra resources the LEA may agree to provide this through Early Years Action Plus or decide to make a statutory assessment.

Children under 2 years

The legal rules about assessments only apply to children over the age of 2 years. However, if parents or professionals working request a statutory assessment for a child under 2, the LEA will decide how to carry out the assessment. Once the assessment has been completed the LEA decides whether to issue a Statement of Special Educational Needs. An SEN statement for a child under 2 describes:

- the child's needs
- the views of parents and professionals
- an account of the help that will be provided
- information about how this help will be monitored and reviewed.

However, it is unusual for a child under the age of 2 to be issued with a statement.

When a child reaches the age of 2, the legal rules for assessing a child and making a statement apply. The procedures for assessment and statements are the same as for children of school age.

Role of the SENCO

The Special Educational Needs Co-ordinator (SENCO), whether in school or pre-school, has responsibility for the day-to-day operation of the setting's SEN policy and for co-ordinating provision for children with special educational needs, particularly through School Action, Early Years Action, School Action Plus or Early Years Action Plus.

The SENCO will have responsibility for:

- liaising with parents and professionals in respect of children with special educational needs
- advising and supporting other practitioners in the setting
- ensuring that appropriate IEPs are in place
- ensuring that relevant background information about individual children with special educational needs is collected, recorded and updated
- further assessment of the child's particular strengths and areas that need development
- planning future support for the child in discussion with colleagues
- monitoring and reviewing action taken
- ensuring that appropriate records are kept including a record of children at Early Years Action or School Action, Early Years Action Plus or School Action Plus and those with Statements of Special Educational Needs.

Training for the SENCO may be provided by the LEA Early Years Partnership.

case study 27.9

Assessment procedure

You are the SENCO for a 24-place nursery school in a rural setting. You and your colleagues are concerned about the development of a 4-year-old boy, Charlie, whose behaviour is causing concern. He mostly plays alone, he has a lack of creative and pretend play and he appears extremely agitated when there is a change of routine, no matter how small this change may be. Charlie also has difficulty with verbal and non-verbal communication. Interactions are rare and involve short phrases which, at times, can be echolalic (repeating what has been said to him).

Charlie's parents are concerned about his behaviour and are looking to you for guidance on how to help their son.

activity

1 Outline the relevant legislation and assessment procedures available to meet Charlie's individual needs.
2 Explain the importance of working in partnership with parents/carers and other professionals, including yourself.

Supporting children with additional needs

If you are to support a child with a disability or a learning difficulty in the most positive and productive way, it is essential that you have an understanding of the child's condition and the strategies and resources that can be put in place to include the child as far as possible in the setting. You need to be aware of health and safety implications and considerations for the layout of the environment. It is useful to remember that a number of strategies that are helpful for children with disabilities or learning difficulties, e.g. ensuring that the acoustics of a room are considered when including a child with a hearing impairment, are helpful for everyone.

There is not always a great deal of published information on some of the rarer conditions, but the support groups can be invaluable and there are usually websites that are very informative, e.g. for conditions such as William's syndrome. You should also remember to consult parents who will most probably have researched their child's condition and may know more about it than many professionals working in the field.

The following are some suggestions for the care/educational needs for some of the conditions described at the beginning of the unit.

Link
Look back at pages 269–284 for more details about the conditions.

Down's syndrome

A child born with Down's syndrome will have a learning disability and will require educational support. However, while there are many similarities among children with Down's syndrome, as each child inherits characteristics from his own family background there will also be significant differences. This will affect the level of care required. In addition there may be possible health difficulties which can include the following.

- There may be impaired hearing due to a tendency to catch frequent coughs and colds, so that glue ear is more likely than in some other children.
- There may be vision problems. Sometimes there is a squint or other associated difficulties. In some children there is a lack of peripheral vision.
- Gross motor skills such as crawling and walking will probably be delayed. Children with Down's syndrome have a tendency to put on weight and this will need to be monitored and a healthy diet followed.
- Around 40 per cent of children with Down's syndrome have a heart problem. Sometimes this is serious enough to require surgery.
- Physical development may be affected and the child may be smaller than her peers. As the young child is floppy and has poor muscle tone, additional physical support will be needed and the advice of a physiotherapist should be sought when including the child in physical activities in school and other settings as some activities may be detrimental to the child's physical condition.

- Children with Down's syndrome will be delayed in their cognitive development but many now successfully access a mainstream education with the support of a differentiated curriculum. Sometimes the child with Down's syndrome may be 'mothered' by other children and while the support of other children in the setting should be encouraged, the child needs to be enabled to develop independence skills.
- As the child's overall development is delayed they will often attend a pre-school setting without having been toilet-trained. Similarly, habits such as putting objects into the mouth tend to continue later in children with Down's syndrome and the 'terrible 2s' usually occur at 3 years of age and beyond. While it should be remembered that all children with Down's syndrome are individuals first and foremost many children do have very affectionate natures but as they become older they may also develop a stubborn streak.
- As the acquisition of language is later in a child with Down's syndrome, the teaching of Makaton signing can be a very useful tool in allowing the child to communicate and alleviating the subsequent frustration. For an inclusive setting, it is important that children and staff learn the Makaton sign language so that they can communicate with the child.
- If a child with Down's syndrome is educated in a mainstream setting they will usually have a Statement of Special Educational Needs and often a teaching assistant is employed to support them in their education and care needs.

Fig 27.18 Child with Down's syndrome in main stream school setting

William's syndrome

Early diagnosis means better understanding of the problems which may arise leading to a happier life for the child and relief and support for the parents. When hypercalcaemia (high blood calcium levels) occurs in the first year or two of life, a low calcium diet is prescribed. Many of the children with William's syndrome have renal and cardiac problems. They may also have dental abnormalities, back and joint problems, raised blood pressure and delayed rate of growth, including low stature and a slight build.

Children with the syndrome have an unusual pattern of abilities and this can lead to artificial expectations of matching ability. For example, initially it may appear that the child's verbal skills are good but the language is often inappropriate and the child may 'talk at' someone rather than having a conversation. Comprehension is poor and this should be taken into consideration when instructions are given and activities provided. Often the child's concentration span will be short adding to the learning difficulties.

There may also be marked gross and fine motor problems and visio-spatial difficulties. There is no one type of school that is ideally suited to these children's needs and finding the most appropriate school will depend on the individual child's level of ability and also on the provision in the particular schools that are available locally.

Cystic fibrosis

The three main areas of care regarding a child with cystic fibrosis are maintenance of nutrition, prevention and control of lung infections and physiotherapy to keep airways clear. All staff need to be aware of the severity of the condition, the importance of diet and medicine, and reminders that the cough is not infectious. Time and space for physiotherapy is needed as is good liaison with school health services.

When a child is too large to be comfortably placed over the knees, treatment will need to take place over a foam wedge. Breathing exercises such as blowing games with bubbles and steaming mirrors can be introduced from about the age of 2. Trampolining is a good form of exercise. From about the age of 5 the child should be encouraged to spit secretions out as the mucus can be observed and indicate infection, changes in stickiness, etc. Swallowing mucus can increase nausea and affect appetite.

The child should be offered full involvement in all activities and wherever possible should make their own decisions about how many strenuous games and activities they can manage. This will depend on the severity of the condition at any one time. The child needs to make friends and have the opportunity to succeed in areas where they can compete equally with their peers, such as music and creative activities.

A childcare worker needs to maintain the balance of a sensitive approach by demonstrating understanding, without over-protecting, in order to help the child take full advantage of the learning opportunities available. The childcare worker should be ready to intervene if the child is picked on by other children due to coughing or expectorating, being underweight and needing regular medication. As with any medical condition, there will be absences from school due to infections so it can be helpful if the key worker or teaching assistant keeps a class diary to help with missed work.

Duchenne muscular dystrophy

The progress of the condition cannot be halted by specific medicines or treatment but good management can ensure good quality of life for the child and limit associated problems. The child should be given the chance to develop wide social relationships, experiences, hobbies and interests that can be continued once mobility is reduced. Muscles need exercise so swimming, ballet, gym clubs and horse-riding should be included in the range of activities which will also help to prevent the child becoming overweight due to being less mobile than his peers.

The child may require up to four hours planned exercises a day which the early years worker may have to help implement, with input from the physiotherapist. Hydrotherapy is often used as a valuable and enjoyable exercise as muscles move more freely in water and are less likely to overstrain. As with other conditions where a child may be using a wheelchair or mobility aids, the environment needs to be checked in order to enable their safe use.

Some boys may have learning and/or behavioural problems, with communication difficulties being the chief area of concern. Computers can be a very useful tool for boys with the condition. However some boys have excellent manual skills and creativity and imagination in the area of design and become very good artists and model makers.

Fragile X syndrome

Fragile X is wide ranging in its effects, from specific learning difficulties and subtle learning problems with an average IQ to severe intellectual disability and developmental delay. Any one child may present only a few of the problems or a whole range of features but in a mild form.

Many adults and children with Fragile X remain undiagnosed because they only have mild learning difficulties and this can mean that they may not get the help and support that they need.

Understanding emotions is an area of difficulty, so social skills groups and programmes can be helpful as many children with Fragile X will have autistic-like symptoms and behaviour. Other strategies used with children on the autistic spectrum such as PECS, Makaton and the TEACCH programme are also helpful, especially where speech and language are affected. Delayed development in these areas is one of the earliest presenting features. Receptive language skills are generally better than expressive language skills.

Link

- See also the section on autistic spectrum disorder, page 324.
- Examples of Makaton are given on page 403, and of PECS on page 128.

Fig 27.19 Child with Fragile X

Boys tend to have more behavioural problems and difficulties with concentration, while girls are more likely to be shy and socially withdrawn and more likely to suffer from anxiety and depression. As girls with Fragile X are less likely to be severely affected, they are more likely to go to mainstream schools. Counselling and training programmes designed to promote self-confidence and self-esteem may be helpful.

Differentiation of the curriculum will almost always be necessary and the support of a teaching assistant may be used. Particular areas of the curriculum that can cause difficulty include mathematics, as conceptual learning is difficult. Handwriting can present problems, while reading and spelling can be relative strengths. Computers are effective learning tools to use with children with Fragile X as they allow for endless repetition of tasks, they are consistent and they have large memories. They give immediate responses and are not personally threatening. Social anxiety can be a key feature of children with Fragile X.

Haemophilia

The effect of haemophilia on a child's lifestyle, growth and development should be minimal and there should be normal growth and life expectancy, not a life of pain. Normal play and schooling is usual. It is important that over-protection is avoided and that normal handling, cuddling and play takes place. When the child is at the toddling stage, sensible protection for knees, e.g. dungarees, is essential. Good dental hygiene is necessary. Toddlers with haemophilia may have more bruises than their peers and false allegations of child abuse have occurred in some situations.

remember Asprin should not be given to any child unless prescribed by a doctor.

It is good practice to seek medical advice if the child falls and hits his head. Normal safety precautions, e.g. stair gates, robust toys with no sharp edges, etc., should be followed. Exercise helps develop strong joints and muscles, better balance and sharper reactions leading to better avoidance of injury. Swimming is especially valuable but physical contact sports are not recommended.

Thalassaemia

With effective treatment a child can attend and thrive in a childcare setting from pre-school to mainstream school. Carers need to be aware that the child is likely to become tired and need extra rest. Symptoms are controlled by regular blood transfusions. Regular, often daily, drugs given by injections under the skin are essential to help prevent too many iron-rich blood cells accumulating in the body with the possible damage to vital organs like heart and liver.

Autistic spectrum disorder

Many children on the autistic spectrum are educated in mainstream schools although some of the most severely affected children may attend special schools, some with a residential facility, or specialist units attached to mainstream schools. They will require social skills training and support in accessing the curriculum in many ways.

Children with autism tend to be good visual learners and therefore a visual timetable can be of great benefit as it can alleviate a great deal of stress. In the timetable, it is important to incorporate a card denoting a change of routine as this can be very difficult for the autistic child to deal with. In whole group settings, such as carpet time, it can be helpful for an assistant or key worker to have a series of cards which can be held up for the autistic child to see so that they behave appropriately (e.g. remain sitting, not calling out). For example, a card may show an ear, depicting listening. This strategy also has the advantage that attention is not unduly drawn to the child.

In some children with autism, the senses are heightened and hearing, for example, may be very acute. This can cause distress in noisy, busy places, so it is important to keep the environment as low stimulus as possible. This can be difficult in a mainstream primary school where there are lots of displays and a very busy atmosphere. Wherever possible the autistic child should have access to a calm, quiet area possibly with his own 'work-station'. This approach is based on a programme developed in North Carolina for people on the autistic spectrum known as TEACCH (Treatment and Education of Autistic and related Communication Handicapped Children). Aspects of the treatment programme include both language- and behaviour-focused intervention programmes.

The five TEACCH concepts are:

- physical structure of the environment
- visual cueing
- the work station
- concept of finish (many autistic children need to learn what this means)
- concept of first work, then play.

Autistic children often take language very literally. It is important to speak very clearly and directly and not use idioms such as 'It's raining cats and dogs'. Some children with autism will have speech difficulties and may benefit from the use of a visual communication system such as the Picture Exchange Communication system (PECS). Other autistic children may find learning Makaton signing beneficial.

Link

Examples of Makaton are given on page 393, and of PECS on page 128.

Other treatments that may be beneficial include music therapy and an intensive one-to-one programme known as Applied Behaviour Analysis (ABA). This is an early intensive behaviour therapy approach which was developed by Dr O. Ivar Lovaas and is carried out by a trained team, usually within the home environment. It is sometimes included on a child's Statement of Special Educational Needs and continued in the pre-school or school setting.

Many children on the autistic spectrum have a number of self-stimulating habits such as hand flapping. This may well be a way of dealing with the ever-present anxiety that is characteristic of anyone on the autistic spectrum. Their reliance on routines and obsessions with activities such as switching lights on and off or watching the washing machine go around may also be comforting to them. They often have obsessions which can be hard to break. However, an obsession, such as an intense fascination with trains, could be worked into a reward system.

Asperger's syndrome

Children with Asperger's syndrome may be highly intelligent, especially in certain areas of the curriculum such as mathematics where the answers are either right or wrong. However other areas of the curriculum such as English, where they may be required to write an imaginative piece of work, or history, where they may be expected to demonstrate empathy with a character from the past, may be problematic.

A differentiated curriculum will be necessary so their skills can be utilised, while support is given with social skills and the use of language appropriate to any given social situation. They will need help in knowing what to do in social situations and with the social skills necessary in making friends and working alongside other people. Often the child with Asperger's syndrome will become fixated on a particular topic which does not hold any interest for other people. Because of their difficulties with social interaction they are not easily able to switch to another topic or understand that the person they are talking to is bored with the subject.

Many schools run social skills groups using material such as that produced by Maureen Aarons and Tessa Gittens, which can be helpful in teaching the rules of social interaction to children with Asperger's syndrome as well as other children who are immature in their social skills.

Programmes such as Carol Gray's Social Stories, where pupils are provided with information about social situations which they can individualise, can also be beneficial.

See page 412 for details of Aarons & Gittens (1999) and Gray et al. (2005).

Children with Asperger's syndrome usually attend mainstream school. As they have language they are often not diagnosed until their other difficulties become more apparent. They can therefore become the targets of bullying as their behaviour is not understood. This can also be because the disability is not clearly visible.

Dyspraxia

Early recognition of dyspraxia enables a child's special educational and social needs to be identified. Action can then be taken to reduce the impact of the condition on the whole family.

It is important that practitioners are sympathetic to the condition and put strategies in place, adapting the curriculum as necessary in order that the child will have a sense of success and self-worth. Very often these children feel a sense of failure and their 'clumsy' behaviour can lead to them being bullied. Frustration and behavioural difficulties may arise from this. Sometimes children with dyspraxia will become the class 'clown' in the hope that others will laugh with them rather than at them.

Poor handwriting is a common symptom and exercises such as those suggested by Mary Nash-Wortham in *Take Time* and Ion Teodorescu and Lois Addy in *Write from the Start* can be useful.

For more information, see Nash-Wortham and Hunt (1997) and Teodorescu and Addy (1998). Details are in the Bibliography on page 412.

Children should have ready access to computers so that they can take pride in written work. Computers also help with reading and spelling and software such as WordShark can be effective tools.

Many children with dyspraxia have difficulties with reading and spelling as limited concentration and poor listening skills and literal use of language have an effect. A child may read well, but not understand some of the concepts in the language. They may be reluctant to read aloud because of articulation difficulties or because they lack self-confidence.

A child with dyspraxia will be late in reaching milestones such as rolling over, sitting, standing, walking and speaking. Strategies and resources should be put into place to assist the child with their fine and gross motor skills and in learning skills such as dressing, forming a correct pencil grip, running, hopping, catching and kicking a ball, doing jigsaws and sorting games.

Young children can be introduced to balancing and co-ordination activities through movement and play. The setting can seek advice from physiotherapists and occupational therapists as to activities for individual children. Most children will benefit from non-competitive activities which require them to improve on their own balancing and co-ordination skills, e.g. doubling the time they can stand on one leg.

Organisational skills will be poor and the older child will need help with these as well as with following instructions. Visual cues and other methods used with children on the autistic spectrum can be helpful, as can social skills groups as the child with dyspraxia often has difficulty in making friends and can appear anxious and distracted.

It is important as the child becomes older and enters secondary school that individual teachers are aware of the child's dyspraxia, in particular the PE teacher and the art teacher as these are two areas where the child's difficulties will be most obvious.

Dyslexia

Early intervention is most effective with dyslexia. The earlier a diagnosis is made and strategies put into place, the better. Multisensory methods and over-learning can help improve literacy skills. With older students the key to success is in improving skills and developing coping and compensatory strategies through an understanding of individual strengths and weaknesses.

Very often dyslexia is not recognised until the child begins to have difficulty with their literacy skills, often unexpected, as they can appear bright in other ways. Some common problems that people working with dyslexic children should recognise are that they may have difficulties in:

- remembering lists of instructions
- organising work
- writing down answers even though they may know them orally
- copying accurately
- writing neatly as their hand skills may be poor
- interpreting symbols if they have a visual memory deficiency.

They may spell the same word incorrectly but in different ways if they do not have a good visual memory, and they may have 'off' days which require extra encouragement and understanding. However common strengths include a good visual eye, good practical skills and excellent imagination.

Strategies

- Presenting material in a variety of ways, i.e. for visual, auditory and kinaesthetic learning styles, e.g. providing pictures, sounds and movements to aid memory retention. The Jolly Phonics programme for teaching sounds is a good example of a multisensory programme. Giving the child the opportunity to use a sand tray to trace letters is a kinaesthetic activity which gives sensory feedback which is important in memory retention.
- Use structured, cumulative and multisensory teaching techniques.
- Avoid asking dyslexic children to copy from a whiteboard. Their short-term memory difficulties will make this activity very difficult for them. Instead they should be given handouts which are clear and not cluttered, preferably in 14 pt Arial font. Alternatively a teaching assistant could scribe for the pupil.

Link
For learning styles, see Unit 18, page 198.

Cerebral palsy

Cerebral palsy is not progressive, i.e. it does not become more severe as the child gets older, although difficulties may become more noticeable. There is no cure for cerebral palsy.

If the children are positioned well from an early age and encouraged to move in a way that helps them to improve their posture and muscle control, they can be supported to develop and achieve more independence for themselves. Physiotherapists and occupational therapists will advise on the appropriateness of any arrangement for an individual child. They may need to show staff how to handle a child in a way that will help him develop the best possible control over his body, and prevent staff back strain or injury. However some key points include:

- Try not to move the child suddenly or jerkily as the muscles may need time to respond to changes in position.
- Do not force movements – let muscles tense and relax in their own time.
- Fear can make muscle spasms worse, so give the child as much support as he needs when you are handling him, being careful not to give him more support than he needs.
- Whatever his size or level of impairment, make sure that he spends time in different positions.
- Try to position the child so that he can see what is going on around him.
- Many physically disabled children are greatly advantaged by properly fitting and supportive seating.
- As a general rule, feet should be flat on the floor, knees bending at right angles, with hips firmly against the back of the seat. Some children will need chairs with arms.

Other difficulties and medical conditions may occur more commonly in people with cerebral palsy. However, just because a person has cerebral palsy does not mean that they will also have other difficulties. The setting would need to take into account any additional needs that a child may have. These may include:

- problems with constipation or sleeping – a doctor or health visitor should be able to offer advice on this
- toileting skills – the degree to which a child is ultimately able to be responsible for their own toileting needs will vary greatly between individuals. Some children, particularly those with severe or multiple impairments, may never achieve full independence in this area of their personal care

- speech and associated difficulties in chewing and swallowing – most children will use speech to communicate, but speech may be delayed or very difficult for a few children and they will need help to support communication. A speech aid might be the best way forward if it is clear that the child will find speaking very difficult, but any child can benefit from using pictures and symbols to support playing and learning. They may also have problems understanding the spoken word. A speech and language therapist will suggest the best way to help an individual child.

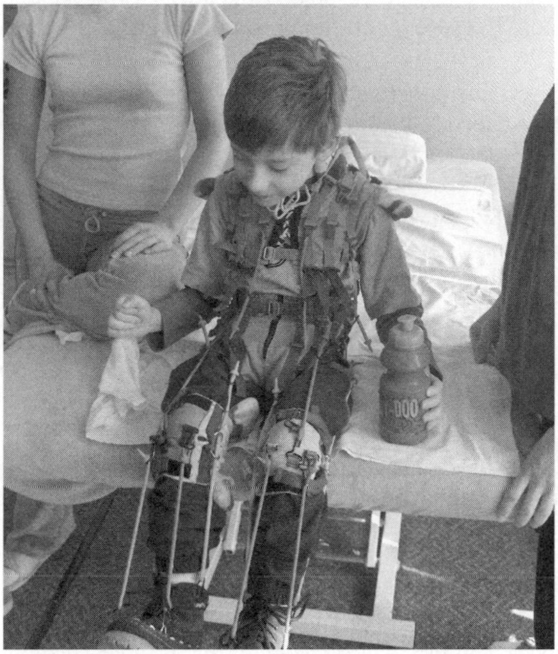

Fig 27.20 Child with cerebral palsy

- feeding difficulties – some children with cerebral palsy cannot suck, swallow or chew easily so eating may be messy. Rubber suction mats can be useful. It may take longer but it is important to take time to ensure that the child has a healthy diet. Staff can encourage a child to feed themselves or make choices about food and drinks. There are special cups and cutlery that might be helpful. Brushing teeth is particularly important when children have eating difficulties since food can easily get stuck in teeth and gums, and this can lead to decay and gum disease
- hearing difficulties – some children with cerebral palsy might be more prone to hearing difficulties
- epilepsy – usually this is well controlled with medication and the setting may only need a volunteer to administer it if the child stays all day. However, the medication might affect the child's behaviour, ability to concentrate or need to use the toilet and these possibilities should be discussed. Where children may have a seizure, staff need to feel confident, through discussion and training, that they are able to deal with it effectively
- distinguishing and comparing shapes – this is to do with visual or spatial perception, i.e. a person's ability to interpret what they have seen, and is not a problem with their eyesight. In the most severe cases these children may appear blind but many children can improve their useful vision with plenty of stimulation and support. Children may have difficulty with pictures, line drawings or writing. We all use spatial awareness to work out where we are in relation to objects and people around us. For some this is a problem. If a child is walking or using a wheelchair themselves, they may bump into things or move into spaces that are far too small. In bookwork they may find it difficult to 'see' an object or a picture in their heads and may need to use real objects for counting and other maths activities for longer than other children
- learning difficulties may be mild, moderate or severe – there may be a specific learning difficulty or problems with a particular activity such as reading, drawing or arithmetic because a specific area of the brain is affected
- a severe cognitive impairment – this means that they cannot reason well or understand their environment fully. Challenging behaviour can be a feature of this group especially when someone cannot communicate effectively.

remember

Even someone very severely affected by cerebral palsy may have average or above average intelligence.

Spina bifida

Toilet needs, mobility and access, specific health needs, continuation of programmes of care such as physiotherapy and occupational therapy and any special dietary requirements are amongst the care needs that you will need to be aware of when there is a child with spina bifida in the setting.

The specific care requirements for a child with spina bifida will depend on how severely affected the child is. This will depend on the position of the lesion – the higher in the spine the malformation is, usually the greater the effect. However, damage in the lower spine is more common. The severity of the condition also depends on how much damage there is to the spinal cord.

In any condition where there is a loss of movement and sensation, there may be pressure sores which you need to be aware of. Pressure sores or ulceration are caused in a child with paralysis who is unable to move about. Movement naturally prevents tissues being deprived of oxygen and sores developing.

Muscles and limbs that do not move of their own accord must be exercised by the carer. A physiotherapist may demonstrate exercises involving gently moving the muscles and joints that the child cannot move themselves, which the carer can follow. Carers will also need to be aware that a child who has lost sensation below the waist will have difficulty in controlling her bowel and bladder. Whatever method of management is used, e.g use of a catheter, the carer will need to support the child and learn about the techniques and help required. Encouraging the child to become independent in the management of bowels and bladder is very important. A high-fibre diet with plenty of fluids to prevent constipation is essential.

For a child who has paraplegia (no movement or sensation below the waist) mobility is primarily achieved through wheelchairs. Children who have more controlled movement may be helped by using crutches and frames. Occupational therapists and physiotherapists will be involved in deciding the most effective way of improving mobility and can advise the setting on how to ensure that the environment is wheelchair-friendly.

Becoming wheelchair proficient and being able to manage small steps and uneven surfaces with confidence are skills that will need teaching. While children with spina bifida are more dependent on their upper limbs (they need strength and power for controlling wheelchairs and crutches), some children are less skilful and dexterous manually than their peers. Activities to develop fine motor skills, e.g. manipulating Duplo, pegboards and playdough are recommended.

case study 27.10

Ayesha

The reception class includes Ayesha who has spina bifida. The teacher has requested that you run a series of activities using the role-play area. One of the targets on Ayesha's IEP is to improve her fine motor skills.

activity

What kind of activities could you introduce in the role play area to address this need?

Attention deficit hyperactivity disorder (ADHD)

Stimulant drugs such as methylphenidate (Ritalin) and dexamphetamine (Desadrine) are often prescribed for children diagnosed with ADHD. They work by stimulating those parts of the brain which control behaviour and regulate activity. The drugs therefore seem to help many children to concentrate and regain control over their actions. As children calm down, they are able to mix better with others and they can respond more effectively to teachers and parents. Children may become less aggressive as well as less hyperactive and their performance at school may improve significantly. It is important to recognise that medication does not cure ADHD, but it can provide a 'window of opportunity' in which children can be helped to manage their own behaviour with clear behaviour management strategies.

Behaviour management strategies that can be helpful to a child with ADHD include:

- arranging the classroom to minimise distractions as you would with a child on the autistic spectrum
- offering a variety of activities during each lesson, alternating physical and sitting-down activities
- setting short achievable tasks and giving immediate rewards when the child completes the task
- keeping class rules clear and simple
- using teacher attention and praise to reward positive behaviour
- giving the child special responsibilities so that other children can see them in a positive light.

Hearing impairment

When working with a child with a hearing loss, practitioners need to be aware of the physical environment, e.g. the pupil needs to be:

- sitting in a favourable position in the room, i.e. near and facing the teacher with the light falling on the teacher's face so that lip reading is possible
- able to see the faces of the other children in group work and classwork
- seated away from noisy areas such as windows and doors.

There needs to be good acoustic conditions in the classroom, i.e. carpet on the floor, curtains, low ceilings with acoustic tiles.

Practitioners need to remember to give audible and clear verbal directions, consider that the correct distance between themselves and the hearing impaired child is 4–6 feet for maximum use of hearing and lip-reading, and check that if a pupil has a hearing aid that is fitted and working correctly. Written material may need to be differentiated in language and presentation and contextual clues should be given throughout the lesson, e.g. main points and key words written on the board.

Visual impairment

Practitioners need to consider the physical environment in the classroom, e.g.

- The pupil needs to be suitably seated in relation to the light source, e.g. window, or to whiteboard or demonstrations.
- The whiteboard needs to have a clean, clear background and writing should be large and clear.
- The classroom should be orderly and reasonably predictable in layout of furniture.

Books and printed materials should be of good contrast with bold, dark letters, lines or figures against light matt background and the layout should be well-spaced with clear delineation. Some children will need texts enlarged and may benefit from coloured paper. It should also be remembered that if spectacles have been prescribed, they must be worn appropriately and properly cared for and kept clean. Audible and clear verbal directions and descriptions directed at the pupil by name should be given, with enough time to complete tasks and opportunities for hands-on experience.

Tourette's syndrome

Most people with Tourette's syndrome are not significantly affected by their behaviours and do not require medication. Relaxation techniques can help to alleviate the stress that can otherwise make tics worse. Behaviour therapies can teach the substitution of one tic for another that is more acceptable.

It is important that Tourette's syndrome is treated early and that people associated with the child with Tourette's understand that the actions and vocal utterances are involuntary. Tics can provoke ridicule and rejection by other children and adults. The child may be bullied, excluded from activities and prevented from enjoying normal relationships. These difficulties may become greater during adolescence.

School children with Tourette's syndrome, as a group, have the same IQ as the population at large. However, some may have special educational needs such as reading and writing difficulties, arithmetic difficulties and perceptual problems. If Tourette's is combined with ADD or ADHD, there will probably be a need for special educational assistance. This may perhaps be in the form of a teaching assistant, especially where the pupil is being educated in a mainstream school. The use of tape recorders and computers can be helpful for those with reading and writing problems. Permission to leave the classroom when tics become overwhelming can be helpful.

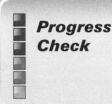

Progress Check

1. Give an example of a genetic condition that is caused by the presence of an extra chromosome.
2. What are the three areas of impairment that a child on the autistic spectrum would be affected by?
3. Give three examples of strategies that are effectively used in order that children with autistic spectrum disorder can access the school curriculum.
4. What are the three types of cerebral palsy?
5. Which areas of learning does dyslexia most commonly affect?
6. What does ADHD stand for?
7. What are the two main duties of the Special Needs and Disability Act 2001?
8. What does differentiation mean?
9. What is an IEP? At what stage of the Code of Practice do children have an IEP and what are the benefits for a child of having an IEP?
10. Give two examples of strategies that settings can use to support a child with low self-esteem.
11. What are the five outcomes of Every Child Matters?
12. What is the role of the Special Educational Needs Co-ordinator?
13. What does a Portage home tutor do?
14. What is the difference between the medical model of disability and the social model of disability?
15. What do you understand by the terms integration and inclusion?

UNIT 35

The Development and Care of Babies and Children under Three Years

This unit covers the following objectives:

- Understand and observe the expected sequence and development of babies and children in the first three years of life
- Know how to help provide physical care requirements for babies and children under three
- Understand how to provide play activities to encourage learning and development
- Understand how to communicate with babies and children under three, interpret their needs and respond to them

During the first three years of life, the human body develops at an incredible rate. This unit takes you from the helplessness of the newborn baby (the neonate) through to the active, investigative stage of the 3-year-old. Care routines such as feeding, bathing and clothing needs are covered here, together with play and its importance in development. The development of communication is discussed and reference is made to the use of and relevance of observation.

grading criteria

To achieve a **Pass** grade the evidence must show that the learner is able to:	To achieve a **Merit** grade the evidence must show that, in addition to the Pass criteria, the learner is able to:	To achieve a **Distinction** grade the evidence must show that, in addition to the Pass and Merit criteria, the learner is able to:
P1 Describe the development, including communication, of babies and young children in the first three years of life page 352		
P2 Outline what needs to be considered when observing babies and children in the first three years of life page 355	**M1** Explain how to undertake observations of babies and young children under three years page 355	**D1** Justify the use of observation of babies and young children in the first three years of life page 355
P3 Identify what can be learned through observation about babies and children in the first three years of life page 355		

To achieve a **Pass** grade the evidence must show that the learner is able to:	To achieve a **Merit** grade the evidence must show that, in addition to the Pass criteria, the learner is able to:	To achieve a **Distinction** grade the evidence must show that, in addition to the Pass and Merit criteria, the learner is able to:
P4 Describe the feeding and routine care of babies and young children under three years page 359	**M2** Explain how babies and young children under three years should be fed and cared for safely page 359	
P5 Identify five different play activities that help to support different aspects of learning and development page 382	**M3** Explain what is meant by challenge in play activities page 398	
P6 Describe the different methods used to communicate with babies and children under three years page 404	**M4** Explain how to interpret needs and respond to babies and young children page 401	**D2** Evaluate the range of methods used in communication with babies and children under three to ensure that understanding is taking place page 406

Understand and observe the expected sequence and development of babies and children in the first three years of life

Development

remember
Every child develops at an individual rate and there are many variations to what is considered normal.

In supporting the all-round **development** of young children, you will need to understand not only what each of the different areas of development are, and what the **maturational** pattern of development is for each of them, but you also need to be able to see how development areas link together, and how you will be supporting the development of the whole child with most of the activities you prepare, actions you take, and opportunities you provide.

Development is usually divided into the categories shown in Figure 35.1.

Fig 35.1 Development

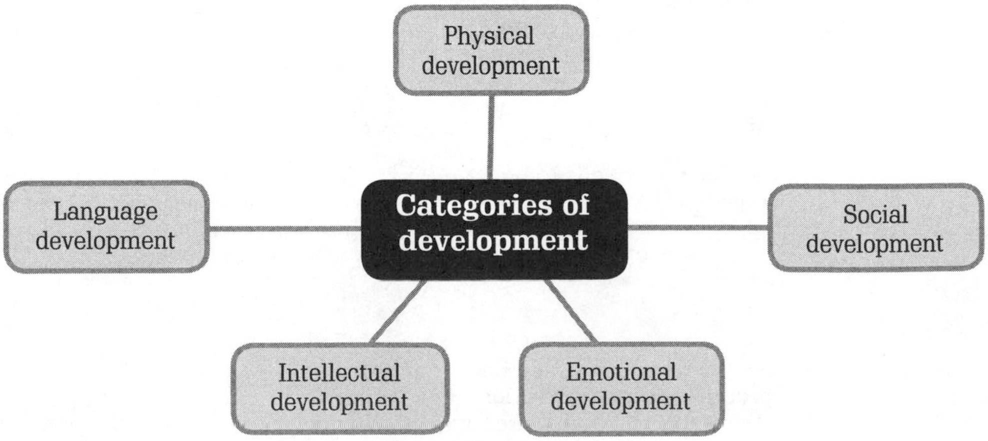

Sequence

As you read through this unit, development details are initially given for the neonate (the first month), and are then discussed under the headings in the diagram, dividing physical development into gross and fine skills, and combining social and emotional development together, and also intellectual and language development.

You will see how developmental progress is sequential, each stage building on the previous one, as skills are learned, consolidated and then developed further. You will also see how the physical development of muscle strength, etc. affects the development of physical control and how stimulation affects interest, curiosity and therefore learning.

Expected pattern of development

Physical development includes the primitive reflexes seen in newborn infants, as set out on page 328. It also involves motor development and manipulation. Motor development can be divided between locomotor skills and non-locomotor skills.

- Motor development
  - Locomotor skills involve the body moving forward in some way. Examples of this are walking, running, hopping.
  - Non-locomotor skills describe the physical movements that take place while stationary. Examples are bending, pulling, pushing.
- Manipulation involves actions using dexterity. Examples are throwing and catching a ball, threading cotton reels and placing one brick on top of another.

Physical skills can be gross (large) or fine. They include movement and balance, and can be either precise or carefree. Movement can involve the whole body or just one part of it.

Development becomes increasingly more complex and more difficult as it progresses. The maturational changes can be described as moving:

- from the simple to the complex – this means that a child learns simple actions, such as learning to stand, before learning the more complex actions of being able to walk
- from cephalo (head) to caudal (tail) – this can be defined as physical control starting at the head and gradually developing down through the body. For example, head control is attained before the spine is strong enough for an infant to sit unsupported, and sitting unsupported is attained before the child is able to stand
- from proximal (near to the body) to distal (the outer reaches of the body) – these terms refer to how a child develops actions near to the body before they develop control of the outer reaches of the body. For example, a child can hug and carry a large teddy bear (arm control) before they can fasten their clothing (finger control)

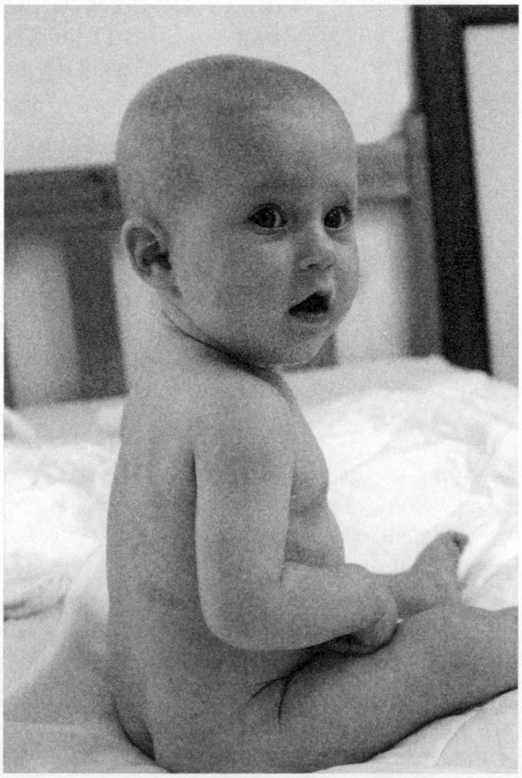

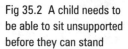

Fig 35.2 A child needs to be able to sit unsupported before they can stand

- from general to specific – the more generalised responses of an infant showing excitement when recognising a favourite carer gradually moves through to the facial smile of an older child on greeting the same person.

The normal neonate

The first month of life is known as the neonatal stage, and the infant is referred to as a **neonate**. Most infants are born at full term and thrive well, settling quickly into a routine with their mother and other carers.

This settling-in period involves many new experiences and the beginning of body processes not previously experienced. In the neonate these include breathing, circulation and digestion of new forms of nutrition (milk).

In the mother this includes the onset of lactation, healing from the trauma of birth and the resettling of the uterus. Each of these are normal processes, but each can also present problems.

Birth

Birth is a traumatic experience for both mother and child. The length of labour and the type of delivery can affect the level of distress experienced by the infant, and therefore how well they are at birth.

All infants are assessed immediately after delivery using a benchmark known as the **Apgar score** (Table 35.1). This is a process of assessment that was devised by Dr Virginia Apgar in 1953, which sets out the vital signs of initial health, indicating whether an infant needs resuscitation or any other form of medical treatment. The five features of the assessment are:

- heart rate – how fast is the infant's heart beating?
- respiration – how well is the infant breathing?
- muscle tone – does the infant appear limp and floppy?
- response to stimulus – does the infant respond when stimulated?
- colour – does the infant's skin colour indicate good circulation?

Each feature is scored after 1 minute, and then again at 5 minutes, continuing at 5-minute intervals as necessary until the infant is responding satisfactorily and the medical team are happy.

Table 35.1 The Apgar score chart

Sign	Score		
	0	1	2
Heart rate	Absent	Less than 100 beats per minute	More than 100 beats per minute
Respiration	Absent	Slow, irregular	Good, regular
Muscle tone	Limp	Some flexion of extremities	Active
Response to stimulus (stimulation of foot or nose)	No response	Grimace	Cry, cough
Colour	Blue, pale	Bluish extremities (body oxygenated)	Completely pink (well oxygenated)

The higher the infant scores, the less likely it is that they will need any treatment. Most healthy infants score nine at 1 minute. They often lose a score due to discoloration of their hands and feet. This is a common occurrence, and is due to their circulation not yet working fully. Infants who are pre-term, of a low birthweight or who have experienced a difficult delivery are more likely to have a lower Apgar score, and a score below five would indicate a very poorly baby. The infants who fall into this category make up a large percentage of those who do not survive or who will have ongoing problems.

A premature, difficult or traumatic birth, particularly if either mother or baby are ill and in need of special care, can also have an effect on the bonding process, due to separation and lack of physical contact, e.g. through the baby being placed in a neonatal care unit, often known as a special care baby unit (SCBU). Health professionals work hard to encourage and maintain links between mothers and their babies in these circumstances, as the bonding that would naturally occur at this time is a vital aspect of emotional development.

Link

Refer to Unit 14, page 114 for more on bonding.

What to expect to see in a neonate

At delivery babies are wet and covered to some degree in mucus, maternal blood and body fluids. Their skin colour will vary due to both their ethnic origin and their state of health, with black babies appearing pale at birth, as the skin pigmentation melanin does not reach its full levels until later on. Most infants are delivered on to their mother's abdomen, and the umbilical cord is clamped and cut shortly after birth. Depending on the type and duration of the delivery, infants vary from being alert and wide awake, to drowsy and unresponsive. Medication given to the mother during labour can have an effect on this.

Fig 35.3 The neonate

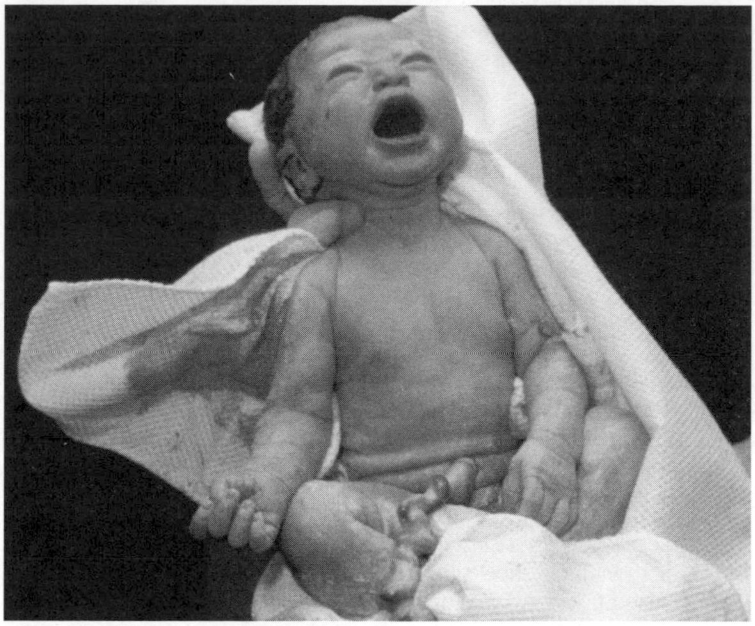

Sleep

At birth the infant will sleep most of the time, mostly waking for feeds and nappy changes. They often fall asleep during the process of these routines too. Sleep patterns change as the infant develops, gradually remaining awake for longer periods.

Head lag

There will be a lack of head control due to under-developed neck muscles, and support is needed during handling. This is often referred to as head lag.

Vernix caseosa

Vernix caseosa may be present. This is a creamy white protective substance, which covers the body of an infant during the latter stages of pregnancy. It is usually seen in pre-term infants, and is often present in full-term infants too. It lubricates the skin and should be left to come off on its own, rather than be washed or rubbed.

Lanugo

A soft, downy hair covering the infant while in the uterus may also be present. It is called lanugo and traces are often found on the back, shoulders and ears at birth.

Fontanelles

Fontanelles are areas of the skull where the bony plates of the skull meet. They enable some movement of the skull during the birth process.

There are two fontanelles on the infant's skull. The posterior fontanelle is a small triangular area near to the crown, which closes within a few weeks of birth. The anterior fontanelle is near the front of the head and is diamond-shaped. It usually closes over by 18 months of age and pulsates at the same rate as the infant's heartbeat.

Fontanelles giving a sunken appearance can indicate that the infant is not getting sufficient fluids, whereas a bulging appearance can indicate a high level of pressure around the brain, or an infection, and this should always be investigated.

Fig 35.4 Fontanelles

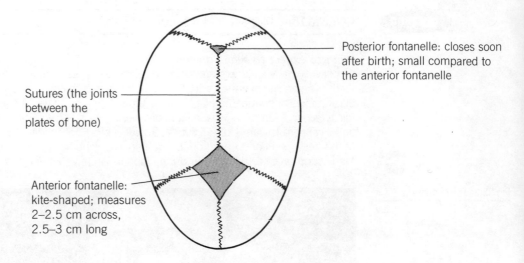

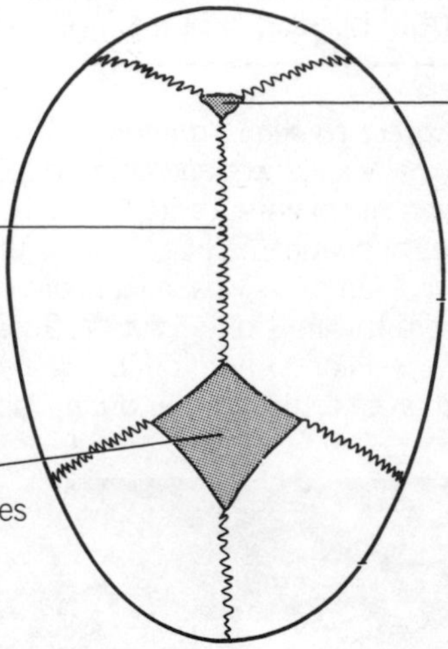

Mis-shapen skulls
Newborn infants often have a flattened or mis-shapen head due to the pressure of passing down the birth canal, or as a result of a forceps or a ventouse suction delivery. In a multiple birth it can occur due to lack of space and it can take some weeks for the natural shape of the skull to realign itself.

Umbilicus
The most well-known sign of the neonate is the umbilical 'stump'. The umbilical cord is clamped and cut at birth, and the clamp will be left to drop off on its own, usually seven to ten days after birth. The stump needs to be kept dry and clean, although actual cleaning of it is not usually recommended.

Swelling and bruising
Some infants show signs of swelling or bruising, normally due to a difficult birth. This tends to ease off within a few days.

Sticky eyes
Sticky eyes are common in the first few days and unco-ordinated eyes are usual. All babies are born with dark eyes and their permanent eye colour is not established until much later on.

Posture
The posture of infants is very flexed and movements tend to be jerky. The extremities (feet and hands) are often bluish in colour due to poor circulation. This soon settles down.

Genitals
Genitalia appear to be swollen in both boys and girls and blood loss from the vaginal area in girls is quite common. Both are caused by the mother's hormones crossing the placenta.

Breasts
The breasts of both boys and girls may be swollen and leak a little milk. Again, this is due to the mother's hormones crossing the placenta and can be seen regularly in both sexes.

Stools
The stools (faeces) of the neonate are a dark, greenish black. This is due to it containing a tarry substance called meconium, which is also very sticky. The colour and consistency of the stools changes within a few days, as the mother's milk comes in or formula feeding is established.

Spots and rashes
Spots and rashes are very common in the first few days but the infant's skin soon settles down. A particularly common type of spots are 'milia', which are tiny white spots often known as milk spots.

Peeling skin
Peeling skin is quite common on the hands and feet, but again this usually only lasts two or three days, and soon settles down.

Neonatal jaundice
Some infants suffer from **neonatal jaundice** where the skin and eyes become yellowish due to the infant's immature liver function and a subsequent rise in levels of bilirubin.

Fig 35.5 Breasts may be swollen and leak a little milk

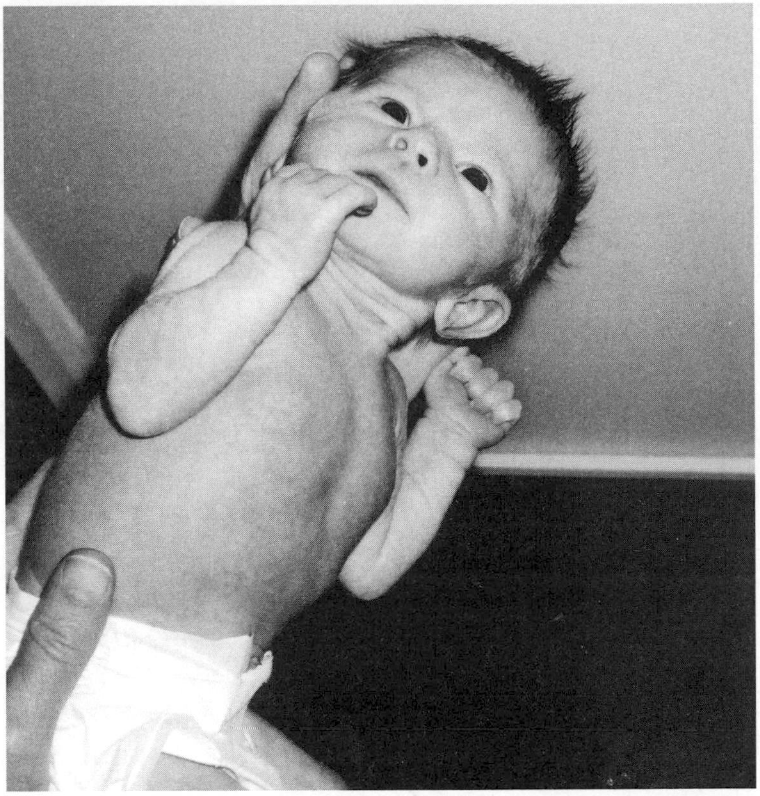

Bilirubin is formed when red blood cells break down and the liver is unable to cope with its workload. It usually occurs (if it is going to) on about day three after birth. Jaundice occurring before 3 days old needs particular investigation as liver disease or sepsis may be present and the infant's life could be in danger. On occasions, jaundice can be a sign of the condition galactosaemia (a metabolic disorder), rubella virus (German measles) or cytomegalovirus (herpes). Some infants with raised bilirubin levels require phototherapy, and some jaundice in breast-fed babies is normal. Liver function problems are monitored by nurses who check the colour of the stools and urine of each infant.

Birthmarks

There are various types of **birthmarks**, including:

- port wine marks – a permanent, dark red mark, often on the face or neck. In the past they were often a permanent disfigurement, but with modern-day technology many of these marks can now be successfully removed or depleted by laser treatment
- strawberry neavei – quite common. These are raised marks full of blood vessels. They are not actually present at birth, but develop in the first few days or weeks. They have usually disappeared by 8 years of age. The full name for this type of neavei is haemangioma

Fig 35.6 Birthmarks

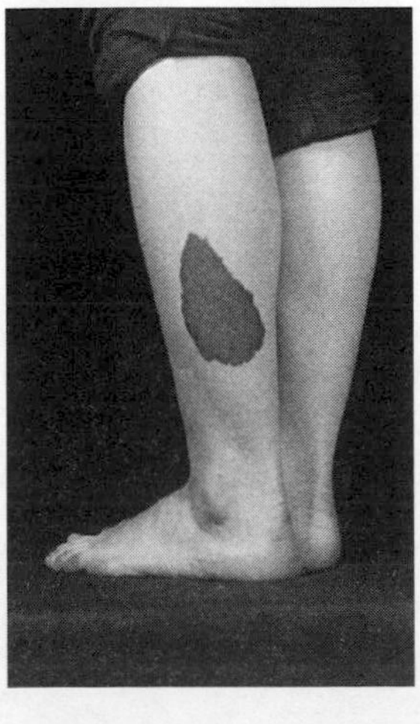

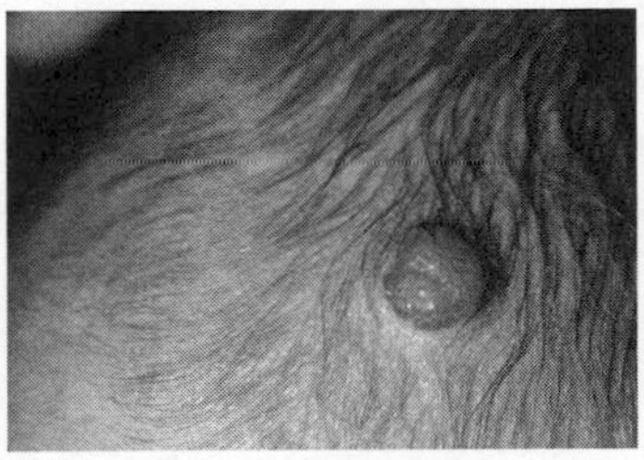

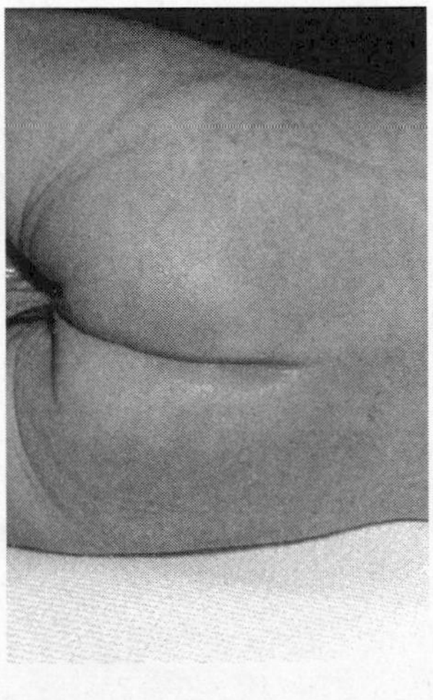

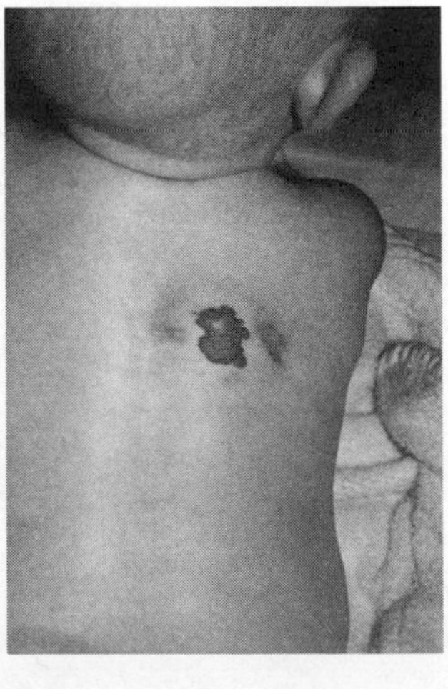

- stork bites – quite common. These are tiny red marks found on the eyelids, the top of the nose and on the back of the neck. They gradually disappear and are not usually a problem
- Mongolian blue spot – dark marks found at the base of the spine on non-Caucasian (non-white) infants. On occasions these marks have been wrongly attributed to physical abuse. They are usually 'mapped' by health professionals in the early weeks to prevent unfounded concerns being raised. Early years workers need to be aware of these marks
- moles – Most people have moles, but some moles can be large and unsightly, for example CMNs (congenital melanocytic naevus). These moles get progressively darker as the infant grows, but they can sometimes be successfully removed or depleted with laser treatment or plastic surgery.

fig 35.7 Rooting reflex

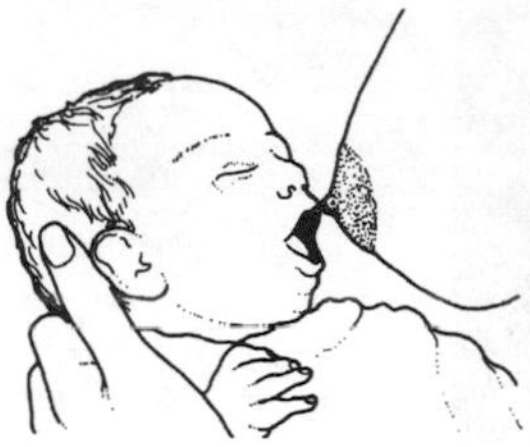

Primitive reflexes

Physically the neonatal stage includes the primary **reflexes**, the infant's posture, gross movements, visual and other sensory responses. The term 'primary reflexes' means 'automatic body reactions to specific stimulation' (Bee, 1992, page 105).

These reflexes include:

- blinking reflex – the neonate reacts to sudden lights, noises or movements in front of the eyes
- rooting reflex – this is where the neonate turns their face towards their mother to locate the breast.
- sucking reflex – infants will usually suck a clean finger, placed gently in their mouth

Fig 35.8 Sucking reflex

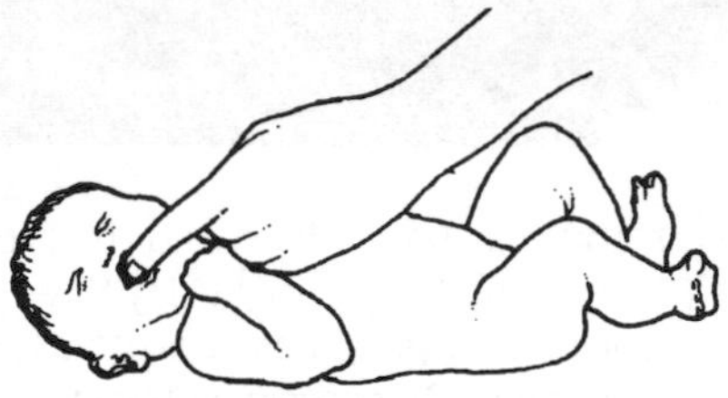

- palmar grasp reflex – the infant holds firmly to whatever touches the palm of their hand (gently stroking the back of the hand will usually release the grasp)

Fig 35.9 Palmar grasp

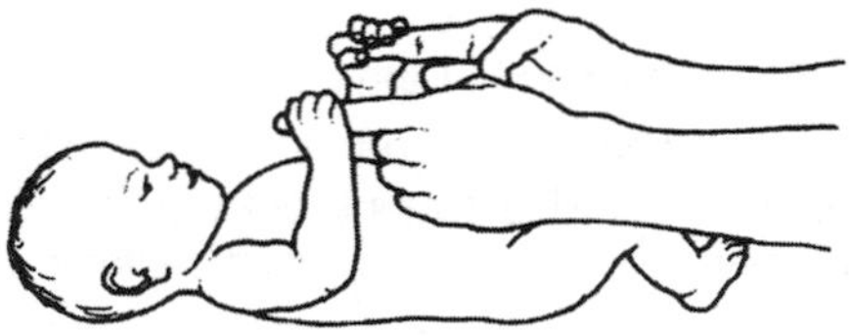

- plantar reflex – touching the sole of the infant's foot with a finger will result in the flexing of their toes towards your finger

- stepping reflex – the neonate's foot responds to contact with a firm surface, resulting in a small 'step' being taken

Fig 35.10 Stepping reflex

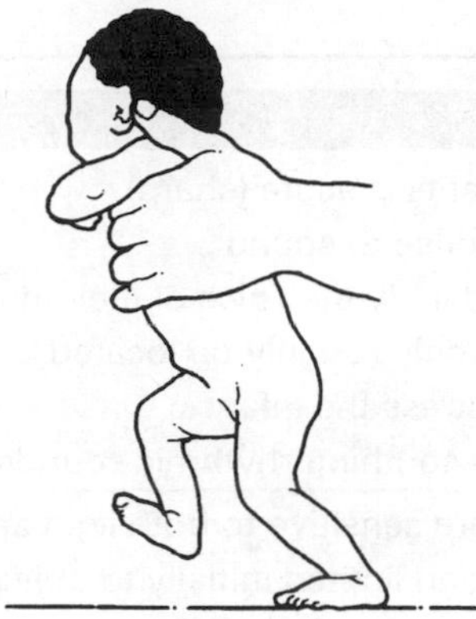

- moro reflex – a sudden movement of the neck is interpreted by the infant as falling. They will throw out their arms with open hands and reclasp them over their chest

Fig 35.11 Moro reflex

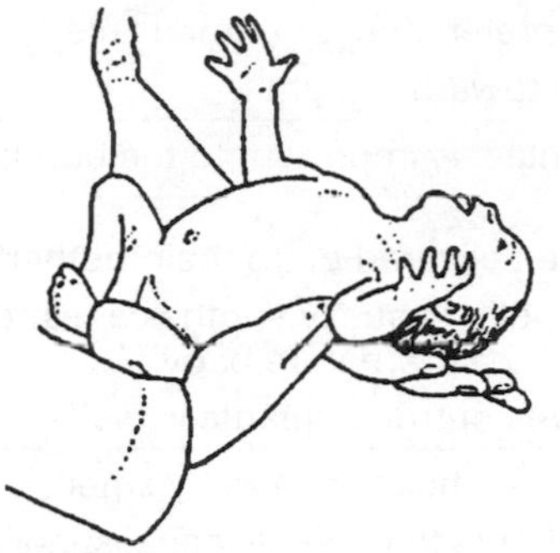

Fig 35.12 Startle reflex

- startle reflex – again the infant throws out their arms at a sudden noise or movement, but the fists remain clenched
- asymmetric tonic neck reflex – when the infant's head is turned to one side, they will respond by straightening the arm and leg on the same side, while flexing the limbs opposite.

Some reflexes stay with us for life, e.g. blinking, but some are lost after the first few weeks (the **primitive reflexes**). The presence of reflexes is an indicator of how well an infant's nervous system is functioning (their neurological well-being). As the brain gradually takes over the body's responses, these primitive reflexes disappear. If the primitive reflexes are still present for longer than is considered usual (they start to diminish at 6 weeks, to be replaced by more deliberate actions), it can indicate that there is a developmental problem with the infant, which may need to be investigated. Their progress will be monitored, together with the usual planned screening procedures.

All infants are usually assessed by a doctor at 6 weeks of age.

The senses

The senses in a neonate are described in Table 35.2.

Table 35.2 The senses in a neonate

Sense	Description
Hearing	■ The hearing of infants is acute (sharp) ■ They blink in response to sound ■ The neonate can identify the voice of their main carer almost immediately ■ Noisy objects can only roughly be located ■ Sudden noises distress the infant ■ Infants respond to soothing rhythmic sounds
Vision	■ Newborn infants are sensitive to both light and sound ■ Vision is diffused and limited initially to objects within about a ■ 30 cm (12 inch) radius ■ Eyes initially do not work together and they will often 'cross' or 'wander' ■ Eye-to-eye contact with the main carer (usually the mother) is an important means of establishing a bonding relationship ■ Infants show a preference for human faces ■ Infants will turn towards a light
Touch	■ Skin-to-skin contact is important to the bonding process, and for breast feeding ■ Most infants are delivered on to their mother's abdomen ■ Contact and handling usually soothes a distressed infant, but may be less welcomed by a premature baby ■ The temperature control of infants is ineffective
Smell	■ Infants can identify their mothers by smell ■ Research has shown that infants can distinguish their mother's milk on a breast pad

Physical development 0–3 years

At birth the infant will sleep most of the time, mostly waking for feeds and nappy changing, and often falling asleep during the process of these routines. Sleep patterns change with the infant gradually remaining awake for longer periods as they develop.

There will be a lack of head control due to under-developed neck muscles and support is needed during handling to ensure that no damage is caused or undue strain placed on the neck muscles.

All babies are born with dark eyes and permanent eye colour is not established until much later on.

The posture of infants is very flexed and movements tend to be jerky. The extremities (feet and hands) are often bluish in colour due to poor circulation.

Posture and motor skills

Immediately after birth, many infants naturally curl into the foetal position with their heads to one side.

Limbs are kept partly flexed and are hypertonic (have tension), and they tend to display jerking movements. The head and neck are hypotonic (weak) and there is no head control, so full support of the head and neck area is needed whenever the infant is handled.

Acceptable range

Throughout childhood **growth** is rapid, being particularly so during the first year, with a steadier rate developing from the toddler stage onwards. Infants and young children are measured using the **centile charts** (see below). These charts enable health visitors and paediatricians (doctors specialising in the care of babies) to monitor development, and to identify any causes for concern in babies' growth rates. Slight differences in the growth expectations of girl infants and boy infants are expected, with boys, on average, being slightly heavier than girls at birth. The 50th centile line is the central line on the centile chart. It indicates what the average is at each age. The upper and lower lines represent the boundary within which 80 per cent of children will fall. A child who falls outside of these boundaries will be monitored more closely and may need further investigation into their development at some stage.

The pattern (or line) formed as a child's measurements are plotted on the centile chart is known as a 'growth curve'.

In the centile charts below, you can see that there are slight differences between the expectations for girls compared to the expectations for boys.

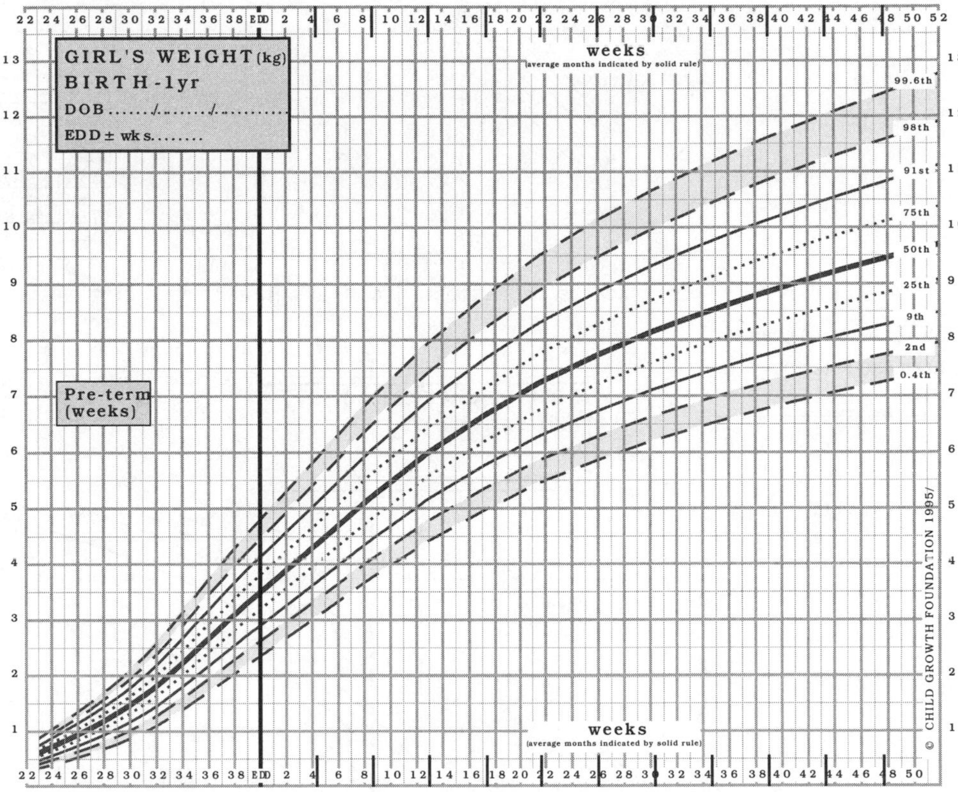

Fig 35.13 A centile chart for the weight of a baby girl

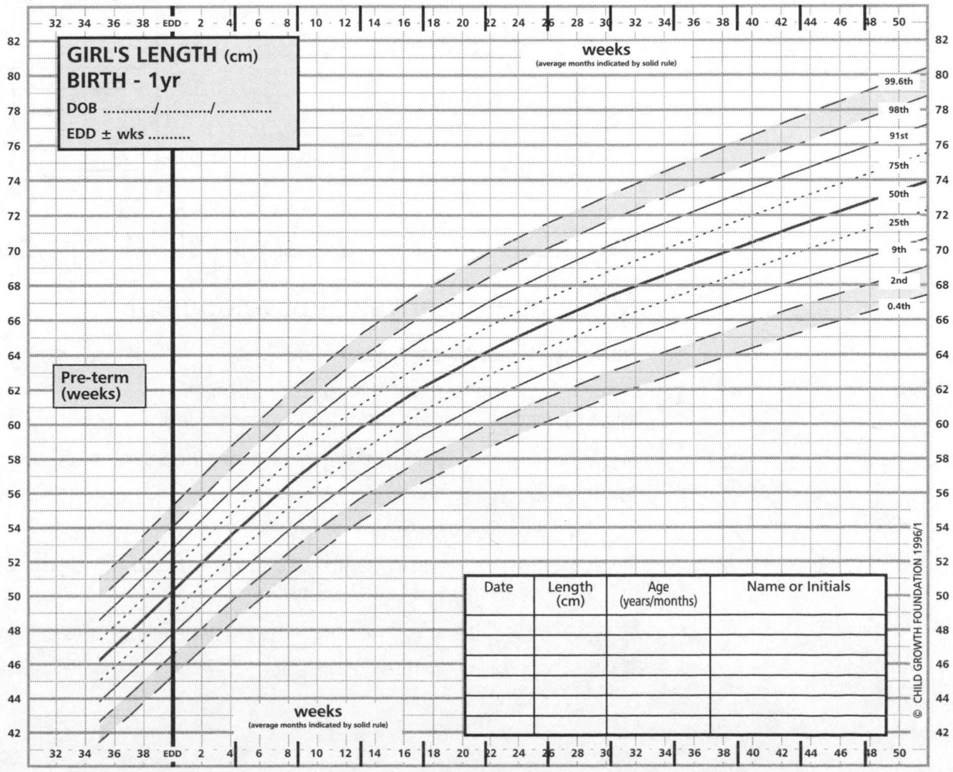

Fig 35.14 A centile chart for the length of a baby girl

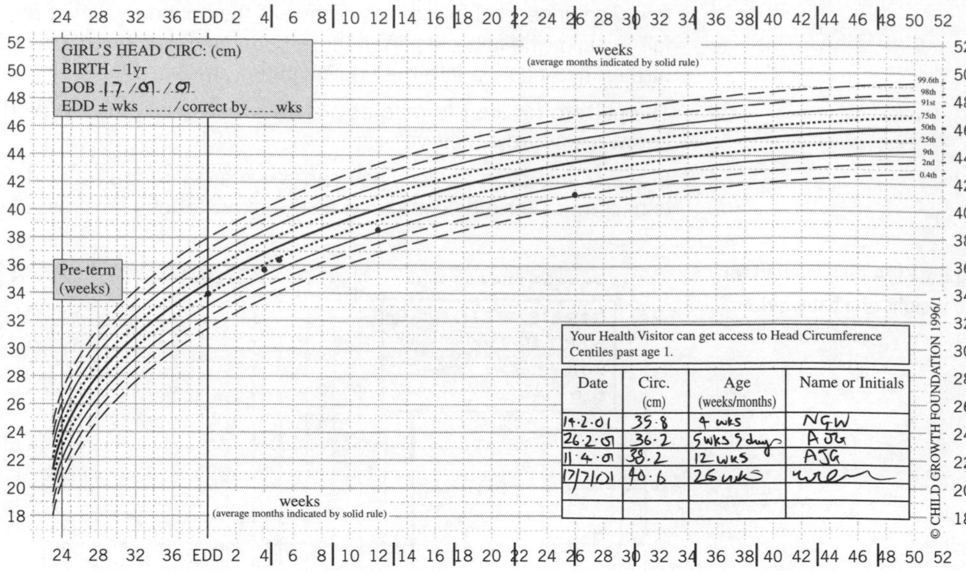

Fig 35.15 A centile chart for the head circumference of a baby girl

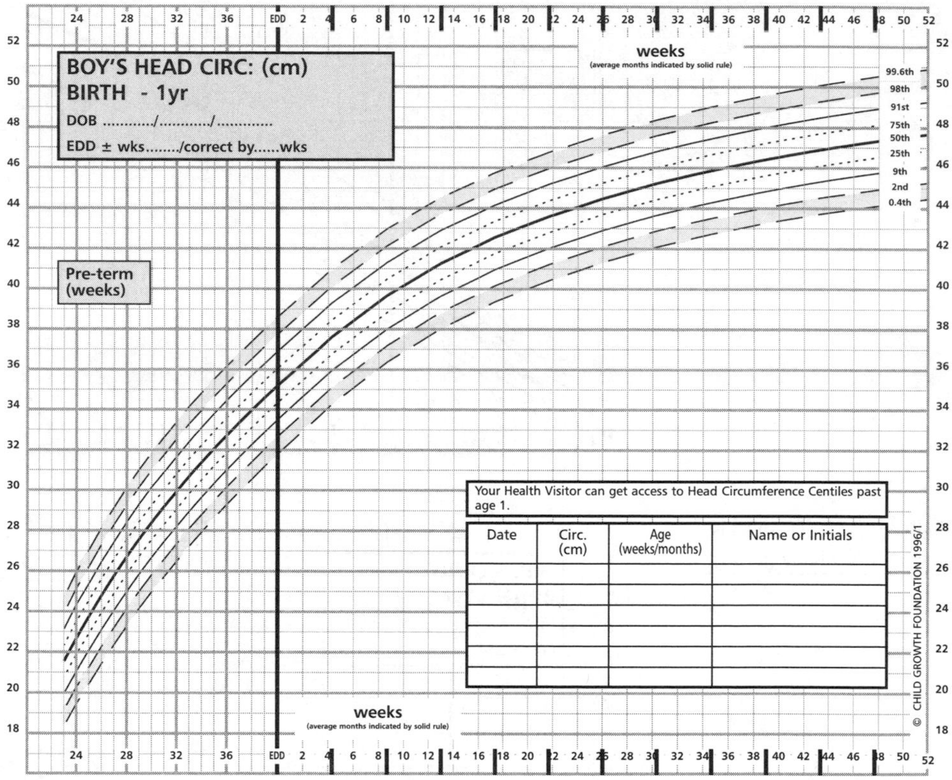

Fig 35.16 A centile chart for the head circumference of a baby boy

Milestones of physical development

Infancy: 1 month to 1 year

A summary of physical skills (gross motor)

- Movements remain jerky and uncontrolled.
- Head lag gradually decreases and head control is usually achieved by 5 months.
- Rolling over is first seen between 4 and 6 months (from back to side), and then from front to back by about 8 months.
- Reaching for objects begins at about 4 months with the ability to pass toys from hand to hand seen from about 7 months.
- At 4 months the infant discovers their own feet and manages to sit with support.
- Sitting alone commences at about 7–8 months, with gradually greater balance developing.

- Crawling can start from 6 months (commando crawling) and traditional crawling from about 8 months. Some infants bear-walk or bottom-shuffle.
- Some infants miss out the crawling stage, and move straight to pulling themselves up on furniture at around 8–10 months.
- Standing alone can occur any time from 10 months, but is more usual at around a year, when generally balance is more established.
- Walking is normally achieved by 12–16 months.

Fig 35.17 Traditional-style crawling usually starts from around 8 months

A summary of physical skills (fine motor)

- Hand and finger movements gradually increase, from the grasping of adults' fingers in the earliest months, through to playing with own fingers and toes, handling and then holding toys and objects from 3–4 months.
- Everything is explored through the mouth.
- At about 7 months, the infant will try to transfer objects from one hand to the other with some success. Pincer grasp (index finger and thumb) is emerging.
- By about 10 months, pincer grasp is developed.
- The infant will pick up small objects.
- Toys are pulled towards the infant.
- Pointing and clapping are deliberate actions for most infants by 10–12 months.
- Controlled efforts when feeding, with some successes.

Fig 35.18 At around a year, balance is quite well established

Toddler: 1 to 2 years

A summary of physical skills

- Standing alone is achieved but they are unable at first to sit from being in a standing position without help. They begin to let themselves down in a controlled manner from about 15 months.
- When walking, hands are held up for balance and the infant's steps are uneven, and they have difficulty in stopping once they have started.
- They can creep upstairs on hands and knees quite safely (not advisable without an adult supervising).
- They begin to kneel.
- By 18 months walking is usually well established, and the arms are no longer needed for balance. The toddler can now back into a small chair, and climb forwards into an adult chair.
- Squatting when playing is now common.
- They can usually walk upstairs holding an adult hand.
- Manipulative skills are developing. Pages of books can usually now be turned quite well, and pencils can be held in a clumsy (primitive) grasp.
- By 2 years the child can usually run safely, starting and stopping at will.
- They are able to pull wheeled toys, with some understanding of direction.
- They are usually able to control a ball to throw forwards.
- Walking up and (usually) down stairs, holding on, two feet to a stair.
- They cannot yet kick a football without falling into it, losing their balance as they kick their foot forward.
- They cannot usually pedal a tricycle.

Fig 35.19 Clumsy (primitive) grasp

Aged 2 to 5 years

A summary of physical skills

- Walking up stairs with alternating feet is usually achieved by 3 years. Up and down on alternate feet is securely seen by 3½.
- At 2½ a child can kick a football gently; by 3 years with force.
- Pushing and pulling of large toys is achieved by 2½.
- Locomotor skills (movement forwards, backwards and so on) improve rapidly during this stage of development.
- Use of pedals is often achieved by 3 years, and a child can steer around corners.
- Balance gradually improves and by 4 years a child can usually stand, walk and run on tip-toes, and navigate skilfully when active.
- From 3 years ball skills increase, catching, throwing, bouncing and kicking.
- Manipulative skills (the ability to use their hands and fingers in a controlled manner) improve.
- Scissor control is developing and greater pencil control is achieved by 3 years.
- By 4 years threading small beads and early sewing is achieved.
- Adult pencil control is usually present by 4 years.

Milestones of social and emotional development

Infancy: 1 month to 1 year

A summary of social and emotional development

- The first social smile is usually seen by 6 weeks.
- Smiling is first confined to main carers, and then in response to most contacts.
- The infant concentrates on faces of carers.
- Pleasure during handling and caring routines is seen by 8 weeks, through smiles, cooing and a general contentment.
- Expressions of pleasure are clear when gaining attention from about 12 weeks and in response to the main carers' voices.
- Social games, involving handling and cuddles gain chuckles from 4–5 months onwards.

- Infants enjoy watching other infants.
- Sleep patterns begin to emerge from about 4 months onwards, although these will continue to change.
- From about 9 or 10 months the infant may become distressed when the main carer leaves them, temporarily losing their sense of security and becoming wary of strangers. This is a normal stage in development.
- Playing contentedly alone increases by 1 year, but the reassuring presence of an adult is still needed.

Fig 35.20 The infant concentrates on the face of her parent/carer

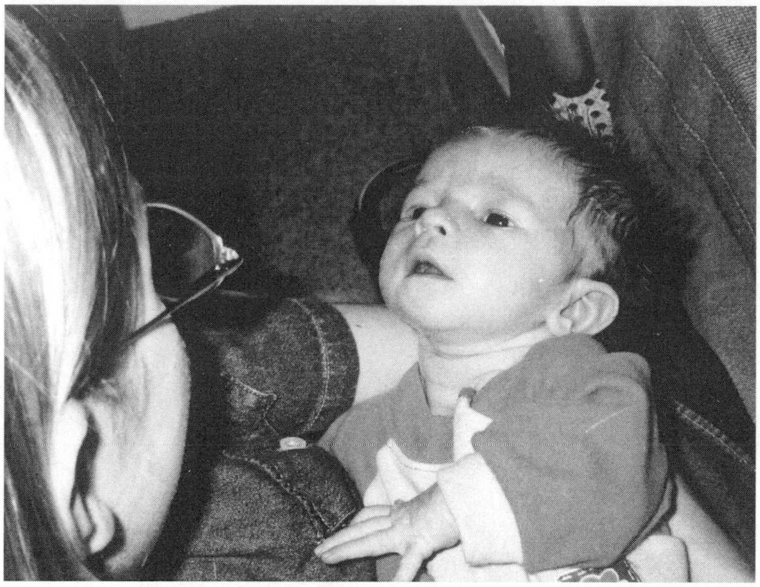

Aged 1 to 2 years

A summary of social and emotional development

- By about 15 months the child will usually indicate a wet or soiled nappy.
- They co-operate (help) with dressing, e.g. holding up arms for a jumper.
- They are dependent on an adult's presence for reassurance.
- Frustration is shown at not being able to achieve their aim – perhaps putting two bricks together, leads to toys being discarded in anger.
- By 18 months feeding self with a spoon is usually very successful.
- The child can confidently handle a cup, but does not put it back down (gives it to adult).
- They remove hats, shoes, etc. but can rarely replace them.
- They make urgent vocalisations when making a demand.
- Bowel control is sometimes attained by 18 months and is usually attained by 2 years.
- By 2 years the child will play parallel alongside others without actually interacting.
- They can be rebellious and resistive and get frustrated when trying to make themselves understood. Can be easily distracted from their tantrums at this age.
- Having no idea of sharing is both common and normal, and no understanding of the need to defer their wishes.
- They follow adult around. Need reassurance when tired or fearful.
- By 2 years they can usually put on hat and shoes, and can reposition a cup on a surface.

Aged 2 to 5 years

A summary of social and emotional development

- At 2½ tantrums are common when needs are thwarted. A child is less easily distracted from them now.
- They are very resistive of restraint, e.g. when having a hand held in a busy shop.
- Mostly they still watch others or play parallel. Occasionally they join in briefly.

- By 4 years a child can eat skilfully and can dress, wash and clean their teeth (with supervision).
- This is a generally more independent age with many children wanting to try things on their own.
- They co-operate with others but can also be unco-operative if wishes are refused.
- They can be very strong-willed.
- At 5 years behaviour is noticeably more sensible and controlled.
- They understand sharing, turn-taking and the need for fair play.
- Co-operative play is constant at 5 years.
- They choose their own friends and play well, and are very protective towards younger children, pets and distressed playmates.

Intellectual and communication skills

As well as physical growth and development, which can be observed and measured quite easily, children develop their knowledge and understanding too. This is often referred to as intellectual (or cognitive) development. The development of knowledge and understanding is closely linked with the development of language and communication skills, and it involves the senses too.

At birth, the infant's nervous system is incomplete and understanding their level of sensory awareness is not easy. It has been established by researchers that an infant's system for vision is not initially strong, but that it develops considerably in the first few months, whereas an infant's hearing is quite well developed right from birth.

Sensory development

The main areas of sensory development studied are vision, hearing and perception.

Visual development

From birth infants turn to look at sources of light. They show an interest in the human face, and researchers (particularly Robert Fantz in the 1950s) have repeatedly shown that the human face receives a greater response than other similar options, e.g. a 'head' with facial features muddled up.

Fig 35.21 Fantz's faces

Within a few days of birth, babies can demonstrate both spontaneous and imitative facial expressions, and the eyes of the newborn infant can at times be seen to move in the direction of sounds. These early visual interactions (eye contacts) between the infant and their carer strengthen the process of bonding and therefore enhance their emotional security.

The stages of visual development are shown in Table 35.3.

Fig 35.22 A newborn infant making eye contact

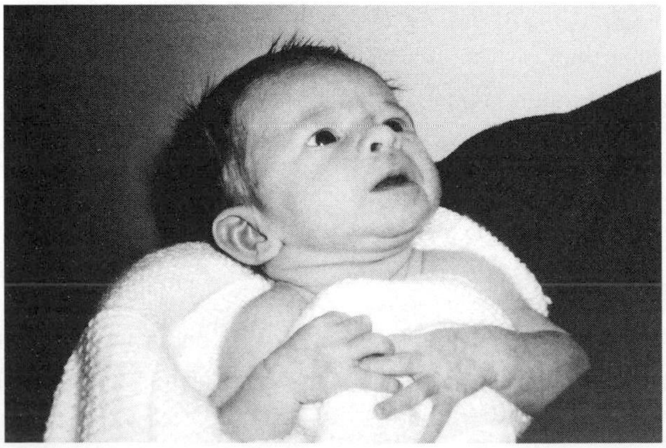

Table 35.3 Stages of visual development

Age	Development of vision
Birth	■ Infant turns to the source of light. ■ Imitative facial expressions are seen, e.g. poking out the tongue. ■ The human face gains the greatest level of an infant's attention. ■ An infant's eyes do not at first move co-operatively.
1 month	■ Infant turns to light source. ■ Staring at face of an adult carer is usual. ■ The eyes are now usually working in co-operation. ■ Vision is held by a bright mobile or similar object. ■ The infant can visually track their mother's face briefly.
3 months	■ The eyes move in co-operation. ■ A defensive blink has been present for some time. ■ The infant follows the movement of main carer. ■ A more sustained visual tracking of face or similar. ■ Infant may now be demonstrating visual awareness of their own hands.
6 months	■ Infant is visually very alert. ■ Infants appear visually insatiable (their eyes fix on anything and everything). ■ Their eyes and head move to track objects of interest.
12 months	■ Hand–eye co-ordination is seen as small objects are picked up using pincer grasp (index finger and thumb). ■ The infant's eyes follow the correct direction of fallen or dropped objects.

Based on Sheridan (1991)

A checklist for visual development

Concerns regarding vision include:

- lack of eye contact with main carer
- no social smile by 6 weeks
- lack of visual tracking of carer's face or bright mobile by 2 months
- lack of visual response to breast or bottle feed
- lack of co-operative eye movement after 3 months
- lack of signs that infant reaches out for toys in response to visual stimulus
- lack of mobility or directed attention by 12 months.

Auditory development

At birth, the hearing of infants is acute (sharp), as their auditory perception (sense of hearing) is not yet cluttered by the sounds of everyday living. They can often be seen responding to sound by blinking and through startled movements (the startle reflex). Newborn infants respond to the sound of their mother or main carer. They also show signs of auditory awareness by turning towards other sounds. Many infants are settled by calming or familiar music, often first heard within the safety of the womb.

Stages in **auditory development** are given in Table 35.4.

Table 35.4 Stages of auditory development

Age	Development of hearing
Birth	■ Startle reactions to sound is normal. ■ Blinking is common in response to ongoing gentle sounds. ■ The infant turns to sounds, including their mother's voice.
1 month	■ Infant is still startled by sudden noises. ■ They stiffen in alarm, extending their limbs. ■ They usually turn to sound of a familiar voice. ■ Also usually calmed by the sound of a familiar voice.
3 months	■ The infant turns head or eyes towards the source of sounds. ■ They often appear to search for location of sounds. ■ They listen to musical mobiles and similar sounds.
6 months	■ They now show considerable interest in familiar sounds. ■ Infant turns to locate even very gentle sounds. ■ Now vocalises deliberately, listening to self. ■ Infant vocalises to get attention, listens and then vocalises again. ■ Infant can usually imitate sounds in response to carers.
12 months	■ Now responds to own name. ■ Infant's behaviour indicates hearing, by appropriate response to carers.

Based on Sheridan (1991)

A checklist for auditory development

Concerns regarding hearing include:

- lack of response to sudden or loud noises in first few months
- lack of response to familiar sounds, either by listening or by being calmed
- no tracking of gentle sounds by 9 months
- no indication of turning to the sound of familiar voice
- limited changes in vocalising from about 6 months
- no obvious response to carers' simple instructions at 1 year.

From 1 year onwards, the development of speech is the greatest indication of how well a child hears, although health problems such as glue ear or repeated ear infections can have an effect on hearing.

Infant perception in general

Perception is the organisation and interpretation of information received from the sensory organs. It helps us to understand all that is happening both to us and around us. Even very young babies can perceive some features of their environment, such as familiar smells and textures, e.g. their mother's skin. Visual perception and auditory perception are two early indicators that development is progressing as expected. Vision and hearing link directly with language and cognition (understanding), and are both assessed specifically at regular intervals during infancy and early childhood.

case study 35.1

Kos

Kos is 6 months old, and his parents are concerned that he doesn't seem to respond to his environment in the way his older brother did at a similar age.

Kos smiles a lot and visually tracks people, and also toys if shown them first. He makes very little noise apart from crying when his needs are not being met, mostly making cooing sounds.

activity

1 Do you think Kos' parents are right to be concerned?
2 If yes, what would concern you about Kos' progress?
3 How would you expect Kos to be responding at this stage?

Milestones of intellectual development

Birth to 1 year

- The infant's main source of learning is to explore orally (with their mouth) throughout most of the first year. Jean Piaget (a psychologist) called this the sensorimotor stage.
- By about 4 months, recognition of an approaching feed is demonstrated by excited actions and squeals.
- By 9–10 months, the infant achieves what Piaget called object permanence. They know that an object exists even if it has been covered up. For example, they pull a cover off a teddy they have seen hidden to 'find' it again.
- The understanding of simple instructions or statements begins from about 9 months, and this is clearly evident by 1 year old, for example, 'Wave bye bye to Daddy'.

Link

See Unit 14, page 103, for information about Piaget.

Fig 35.23 The infant's main source of learning is to explore orally

1 to 2 years

- Toddlers of this age are very curious, and they investigate everything they can.
- They are interested in all that happens around them.
- A precise pincer grasp (index finger and thumb) is seen now.
- They enjoy putting objects into containers.
- They take toys to their mouths less often now.
- They enjoy activities that need fitting together, e.g. simple construction or a 'build up' clown.
- They will place an object on another – a two-object tower.

Fig 35.24 A busy toddler

2 to 3 years

- From 2 years they rarely take toys to mouth.
- Brief imitation is seen of everyday activities, e.g. the feeding of a doll.
- They are usually content to play alone.
- Simple role play is demonstrated.
- They can build six to eight objects into a tower.
- They can follow simple instructions, for example, 'Fetch your shoes please'.
- They can succeed with simple jigsaw puzzles.
- Vertical and horizontal lines are drawn.

3 to 5 years

- Children of this age can usually draw a person with the main details.
- Role play is frequent and detailed by 5 years of age.
- Floor play is very complex; cars, train sets, farms, and so on.
- Understanding of time, linked to routine is emerging, e.g. they begin to understand that they will be picked up from pre-school after the singing has finished.

Language development

As with every aspect of development, children develop language at differing rates within what is considered to be the normal range. This process of language development can be divided into ten basic stages. They are:

1. Non-verbal communication/expression
2. Speech-like noises
3. Controlling sounds, using mouth and tongue
4. Imitating sounds
5. First words
6. Development of vocabulary (50 words is usual at 2 years)
7. Putting words together to form simple phrases and sentences
8. Use of grammar
9. Use of meaning
10. Using language to develop other skills, e.g. early literacy.

Table 35.5 Stages of language development

Age	Understanding	No. of words	Type of words	Average length of sentence
3 months	Soothed by sound	0	Cooing and gurgling	0
6 months	Responds to voice tones	0	Babble	0
12 months	Knows own name and a few others	1	Noun (naming word)	1 word
18 months	Understands simple commands	6–20	Nouns +	1 word
2 years	Understands much more than they can say	50+	Verbs and pronouns (action + name)	1–2 word phrases
2½ years	Enjoys simple and familiar stories	200+	Pronouns: I, me, you Questions: What? Where?	2–3 word phrases
3 years	Carries out complex commands	500–1000	Plurals Verbs in present tense Questions: Who?	3–4 word phrases
4 years	Listens to long stories	1000–1500	Verbs in past tense Questions: Why? Where? How?	4–5 word sentences
5 years	Is developing the ability to reason	1500–2000	Complex sentences with adult forms of grammar	

Speech sounds

Speech sounds in the English language are made up of consonants and vowels. The approximate sequential development of consonants in the English language is:

- 2 years – m, n, p, b, t, d, w
- 2½ years – k, g, ng (as in sing), h
- 2½–3 years – f, s, l, y
- 3½–4 years – v, z, ch, j, sh
- 4½ years onwards – th (as in thin), th (as in the), r.

Double consonants such as sp, tr and fl and also the sounds r and th, can develop as late as 6½ years in some children.

Link

See also the section on communicating, pages 398–407.

Nature–nurture theory

One of the fiercest debates regarding development has been whether it is influenced by nature, or through nurturing. Theorists who believe in influences of nature are known as nativists. Those who put forward theories about nurturing are known as empiricists.

Nature

Nativists believe that children are born ready to achieve whatever they achieve. They believe that a child's genetic make-up influences both behaviour and learning.

Nurture

Empiricists believe that the environment into which a child is born, together with the way they are raised and guided by parents and carers, is the main influence.

Today, most people agree that a combination of both nature and nurture influence the overall development of a child. Biological factors such as chromosome make-up and dominant and recessive genes determine the physical characteristics of each individual, and these factors in turn influence the achievements and choices each individual makes.

Link

Refer also to Unit 14 , page 98 for more on the nature–nurture debate.

Professional Practice

- It can be helpful to think about the factors that have influenced your own development. Which were due to nature, and which were due to nurture?

activity
INDIVIDUAL WORK 35.1
P1

Explain the different aspects and stages of development, describing what stage you would expect a child to have reached by at least two of the following ages:

3 months

6 months

12 months

2 years

3 years.

Frameworks for effective practice

The development of children from birth to three years has been specifically supported through government guidelines through the **Birth to Three Matters** strategy, which was divided into four main aspects, as illustrated below in fig 35.25. It has now been superseded by the Early Years Foundation Stage (EYFS) which incorporates the support of development from 0 to 5 years, as shown in fig 35.25(a). The EYFS sets out children's development in six overlapping are brackets, as a useful guide. These are ;

0–11 months

8–20 months

16–26 months

22–36 months

30–50 months

40–60+ months

The EYFS will become mandatory from September 2008 with many early years settings working with it since 2007.

Professional Practice

- You will be able to note many obvious links between both frameworks.

Fig 35.25 The four aspects of Birth to Three Matters

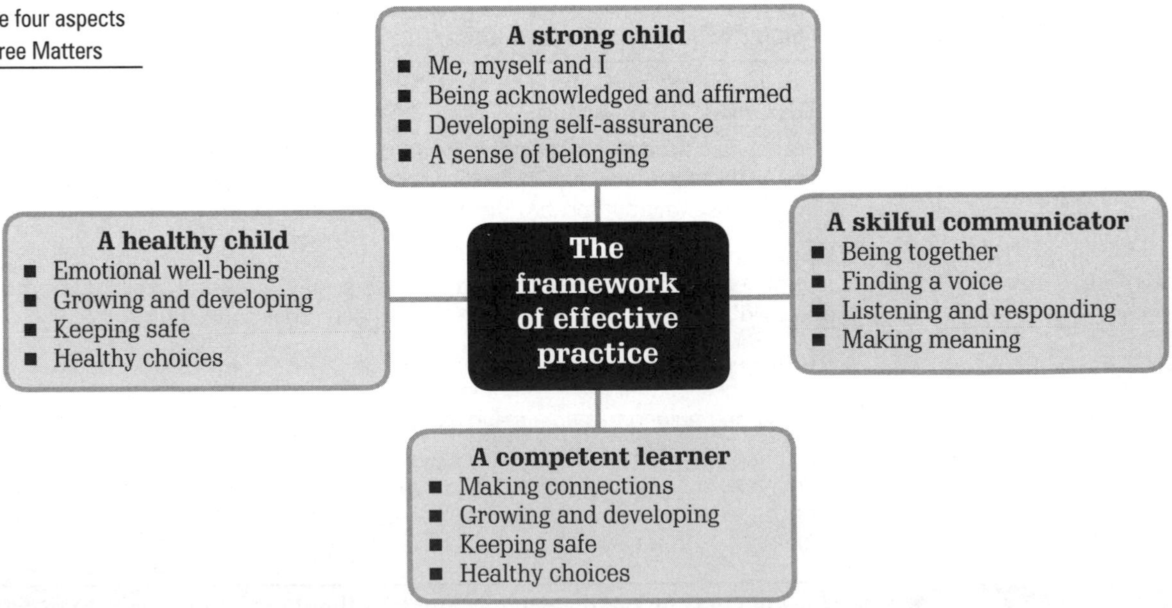

Fig 35.25(a)

THE EARLY YEARS FOUNDATION STAGE PRINCIPLES

The Early Years Foundation Stage Setting the Standards for Learning, Development and Care for children from birth to five

A Unique Child	Positive Relationships	Enabling Environments	Learning and Development
Every child is a competent learner from birth who can be resilient, capable, confident and self-assured	Children learn to be strong and independent from a base of loving and secure relationships with parents and/or a key person	The environment plays a key role in supporting and extending children's development and learning	Children develop and learn in different ways and at different rates and all areas of Learning and Development are equally important and inter-connected
1.1 Child Development ■ Child development ■ A skilful communicator ■ A competent learner 1.2 Inclusive Practice ■ Equality and diversity ■ Children's entitlements ■ Early support 1.3 Keeping Safe ■ Being safe and protected ■ Discovering boundaries ■ Making choices 1.4 Health and Well-being ■ Growing and developing ■ Physical well-being ■ Emotional well-being	2.1 Respecting Each Other ■ Understand feelings ■ Friendships ■ Professional relationships 2.2 Parents and Partners ■ Respecting diversity ■ Communication ■ Learning together 2.3 Supporting Learning ■ Positive interactions ■ Listening to children ■ Effective teaching 2.4 Key Person ■ Secure attachment ■ Shared care ■ independence	3.1 Observation, Assessment and Planning ■ Starting with the child ■ Planning ■ Assessment 3.2 Supporting Every Child ■ Children's needs ■ The learning journey ■ Working together 3.3 The Learning Environment ■ The emotional environment ■ The outdoor environment ■ The indoor environment 3.4 The Wider Context ■ Transitions and continuity ■ Multi-agency working ■ The community	4.1 Play and Exploration ■ Learning through experience ■ Adult involvement ■ Contexts for learning 4.2 Active Learning ■ Mental and physical involvement ■ Decision making ■ Personalised learning 4.3 Creativity and Critical Thinking ■ Making connections ■ Transforming understanding ■ Sustained shared thinking 4.4 Areas of Learning and Development ■ Personal, Social and Emotional Development ■ Communication, Language and Literacy ■ Problem Solving, Reasoning and numeracy ■ Knowledge and Understanding of the World ■ Physical Development ■ Creative Development

Based on material from the department for education and skills 2007

- Further details of the EYFS can be downloaded at www.standards.dfes.gov.uk/eyfs/. Information is likely to continue to be updated on the website up to and after its full implementation.
- In Wales there will also be changes, with the new Foundation Phase curriculum also being put into place in 2008. Details of the Foundation Phase can be found at www.wales.gov.uk.

Reporting concerns, data protection and use of personal information

On occasions, it will be necessary to refer a child to another professional. This could be for health, developmental, care or learning needs. As a student, if you have any concerns about a child for any reason, you should speak to your placement supervisor or to the child's key worker. It is likely that some needs would be managed within the setting, with the staff and resources already available. At other times, additional or one-to-one support will be required and an extra member of staff may be brought in, or the child may have a Portage worker who will give guidance to other carers.

Refer to Green (2007a), Unit 8, for more on supporting children with a disability or special educational need, and Unit 27, p. 257.

A child may also have to be referred because of suspected neglect or another form of abuse. Each setting has a member of staff designated to make such referrals to the local child protection team. It is inappropriate for you as a student to make the referral yourself. You must always talk to your placement supervisor.

Refer to Green (2007), Unit 5 for more on child protection issues.

Any concern about a child in your care must always be reported. There are guidelines and legislation regarding reporting, storing and sharing information on children.

Confidentiality

It is expected that confidentiality will always be maintained. At times you may become privy to information about a child or their family. You will have received this information for a purpose, and in trust. You will have received it on a 'need-to-know' basis. Confidentiality forms part of your role as a professional. It also applies when carrying out observations.

Data protection

The Data Protection Act 1998 covers any information kept on paper or on a computer. This Act is relevant to you not only as a student, in relation to the information you use in writing your assignments, observations and recordings, but also as a practitioner, writing observations and maintaining records of babies and children.

Parents should be kept informed of any concerns about their child, and should also have access and be welcomed to read their child's file. It is inappropriate, however, for a parent to find out about observations made of their child, and any concerns staff may have, simply by reading the file. Concerns and notes on development should always be discussed with them.

Observations

When working with babies and children under 3, you will need to carry out a range of **observations**. These will be both formal and informal. Observations are used to note progress, assess needs and to enable accurate feedback to be given to parents and in some cases health care professionals. They also help day care staff ensure that safe practice is carried out at all times.

When carrying out observations you will need to take into consideration:

- parental permission
- the importance of accuracy
- using both formal and informal observation methods
- how you record your observations
- language and recording formats used
- the recording procedures of the setting you are working in
- why you are carrying out the observations and what you hope to gain from them.

To refresh your understanding of observing babies and young children, refer to the work you have done for Unit 3 and also to Green (2007), Unit 8, where the role of observation is discussed together with explanations of how to carry out a range of different observation methods.

Observing babies and young children helps to:

- inform future planning
- learn about individual children's interests and needs
- identify links between circumstances and behaviour
- note changes in behaviour
- get to know a child better
- identify any safety issues
- gauge the success of activities or resources

- monitor any concern that may already have been raised
- assess a child's state of health
- assess a child's overall stage of development
- assess a child's progress.

The above bullet points are developed further in Unit 3 of Book 1.

activity
INDIVIDUAL WORK 35.2
P2
P3

Write a letter to an imaginary parent asking for permission to carry out observations on their baby or child. Explain how you will carry out your observations and outline what you consider you can learn about a child through observation.

activity
GROUP WORK 35.3
M1
D1

Prepare a talk, justifying the use of observation of babies and young children and explain how to carry them out. Each member of the group should research and provide observation examples to support the aims of the talk.

NB Ensure that issues of confidentiality are upheld at all times.

Know how to help provide physical care requirements for babies and children under three

Feeding

Everyone working with young babies needs to be able to make up a formula feed accurately, and also know how to store breast milk, previously expressed by the mother, to give to the infant during time within their care. Supporting a mother's choice of feeding is important.

Link

- These important procedures are explained in Unit 11, Diet and Nutrition for Children.
- Refer to pages 2–13 where you will information on:
  - breast feeding and lactation
  - fore milk and hind milk
  - advantages and disadvantages of breast feeding
  - advantages and disadvantages of formula feeding
  - preparing and giving formula feeds
  - winding positions
  - sterilising methods
  - storage of feeds, both breast and formula.

Weaning

Babies grow at their fastest rate during their first year and it is important that they are given a healthy and varied diet. This means a good balance of calcium, protein, carbohydrates and fats, together with a range of vitamins and minerals.

Ideally infants should remain on a full milk diet until around 6 months. Research has suggested that this could help lower their chances of developing an allergy or intolerance to some foods. However, no baby should be allowed to go hungry and when they clearly begin to be less satisfied with a purely milk diet, whether breast or formula, an introduction to solid food becomes appropriate.

This transition into mixed feeding is called weaning. Breast and formula milks do not have sufficient iron for continued healthy development, and prolonged (exclusive) milk feeding will not provide enough of this important mineral. Initially the baby has sufficient stocks of iron taken from their mother during pregnancy, and during the earliest months the baby's digestive system is not usually mature enough to cope with the components of solid food. It is unusual for an infant to begin solid food before 4 months.

Milk remains an important part of the baby's diet until they are at least a year old. The aim of weaning is to introduce babies to a variety of textures, tastes and experiences to integrate them fully into family mealtimes. As the level of solid food intake increases, the milk feeds will decrease until the baby is having sufficient solid food at a 'mealtime' to be satisfied with a drink of water to accompany it.

Fig 35.26 Enjoying solid foods

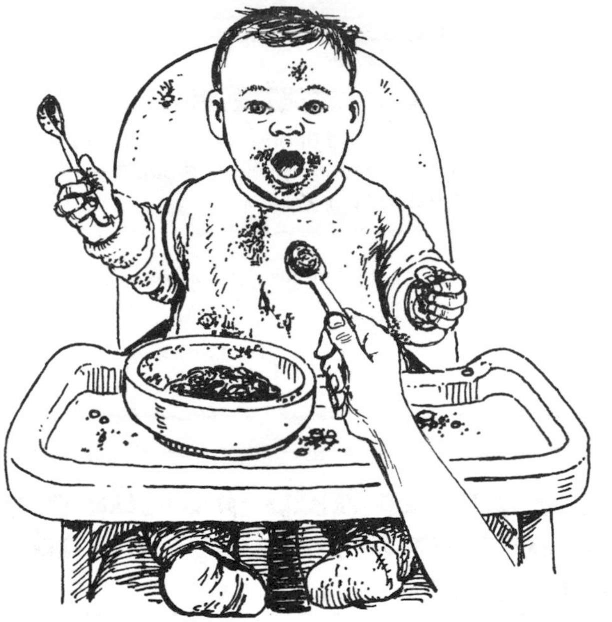

remember

Weaning is an important part of development, both socially and physically. It is not usually beneficial to an infant to hold back the start of weaning for any length of time, even if they still seem content with their milk feeds.

Weaning should be a pleasurable experience for both carer and child, encouraging the infant to explore new tastes over a period of time. It should not be a situation of stress or tension. At times it can be difficult to get a baby interested in trying to take solids from a spoon, but it is important to keep on offering it to them, without worrying about regular refusals. The baby will get there in time and in the early stages of weaning the baby will still be having all of their milk feeds and so will not be losing out nutritionally.

Do not introduce weaning (or a new food) when the baby is unwell or tired.

Offering half of the milk feed before the solids and half afterwards works well for most babies, but each baby is different and they will soon indicate their preference!

Link

More information on weaning can be found in Unit 11, Diet and Nutrition, page 13.

Nutritional requirements of babies and children under three years

As with children and adults of all ages, babies and toddlers need a balanced diet which includes foods from the four main food groups.

A well-balanced diet is one that provides all the nutritional requirements for growth, maintenance and development of the body. What we eat helps us to repair and maintain our body tissues, supports the functioning of muscles and organs and helps to prevent infection. It also supplies us with the energy we need in order to function from day to day.

The four main food groups are:

- proteins, which help growth, development and tissue repair
- carbohydrates, which provide energy

- vitamins, minerals and fibre, for general good health and the prevention of illness
- dairy products, which are high in calcium, enhancing and maintaining bones and teeth.

A fifth food group – fats and oils – are higher energy-giving foods, which are essential to children, but should be consumed sparingly by adults.

Many foods contribute to more than one food group, e.g. meat is a good source of iron, and pulses are a good source of fibre. Look at the illustrations below, which indicate where the main benefits of each food lie.

Fig 35.27 The food groups

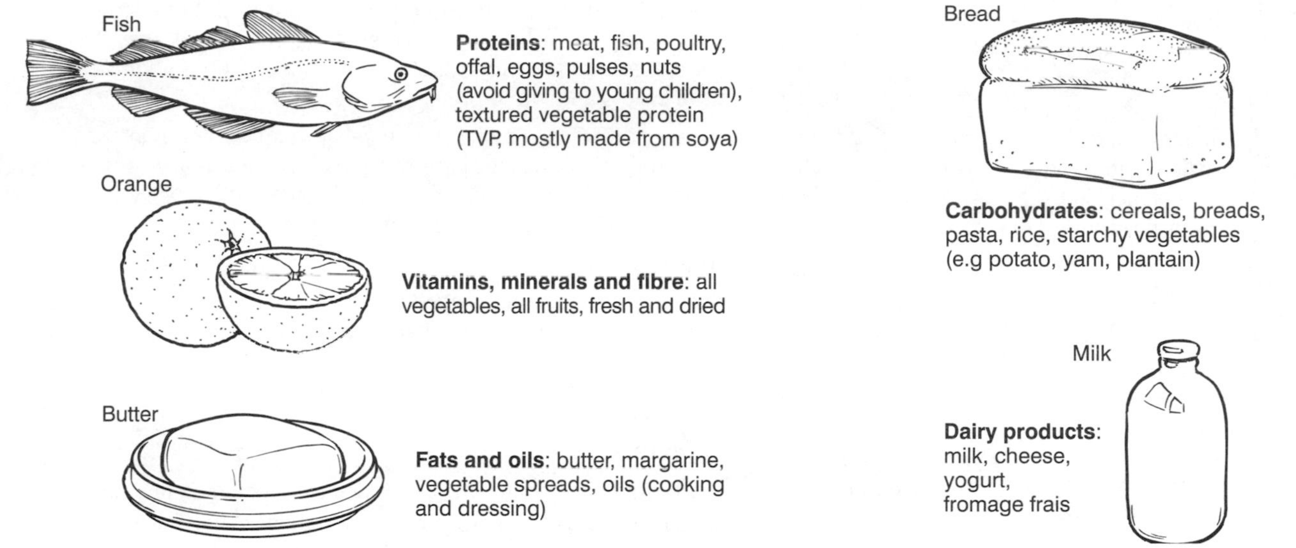

Fish
Proteins: meat, fish, poultry, offal, eggs, pulses, nuts (avoid giving to young children), textured vegetable protein (TVP, mostly made from soya)
Bread
Carbohydrates: cereals, breads, pasta, rice, starchy vegetables (e.g potato, yam, plantain)
Orange
Vitamins, minerals and fibre: all vegetables, all fruits, fresh and dried
Milk
Dairy products: milk, cheese, yogurt, fromage frais
Butter
Fats and oils: butter, margarine, vegetable spreads, oils (cooking and dressing)

Link

A more detailed explanation of each food group can be found in Unit 11, Diet and Nutrition page 17.

Estimated average requirements (EARs)

Table 35.6 shows the estimated average requirements (EARs) for energy in the UK (per day) for children aged 0–3 years. As the infant becomes more active, their energy levels increase, and again this indicates the need for solid foods to complement the nourishment of the milk feeds.

Table 35.6 Estimated average requirements (EARs) for energy in the UK (per day), birth to 3 years

Age range	Males		Females	
	MJ	kcal	MJ	kcal
0-3 months	2.28	545	2.16	515
4–6 months	2.89	690	2.69	645
7–9 months	3.44	825	3.20	765
10–12 months	3.85	920	3.61	865
1–3 years	5.15	1230	4.86	1165

Vitamins and minerals

Like adults, babies and young children need a range of vitamins and minerals to help them develop and to maintain health. These include:

- vitamins A, B group, C, D, E and K
- minerals such as calcium, fluoride, iodine, iron, sodium chloride
- trace minerals such as potassium, phosphorus, magnesium, sulphur, manganese and zinc.

Link

Tables on pages 19 and 20 of Unit 11 explain the sources and functions of many of these vitamins and minerals.

> **remember** Children have preferences, just as adults do, and these preferences should be taken into account up to a point. It is, however, important to provide a balance between allowing children to select what they eat and do not eat, and encouraging them to try a range of different foods. A dislike of one food or drink does not automatically mean the child is being 'fussy'.

Children need a diet that is high in protein and carbohydrates in order for it to meet their high energy needs. Ideally the carbohydrates should be provided in the form of starchy foods, such as potatoes, bread and cereals.

Providing meals that include variation in colour and texture will make them more appealing to children. This will be particularly important if you are catering for a 'fussy' or reluctant eater.

Introducing new foods to children can sometimes be met with resistance. It is important to only introduce one new food at a time, ideally alongside a portion of something they like, encouraging them to eat a little of both.

Giving children a large portion of food can be off-putting for them. It is far better to have them eat all of a small meal, rather than just half of a larger meal. This encourages the good habit of 'finishing' a meal, and lessens any possibility of conflict. The portion size can gradually be increased as the child's appetite grows.

Encouraging children to have a drink of water with their meals is another good habit to develop. Many children will automatically ask for juice or squash, without really considering water. If they have been offered it regularly when very young, they are more likely to continue to drink it later on too, which is a healthy recommendation.

Cultural and other dietary needs

Many children have specific dietary needs. These need to be clearly understood by all staff in the setting. This may include a child who is vegetarian or vegan by parental or personal choice, whose culture includes specific dietary requirements, or a child who has an allergic reaction to certain foods, or a medical condition that is affected by certain foods.

Professional Practice

- **Read through the menus for the children in your placement to see how dietary needs are incorporated, and how many cultures are represented within the menus. This will help you plan meals for children yourself for the future.**

> **remember** When an infant or a child is unwell, it is not an appropriate time to introduce new foods.

Diet and the unwell child

Children who are unwell are likely to be more selective in what they want to eat, and it is often more appropriate to allow them to eat what they feel like eating, rather than insist they try something they do not want, resulting in little food being consumed. Again, portion size is important. An unwell child will usually require far less food at each meal than usual.

Professional Practice

- **Processed foods contain many hidden ingredients, such as sugar and salt. Whenever possible, offer children fresh foods and use fresh ingredients in your cooking. Do not provide salt or sugar at the table for children to add to their meals as this can become an expectation and set up bad habits for the future.**

Overcoming feeding difficulties and food allergies

At times babies can repeatedly refuse solid foods. It is important during these periods to consider the following questions:

- Is the child unwell?
- Are they teething?
- Are you giving them too many new foods too quickly?
- Are you offering food at the right consistency?
- Are you feeling anxious about the weaning process, and possibly passing your anxiety on to the child?

It is important to make sure that you:

- make mealtimes a pleasure, not a battle
- make gradual changes to the consistency of foods
- only offer one new food or new consistency at a time
- only offer new foods when the infant is well and content
- offer a new food alongside a familiar food, to ensure that at least part of the meal is eaten.

remember

Feeding can be messy, so feed babies in a suitable environment. Babies need to try to feed themselves in order to learn. Happy meal times will encourage a positive attitude to food and eating later on.

Babies experimenting with feeding themselves

Babies enjoy trying to feed themselves. They can usually cope with finger foods from 8 months onwards, and suitable foods would include rusks, fingers of soft bread, pieces of pear and slices of banana. When the infant shows an interest in trying to handle the spoon, give them a spare one. You will then remain in control of the feeding process, while satisfying their curiosity and skill development.

Complying with parental wishes relating to feeding babies

When working in care settings you will need to be aware of a variety of dietary needs. These can be for:

- medical needs, for chronic conditions such as lactose intolerance, gluten intolerance or food allergy
- cultural needs, heeding the forbidden or restricted foods and food combinations of some cultures
- social needs/family choice, which would include being vegetarian or vegan.

Parents' wishes regarding their child's diet need to be valued. It is perfectly acceptable to seek their advice regarding meeting their child's needs. Most parents will be pleased that you have shown an interest and taken the time to ensure you are providing for them appropriately.

activity
INDIVIDUAL WORK 35.4

P4

M2

Produce two charts, one for a baby and one for a toddler, showing a suitable daily care and feeding routine.

Link

You may find it helpful to refer back to Unit 11,where diet and nutrition are covered in more detail. Topics include:

- weaning and types of foods to introduce
- food allergies and food intolerance
- main food groups
- food preferences
- potential effects of food additives on children
- vegetarian and vegan diets
- cultural food practices
- malnutrition, obesity and under-nourishment
- nutrient deficiencies, e.g. rickets, anaemia
- principles of good food safety practice.

Routine care

Washing, dressing and nappy changing

Hygiene must always be a top priority when dealing with body fluids of any kind. This includes nappy changes. In day care settings, the use of disposable gloves is now the norm, whereas in a home setting good personal hygiene practice should be sufficient.

Babies are usually topped and tailed in the mornings, and bathed in the evening before being put to bed. **Topping and tailing** involves washing the face and refreshing the top half of the body, together with changing the nappy.

Topping and tailing

Preparation

Get everything ready in advance. You will need:

- towel
- changing mat
- bowl of cooled boiled water
- bowl of warm water
- cotton wool
- barrier cream (if using)
- a clean nappy
- a fresh set of clothes
- access to a nappy bucket (for towelling nappies) or
- a nappy sack (if using disposables)
- access to the laundry basket for clothes.

remember

Cleansing of a girl's nappy area should always be by wiping from the front to the back to avoid any infection from the bowels passing into the vaginal area. Cleansing of a boy's nappy area does not necessitate the pulling back of the foreskin. Excessive cleaning can actually cause irritation and infection, rather than preventing it.

Method

1 Place baby on changing mat and undress to their vest and nappy.

2 Using the cooled boiled water, wipe each eye from the nose corner outwards, using each piece of cotton wool only once.

3 Repeat two or three times for each eye.

4 Dry gently with the corner of a clean towel.

5 Gently clean ears and around the face using moistened cotton wool, ensuring that you reach all the creases, particularly under the chin and behind the ears. Dry gently.

6 Using a larger piece of moistened cotton wool, freshen up the baby's armpits and hands, removing all fibres collected between the fingers. Dry gently.

7 In newborn babies check that the umbilical stump is clean, but do not clean it unnecessarily. Whenever possible, it should be left alone. (They tend to shrivel up and drop off seven to ten days after birth.)

8 Remove soiled nappy and place in bucket or nappy sack.

9 Clean the nappy area thoroughly, with warm water (or baby wipes if used), ensuring that you clean all creases, wiping from the front to the back.

10 Put on clean nappy (applying barrier cream if used), dress and have a cuddle!

Changing nappies

Parents and carers today have a vast array of choices regarding the type of nappies they use. Disposable nappies are extremely absorbent and can be easy to use, but they are expensive and are a significant environmental concern. Towelling nappies are cheaper to use, but they have to be washed and dried. In many areas there are nappy laundering services. These are expensive to use, but sometimes appeal to the environmentally conscious parent, who does not want to bother with the extra washing themselves. Towelling nappies have been revolutionised. They can be bought ready 'shaped', often used with a waterproof wrap. These nappies are usually secured with a Velcro-type fastening (aplix), poppers or a nappy nipper (a three-pronged rubber grip). If the infant in your care wears nappies made from folding towelling squares, you will need to know how to fold them. There are a number of ways to do this, as shown in Figure 35.28.

remember

A baby or child should never be left alone on a raised changing surface. All resources needed should be gathered in advance.

There should be separate nappy-changing facilities in every appropriate care setting. The surfaces used should be safe, clean and offer privacy. Each baby or child needs to have their own changing items labelled and stored separately. Creams and lotions should not be shared between children. Staff should follow hygiene protection practices as directed by the policy of the setting.

Bathing

Bathing young babies is usually very pleasurable, and can be carried out by either the 'traditional' method or the 'modern' method. You need to be able to carry out both methods, to meet with parental preferences.

Traditional method

Prepare everything in advance, ensuring that the temperature of the room is suitable (at least 20° C/68° F) with no draughts, and that all windows and doors are closed. All that you

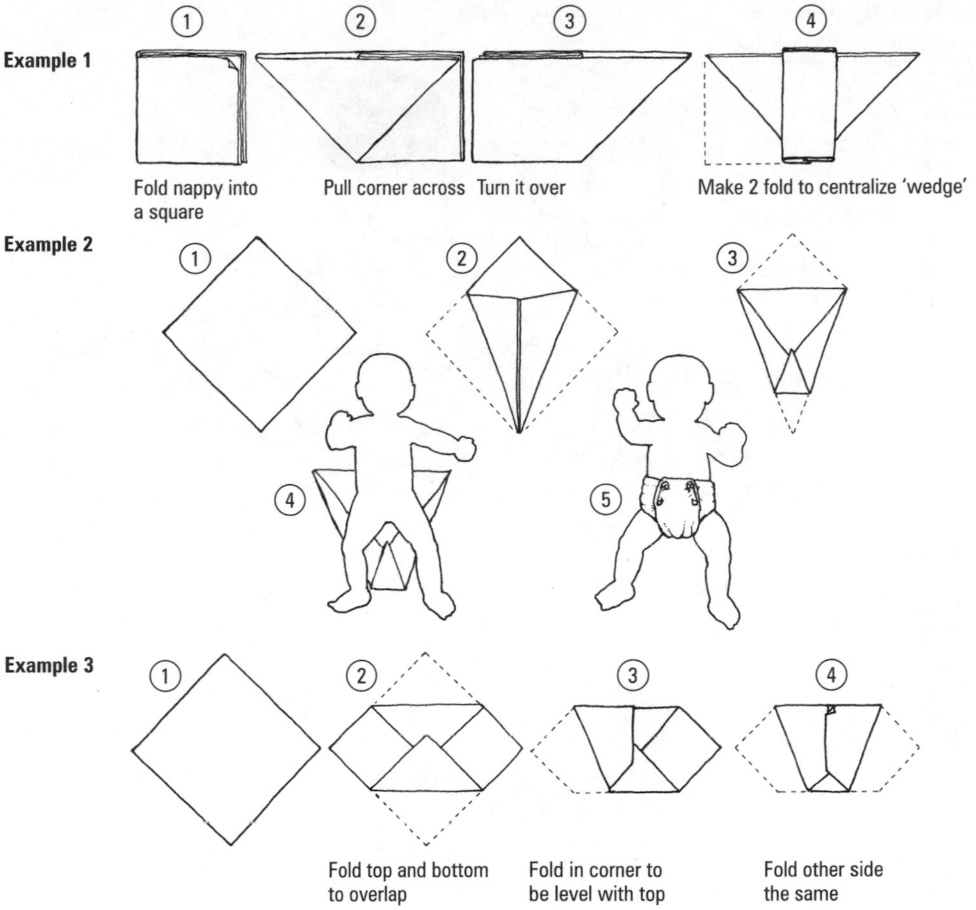

Fig 35.28 Methods of folding traditional nappy squares

will need must be to hand, and the bath should be in a safe and secure place. A special bath stand or a firm surface is ideal, but many people choose to place the baby bath in the family bath or on the floor. Any of these options are acceptable.

You will need:

- bath, with water at 37° C – always check this before putting the baby in (using your elbow or preferably a bath thermometer)
- changing mat
- towels
- cotton wool
- bowl of cooled boiled water (for the eyes)
- shampoo (if using)
- soap
- barrier cream (if using)
- a clean nappy
- a fresh set of clothes
- access to a nappy bucket (for towelling nappies) or
- a nappy sack (if using disposables)
- access to a laundry basket for clothing.

Fig 35.29 The traditional method for bathing a baby

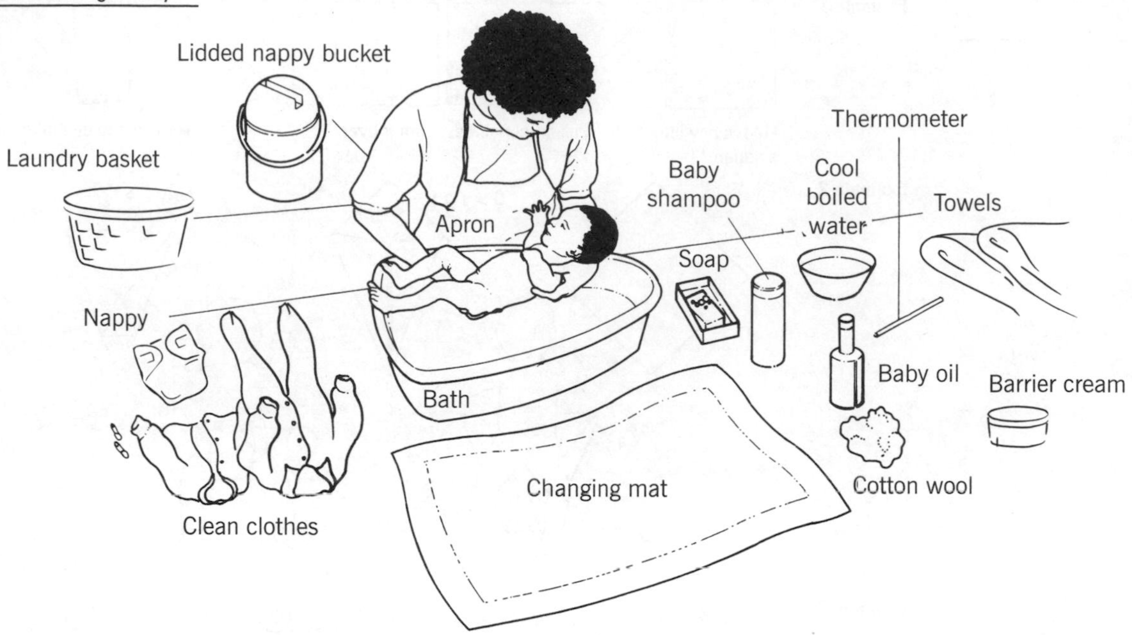

How to do it:

1 Undress baby to just their nappy and wrap them in the towel with the top corner folded away from you.

2 Wash eyes and face as in topping and tailing guidelines above.

3 Hold baby over the bath (still wrapped in towel) under your arm, resting on your hip.

4 Gently wet their hair all over.

5 Add shampoo or soap and rub in gently but firmly.

6 Rinse their hair by leaning baby backwards over the bath, towel drying their hair with the folded-over corner of the towel.

7 Lay baby across your lap and remove nappy, cleansing away excess faeces.

8 With your spare hand gently wet and soap baby all over, turning them by pulling them over towards you, holding shoulder and thigh, and on to their tummy. When their back and bottom are also soaped, turn again in the same way (always towards you).

9 Supporting the baby's head and neck with one hand and their bottom with the other, lower them into the bath.

10 Gently rinse baby all over, continually supporting the head and neck with your wrist, and holding their shoulder and arm.

11 When ready to be dried, lift baby on to your lap, wrap in towel and cuddle dry!

12 Apply nappy and clothing as before.

13 Brush or groom hair as appropriate.

14 Trim nails as necessary using blunt baby scissors (with parents' permission).

remember Always keep hold of the baby, by firmly holding the arm and shoulder furthest away from you. Even very young babies can move suddenly.

Other points to remember:

- Babies usually have a feed after a bath and are then put down to sleep.
- Only use talcum powder if parents insist. It has been suggested that it may link to the development of asthma in early childhood.
- Cultural practice regarding hair care, use of oils and creams should be adhered to.
- Never poke cotton buds into ears, noses and so on.
- Babies need total supervision by a responsible adult at all times when being bathed.

Modern method

How to do it:

1 Bath water, clothing and so on needs to be prepared in the same way as with the traditional method.

> **remember**
> Using a bathing preparation can make the water (and baby) quite slippery, so particular care is needed in holding the baby securely. If a bathing preparation causes irritation of the baby's skin, do not continue its use. Some preparations irritate a baby's skin in the early weeks but can be used without problems later on.

2 A bathing preparation is added to the water.

3 The baby is lowered into the water after the eyes and face have been washed.

4 Soaping of the baby is by using the 'bubble bath'.

5 The process then continues as the traditional method.

Bathing older babies

From 7 or 8 months onwards, babies can progress into the family bath, although some babies will prefer the security of the baby bath for far longer. They are usually much more active by this time and the additional room for splashing is appreciated. They are often able to sit alone quite well, but remember that the water will make them buoyant and you will need to be ready to support them if they slip.

Other points to remember:

- The same precautions are needed regarding temperature, preparation and supervision as with younger babies.
- Ensure that the baby cannot touch the hot tap, which remains hot for some time after use.
- Do not have the water too deep, or the baby will float.
- Sitting on a rubber mat can help them feel more secure.
- A range of containers and bath toys will be enjoyed.
- Many babies enjoy bathing with a parent.

Fearful babies

At times a baby may become fearful of water. This may be due to an incident such as:

- slipping in the bath
- disliking water getting in their eyes
- stinging eyes from soaps or shampoos.

You should ensure that you:

- always hold babies securely when in the bath
- never allow babies to try and stand in the bath
- always use non-stinging products, especially designed for babies' delicate skin
- use a hair ring to keep water out of their eyes, if they dislike the sensation
- do not make a big issue of bathing if it becomes a battle – often if you omit the bath or the hair wash for a couple of days, the issue will go away, as the baby 'forgets' it was a problem.

> **remember**
> Although most parents and carers like to freshen their babies at the end of each day with a bath, it is not absolutely essential. A good wash using the top and tail method can also maintain good health care.

Clothing for babies and children

Adults need to take responsibility for what the children in their care wear, as young children are not able to make an 'informed' choice for themselves. However, those who are able to will state their preferences with no regard to temperature, weather or planned activity.

Babies

Clothing for babies needs to:

- be easy to put on and take off
- have room for them to grow
- allow unrestricted movement
- be suitable for the time of year and temperature of the environment they are in
- avoid cramping of their toes (e.g. in all-in-one suits)
- be free from long ties or ribbons (to avoid choking)
- be free from loose buttons or poppers (another choking hazard)
- be free from looped edgings on seams that may catch their fingers
- avoid lacy designs that may also catch small fingers
- be easy to wash and dry
- be made of natural materials such as cotton to allow the baby's skin to breathe
- not involve fluffy materials or wools such as mohair as this can irritate noses and get in hands and mouths

- be of a suitable length for dresses not to get caught when toddling or crawling
- be washed in non-biological powders to avoid reactions to the harsh detergents in many modern washing agents.

Fig 35.30 A baby's clothing

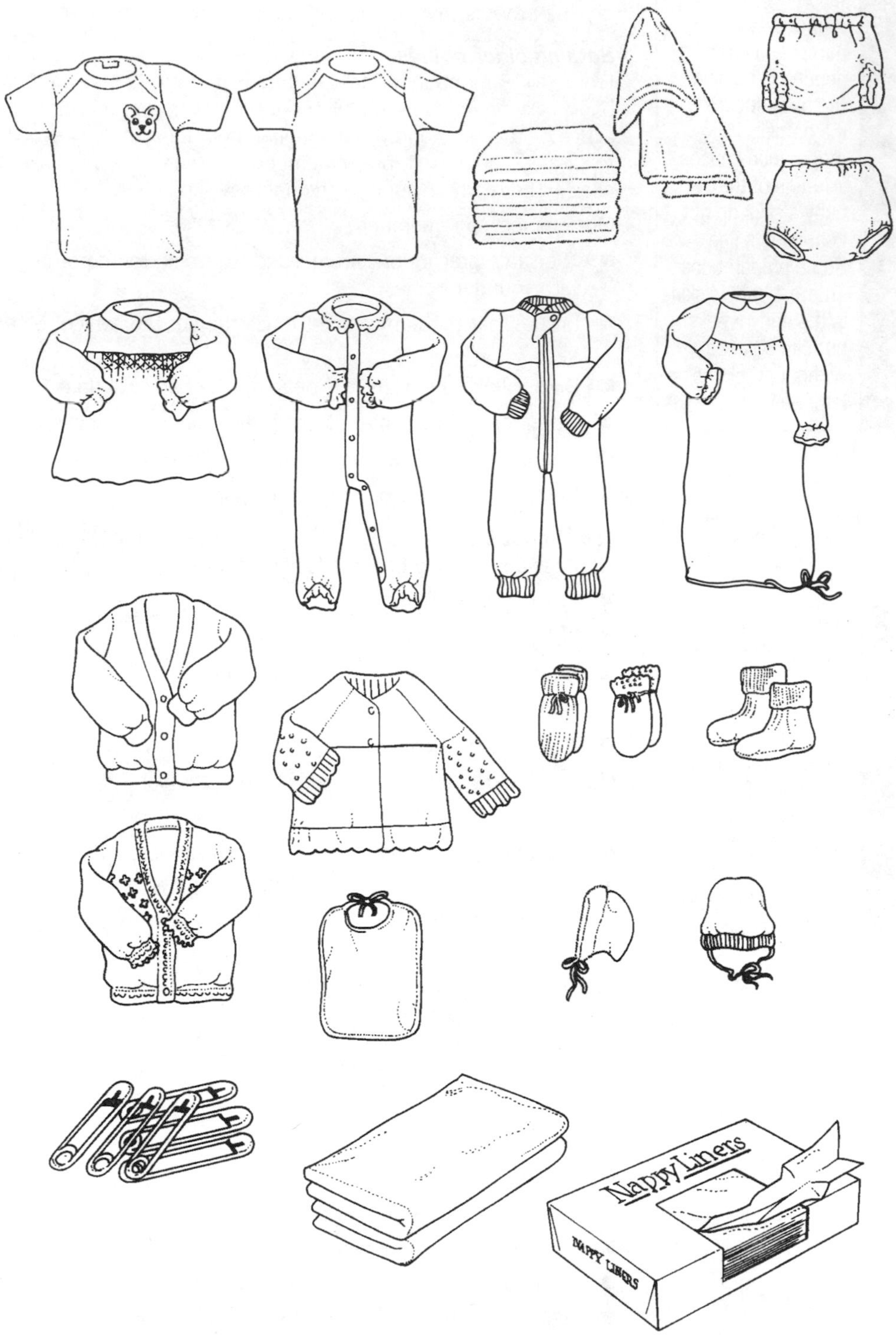

remember

Babies are not able to control their body temperature and could therefore become overheated. So it is better for them to wear several layers of clothes that can be removed or replaced according to temperature, than one warmer layer that offers no opportunity for adjustment.

remember

When a baby is ready to have their first pair of proper shoes, it is important to have their feet measured and shoes fitted by a foot care specialist.

Babies' feet are very delicate and their bones are still forming. Therefore they should not be given shoes before they are walking, as this can hinder the natural growth and development of their feet, leading to deformity. Socks, all-in-one suits and bootees should all have sufficient room for natural movement and growth.

Children

Clothing for children needs to:

- be easy to put on and take off, to encourage independence
- allow for growth, as the growth rate of children is so rapid

- allow unrestricted movement, particularly for outdoor play
- be suitable for the time of year and temperature of the environment they are in
- be free from long or loose ties or ribbons that could get caught during play
- be kept in good repair and regularly washed, setting a good example regarding cleanliness
- be easy to wash and dry
- be made of natural materials to allow skin to breathe
- be of a suitable length to avoid the possibility of tripping
- be suitable for the activities being undertaken, enabling them to play without worrying they might spoil a special outfit
- allow for temperature adjustment, therefore several layers are better than one thicker garment

Fig 35.31 Children's clothing should be suitable for the activities being undertaken

remember It is unhealthy for a child to wear trainers for long periods of time.

Children's feet develop quickly and it is not uncommon for a child to need four pairs of new shoes during the course of one year. Foot care specialists recommend that children should have their feet measured every 12 weeks and sooner if there is any concern about cramping of toes or if soreness occurs. It is important that sock sizes are monitored, as socks that are too small can cause damage to the structure of a child's feet.

Caring for a baby's environment

Room temperature and suitable levels of ventilation are important factors in looking after a baby. Any room where a baby spends much of their time should be a constant 20° C (68° F) day and night. A room thermometer should be placed on the wall in the baby room of the setting and should be checked regularly, adjusting the heating accordingly.

Overheating of babies is thought to be a contributory factor in sudden infant death syndrome (cot death), and recommendations are that babies should not be piled high with blankets. Just a sheet and two layers of blankets will normally be sufficient.

remember A blanket folded in half counts as two layers.

Duvets and baby nests are no longer recommended, as they do not allow for temperature regulation. Cot bumpers are also advised against as they add extra warmth to a baby's cot, as well as having the potential for suffocation.

Having a well-ventilated room will help to prevent cross-infection and make the working or living environment a more pleasant place to be, both for the baby and for their carers.

Professional Practice

- You can check if a well baby is too warm or too cool by feeling their abdomen. If it feels warm and clammy, they are hotter than necessary. An abdomen that is slightly cool to touch is usual.
- Removing a layer of clothing should be sufficient to keep them at a more comfortable temperature.
- Cool hands and feet do not automatically indicate a 'cold' baby.
- The circulation of young babies is not as fully developed as adults and older children, and many babies have cool extremities, especially before they become mobile.
- If you are concerned that a baby is unwell or has a raised temperature, always check it with a thermometer and seek medical advice as necessary.
- Normally body temperature is between 36 and 37° C.

A high temperature (pyrexia)

Normal body temperature is between 36 and 37° C. A temperature above 37.5° C indicates **pyrexia** (fever). Young children's temperatures are often a sensitive indicator of the onset of illness and a raised temperature should never be ignored.

Check for overheating in the first instance by:

- removing clothing or a layer of bedding
- reducing the temperature of the room
- sponging the child with a cool flannel.

If fever is suspected:

- take the child's temperature and record the outcome
- remove clothing or a layer of bedding
- sponge with a cool flannel
- offer plenty of fluids
- use a fan to circulate cool air around them
- observe the child carefully, particularly very young babies.

remember

Parents should always be informed if a child has become unwell, even if they appear well again by the time they are collected.

Febrile convulsions

Febrile convulsions can occur in some children when their temperature rises, involving loss of consciousness, flickering of eyes and general jitteriness.

- A child who has one febrile convulsion is more likely to have another. It does not however mean that they have developed epilepsy.
- Medical advice should be sought if a febrile convulsion occurs.
- The child should be placed in the recovery position when the convulsion is over while medical advice is sought.
- The child needs reassurance and rest following a febrile convulsion.

Professional Practice

- A baby's environment and care **routines** must be constantly monitored for their suitability, as they will need to be adjusted as the infant gets older, in order to meet their changing developmental needs. These needs will include:
  - sleeping patterns, as the infant gradually has longer periods of wakefulness
  - feeding times, incorporating the introduction of weaning
  - amounts of time spent specifically playing with them
  - time for stimulation, involving games, music, outings, and so on
  - time for rest and relaxation, sleep, cuddles and books.
- Babies need a routine that is not rigid but provides continuity and security for them. A secure baby is usually a settled baby. Babies have periods of wakefulness and periods of deep sleep. They can appear very alert and content at times, and restless and irritable at others. A baby's day needs to include:

- sufficient feeds for their current age, weight and level of development
- sufficient extended periods of sleep
- time for love and cuddles
- stimulation through toys, adult communications and through the general environment
- regular changes of nappies
- opportunities for fresh air.

Maintenance and cleaning in the nursery

- Carpeted surfaces should be vacuumed regularly.
- Washable (non-slip) floors should be cleaned with a mop (disinfected).
- All surfaces used for making up, or standing feeds upon, should be thoroughly cleaned with an anti-bacterial product.
- All general surfaces should also be kept clean with an anti-bacterial product.
- Soft toys should be washed regularly.
- All toys should be cleaned regularly with an anti-bacterial product.
- Thermometers must be checked regularly to ensure that rooms are kept at an appropriate temperature (18–20° C/65–68° F).
- Lighting must be adequate for safe working practice.
- Good ventilation reduces the risk of cross-infection.
- Ventilation points need to be kept clean, to avoid a build-up of dirt and bacteria

Safety equipment suitable for the development stages of babies

In any setting that cares for babies and young children, there should be an awareness of safety marks, and the need to buy toys and equipment that have been tested and safety marked whenever possible.

Safety equipment needed for the different stages of a baby's development includes the following.

For newborn infants

- A safe surface on which to change the baby
- A cat/insect net
- A sturdy cot, Moses basket or carry-cot that conforms to current safety standards
- A suitable mattress, again that conforms to current safety standards and is the correct size for the cot
- An appropriate (rear-facing) car seat

Avoid cot bumpers, quilts and duvets, which have been linked to the overheating of young babies that can contribute to cot death.

When the baby sits up

- Be aware of new areas that can be reached by the baby.
- Flexes should be kept out of reach.
- Hot food should not be placed in front of the infant, in case they topple on to it.
- Harnesses are definitely needed in chairs, prams and strollers.
- Do not change the baby's car seat round until they reach the correct weight (as indicated on the car seat).

When the baby can crawl

- Play pens can be useful.
- Fire guards prevent the baby accessing fires.
- Electric socket covers should be used.
- A video guard can be bought.
- Safety gates are needed at top and bottom of stairs, and possibly across the kitchen too.

- Toilet lid catches can be useful.
- Trailing leads need to be secured.
- Sharp corners need to be protected with transparent 'corners'.
- Safety glass (or a special safety film) should be placed in all full-length glass doors.
- Remove overhanging tablecloths.
- Keep cleaning fluids up high, preferably shut away out of sight.
- Hot drinks should be kept out of the baby's reach.
- Be aware of pet food and pet water bowls.
- Be aware of loose carpet fibres, which can cause choking if swallowed.
- Strong netting is needed over garden ponds.

When the baby is standing, climbing or toddling

- Cooker bars help to protect from saucepan spills.
- Keep cooking handles turned inwards at all times.
- A fridge lock may be needed.
- Catches are needed on windows, doors and drawers.
- Safety glass, or safety film on doors, and low windows, and on glass coffee tables.

General safety points

- Smoke alarms should be installed.
- Safety mats in baths are important.
- Slam stoppers on doors, to prevent fingers being trapped, are extremely useful.
- Razors, chemicals and medicines should be kept locked away securely.
- Cold water should always be added to baths before hot water.
- Toys should be checked regularly to ensure they are whole, undamaged and clean.

Safety marks

Safety marks are listed in Table 35.7.

Hygiene and protection practices

It is important that all care staff understand the health and safe practice procedures for the setting. This helps prevent the spread of illness and infection.

Link

Refer to Unit 11, page 32, for more on this important aspect of caring for children.

Safe disposal of waste

Soiled nappies and clothing need to be safely and hygienically dealt with. Every care setting should have a policy regarding:

- the safe disposal of nappies, baby wipes, etc.
- the safe disposal of cleaning materials
- the sending home of soiled clothing.

If the setting washes soiled items on site, they should be sluiced in a sink kept for that purpose and washed on the appropriate heat setting of an industrial-strength washing machine. Blood-stained garments are likely to benefit from an initial rinsing on a cold water cycle.

If garments are sent home with the child, they should be sluiced off to remove excess body fluids, double bagged and tied securely to prevent leakages.

Disposable nappies and any items used during care routines should again be securely bagged and disposed of in a waste bin set aside for that purpose.

Care of skin, teeth and hair

Skin care is important because it is the front line area of defence for the body as it comes into contact with the environment. It is necessary to protect the skin from short-term problems:

- discomfort
- irritation
- infection.

Table 35.7 Safety marks

Mark	Name	Meaning
	BSI Kitemark	Indicates a product has met a British safety standard and has been independently tested
	Lion Mark	Indicates adherence to the British Toy and Hobby Association Code of Practice and ensures a product is safe and conforms to all relevant safety information
0-3	Age Warning	Indicates: 'Warning – do not give the toy to children less than 3 years, nor allow them to play with it'. Details of the hazard, e.g. small parts, will be near the symbol or with the instructions
BEAB Approved	BEAB Mark of the British Electrotechnical Approvals Board	Indicates that electrical appliances carrying this mark meet a national safety standard
	BSI Safety Mark on gas appliances, light fittings and power tools	Indicates the product has been made and tested to a specific safety standard in accordance with the British Standards Institute
RES STANT	Safety Mark on upholstered furniture	Indicates upholstery materials and fillings have passed the furniture cigarette and match tests – a lighted cigarette or match applied to the material will not cause the article to burst into flames
LOW FLAMMABILITY TO BS 5772 KEEP AWAY FROM FIRE LOW FLAMMABILITY TO BS 5772	Low Flammability labels	Children's pyjamas, bathrobes made from 100% Terry towelling and clothes for babies up to 3 months old must carry a label showing whether or not the garment has passed the Low Flammability Test. Either of these two labels is acceptable. Always look for these labels when choosing such garments
KEEP AWAY FROM FIRE	Keep Away From Fire label	Indicates the garment is not slow burning and has probably not passed the Low Flammability Test. Great care must be taken anywhere near a fire or flame

It is also necessary to protect the skin from long-term problems:

- sunburn
- sun damage (that can lead to skin cancers)
- scarring from repeated irritation or infections.

Babies have sensitive skin and many of our everyday products are far too harsh for them. It is therefore important to use specially prepared baby products suitable for sensitive skins during all care routines.

Skin types

Skin types vary, as do family practices, and it is important that in any setting the preferences of parents are taken into account. Most day care settings ask parents to provide their own products and these are clearly labelled and kept solely for the use of their baby.

case study 35.2

Jerome

Jerome is West Indian and his skin tends to be very dry. His parents rub cocoa butter into his skin after his bath. They also massage his skin with oil, particularly his arms and legs, at each nappy change. They have supplied Jerome's nursery with a bottle of oil, and asked them to continue this practice during the day.

activity

1 What precautions, if any, need to be in place here?
2 Who should carry out the massage?

Professional Practice

- Babies with black skin have a greater tendency to dry skin than those with other skin types.

remember

Any oil used on babies and young children should be free of nut traces (almond oil used to be popular but is no longer used), as there is concern about links with the increase in nut allergies in young children. Many specialists recommend the use of organic sunflower oil, which is what Jerome's parents use.

Eczema

Eczema is a common complaint in young children which produces a dry, scaly, itchy skin. Children with this condition will need particular support during bad phases. Some will need to have prescribed ointments applied during the day. Staff taking on this role should wear disposable gloves to reduce the risk of passing any infection on to the child, and also to prevent themselves from absorbing the ointments or creams (which often incorporate corticosteroids) into their own skin.

Note: Older children with eczema may need to be encouraged to wear gloves during activities such as sand play to avoid exacerbating their condition. They should be taught to wash and dry their skin carefully and thoroughly.

Skin infestations and conditions

From time to time **skin infestations** and infectious conditions can occur in early years settings. These can spread very quickly, but preventive measures for cross-infection, which should be standard practice, should help contain them to some extent. There will usually be a policy regarding the admittance of children and babies with an infectious condition. Ask your current placement setting if you can see what is included in their policy. Skin infestations and infectious conditions include:

- scabies
- impetigo
- hand, foot and mouth disease.

Scabies

- *What is scabies?* Scabies are tiny parasites that burrow into the skin. They are sometimes known as itch mites due to the intense itching they cause, particularly at night. It is an extremely infectious condition, which is passed on by physical contact, either from person to person, or via towels, flannels and bedding.
- *Identifying scabies* The scabies mites burrow into the skin, leaving thin track marks under the skin where they have passed through. The itching causes redness and sore patches, which may at times be mistaken for eczema.
- *Treatment* Scabies will not disappear without treatment. A special lotion prescribed by the GP is needed, and each individual who has been in contact with the infected child needs to be treated. This usually includes their whole family and the staff in their care setting who have worked closely with them.

Impetigo

- *What is impetigo?* Impetigo is an extremely infectious skin condition, which often affects the mouth and nose. It also affects the nappy area of babies. It is caused by bacteria, which enter the body through a break in the skin. As with scabies, it is passed on by physical contact, either from person to person, or via towels, flannels and bedding.
- *Identifying impetigo* Red skin with tiny blisters is the most noticeable sign. The blisters weep and gradually crust over with yellowish scabs.

- *Treatment* Antibiotic creams will be needed from the child's GP. It is important to try to avoid cross-infection, and to discourage children from scratching. Babies and toddlers may benefit from wearing cotton gloves at night. Scarring can occur if scratching is intense. Complications are a possibility, causing a general infection of the body, which can affect the child's kidneys.

Sun care

Research has shown how seriously our skin can be damaged by the sun's rays, and children and babies should not be exposed to the sun for more than a very short period of time. Babies should be kept in the shade whenever possible (watch out for the sun moving round if they are in prams or pushchairs) and outdoor play in sunny areas should be restricted, particularly around midday when the sun is at its highest point.

Hats should be worn, and each setting should have a policy regarding the application of sun creams. Sunscreen creams and lotions for children and babies should be of the highest factor, or be a total sun block. Written parental permission should be obtained before staff apply cream to any child.

Hair care

Hair care is needed to prevent infestation from head lice and to encourage good grooming for the future. Again, cultural practices differ. Muslim babies will have their heads shaved within 40 days of birth as part of cultural tradition, and many Caribbean parents traditionally weave and plait their babies' hair at a very early age.

Washing the hair of babies can at times be traumatic, as not all babies are happy to have water in their eyes. Hair rings can be purchased, which prevent water from reaching the eyes and can make for a happier bath time. Hair washing products should always be 'non-stinging' to the eyes. There are plenty of different products available.

Dental care

The brushing of a baby's teeth should commence as soon as the first ones arrive, and definitely when a baby has corresponding teeth top and bottom. Soft baby toothbrushes are specially designed for the delicate gums and first teeth, and their regular use will encourage the baby into a habit of good oral health care for the future. In day care settings each baby and child should have their own toothbrush, which should be labelled and kept separately.

It is important to teach children the correct amount of toothpaste to use, and to remember that toothpaste should not be swallowed. Cleaning of teeth should be encouraged after eating and before bed.

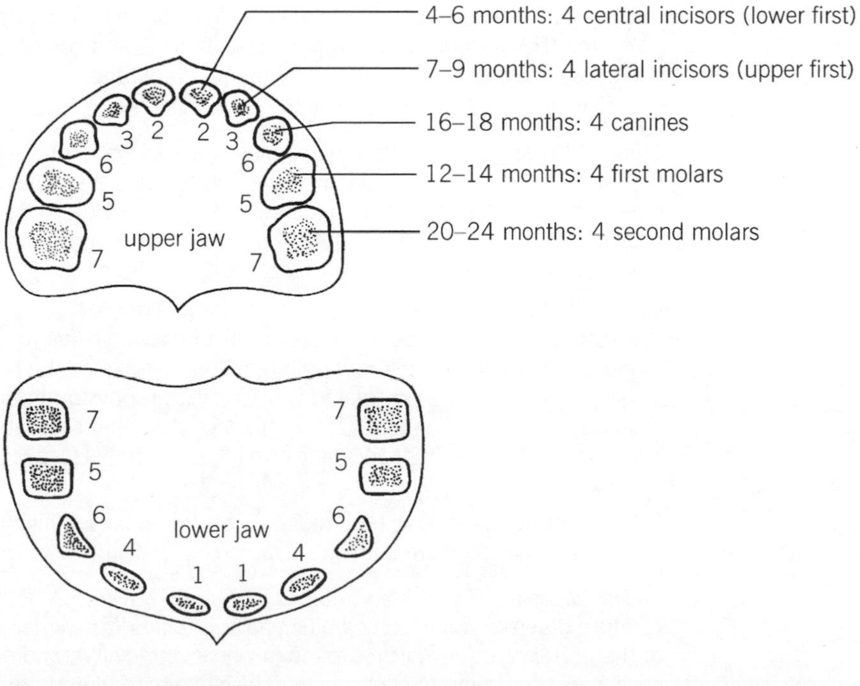

Fig 35.32 The usual order in which milk teeth appear

Toilet training

Bowel and bladder control cannot be achieved until a child is both physically and emotionally ready to do so. The nervous system needs to be mature enough for physical control to take place, and a child needs to be both interested in using a potty and willing to sit on it. The age at which control is attained varies enormously, and the development process needs to be child-led, not thrust upon them by an adult.

Having a potty around for a child to gain familiarity is useful, with positive comments given when they show interest in it. Generally, potty use should take place in the bathroom of the setting, giving the child privacy and restricting any risk of cross-infection.

Professional Practice

- Once a child has started to gain bowel or bladder control, it is important that accidents are dealt with in a matter-of-fact manner, and the child is not made to feel anxious.

Minor bowel and bladder problems in children

All children suffer from diarrhoea and constipation at some point. These are usually due to gastro-enteritis, a viral infection (diarrhoea) or changes in the diet (constipation). They are unpleasant conditions, but rarely serious.

Diarrhoea

Avoiding food and drinking plenty of clear fluids usually helps a child remain hydrated until the virus has passed. If, however, a child suffers from vomiting and diarrhoea for a considerable length of time, they may begin to dehydrate (the water content of the body falls), particularly babies and toddlers, and medical attention will be important to ensure that their body is rehydrated.

Link

More information on common illnesses in children, including gastro-enteritis, can be found on page 36.

remember

Laxatives should never be given to a child without medical advice.

Constipation

Usually, increasing the child's consumption of roughage (fruits and vegetables in particular) will reduce the problem, and improve their health in general too. If the problem continues, advice from a health professional may be needed.

More serious bowel and bladder problems

Children with certain chronic conditions suffer from either intermittent or constant bowel problems. This includes children with cystic fibrosis and coeliac disease. Both of these conditions are regularly diagnosed by the toddler stage.

Cystic fibrosis (CF)

Cystic fibrosis is a condition that is mostly associated with respiratory problems, due to the sticky secretions that build up in the lungs, but is a serious digestive condition too. The digestive tract is affected due to the pancreas not being able to produce the appropriate enzymes needed to break down the food and absorb it into the body's systems. It is often identified shortly after birth due to a blockage at the opening of the intestine called a meconium ileus.

Infants that are not diagnosed shortly after birth usually fail to thrive during the first few months due to the malabsorption of food. Their stools will be fatty and have an offensive smell. The sticky lungs are treated with percussion physiotherapy of the chest several times each day to loosen the secretions. Antibiotics are given to treat chest infections. The digestive tract is treated by giving pancreatic enzyme supplements, taken before each meal. These help the body to absorb food.

Children with cystic fibrosis need a diet that is low in fat but high in protein and carbohydrates. It is a life-limiting condition, but current research is moving forward very positively.

Coeliac disease

Coeliac disease is a condition affecting the lining of the small intestine. It is an intolerance of the protein gluten, which is found in wheat, barley, rye and oats. Symptoms indicating coeliac disease begin to show once foods containing gluten are introduced to the infant's diet. Sufferers of this condition fail to thrive in the usual way, by not putting on weight and being continuously low on the centile growth charts. Children are lethargic and pass pale, unpleasant stools.

The condition can be confirmed through blood tests and/or a biopsy of the jejunum (part of the small intestine).

The only way to control the symptoms of coeliac disease is for a gluten-free diet to be adopted. This will be necessary for life. Advice will be given to the family from a dietician, as gluten is found in many everyday foods, and establishing what is suitable and what must be avoided can take time.

If coeliac disease remains untreated, it can lead to iron deficiency anaemia and possible long-term problems with bone density. Calcium supplements are often given throughout life.

Physical signs of illness

Most babies are born with a degree of immunity passed to them from their mother via the placenta. Those who are breast-fed continue to benefit from their mother's protection during the early months. Although the common childhood illnesses are mostly seen from the toddler stage onwards, it is possible for young babies to also be affected, as they come into contact with older siblings with an infectious condition or when an infection enters their early years care setting.

Signs and symptoms of common illnesses

There are many common childhood illnesses. Most last only a short period of time, but can be very unpleasant during the process. Others, such as meningitis, are far more serious. Long-term consequences can result from some conditions and the severity of conditions such as measles, particularly in children who have not been immunised, should never be under-estimated. In being able to identify some of the common conditions, you will be able to help prevent cross-infection of the condition by notifying parents and carers, and arranging to exclude the affected child from the setting.

Common childhood illnesses include:

- chickenpox
- rubella
- measles
- mumps
- hand, foot and mouth disease
- coughs and colds
- gastro-intestinal problems
- asthma.

remember
A serious condition that all early years workers should also know about is meningitis.

Chickenpox

What is chickenpox?
Chickenpox is an itchy and highly contagious condition, which is spread by **droplet infection** (tiny droplets of moisture from the nose or mouth of another person). It causes spots that blister, weep and subsequently crust over.

What causes chickenpox?
It is a viral infection called herpes zoster. The same virus can cause shingles in adults who have previously had chickenpox, if exposed to the virus a second time.

Recognising chickenpox
Spots appear in groups, initially on the torso and then more 'groups' of spots appear anywhere on the body over several days. The spots turn into fluid-filled blisters, which weep and then dry after about three days. As the spots appear in successive groups, they will also dry up in successive groups.

Initial actions
- Comfort and reassurance are needed.
- If initial spots appear in a day care setting, parents need to be contacted.
- Paracetamol is usually given to reduce the discomfort.
- Antihistamines can be useful in reducing the irritation.
- Calamine (or similar) lotion can be applied to the spots to soothe them.
- Using bicarbonate of soda in a cool bath can also help reduce the itching.

Ongoing care

- Paracetamol is usually given as needed, for example to reduce a raised temperature.
- Calamine and bicarbonate of soda can continue to be used over a few days.
- Ensure the child has plenty of fluids and is kept comfortable.
- Cut fingernails short to avoid scratching.
- In young babies cotton mittens can be useful.

Possible complications

- Some children have internal spots; nostrils, throat, vagina, anus.
- Secondary infections can occur through scratching.
- Encephalitis, inflammation of the brain, is rare but serious.
- Pneumonia, inflammation of the lungs, is also rare but serious.

Immunisation

No **immunisation** is available at present, but a vaccine is currently being developed. It is important that pregnant women and children and adults with a reduced immunity due to conditions such as leukaemia or HIV are not exposed to the chickenpox virus.

Incubation period and potential to infect others

- The incubation period for chickenpox can be up to 21 days.
- Children are infectious for about three days prior to the first spots appearing.
- They remain infectious until all the scabs have dried over.

NB Paracetemol is only given when necessary, and by approved staff, for a range of childhood illnesses, unless the child is allergic to it, in which case advice must be sought regarding an alternative.

Rubella (German measles)

What is rubella?

Rubella is usually only a mild condition in children. It involves a high temperature and an all-over rash.

What causes rubella?

Rubella is passed as a virus through droplet infection.

Recognising rubella

The appearance of the rash is usually preceded by a raised temperature. The all-over pale rash, which usually starts on the face, does not itch. Glands are often swollen behind the ears and in the neck.

Initial actions

- Paracetamol can be given to reduce the temperature.
- Drinking plenty of fluids should be encouraged.

Ongoing care

- Avoid contact with women who are or could be pregnant as contact during the first 12 weeks can affect the foetus.
- No other special care is needed, and children usually recover quickly.

Possible complications

- In children and adults there are unlikely to be complications.
- To an infected foetus, complications can include:
  - loss of hearing or vision
  - impaired hearing or vision
  - heart deformities
  - learning difficulties.

Immunisation

Rubella vaccine is given as part of the MMR triple vaccine at aged 15 months and 4 years.

Incubation period and potential to infect others

- The incubation period for rubella is 14–21 days.
- Children are infectious from about seven days prior to the rash appearing and until four to five days afterwards.

Measles

What is measles?
Measles is a highly contagious virus with a distinctive rash. It can be a very serious condition.

What causes measles?
The virus is passed through droplet infection.

Recognising measles
Children usually appear unwell for three to four days before the rash appears. Runny nose and general cold symptoms are common. The rash is dense, blotchy and red, usually starting on the neck and face before spreading down over the whole body. White spots form inside the mouth or on the cheeks (Koplik's spots). Eyes become sore and an avoidance of bright lights is common.

Initial actions
- Paracetamol should be given to reduce the raised temperature.
- Plenty of fluids should be encouraged.
- Children would only be visited by a GP in exceptional circumstances, but in most health authorities will usually be seen by a health visitor to confirm diagnosis, and referred to the GP if necessary.
- Children will normally be most comfortable resting with curtains closed to reduce the light.

Ongoing care
- Paracetamol can be given as necessary.
- Continue to ensure a high fluid intake.

Possible complications
- Eye infections may need antibiotics.
- Ear infections may need antibiotics.
- Hearing needs to be checked within a few weeks of illness if ears were affected.
- Inflammation of the brain can occur (encephalitis).

Immunisation
Measles vaccine is given as part of the MMR triple vaccine at age 15 months and 4 years.

Incubation period and potential to infect others
- The incubation period for measles is 8–14 days.
- Children are infectious from the day before the symptoms appear until four to five days afterwards.

Mumps

What is mumps?
Mumps is an inflammation of the salivary glands. These are found in front of and below the ears. It can be a very painful condition.

What causes mumps and how is it spread?
It is caused by a virus and is spread by droplet infection.

Recognising mumps
Initially children feel unwell for two or three days before the swelling occurs. Swelling and tenderness occurs on either or both sides of the face. A raised temperature is usual and earache is common. Eating and drinking can cause pain due to restricted movement of the jaw.

Initial actions
- Paracetamol can be given to reduce the temperature.
- Drinking plenty of fluids should be encouraged (using a straw might be helpful).

Ongoing care
- Timing paracetamol to be given shortly before meals will help pain when eating.
- Easy-to-eat foods should be offered such as soup, jelly or stewed fruits.

Possible complications
- Hearing loss or even deafness.
- Meningitis – inflammation of the meninges.
- Orchitis – inflammation of the testes (unusual in young children).

Immunisation
Mumps vaccine is given as part of the MMR triple vaccine at 15 months and 4 years. Having the condition provides the body with natural immunity

Incubation period and potential to infect others
- The incubation period for mumps is 14–21 days.
- Children continue to be infectious for several days after the symptoms have appeared.

Hand, foot and mouth disease

What is hand, foot and mouth?
This is a mild, but highly infectious condition, which is common in children of pre-school age. It is in no way connected to foot and mouth disease found in cattle and other hoofed animals.

What causes hand, foot and mouth?
It is a viral condition spread by droplet infection. The virus is called coxsackie.

Recognising hand, foot and mouth disease
A child's temperature may be raised slightly. Very small blisters are often found inside the cheeks, which may ulcerate. Blistery spots with a red surrounding edge appear about two days after the mouth blisters on hands and fingers, and tops of feet.

Initial actions
- Paracetamol can be given to reduce the raised temperature.
- Give plenty of fluids. Avoid anything that might irritate the sore mouth.
- Foods suitable for a slightly sore mouth should be offered.

Ongoing care
Prolonged mouth blisters may require an appointment with the GP.

Possible complications
No real complications have been noted.

Immunisation
There is no immunisation available for hand, foot and mouth disease.

Incubation period and potential to infect others
There is no known incubation period.

case study 35.3

Russell

Russell is 6 and is in the Year 2 class at your placement. He was not his usual bright and cheerful self this morning and did not run around at playtime as he usually would. Russell is now running a raised temperature and has a pale rash on his face. He says his ears hurt and his neck feels lumpy.

activity

1 What do you think might be wrong with Russell?
2 How should he be cared for?
3 Might there be any long-term health problems linked to Russell's illness?
4 If yes, what might they be?

Coughs and colds

What are coughs and colds?
Coughs and colds can vary from the very mild to quite severe. They can be highly contagious.

What causes coughs and colds?
Coughs and colds are caused by viral infections. They are passed through droplet infection. Coughs can also be part of another condition, such as bronchitis or pneumonia.

Recognising coughs and colds
Colds usually start with a raised temperature and runny nose and eyes. Accompanying coughs can be dry and ticklish, or deep and chesty.

Initial actions
- Paracetamol can be given to reduce the raised temperature.
- Plenty of fluids should be offered.

Ongoing care
Continue to give paracetamol as necessary.

Possible complications
- Ear infections may require antibiotics.
- Chest infections may require antibiotics.

Immunisation
There is no immunisation for the common cold.

Incubation period and potential to infect others
Each cold virus is unique and so there is no known incubation period.

Gastro-enteritis

What is gastro-enteritis (vomiting and diarrhoea)?
Gastro-enteritis is the most common irritant of the stomach and intestinal lining.

What causes gastro-enteritis?
It is caused by bacteria and viruses. It can be passed in food due to poor hygiene during food handling, by **direct contact** or **indirect contact**.

Recognising gastro-enteritis
Children appear unwell, lethargic and miserable before the onset of the main symptoms, which include:

- vomiting
- diarrhoea
- raised temperature
- loss of appetite.

Initial actions
- Only clear fluids (cooled boiled water) should be given for 24 hours.
- Re-hydration drinks may be used for children over the age of 1 year, particularly if symptoms are severe.

Ongoing care
- Breast-fed babies should continue to breast feed as usual.
- If there is no improvement, medical advice should be sought, particularly in very young children.
- Continue with clear fluids, together with 'ice-pops' to give the child some sugar.
- Light foods should be offered when appetite returns.
- Diet drinks are not considered to be suitable for children.

Possible complications
- Dehydration can easily occur in very young children and babies.
- If children cease to pass urine frequently, medical advice should be sought.
- Intravenous fluids may need to be given in severe cases.

Immunisation
There is no immunisation available.

Incubation period and potential to infect others
- Strict hygiene is needed to try and minimise the spread of infection.
- Gastro-enteritis often 'sweeps' through families, nurseries and schools.

Asthma

What is asthma?
Asthma is a condition of the lungs.

What causes asthma?
It is a narrowing of the airways that can be caused by a variety of 'triggers', e.g.

- infections
- going out into the cold air
- cigarette smoke
- exercise
- allergies.

Recognising an asthma attack
There may be:

- coughing
- shortness of breath
- wheezing
- a tightness in the chest area.

Initial actions

- It is important to keep calm in order to encourage calm in the child
- If it is a child's first attack, seek medical help

Managing an attack
Keene (1999) sets out a ten-point plan for managing an asthma attack:

1. Reassure the child.
2. Encourage relaxed breathing – slowly and deeply.
3. Loosen tight clothing around the neck.
4. Sit the child upright and leaning forward, supporting themselves with their hands in any comfortable position.
5. Stay with the child.
6. Give the child their bronchodilator to inhale if they are known asthmatics – dosage according to the GP's instructions.
7. Offer a warm drink to relieve dryness of the mouth.
8. Continue to comfort and reassure. Do not panic as this will increase the child's anxiety which will impair their breathing.
9. When the child has recovered from a minor attack they can resume quiet activities.
10. Report the attack to the parents when the child is collected. If the child is upset by the episode the parents should be contacted immediately.

An ambulance should be called if:

- it is the child's first attack
- after 5–10 minutes there is no improvement in the child
- the child becomes increasingly distressed and exhausted
- blueness of lips, mouth or face begins to occur.

Ongoing care
There are two different types of inhalers:

- preventers, which contain medicines to reduce the swelling and mucus in the airways; they are usually in brown/orange inhalers and are used on a regular basis to prevent asthma attacks
- relievers, which contain medication that dilates the airways; they are usually in blue inhalers and are used to relieve symptoms of wheezing and coughing when an attack occurs or are used prior to exercise to prevent an attack.

Possible complications
Each year a small number of children die during an attack.

Immunisation
There is no immunisation available.

Incubation period and potential to infect others
Asthma cannot be passed on to others.

Meningitis

Meningitis is not common, but it is serious, and every practitioner working with babies and children needs to know about it.

What is meningitis?
Meningitis is an inflammation of the protective covering of the brain and spinal cord, known as the meninges.

What causes meningitis and how is it spread?
Meningitis can be caused by different organisms, and can be either viral or bacterial. Bacterial meningitis is always the more serious type.

Recognising meningitis
Symptoms for both viral and bacterial meningitis are similar in the early stages.

In babies:

- high temperature
- drowsy and irritable
- vomiting
- crying and restless
- fontanelles may bulge in a very young baby due to pressure inside the skull.

In children:

- headache
- vomiting
- averting eyes from the light (photophobia)
- a stiff neck (the muscles become rigid making it difficult for the neck to be moved forward towards the chin).

Particularly important

- In bacterial meningitis the symptoms will rapidly increase and the child will quickly become very ill.
- Septicaemia may develop (infection of the blood).
- The septicaemia rash looks like bruising appearing.
- The septicaemia rash is flat with dark, purple or pink spots.
- The septicaemia rash does not fade or disappear when pressed (try this with a glass).
- The development of the septicaemia rash is an extreme emergency.

Initial actions

- Always call an ambulance if meningitis is suspected or take child to hospital yourself if this is quicker.
- Keep child in a darkened room until emergency services arrive.
- Reassure the child as best you can and try to reduce their temperature.

Ongoing care

- Intravenous antibiotics will be given by doctor or hospital staff.
- A lumbar puncture (cerebrospinal fluid taken from the spinal canal through a fine hollow needle) is carried out to check that the condition is meningitis, and to identify the correct type of the condition.

Possible complications
There are not usually any complications with viral meningitis. Bacterial meningitis can cause deafness, brain damage, epilepsy and, in some cases, death.

Immunisation
Vaccinations are only available against bacterial forms of meningitis.

- Haemophilus influenzae type b (Hib) and meningitis C is given to infants as part of the infant screening programme.
- Meningitis C vaccine is offered to teenagers and young adults who have not benefited from the introduction of the infant screening programme.

Incubation period and potential to infect others

- The incubation for meningitis can vary between two and ten days.
- At times local communities are screened for signs of meningitis following an outbreak. This usually involves throat swabs and prophylactic antibiotics (used as a preventive measure). On occasions schools, pre-schools, etc. may close temporarily to avoid further risk of infection.

Appropriate responses to illness

Every early years setting has a policy and procedure for dealing with illness. It is important that you familiarise yourself with these. They will set out where children need to be taken (a separate room or screened area), who telephones a child's parents and when, and who telephones for medical advice or the emergency services. It will also cover the storage and administration of medicines

As an early years practitioner, it is inevitable that you will from time to time have to deal with children who are unwell. This covers both minor sniffs and sniffles to the sudden onset of tummy upsets, childhood illnesses and more serious infections. It is important that you are able to recognise signs that may indicate an unwell child.

As well as a child crying, sitting quietly without interest in activities and clearly not being their usual self, signs of illness include:

- pallor – sickly pale skin tone
- fever – a raised temperature above 37.5° C
- rashes – spots, blisters and blemishes
- breathlessness – often associated with asthma and allergies.

Understand how to provide play activities to encourage learning and development

Play activities

Identifying and choosing play activities

Play and learning go hand in hand. Babies and young children learn through exploration, and that exploration is their play. From the moment an infant finds his toes, or waves his fingers in front of his face, he is starting to play. The **turn-taking** exchanges of vocalising and visual focusing are all early play. The infant explores through all of their senses.

As an early years practitioner, you will need to provide a range of stimulating experiences for the babies and toddlers within your care. This does not necessitate expensive toys and resources. Many stimulating opportunities are found within the home or care environment, and through the responses of the adults caring for them. It is important to remember that the adults in a child's life are a vital resource for them too. They each offer knowledge, skills and experience drawn from their own upbringing, education and general experiences within life.

> **remember** Items suitable for a 3-year-old are unlikely to meet safe care practices for a baby.

This section of the unit sets out a range of ideas for stimulating the under-3s. There are, of course, many more and, as your practical experience grows, you will build up a mental list including an assortment of resource ideas and activities, some needing forward planning, but many offering spontaneous entertainment and stimulation. Finding new ideas is an area of practice that you will find never ends. Practitioners with many years experience continue to discover fresh ideas or new ways of doing things.

Professional Practice

- All activities and resources should meet safety standards and be checked, cared for and replaced according to the practice of the setting.
- The use of risk assessment procedures helps to identify any potential problems in advance, providing the time to withdraw items or adjust the age group they are offered to.

i To remind yourself of safety marks and symbols, refer back to your college notes from studying Unit 2, Positive Environments for Children's Care, Learning and Development, or refer to Green (2007).

Activities need to be carefully thought through for the baby or child being cared for. As a general guide the selection of activities and/or resources offered should:

- be appropriate for the age and stage of their development
- be stimulating
- hold attention
- provide **challenge**, but with achievable outcomes
- provide opportunities for making choices.

As a carer you should:

- plan for each child and provide suitable resources and activities to meet their needs
- supervise and observe the individual child's responses to help inform your planning for them for the future
- encourage them to explore new items, and at times present resources in different ways to help the infant explore from a different perspective
- give praise and show delight in their discoveries
- support their development by at times modelling the use of unfamiliar resources or activities.

Professional Practice

- Children respond well to praise and encouragement, and this applies to babies too. When interacting with babies, you can make them feel wanted and valued as a person by remembering to:
- give them your full attention
- mimic their actions, showing pleasure
- make eye contact with them
- offer objects to them and accept objects when they offer them to you.

Planning a suitable environment

Babies and toddlers need sensory experiences, so it is important to ensure that each sensory area is considered in turn and resourced accordingly.

Fig 35.33 Sensory areas

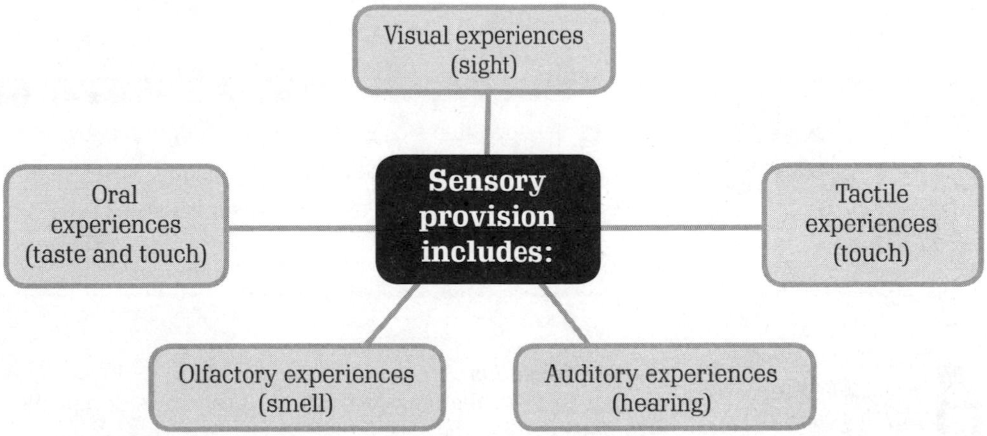

Suggestions for sensory play could include the following.

Visual experiences

To encourage visual experiences (sight) try providing:

- three-dimensional mobiles
- safety mirrors
- bubble tubes

- bubbles for blowing
- balloons and streamers.

Tactile experiences

To encourage tactile experiences (touch) try providing:

- textured mats and 'surprise' bags
- natural wooden items
- messy play such as finger-painting
- silk scarves and hankies
- malleable play such as sand and dough
- blocks and cotton reels.

Auditory experiences

To encourage auditory experiences (hearing) try providing:

- wind chimes
- music boxes
- rattles, shakers and bells
- objects to bang (box and spoon)
- music to listen to and bounce, jiggle, clap and wave to.

Experiences involving smell

To encourage olfactory experiences (smell) try providing:

- wooden items permeated with smells such as lavender or lemon
- bags of herbs, lavender or flowers
- scented tissues inside a box or cloth bag
- citrus fruit (changed regularly).

Experiences involving taste and touch

To encourage oral experiences (taste and touch) try providing:

- hard objects in different shapes
- squashy objects made from various materials
- spoons and cups
- feely books
- textured mats.

activity
GROUP WORK 35.5
P5

1 Select five play items or experiences each from a baby setting you are familiar with.
2 Discuss which senses each item will stimulate.
3 Produce a visual chart to explain how each sensory area is being stimulated.

remember

When planning play for babies and toddlers an important consideration is the positioning of visual stimuli around the room.

Visual stimulation

Because of the different physical stages of a baby's development, they need **visual stimulation** when they are:

- lying on their backs (supine)
- lying on their tummies (prone)
- when sitting, either propped up with cushions or in a chair
- while moving around.

See the illustrations below.

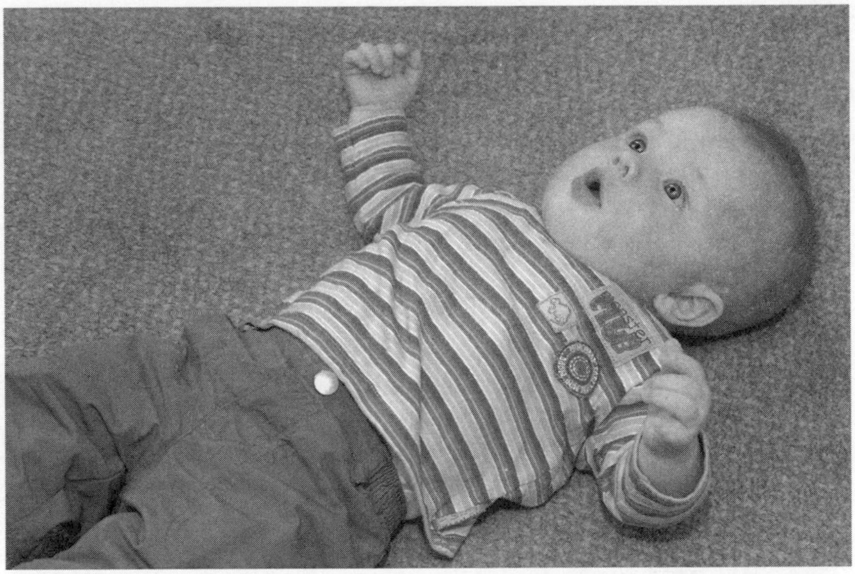

Fig 35.34 Babies who are supine (lying on their backs)

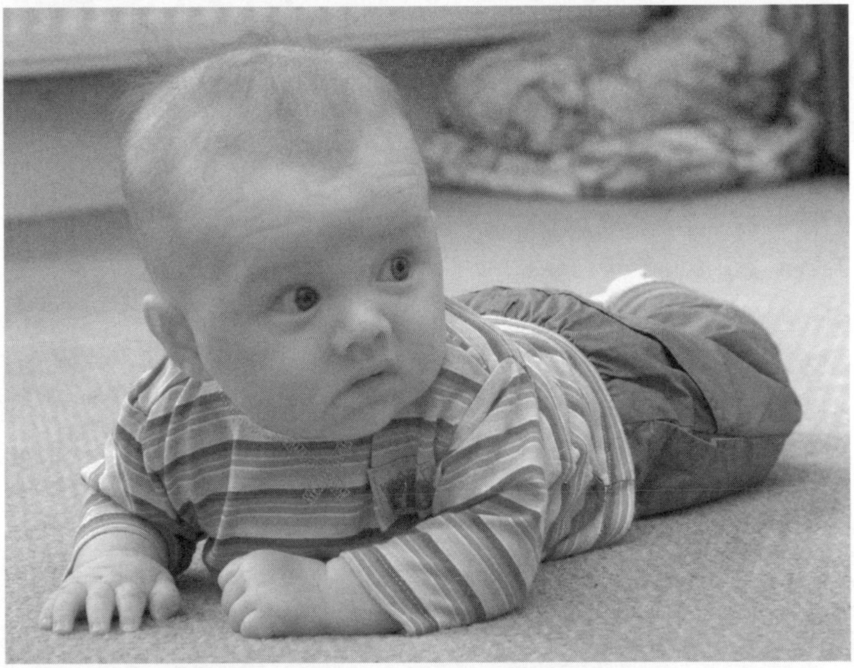

Fig 35.35 Babies who are prone (lying on their tummies)

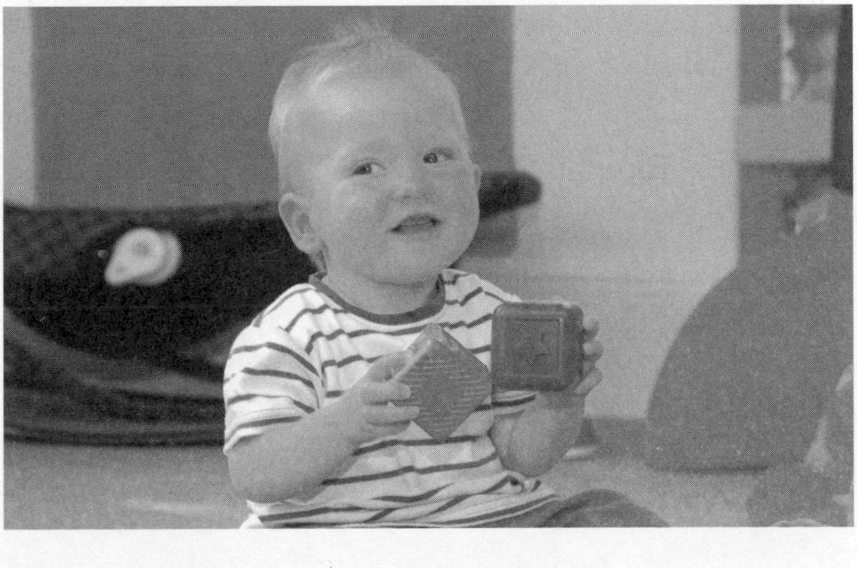

Fig 35.36 Babies who are sitting or are propped up on cushions

Fig 35.37 Crawlers and bear walkers

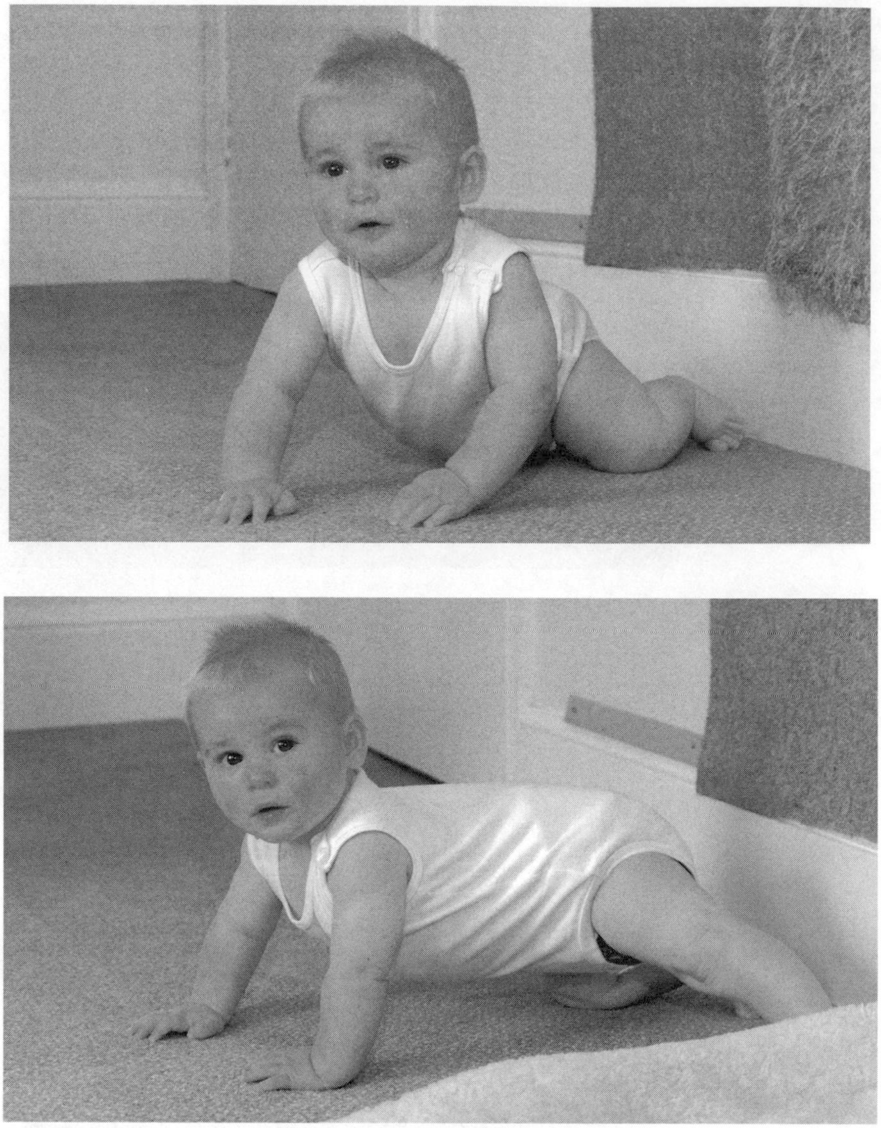

Fig 35.38 Toddlers and those who are standing or pulling themselves up

Visual stimulation is therefore needed on a range of levels to meet the changing needs of babies and toddlers at different stages in their development. Try lying down on the floor to

see the room from the viewpoint of the baby. How good or how limited is your vision? Give consideration to the following ideas.

Try positioning items of interest:

- at skirting-board levels (e.g. safety mirrors)
- on windows and on walls (e.g. pictures, designs, areas of colour)
- on the wall behind and immediately above a sofa (a great place for a safety mirror)
- as objects hanging from ceilings (mobiles, balloons and wind chimes are favourites)
- as attachments to prams, cots, highchairs, etc. (e.g. music boxes, soft toys and wobbly objects).

Fig 35.39 Stimulating play is an essential part of a child's experience

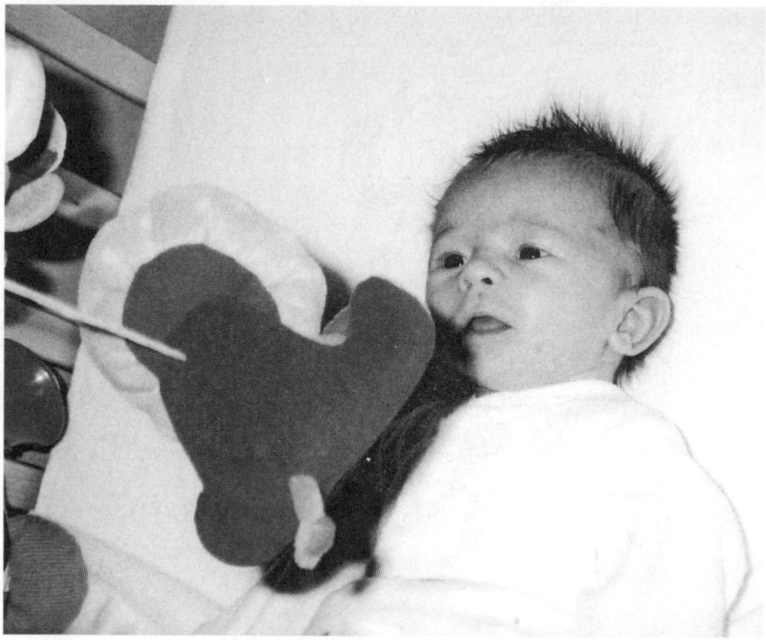

Helping babies and children choose activities that meet their needs

From around 6 weeks, babies benefit from an activity frame or something similar that can be placed above them, encouraging them to focus visually and aurally on the items hanging in front of them and enjoying tactile experiences too, as they come into contact with the items during their natural body movements. Eventually, these movements become more intentional, and repeated actions will be observed, often in response for the 'reward' of a noise or visual 'experience' (movement, reflection or fluttering of material). Opportunities to play at bath time or when having their nappy changed give freedom from the restriction of clothes, allowing full leg mobility, and should be encouraged whenever possible.

Outside

Babies enjoy being outside watching the leaves on trees fluttering and taking in the sounds and smells of the garden. Fresh air is good for them, but they should never be left unsupervised. Care should be taken to ensure that prams are not positioned in the sun, as a baby's delicate skin burns extremely easily. Whenever possible allow a baby to lie out of doors in warm weather without a nappy on, as exposure of the nappy area to fresh air is healthy and stimulating for their skin too. Although most professionals agree that taking a baby out each day is a good idea, this does not apply if the weather is particularly cold, or is foggy.

remember Babies absorb information from all around them and will benefit from as wide a range of experiences as it is possible to give them.

Stimulating play for older babies

As they develop, older babies will be interested in a range of household articles. Sturdy boxes can be handled easily, being passed from hand to hand from about 6 months onwards and knocked together as manipulative control is developed. They will also enjoy banging things in order to make a noise. A useful item for this is a wooden spoon on a saucepan lid or the tray of their high chair. Babies enjoy activities that enable them to explore by themselves through all of their senses. An excellent resource for this is a treasure basket.

Treasure baskets

Infants from about 6 months of age will enjoy exploring a **treasure basket**. They ideally need to be able to sit up securely in order to benefit from the freedom to explore. A treasure basket includes a range of objects that are made of natural materials that can be easily handled by the infant. They should be selected carefully to **stimulate** all the senses, and they should be completely safe. The infant should be allowed to focus on the objects they are handling without distraction from the adult or older children. Nothing in a treasure basket should be made of plastic or any man-made materials.

Fig 35.40 From about the age of 6 months, a baby will enjoy exploring a treasure basket

remember

The objects included in a treasure basket need to be kept very clean. They should not have sharp or rough edges or be at risk of 'coming apart', and none should be small enough to be swallowed, or put up noses. The infant will need supervision while exploring their treasure basket, but not direct adult intervention. The adult's role is to provide, to oversee and to allow freedom of exploration.

The original treasure basket principle can be extended to providing baskets of items of a particular type. Examples could be shiny objects, furry objects, sparkly objects, metal objects, etc.

Professional Practice

- Some older children with a special need may also benefit from exploring a resource prepared along the lines of a treasure basket.

Stimulating play for toddlers and young children

Toddlers enjoy a range of play activities, from developing new ideas for games using 'baby' toys, through to exploring the range of activities also enjoyed by the over-3s. Their first encounters with activities such as sand, painting, model-making, clay, construction materials, etc. will often highlight the limitations of their manipulative dexterity, their creativeness, and at times their confidence in trying new experiences, compared with the over-3s. The adult role here is to provide opportunities, encourage participation in their own time at a level they are secure with and, when appropriate, model actions and make successful (and unsuccessful) attempts at achieving voiced intentions for them. As with all aspects of development, children progress at different rates.

Popular activities/resources for toddlers and children up to 3 years old include:

- push-along toys, e.g. brick trolley, dog on wheels
- pull-along toys, e.g. caterpillar, train
- climbing frames, tunnels, trikes, etc.
- resources to support mimicry of real life, e.g. telephones, tea sets, shopping bags
- dolls, dolls' clothes and bedding

- books needing greater concentration and 'staying power'
- dressing-up clothes and associated accessories
- simple construction materials: Sticklebricks, Duplo, Megablocks, Popoids.

In many ways, 2- and 3-year-olds enjoy the same range of activities as the over-3s, they just use them differently according to their stage in development.

A range of play activities is set out in Unit 4, page 217, of Green (2007) showing how activities link to a child's development. Refer to that section to support your understanding of this unit.

Linking play to development

Understanding which areas of development are supported by which activities comes with experience. Sometimes it is obvious, e.g. providing creative play with crayons and pencils clearly helps manipulation skills, and encouraging play on climbing frames, through tunnels and generally running around clearly help large motor skills to develop, but it is much more complex than that. Most activities offer stimulation and support for more than one development area.

Consider Henry, aged 2 years 9 months, who is engaging with a play-tray type puzzle. How many areas of development are involved in this one play experience?

During this type of play experience, Henry is using fine motor (manipulation) skills to move and adjust the puzzle pieces into place. He is using cognitive (intellectual) skills as he considers shape, order or the picture involved. Gaining satisfaction on completion of the puzzle links to Henry's emotional development and feelings of self-esteem and pride.

Henry talks to his key worker about the puzzle, and shares his pleasure with them. Through these actions Henry is using communication skills and is also socialising.

Activities to support development

Sometimes it is easy to see the learning value of activities and toys, e.g. a push-along dog clearly helps the development of balance and walking in toddlers. Sometimes, however, the learning value is less obvious. The following pages set out a range of popular activities, noting the support they give to different aspects of children's development. The activities are set out under the following headings:

- social development
- emotional development
- physical development
- intellectual development
- language development.

Construction play

Fig 35.41 Construction play encourages social development

Social development

- Developing confidence in selecting resources
- Sharing resources with others
- Negotiating exchanges of resources
- Asking and responding to requests
- Building, using own ideas from observations of their own environment

Fig 35.42 Construction play encourages emotional development

Emotional development

- Showing satisfaction with own achievements
- Showing frustration and disappointment if their intentions fail

Fig 35.43 Construction play and physical development

Physical development

- Handling resources with increasing confidence and skill
- Manipulative skills development with smaller construction pieces
- Precision and increased ability to place pieces carefully
- Large motor skills development when using large boxes, tables, chairs, etc.
- Use of senses to explore shape and texture, e.g. Sticklebricks, Duplo, Popoids

Fig 35.44 Construction play encourages language and intellectual development

Intellectual development

- Increased ability to understand how pieces fit together
- Development of planning and intention
- Increased understanding of stability and strength
- Increased understanding of weight and height
- Increased understanding of the differences between resources
- Increased ability to select and group pieces together by size, shape, colour, etc.
- Helps develop sustained concentration

Language development

- Development of new words and terminology, e.g. build, construct, stability, planning
- Describing plans and intentions
- Discussing ideas and what they are doing

Sand play

Fig 35.45 Sand play helps increase physical control

Social development
- Playing alongside or with others
- Development of the ability to interact
- Imitating the actions of others
- Passing and exchanging tools and resources
- Sharing tools and resources

Emotional development
- Sand can be a soothing experience
- Sand can be a very satisfying experience
- It is a safe, non-fail activity – you cannot play with sand 'wrong'
- Development of confidence in interacting with others

Physical development
- Handling the sand, experiencing the feel and textures of both the sand itself and the various tools that may be provided (sensory experiences)
- Manipulative development – the skills needed to use both dry and wet sand
- Increasing control over body movements

Intellectual development
- Understanding about the properties of sand
- Dry sand pours
- Wet sand moulds, etc.
- Learning that adding water can alter the sand and the type of play
- Increased understanding of absorbency
- Increased understanding of the effects various sand 'tools' can have
- Helps develop sustained concentration

Language development
- Development of new words and terminology, e.g. sift, sieve, pour, trickle, mould, pat, shape
- Increased ability to express ideas and plans

Water play

Social development
- Playing alongside and then with others
- Selecting tools and resources
- Sharing and passing tools to others
- Swapping and negotiating for tools
- Asking for tools and resources and responding to requests

Emotional development
- Water can be a soothing experience
- Water allows a sense of achievement
- It is a non-fail activity – you cannot play with water 'wrong'
- Displaying expressions of pleasure and excitement at new and favourite activities

Physical development
- Increased manipulative skills
- Increased control over body movements
- Handling the water, noting the feel, texture, etc.
- Physically tipping, pouring from one container to another

Intellectual development
- Increased understanding of what water can do
- Investigating and trying out ideas
- Increased understanding of full up and empty

- Increased understanding of volume and capacity
- Increased understanding of floating and sinking
- Helps develop sustained concentration

Language development
- Development of new words and terminology, e.g. float, sink, pour, swish, splash, empty, full, more, less, greater than, less than, heavier, lighter

Dough play

Fig 35.46 Dough provides opportunities to develop a range of manipulative skills

Social development
- Alongside or with others
- Developing confidence in their own ability to interact with others
- Sharing
- Asking for resources or tools and responding to requests
- Passing tools to others

Emotional development
- Dough is a very satisfying medium to use
- It is a non-fail activity – you cannot play with dough 'wrong'
- Actions can be repeated and developed – you can make, squash and remake

Physical development
- Handling the dough – experiencing the feel and texture
- Manipulative skills development – rolling, prodding, poking, pulling, pushing, moulding
- Increased control over body movements
- Developing an increased control of the tools – knives, cutters, forks, rolling pins, graters, etc.

Intellectual development
- Increased understanding of which tools are appropriate for which actions
- Selecting tools for intended actions
- Developing planning skills to make intended 'end results'
- Helps develop sustained concentration

Language development
- New words and terminology to describe the various actions, e.g. rolling, pressing down, forming a ball
- Describing texture and how each action feels
- Increased ability to explain ideas and make suggestions

Role play, including dressing up

Physical development
- Large motor skills development as they dress and undress
- Manipulative development skills as they manoeuvre buttons, zips, etc. with increased control and dexterity
- Precision and dexterity is seen as children lay the table, set out the items for a shop, etc.

Social development
- Imitation of others – being mummy, making dinner, brushing a doll's hair, going shopping
- Linking up with the games of others
- Co-operative play, planning who will be who, and what each will do
- Demonstrating understanding of social greeting and politeness – hello, please, thank you, etc.

Emotional development
- Increased confidence in interacting
- A sense of release and understanding through acting out situations that may concern, confuse or worry them, e.g. a new baby at home, mummy crying, going into hospital
- Development of understanding how other people might feel
- Role play offers opportunities for children to move in and out of reality, as their needs arise

Intellectual development
- Demonstrating understanding of different people's roles
- Demonstrating understanding of cooking processes – cakes go in the oven, pans go on the hob, etc.
- Demonstrating understanding of shopping processes – asking for items, paying for them, taking them home
- Selecting appropriate resources for different roles
- Using one object to pretend it is something else (symbolic play)
- Opportunities for matching, grouping and pairing – cups to saucers, knives to forks, etc.
- Demonstrating knowledge of various situations – hospitals, cafés, etc.
- Responding to ideas and situations

Language development
- Opportunities for conversation
- Opportunities to express ideas from their own imagination
- Using language to organise and make suggestions
- Interacting with others
- Development of new vocabulary as new 'game situations' arise
- Writing skills develop as they make shopping lists, menus for the café, etc.

Activities involving paint

Social development
- Opportunities to make choices – choosing colours, paper sizes, etc.
- Sharing ideas with others
- Using observations as a basis for pictures

Emotional development
- Paint is satisfying and non-competitive – you can't paint your own picture 'wrong'
- Opportunities to show pleasure and excitement at new and favourite activities
- Development of confidence in joining in the 'messiest' activities

Physical development

- Manipulative skills development when using pens, brushes, rollers, etc.
- Increased control of body movements
- Handling paint textures – runny paint, thick paint, etc.
- Handling and using the various alternative 'tools', e.g. sponges, print blocks, straws, rollers
- Learning how to fold paper and card for printing and making cards, etc.

Intellectual development

- Developing the ability and confidence to make choices
- Mixing colours to make additional colours
- Choosing colours, showing understanding to illustrate specific things, e.g. blue for the sky, green for the grass
- Experimenting with new ideas and activities – printing, etc.
- Developing and identifying patterns in colours, shapes, etc.
- Using paint to demonstrate what they have observed

Language development

- Using language to describe colours, textures, etc.
- Using language to describe ideas and intentions
- Discussion of what they have painted or created

Junk modelling

Social development

- Developing confidence in selecting materials
- Observing others and learning from them
- Sharing and negotiation skills regarding resources

Emotional development

- Satisfaction when model is complete
- Pride when showing models, or having them admired
- Learning to deal with frustration if model falls apart
- Learning to deal with disappointment if not enough of a certain size box, etc.

Physical development

- Manipulative development skills
- Increased control of body movements
- Increased ability to hold items in place while constructing
- Development of use of staplers, fasteners, tape, etc.
- Handling a range of materials – texture, feel, etc., e.g. glue is sticky, Sellotape is tacky
- Increased understanding of safety issues, such as the safe use of scissors

Intellectual development

- Increased understanding of how things hold together
- Making choices regarding which junk items to use
- Planning from their own imaginations, e.g. rockets, space ships
- Planning from observations of their environment, e.g. making a vacuum cleaner
- Increasing their understanding of stability and instability
- Increasing their understanding of strength
- Developing understanding of the need to negotiate regarding the space to build and the items required to build something specific
- Helps develop sustained concentration

Language development

- New words and terminology regarding shape, size, materials
- Asking for items and resources

- Using language to describe their model
- Using language to describe their plans and intentions
- Discussion of the size, shape, colour and use of their models.

Books and stories

Fig 35.47 Enjoying a story

Social development

- Often a shared experience
- Can be one-to-one or in a group
- Helps children learn about their social world (families, holidays, everyday situations)
- Helps extend understanding of situations that may cause concern (new baby, moving house, having a tantrum, illness)
- Helps develop observation skills
- Often offers opportunities to join in with actions – to be part of a group

Emotional development

- A range of emotions can be explored (having a new baby, having tantrums, worries about moving house, going into hospital, etc.)
- The repetition of familiar stories and the repeated sequences in many books is comforting to most children
- Books and stories offer opportunities to express emotions, for example, laughter, mock 'fear', etc.

Physical development

- Manipulative skills development through handling books appropriately – turning pages, holding books the right way up, holding books still while looking at them
- Hand–eye co-ordination skills in following the text even before they can read
- There are often opportunities for actions alongside stories

Intellectual development

- Developing an understanding of how books 'work' – from top to bottom and left to right (in English)
- Understanding that books can be both for pleasure and a source of information
- Children learn a great deal about their own environment through the stories they hear and the books they look at
- A child's understanding is consolidated by the repetition of familiar stories

Language development

- Development of new words and terminology:
  - about new objects, new situations, other cultures
  - through joining in with repetition

- through describing what will happen next
- through suggesting what might happen next

Musical instruments

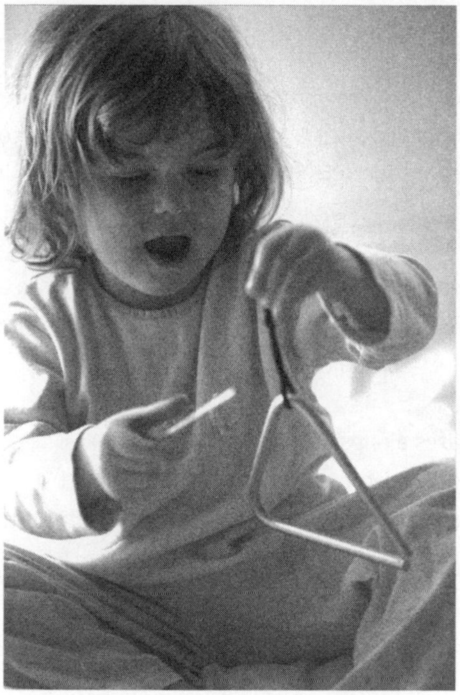

Fig 35.48 Playing musical instruments

Social development

- Often a joint activity with others
- Children learn to play co-operatively
- Development of understanding how to respond to instructions and guidance regarding when to start and when to stop
- Taking turns to play

Emotional development

- There can be an emotional release through music
- Gentle sounds can soothe a distressed child
- Bold sounds can liven up a sad or unusually quiet child
- Children learn to enjoy and value the sounds and instruments of their own culture
- Children learn to enjoy and value the sounds and instruments of other cultures
- Understanding of the need to consider other people can be learnt through taking turns to listen to each other play

Physical development

- Manipulative skills development through the use of instruments
- Large motor skills development through the opportunities to balance, dance and march to music (locomotion)
- Developing the ability to move rhythmically
- Linking music to dance and movement
- Learning about the different feel of various instruments, e.g. cymbals – metal, drums – skins, maracas – wooden, shakers – gourds (a hollowed-out fruit)

Intellectual development

- Increased knowledge of the origins of instruments and music
- Increased knowledge of the different types of sounds that can be made
- Sequencing and patterning within music
- Linking music to dance and movement

- Understanding the changes in pitch, tempo, etc.
- Helps develop sustained concentration

Language development
- increased vocabulary, e.g.
  - sound names
  - instrument names
  - rhythmic words: slow, slow, fast, fast, slow
  - development of voice pitch and how it can be changed to match different instruments
  - increased listening skills

Puzzles

Social development
- With younger children this is often a shared activity with an adult
- Floor puzzles are usually enjoyed in pairs or small groups
- Pictures often depict objects or situations from children's own environment and experience

Emotional development
- Confidence increases alongside skill development
- Satisfaction is experienced when puzzles are completed
- Learning to deal with frustration if puzzle becomes difficult to achieve

Physical development
- Manipulative skills development
- Increased ability to handle small pieces
- Increased ability regarding hand–eye co-ordination

Intellectual development
- Developing understanding of how to match pieces to gaps, identifying shape, size, etc.
- Learning through trial and error in the earliest stages
- Demonstrating understanding of processes by matching pieces to accompanying pictures
- Helps develop sustained concentration
- Eventual development of memory regarding the completed picture, helping the child visualise what they are trying to achieve

Language development
- Using language to talk about the picture
- Using language to talk about shapes, size and how to position pieces
- New words, e.g. place, hold, edges, twist, turn, flat, turn over, etc.

Stacking toys and posting boxes

Fig 35.49 Building with blocks

Social development
- Initially this would be a shared activity with an adult or older sibling
- Children learn to build jointly with another person
- Knocking down the tower would be another joint fun action
- Working together, the adult will help the child (perhaps hand over hand) to guide them to success in posting a shape in a post box or shape sorter
- Opportunities for child to select which piece to post, or which piece to stack next

Emotional development
- Satisfaction and pleasure is seen when successful
- Pleasure and excitement is seen in knocking down the tower
- Increased confidence is developed in line with increased physical (manipulative) skills

Physical development
- Manipulative skills development – handling with increasing control
- Precision and positioning skills
- Hand–eye co-ordination
- Exploration of shapes with both hands and mouths

Intellectual development
- Learning to stack by size (beakers and rings)
- Learning to enclose by size (beakers, 'Russian doll'-style objects)
- Matching shapes to correct shape holes
- Learning by trial and error
- Counting opportunities as stacking and sorting objects occurs
- Learning about colours as each colour is stated for them by the adult

Language development
- Shape names are introduced by the adult
- Colour names introduced by the adult
- Counting
- Introducing vocabulary, such as biggest, smallest, bigger than, etc.

Threading reels and buttons

Social development
- Often playing alongside or with others
- Making decisions and selecting resources
- Asking for resources and responding to requests
- Sharing and swapping resources

Emotional development
- This is a calm, satisfying activity
- A sense of pleasure is seen in achievement
- Children enjoy being able to make their own choices

Physical development
- Manipulative skills development
- Hand–eye co-ordination
- Increased control over body movements
- Handling the threading of objects with increased ability and precision

Intellectual development
- Developing the ability to sequence by shape, size and colour
- Developing the ability to group by shape, size, colours, etc.
- Learning to plan and have intentions
- Learning to add on and count
- Learning to take one away
- Helps develop sustained concentration

Language development

- Development of words and terminology:
    - colour names
    - shape names
    - counting
    - using language to ask for and negotiate
    - using language to talk about length, purpose, etc.

activity
INDIVIDUAL WORK 35.6
M3

Explain what is meant by challenge in children's play, giving a variety of examples across the age range up to 3 years.

Understand how to communicate with babies and children under three, interpret their needs and respond to them

Communication between human beings, whatever their ages, involves:

- facial expressions
- tone of voice
- body posture
- expression of meaning through the use of both words and symbols.

Development

Language development is affected by all other aspects of our development too. For example, socially and intellectually an understanding of the need to interact with others as a means of communication is vital, as are the physical abilities of vision, hearing and speech. Without these, it can be difficult for language to develop normally.

Sequence in which communication develops

Link

The ten main stages of language development, through which most infants pass, are set out on page 350, together with a chart illustrating how and when the first words are produced, the type of words that appear first, i.e. nouns before verbs and pronouns, and how these develop into phrases and the asking of questions. You may find it helpful to remind yourself of these sequences before you read on.

How and why babies communicate from birth

Communication with babies can be both verbal and **non-verbal**. Pre-verbal communication is a vital part of supporting an infant's future language skills. It is seen as the adult encourages the baby to take a share in the conversation, asking them questions and supplying them with answers or making reaffirming comments following a pause in which the infant adds their own vocalisations. Welcoming the vocal sounds of babies encourages them to vocalise further.

Babies are born ready to communicate and they respond from birth to both voice and touch, quickly recognising their main carers.

Professional Practice

- Taking time to observe an adult with a young baby will give you an example of how you too can 'converse' with a baby in their earliest weeks.

Pre-verbal stage

When you spend time with a young baby you will find that talking to them and watching them respond to you will automatically be encouraging and enhancing their communication with you. This 'turn-taking' between carer and infant was identified by Stern in the 1970s, who put forward the theory that infants learn the basis of their social interactions in this way.

Motherese

The term **motherese** is what we often call baby talk. Motherese speech:

- has a higher pitch than that used with other people
- is slower, with simplified words and phrases usually being employed
- includes frequent pauses, to facilitate the turn-taking
- mostly consists of key words linked to the current situation, e.g. naming words if playing jointly with a toy (nouns), or action words (verbs) when moving the infant or referring to a specific action.

Examples include 'Here is teddy' or 'Up you come for a cuddle'.

Adults communicate with babies in many ways. Some of the most important ones are:

- eye contact during breast or formula feeds
- turn-taking vocally or visually
- initiating 'conversations' with babies as you play
- observing the needs of babies through their **body language** or facial expression
- responding to their cries
- encouraging them to vocalise
- showing appreciation of their vocalising
- giving praise
- calling to them when out of their visual range
- stimulating them aurally
- stimulating them visually.

case study 35.4

Mary

Mary works in the baby room. She is preparing a formula feed for William, who is 6 months old. William is in his chair, and Mary is currently out of his line of vision as she gets his bottle ready. She calls to him in a sing-song voice, pausing to hear him make a noise in response, before calling him again. When she brings his feed to him, Mary takes him out of his chair and cuddles him on her lap while he is fed. He watches her face, and she smiles at him, talking quietly to him all the time.

activity

1. Which forms of communication listed above do you consider that Mary used?
2. Do you think there were opportunities for any other form of communication to have taken place?
3. What might be the outcome for a baby who does not have opportunities for communication?

Responding to children

Responding to pre-verbal speech

Babies become distressed for lots of reasons. It may be because they are tired, wet, hungry, uncomfortable, unwell, teething or simply bored. Working out what is the cause of their distress is not always easy. If a young baby is distressed at the same time every day, it can often be attributed to a condition known as **colic**. Mostly, when a baby cries, they are trying to tell us something.

Fig 35.50 Identifying a baby's needs

Why is the baby crying?

My tummy hurts
If a baby is distressed at the same time of day every day, it can often be attributed to colic. Colic is a painful condition, common in the first four months, in which the baby pulls up their legs indicating abdominal pain and is very difficult to console. There is no known cause for colic and it tends to disappear by itself by the time the baby reaches four months old. It is, however, distressing for both baby and carer and advice from a health visitor is advisable. The baby is usually thriving well in spite of the colic and no other symptoms are displayed.

I'm tired
Babies become over-tired if they do not have sufficient periods of restful sleep, and a baby who is constantly disturbed may become irritable. It is important to allow babies an extended period of sleep whenever possible.

I want my nappy changed
A wet or soiled nappy is uncomfortable, and most babies prefer to be clean and dry. Regular changing of babies helps prevent the development of nappy rash, as does allowing fresh air to their bottoms by leaving them to kick freely at some point each day.

I'm so bored
Sometimes, however, babies are simply bored, and so it is important to offer them stimulation. Mobiles over the cot or hanging from the ceiling are ideal visual stimulants and musical toys will stimulate them aurally. Babies also enjoy the company of their carers and will respond with pleasure and recognition from a very early age.

Please leave me alone
Sometimes babies become distressed when being handled, but this is usually a stage that passes quickly. Handling should be gentle and kept to a minimum until they find it more pleasurable.

I'm too hot
A baby who is too hot or too cool may also cry in discomfort. Adjusting the temperature of the room or their clothing will usually help.

My gums hurt
If a baby is unwell or teething, they may simply want to be cuddled. For a teething baby, a refrigerated teething ring will help cool down their gums and firm flexible teething toys will give them something appropriate to chew hard on. Preparations are available to rub onto the gums to alleviate discomfort of the gums and paediatric paracetamol can be given in times of extreme discomfort.

I want my bottle
A hungry or thirsty baby is often the easiest to identify as they tend to root for the breast or bottle when picked up or suck on whatever passes their mouth. In a day-care setting, making a note of the time and amount of feed taken by the baby helps you to anticipate their next feed time and is a general requirement of those caring for babies.

remember
Babies are best dressed in layers of lightweight clothing that can be taken off or added to as necessary.

Sometimes babies will simply want a drink in the same way as adults and older children do. Small amounts of cooled boiled water can be introduced to even very young babies, especially in hot weather.

Every baby is different. Each baby has their own individual personality. Some babies cry much more than others. It is possible to over-stimulate a baby, tiring them and causing irritability. Illness must never be ruled out, but will usually be considered when other causes have been eliminated unless additional symptoms are present. Offer support to parents of a constantly crying baby as it can be very draining.

Professional Practice

- It can be useful to find out about support groups such as Cry-sis, collecting copies of their information that could be given to parents or carers of a regularly distressed infant.

activity
INDIVIDUAL WORK 35.7
M4

Describe three situations you have observed where a baby or young child has been distressed.

- What, if any, signs did they give beforehand?
- How was their distress dealt with?
- Would you have done anything different?
- What have you learned from these examples about interpreting and responding to needs?

By about 4 months, recognition of an approaching feed is demonstrated by excited actions and squeals. This is communication.

- Language develops through cooing, gurgling, excited squealing and changing tones of their own voice.
- By 5 months, the infant's enjoyment of their own voice is obvious. Chuckles and laughs are evident.
- By about 8 months, the infant babbles continuously and tunefully, e.g. mamamama babababa.
- First 'words' may be apparent by a year, usually dada, mama, baba.
- Understanding of simple instructions or statements begins from about 9 months, and is clearly evident by a year.

Link Refer to page 350 for more about language development.

An example of one infant's language development is given in Table 35.8.

Table 35.8 An example of the language development of an infant

Age	Understanding	No. of words	Type of words or sounds	Average length of sentence
3 months	Calmed by Mummy's voice and by music (e.g. Pachelbel's Canon and Sinead O'Connor)	0	Chuckles , coos and gurgles conversationally, turn-taking with adults	0
6 months	Responds to familiar voices	0	Babbles almost incessantly, mainly using the sounds 'ummm' and 'yi yi yi'	0
12 months	Knows own name and a few others	2	'In air?' (Who's in there? or What's that), 'dor' (dog), 'hooray'	1 word
18 months	Repeats her own new word – 'gollygollygolly' and understands 'car' and 'duck'	8	Nouns plus gobbledegook	1 word
2 years	Understands much of what is said to her. Enjoys simple and familiar stories	Approximately 120, some clear, others less so	Verbs and pronouns, e.g. 'Mummy fine it' (Mummy find it), 'Daddy a gate' (Daddy's opening/shutting the gate'), 'boon in sky' (the hot air balloon is in the sky')	2–3 word phrases, e.g. 'bean a sausee' (beans and sausages), 'cackers a chee' (crackers and cheese), 'socks a pink' (the socks are pink)

Green (2004a)

Professional Practice

- During your placement experience you will notice differences in speech, questioning and grammar of children at different ages and stages. You will probably notice that some children will be quite advanced in their speech, but are perhaps less skilled physically, or a very physical child may communicate less well. This demonstrates how very few children are 'advanced' in all developmental areas.

Communication development through bonding

Forming a bond is a child's secure two-way relationship with a parent or regular carer.

Link

Bonding (attachment) is discussed in Unit 14, page 98.

remember

The role of a carer is significant to the baby and their development, but within a care setting, it is not usual for staff to carry out massage with the babies. Permission is always needed from parents.

One very pleasurable way of developing a bond with a baby is through baby massage.

Baby massage

Baby massage is a popular and important means of communication between an adult and a baby, as it enhances the adult's understanding of the baby's needs. Baby massage involves eye contact, touch, smiling and other pleasurable facial expressions, and as it involves such close contact, interaction between parent and baby, or carer and baby is heightened. Baby massage is also used by therapists to help mothers who are suffering from postnatal depression. It strengthens their contact with their baby and encourages the bonding process.

Baby signing

Baby signing is another form of communication. In some early years settings, signing with babies is a new strategy being developed, but always with the agreement of the babies' parents. There are programmes to help train staff and parents, and the thinking behind it is that during the pre-verbal stage, the infant can make themselves understood more easily by using a simple sign indicating that they need a drink, or wish to go to sleep, etc. This communication aid may help avoid some of the frustration felt by infants who are unable to make themselves understood.

Signed languages

There is a range of languages using signs and visual aids. These can help build up a channel of communication for babies, children (and adults) of any age who are unable to communicate verbally, or who find verbal communication very difficult.

Signed language often involves facial, hand and body movements and is used by deaf people, those whose hearing is impaired, people with certain forms of disability and by many people communicating with them. There are a number of different forms of sign language, and each is a language in its own right. Each language has its own rules with regard to grammar and how words are put together. Examples include:

- sign language
- Makaton
- Bliss symbols
- cued speech
- Braille
- Picture Exchange Communication System (PECS).

Makaton, Bliss symbols and the PECs system can be used from a very young age.

Sign language

Fig 35.51 The standard manual alphabet: each of the letters is represented by different hand positions

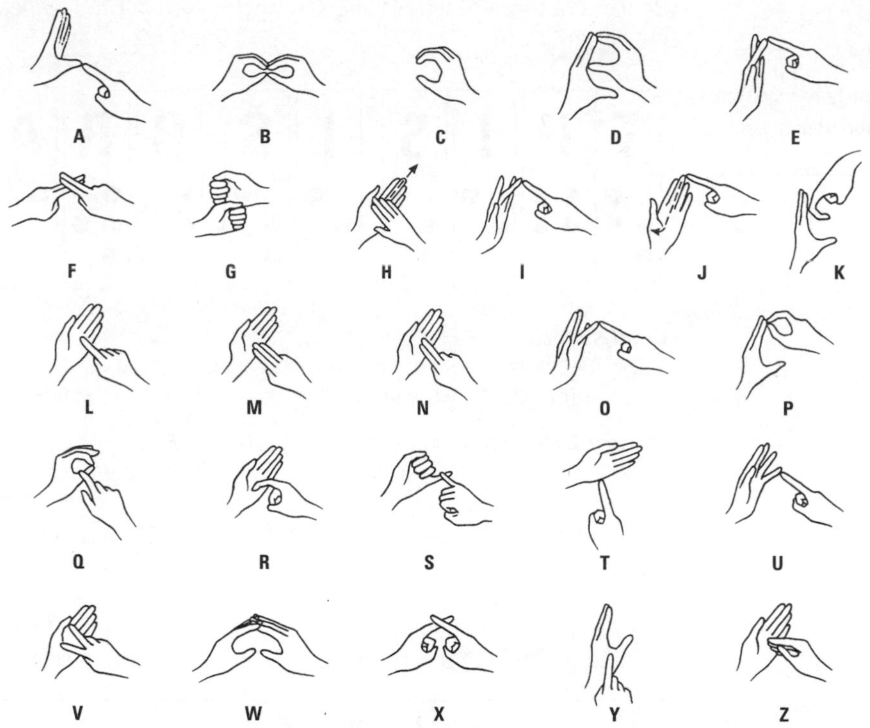

The standard manual alphabet: each of the letters is represented by different hand positions

Bliss symbols

These form 'a universal language of pictographic symbols, which is used by people with reading and writing disabilities' (Mukherji & O'Dea, 2000).

Fig 35.52 Bliss symbols: each child using this system has their own chart of the symbols that they wish to use

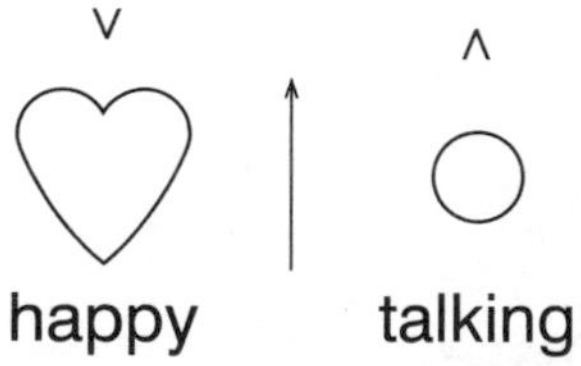

Bliss symbols: each child using this system has their own chart of the symbols they wish to use

Makaton

This is 'a basic signing system using signs borrowed from British sign language; it is used by people who have severe learning difficulties' (Mukherji & O'Dea, 2000).

Fig 35.53 Makaton signs: a system used by many children and adults who have communication difficulties

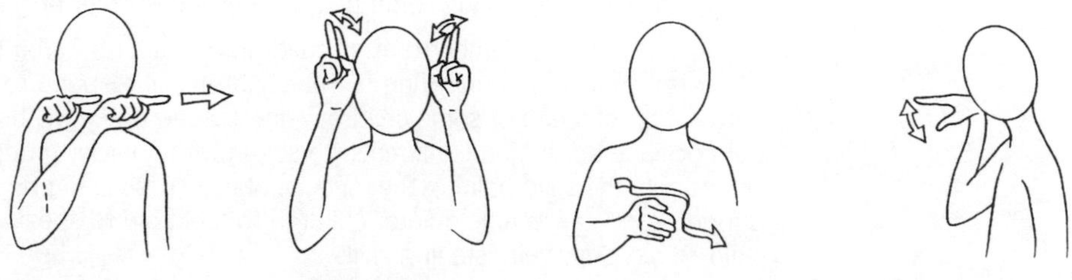

boy
Brush right index pointing left across chin

rabbit
Palm forward 'N' hands, held at either side of head, bend several times to indicate ears

fish
Right flat hand waggles forward like a fish swimming

bird
Index finger and thumb open and close in front of mouth like a beak

Braille

Braille is 'a touch-based reading and writing system used by people who are blind' (Mukherji & O'Dea, 2000).

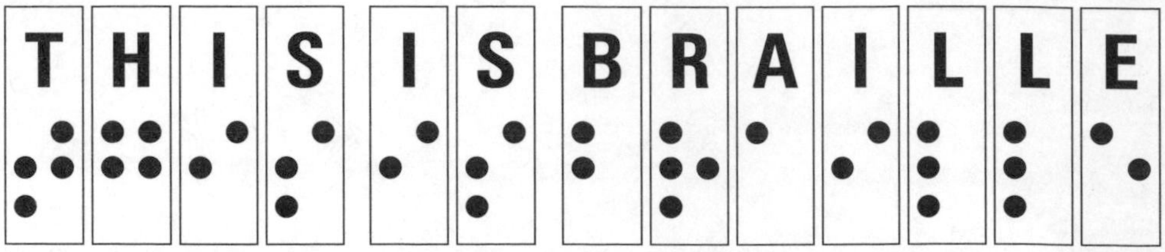

Fig 35.54 Braille is a system of letters made from raised dots

Cued speech

Cued speech is 'a system of eight hand shapes made in four locations near the face to assist children (or adults), who are deaf, in lip-reading' (Mukherji & O'Dea, 2000).

Picture Exchange Communication System (PECS)

Initially, this system uses pictures of items of specific interest to the child, e.g. preferred foods, toys and activities. The child is encouraged to select a picture and hand it to the adult to indicate their request. Each picture is backed with a Velcro fastening and can be placed on a picture exchange board.

As the child's ability to communicate using this system develops, the adult introduces pictures to assist in the building up of sentence structures, and the child selects pictures from a board, locates the adult and hands the pictures or requests to the adult.

Link

See Unit 14, page 127, for more about PECS.

activity
INDIVIDUAL WORK 35.8
P6

Produce a chart to describe the different methods of communicating with babies and children under 3 years that you have observed in your placement.

Responding to children

Relationships with babies and young children are built on familiarity, stability and continuity of care. The way in which you respond to a baby or young child will impact on the communication channel between you and how well you 'tune in' to each other, on the infant's self-esteem (their feeling of being worthy and valued by their carers), and how well they settle into your care.

As the adult carer, you need to be an interested enabler of the children you care for. You will be able to enhance their confidence in themselves and their interest in 'trying again' through acknowledging what they do and encouraging them as they attempt new activities or experiences such as telling something to a group of their peers.

It is important to remember that all children are different. You will need to develop a range of strategies for communicating. Some children will respond to one form of communication better than others. For some children, one-to-one times will be extremely important as they will not have developed confidence to speak within larger groups. Circle time experiences, where only the child holding the 'special object' (this could be a special teddy, large shell, puppet, etc.) can enable quieter children to feel able to speak, and help the over-enthusiastic child to develop their listening skills.

With babies, most enjoy the close comfort of a cuddle when you talk to them, but some do not. You will need to be aware of individual preferences and adjust your approach accordingly.

Communication barriers

Barriers to communication can be social, emotional or cultural. You will need to be aware of the barriers shown in Figure 35.55 and how they can potentially prevent communication taking place.

When communication breaks down for a child they will often only be able to express this through actions. The tantrums often seen during the 2–3-year-old stage are an example of this. You will need to find appropriate ways of managing unwanted behaviour. This is part of emotional development and links to the frustrations of not being able to communicate fully.

Fig 35.55 Barriers to communication

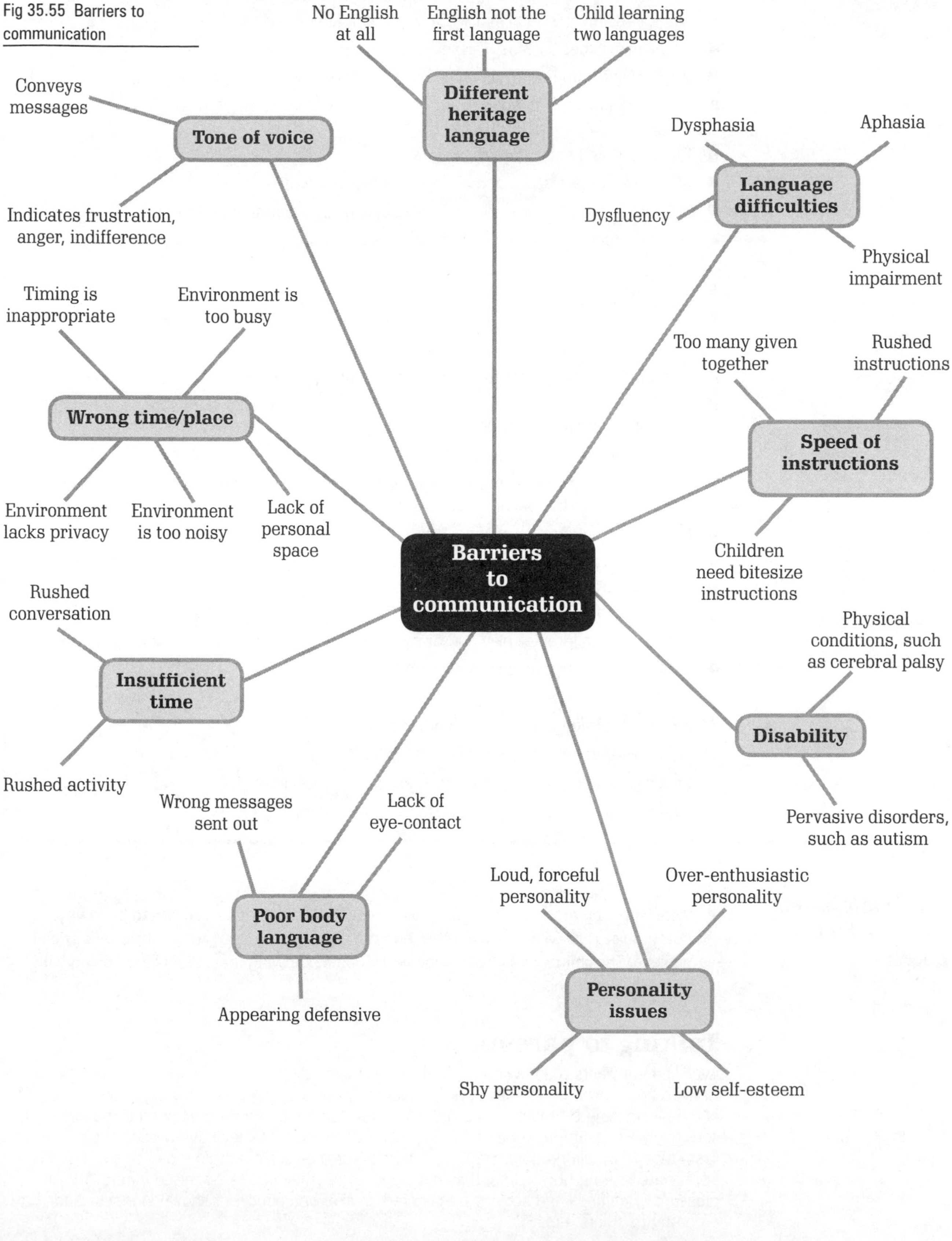

activity
INDIVIDUAL WORK 35.9

D2

Consider the following list of ideas aimed at enhancing communication:

- Greet everyone as they arrive, and give a verbal farewell too
- Read stories and share poems as a group, enjoying excitement and outcomes together
- Sing or say rhymes such as 'Head, shoulders, knees and toes'
- Play circle games such as 'Farmer's in the den'
- Play rocking games such as 'Row, row your boat'
- Use descriptive terms when eating (yummy), bathing (splish, splash), walking through leaves (crunch, crunch), etc.
- Play music and encourage moving to it
- Make eye contact especially during one-to-one activities
- Talk, smile and use physical contact such as tickling during care routines
- Whisper during one-to-one times, at the start of story reading or perhaps when putting to bed
- Join in with games and laughter
- Give a message to be passed on to someone else
- Encourage description of what children are doing
- Describe for babies what they are seeing, hearing or feeling
- Provide instruments and encourage children to make differentiated sounds, e.g. loud and soft, high and low, short and long
- Use pictures of facial expressions to talk about emotions
- Show pictures of regular routines and discuss the order they happen, the importance of them to each individual and their preferences
- Make a tape of familiar sounds. Which can be identified?
- Play memory games, such as 'I had in my basket …'
- Provide co-operative play opportunities such as role-play areas, drama situations (stories such as 'The Three Bears' and 'The Three Little Pigs' can be great fun)
- Photograph children at play and discuss with them what they were doing
- Provide software packages to develop ICT skills

1. Which encourage one-to-one communication?
2. Which encourage communication with others?
3. Which encourage talking, and which encourage listening?
4. How can you identify when understanding has taken place?

Professional Practice

- **Whenever you are with children, take as many opportunities as you can to build your communications with them. You will find out more of what they think, enjoy and hope to achieve. The children will feel valued and wanted, knowing that adults enjoy being with and talking with them.**

Talking to parents

Every parent wants to know how well their child is settling into their early years setting. They want to hear how they are developing, what they enjoy doing, who they enjoy being with and also anything that becomes a problem. Developmental milestones need to be dealt with sensitively. For example, a parent does not wish to hear that they have missed their child's first steps (they will no doubt see this 'miracle' for themselves within a day or so), but will appreciate hearing how helpful they have been, how they have recognised carers, shown pleasure at routines and activities, mastered control of a pencil, or shown kindness and empathy to others, etc.

A child's key worker will be the main person to keep parents informed and updated. It is important that any communication with a child's parent is kept as positive as possible. In the event of having to discuss the difficult issue of unacceptable behaviour, it is helpful if praise can at first be given for what the child has done well.

It is the responsibility of the setting to arrange regular feedback to parents about their child. For some settings, this will take place on a daily basis, usually at collection time. In other settings, a home–setting book enables written comments to be added each day, and provides a two-way communication with parents, helping them to notify carers of any potential problems (e.g. a family occasion or crisis resulting in lack of sleep), or concerns they may have (e.g. child suddenly reluctant to go to nursery).

Progress Check

1 What primitive reflexes can you explain?
2 What is perception?
3 When would you become concerned that a child's hearing might be impaired?
4 When would you become concerned that a child's vision might be impaired?
5 What does the Apgar score measure?
6 Explain the developmental terms simple to complex, cephalo to caudal, proximal to distal and general to specific.
7 Which birthmark is only found on dark-skinned infants?
8 Which fontanelle closes by 18 months of age?
9 Why are black infants usually pale at birth?
10 Why is breast milk best for babies?
11 Why is weaning usually introduced at about 6 months?
12 Give ten examples of stimulating activities for a baby.
13 Give ten examples of stimulating activities for a toddler.
14 Explain a variety of ways that communication can take place with a baby.
15 How does observing a baby or young child help you to care for them?

Glossary

Accommodation Jean Piaget's term for the process by which a child modifies their understanding to acquire a new concept

Active listening Ensuring that you are focusing on what you are listening to

Advocacy Representing another individual or speaking on their behalf

Allergy Allergies are due to the immune system mistakenly believing that a food or substance (that is usually perfectly safe) is harmful, creating antibodies to fight it off

Apgar score Health score given to a baby at birth, recorded on a chart

Aphasia Inability to express thoughts in words

Appendicular skeleton Parts of the skeleton that are attached to the axial skeleton in some way, i.e. shoulders (pectoral girdle), hips (pelvic girdle), arms and legs

Assessment An evaluation of, for example, someone's needs, the quality of a learner's work, or potential risks

Assimilation Jean Piaget's term for a child trying to understand a new concept by fitting it into their present understanding

Asthma A condition affecting the lungs and breathing, often caused by allergy

Auditory development The development of hearing

Aural stimulation Stimulation through sound

Axial skeleton Parts of the skeleton that lie along its main axis, i.e. skull, vertebrae, ribcage and sternum

Baby massage A pleasurable form of physical contact, which aids relaxation and can help the bonding of parent and child

Baby signing A scheme to enable hearing babies to make their needs known prior to acquiring speech

Barrier to communication Any obstruction to understanding between more than one individual

Birthmark A mark or blemish on the skin at birth, or appearing shortly after birth

Blood Essential for life, blood is made up of plasma, red cells and white cells. Blood is categorised into blood groups A, B, AB or O with a substance known as Rhesus factor either present (Rhesus positive blood) or absent (Rhesus negative blood). Blood type varies from person to person

Blood pressure The measurement of pressure just after the heart has contracted (systolic pressure) and once it has relaxed again (diastolic pressure)

Blood vessels Part of the circulatory system. They include arteries, capillaries and veins

Body language Non-verbal signals, including gestures and facial expressions

Bonding The close relationship formed between a child and one or more of the main carers

Bone Each element of the skeletal system

Caudal Referring to the lower parts of the body

Centile chart A chart used to record the growth in infants and young children

Central nervous system The brain and the spinal cord

Cephalo Referring to the head

Challenge An experience that will help develop a skill or aspect of learning

Chickenpox A common childhood illness

Circulatory system The body's system for blood moving around the body

Coeliac disease An intolerance to the protein gluten in wheat, rye, barley and often oats too

Cognitive development The development of knowledge through thinking and problem-solving

Colic Acute spasmodic abdominal pain common in young babies

Communication The means of passing and receiving information

Confidentiality Keeping information to yourself; not passing on information inappropriately, thereby respecting the privacy of others

Congenital A condition present at birth, e.g Down's syndrome

Connective tissue Together with ligaments and tendons, connective tissue helps join bones together

Conservation Being able to understand change in quantity, size and number; the term is often associated with Jean Piaget

Cooled boiled water Used to prepare formula feeds and to clean the eyes of newborn babies

Cross-infection The passing of infection from one person to another

Cultural food customs Guidance and taboos regarding the preparation and consumption of foods which differ between cultural groups

Cystic fibrosis The most commonly found inherited disorder in the UK, affecting the lungs and digestive system

Data protection Regulations regarding the safekeeping of personal details etc.

Development The changes that take place as an individual grows and ages

Developmental delay The term often used when a child's development is not following the pattern of averages (or norms)

Developmental norms Typical patterns of growth and development

Diaphragm The muscle that initiates the body's breathing process

Differentiation The various strategies teachers and other professionals use to enable pupils with diverse learning characteristics to participate in the mainstream programme, to ensure that all children maximise their potential and receive a curriculum through which they can experience success

Direct contact Cross-infection through contact with an infected individual

Distal A distance away from the central point (of the body)

Droplet infection A common cause of cross-infection

Dyscalculia Difficulty in sequencing and in understanding concepts, rules and order

Dysfluency Being unable to speak words fluently, stammering; a common (temporary) occurrence in young children

Dysgraphia Difficulty in controlling pen or pencil, causing problems with letter formation, and consistency of size and shape of letters and numerals

Dyslexia A neurological disorder affecting the fluency and accuracy of reading and writing

Dysphasia Difficulty in expressing thoughts in words

Dyspraxia A sensory disorder affecting the organisation of movement skills

Early Years Foundation Stage (EYFS) A statutory framework for the Learning, Development and Care of Children from birth to five

Elision The omission of the endings of the first word of a two-word pairing

Enactive mode of representation
The child learns through first-hand experiences

Environmental factors
Any influences from outside an individual that could have an impact on the individual in any way

Evaluation Reflecting on and giving consideration to a past event, action or project

Expiration The process of breathing out

Eye contact Looking directly at an individual when conversing or explaining something to them

Febrile convulsion A minor fit due to a raised temperature

Foetal alcohol syndrome (FAS) Physical and cognitive abnormalities often found in children born to alcoholic mothers

Food additives Additional items added to foods to extend shelf life, keep foods free of disease etc.

Food contamination Anything that renders food unfit for consumption. Contamination can be chemical, physical or biological

Food groups The grouping of food types into categories that provide similar nutrients, e.g. carbohydrates, proteins

Food poisoning Illness caused by a variety of bacteria and/or poor kitchen or personal hygiene practices

Food safety A range of regulations regarding the production, handling and preparation of foods

Fore milk The breast milk initially received by an infant that satisfies immediate hunger

Foundation Stage Curriculum A government-led curriculum for children from age three years superseded by the Early Years Foundation Stage (EYFS)

Gastro-enteritis The most common irritation of the stomach and intestines. It can be caused by bacteria or a virus and is passed on either by direct or indirect contact. Poor hygiene is usually the main cause of cross contamination

Growth Increasing in size, height, weight, and so on

HACCP Hazard Analysis Critical Control Point should form part of risk assessment procedures

Hand, foot and mouth disease A relatively common childhood illness

Health The state of well-being

Hind milk The richest type of breast milk

Holistic approach An approach that takes account of the whole person

Homeostasis The body's control mechanism for balancing its metabolism

Hygiene control Preventative measures to avoid cross contamination, e.g through : kitchen hygiene, personal hygiene, safe food handling practices

Iconic mode of representation Thinking using mental images (the term is associated with Jerome Bruner)

Immunisation A process of giving vaccinations (usually to children) to prevent illness and to help eradicate certain medical conditions from society

Inclusion Disabled children and young people learning together in ordinary pre-school provision, schools, colleges and universities, with appropriate networks of support, enabling pupils to participate in the life and work of mainstream institutions to the best of their abilities, whatever their needs

Indirect contact Cross-infection where there is no specific contact with an infected individual

Inspiration The process of breathing in

Intolerance An inability within the body to deal with certain foods or substances, e.g. lactose or gluten

Joints The various links between bones. Joints can be fixed, cartilaginous, ball and socket, hinged, gliding or pivotal

Kinaesthetic learners Individuals who learn best through active involvement

Lactation The production of milk from the breast

Language acquisition device In the theory of language development associated with Noam Chomsky, the term for a hypothetical inborn mechanism in the brain that predisposes children to acquire language

Malnutrition An imbalance of nutrients

Managing behaviour Methods of reducing undesirable behaviour in children

Maturational To do with the biological process of development

Measles A childhood illness, mostly controlled by immunisation schedules

Meningitis A serious infection of meninges

Metabolism The process of breaking down food, and either using or storing it

Motherese The voice tones often used by adults when talking to infants

Motor skills The physical skills of locomotion, non-locomotion and manipulative dexterity

Movements and levers The 'load and effort' processes involved in the body's ability for movement

Mumps A childhood illness, mostly controlled by immunisation schedules

Muscular system Part of the body's system to enable movement. There are three categories of muscle, i.e. skeletal, cardiac and involuntary muscles

National Curriculum The curriculum followed by children in all state schools

Natural immunity A degree of immunity present in the body without the use of vaccination

Nature–nurture debate The question of whether individuals acquire knowledge through their genetic inheritance or through what they experience from birth onwards

Neonatal jaundice A problem with the function of the liver during the first weeks of life

Neonate An infant in the first month of life

Non-verbal communication The messages that are given through body language and facial expression

Observation A method of studying behaviour by watching and recording what the people being studied do

Over-nutrition The intake of more nutrients than the body requires

Pathogen A micro-organism, such as a bacterium or virus, that causes disease

Perception The process by which the brain makes sense of information received from the senses; insight or awareness

Peripheral nervous system The body's automatic nervous system

Persona dolls Dolls designed to represent children from various cultures and/or with a range of disabilities or issues

Pest control The control of infestations such as rats, mice, cock-roaches

Physical environment The surroundings (building, room layout, lighting, ventilation, etc.)

Physical impairment The loss or partial loss of physical action, e.g. mobility

Planning Looking ahead, preparation usually based on observation and assessment

Policies A set of principles used as the basis for decisions or actions

Portage A daily home teaching programme specified for the individual child

Prejudice An opinion formed in advance, a prejudgement

Primary National Strategy A government-led programme, setting out the core learning for both mathematics and literacy

Primitive reflexes Reflexes present at birth, many of which gradually disappear as the central nervous system develops

Principles of diet and nutrition The basis of healthy eating

Proximal Close to the central point (of the body)

Pyrexia A high temperature, fever

Reflex An involuntary response to a stimulus, for example blinking

Reinforcement Practice and repetition to help consolidate learning

Respiratory system The body's system for breathing

Risk assessment An assessment of risk according to appropriate parameters, e.g. age of children

Routines A set procedure that should meet the needs of all concerned

Rubella The medical name for the childhood condition often known as German Measles. It is mostly controlled by immunisation schedules

Safety marks National standards regarding safety, printed on the packaging of objects to guide consumers as to their suitability for the intended use or recipient; found, for example, on toys, baby equipment, electrical appliances

Scaffolding A term usually associated with Jerome Bruner; the adult supports and extends a child's learning

Schema An internal representation of knowledge, which is adapted through assimilation and accommodation

Screening Tests carried out to identify if an individual is showing signs of a disease or may be predisposed to develop it. Screening of the foetus/embryo is carried out during pregnancy; screening is also done during childhood. Sometimes, whole populations are screened as a public health measure

Senses Vision, hearing, taste, touch and smell

Sensory impairment The loss or partial loss of one or more senses, e.g. vision or hearing

Signed language Communication without the necessity for speech

Skeletal system The framework of the body's bones, divided into the axial skeleton and appendicular skeleton

Skin care Appropriate care of different types of skin

Skin infestation A treatable skin problem such as scabies

Social constructivist theory The theory that children learn by exploring a range of experiences and objects from everyday life, for example in play

Social learning theory The theory that children learn by observing and copying others; supported by the results of Albert Bandura's Bobo doll experiments

Specific needs An identified requirement that will enable an individual to meet their potential

Standard Attainment Tasks (SATs) Tests carried out at regular intervals during formal schooling

Stereotyping Categorising people according to their group, not seeing their individuality

Sterilising techniques Methods of ensuring that utensils (bottles, teats, etc.) used for babies are free from bacteria

Stimulate To arouse curiosity, interest and development

Stimulating play Activities or objects which stimulate

Symbolic mode of representation Being able to use symbols such as language or number to represent the world (the term is associated with Jerome Bruner)

Syndrome A collection of signs or characteristics

Theoretical perspectives Theories or explanations involving abstract ideas and philosophies

Topping and tailing Washing a baby's facial area and changing its nappy

Treasure basket A small basket of natural objects; ideal for babies from about six months of age, it enables exploration of a range of natural materials, smells and shapes

Turn-taking Responses made by young babies to adults when they make 'conversation' with them. This can be an expression, a movement, a smile or a sound

UN Convention on the Rights of the Child This international constitution was adopted by the United Nations Assembly in 1989 to uphold agreed rights for children whenever possible

Under-nutrition Insufficient nutrients to meet the needs of the body

Vegan diet A diet avoiding all foods derived from or produced by animals

Vegetarian diet A diet avoiding all foods derived form animals

Visual stimulation Stimulation through sight

Weaning The introduction of solid food to young babies

Zone of proximal development (ZPD) The term used by Lev Vygotsky for the area between the child's actual development and the potential level that they could achieve with additional support from the adult

Bibliography

Aarons, M. and Gittens, T. (1999) *Social Skills Programmes: An Integrated Approach from Early Years to Adolescence*, Speechmark

Ashman, C. and Green, S. (2005) *Managing Environment and Resources*, David Fulton, London

Athey, C. (1990) *Extending Thought in Young Children*, Paul Chapman, London

Baston, H. and Durward, H. (2001) *Examination of the Newborn. A Practical Guide*, Routledge, London

Beaver, M., Brewster, J., Jones, P., Keane, A., Neaum, S. and Tallack, J. (2001) *Babies and Young Children*, Nelson Thornes, Cheltenham

Bee, H. (2003) *The Developing Child,* Allyn & Bacon, Boston, MA

Bilton, H. (2004) *Playing Outside*, David Fulton, London

Birkett, V. (2004) *How to Support and Teach Children with SEN*, LDA, Wiltshire

Boulton, J. and Ackroyd, J. (2004) *Role Play in the Early Years* series, David Fulton, London

Boyd, L. (2004) *Construction*, David Fulton/Routledge, London

Brown, T. and Leibling, H. (2005) *The Really Useful Maths Book,* Routledge, London

Bruce, T. (1991) *Time to Play in Early Childhood Education*, Hodder & Stoughton, London

Bruce, T. (2004) *Early Childhood Education*, 2nd edition, Hodder & Stoughton, London

Canter, L. and Canter, M. (2001) *Lee Canter's Assertive Discipline: Positive Behaviour Management for Today's Classroom*, 3rd edition, National Education Service, Bloomington, Ind.

Cullis, T., Dolan, L. and Groves, D. (1999) *Psychology for You*, Nelson Thornes, Cheltenham

Dare, A. and O'Donovan, M. (1996) *A Practical Guide to Child Nutrition*, Nelson Thornes, Cheltenham

Dare, A. and O'Donovan, M. (1997) *Good Practice in Caring for Young Children with Special Needs*, Nelson Thornes, Cheltenham

Dare, A. and O'Donovan, M. (1998) *A Practical Guide to Working with Babies*, 2nd edition, Nelson Thornes, Cheltenham

Dare, A. and O'Donovan, M. (2002) *Good Practice in Caring for Young Children with Special Needs*, 2nd edition, Nelson Thornes, Cheltenham

DfES (2001) *Special Education Needs Guide for Parents and Carers*, DfES, London

DfES (2004) *Removing Barriers to Achievement*, Stationery Office, London

DfES (2006) *Primary Framework for Literacy and Mathematics*, Stationery Office, London

Donaldson, M. (2003) *Children's Minds*, Harper Collins, London

Drake, J. (2001) *Planning Children's Play and Learning in the Foundation Stage*, David Fulton, London

Dyson, A. and Meredith, L. (2006) *Feeding the Under 5s*, David Fulton, London

Family Information Service (2006) *A Directory of Services for Children with Additional Needs*, 2nd edition, Bath & North-East Somerset Council

Gerhardt, S. (2004) *Why Love Matters,* Brunner-Routledge, Hove

Gilbert, P. (2000) *A-Z of Syndromes and Inherited Disorders*, 3rd edition, Nelson Thornes, Cheltenham

Gray, C. and White, A.L. (eds.) (2001) *My Social Stories Book,* Jessica Kingsley, London

Gray, C., Howley, M. and Arnold, E. (2005) *Revealing the Hidden Social Code: Social Stories for People with Autistic Spectrum Disorder*, Jessica Kingsley, London

Green, S. (2004a) *Baby and Toddler Development Made Real*, David Fulton, London

Green, S. (2004b) *Outdoor Play*, Scholastic Ltd, Leamington Spa

Green, S. (2005a) *Food and Cooking*, David Fulton, London

Green, S. (2005b) *Role Play*, David Fulton/Routledge, London

Green, S. (2006) *Books, Stories and Puppets*, David Fulton, London

Green, S. (2007) *BTEC National Children's Care, Learning and Development*, Book 1, Nelson Thornes, Cheltenham

Green, S. (2007a) *BTEC First Children's Care, Learning and Development*, Nelson Thornes, Cheltenham

Halliwell, M. (2003) *Supporting Children with SEN: A Guide for Assistants in Schools and Pre-Schools,* David Fulton, London

Harpley, A. and Roberts, A. (Green, S. ed.) (2006) *From Birth to 3* series, David Fulton, London

Harpley, A. and Roberts, A. (Green, S. ed.) (2007) *Helping Children to be Competent Learners*, David Fulton/Routledge, London

Head, J. (1999) *Understanding the Boys: Issues of Behaviour and Achievement,* Routledge Falmer, London

Honeybourne, J. (2007) *BTEC National Sport: Development, Coaching and Fitness,* Book 1, Nelson Thornes, Cheltenham

Jarvis, M. (2001) *Angles on Child Psychology*, Nelson Thornes, Cheltenham

Keene, A. (1999) *Child Health: Care of the Child in Health and Illness*, Nelson Thornes, Cheltenham

Kulochova, J. (1972) 'A severe deprivation in twins: a case study', *Journal of Child Psychology and Psychiatry*, 13, pp107–14

Mackonochie, A. (2004) *Toddlers Tantrums and Other Bad Behaviour*, Carroll & Brown, London

Maines, B. and Robinson, G. (1998) *All for Alex: A Circle of Friends*, Lucky Duck Publishing

Martin, T. *et al.* (2005) *The Really Useful Literacy Book*, Routledge Falmer, London

Money, J. (2001) *Blueprints: Physical Education*, 2nd edition, Nelson Thornes, Cheltenham

Mooney, C.G. (2000) *Theories of Childhood*, Redleaf Press, St Paul, Mn

Moyles, J. (1989) *Just Playing? The Excellence of Play*, Open University Press, Milton Keynes

Moyles, J. (ed.) (1994) *Just Playing? The Role and Status of Play in Early Childhood Education*, Open University Press, Milton Keynes

Mukherji, P. and O'Dea, T. (2000) *Understanding Children's Language and Literacy*, Nelson Thornes, Cheltenham

Nash-Wortham, M. and Hunt, J. (1997) *Take Time: Movement Exercises for Parents, Teachers and Therapists of Children with Difficulties Speaking, Reading, Writing and Spelling*, 4th edition, Robinswood Press, Stourbridge

Palmer, S. and Corbett, P. (2003) *Literacy: What Works?* Nelson Thornes, Cheltenham

Parker, L. (2006) *How to Avoid Illness and Infection*, David Fulton, London

Pennington, D. *et al.* (2003) *Advanced Psychology: Child Development, Perspectives and Methods*, Hodder & Stoughton, London

Phillips, C. (1996) *Family-Centred Maternity and Newborn Care*, 4th edition, Mosby Publishers, London

Pound, L. (1999) *Supporting Mathematical Development*, Open University Press, Milton Keynes

Price, L. (2003) *Primary School Gymnastics*, David Fulton, London

QCA (2000) *Curriculum Guidance for the Foundation Stage*, Stationery Office, London

QCA (2003) *Foundation Stage Profile Handbook*, Stationery Office, London

Robertson, J. and Bowlby, J. (1952) 'Responses of young children to separation from their mothers', *Courier of the International Children's Centre, Paris II*, pp131–40

Rogers, B. (2002) *Classroom Behaviour*, Paul Chapman, London

Rutter, M. and the English and Romanian Adoptees Study Team (1998) 'Development catch-up and deficit after severe global early deprivation', *Journal of Child Psychology and Psychiatry*, 39, pp465–76

Ryder Richardson, G. (2006) *Creating a Space to Grow*, David Fulton, London

Schaffer, R. and Emerson, P. (1964) 'The development of social attachments in infancy', *Monographs of the Society for Research in Child Development*, 29, no. 94

Severs, J. (2003) *Safety and Risk in Primary School Physical Education*, Routledge, London

Sheridan, M. (1991) *From Birth to Five Years: Children's Developmental Progress*, NFER Nelson, Windsor

Spann, M.B. (1998) *Exploring Numbers 1 to 100*, Scholastic, Leamington Spa

Swanson, N. (2001) *The Good Child Guide*, Aurum Press, London

Tassoni, P. (2003) *Supporting Special Needs: Understanding Inclusion in the Early Years*, Heinemann, London

Teodorescu, I. and Addy, L. (1998) *Write from the Start: Unique Programme to Develop the Fine Motor and Perceptual Skills Necessary for Effective Handwriting*, LDA, Wisbech

Vickerman, P. (2007) *Teaching Physical Education to Children with Special Educational Needs*, Routledge, London

Walker, C. (1998) *Eating Well for the Under-5s in Child Care*, The Caroline Walker Trust, St Austell

Wall, K. (2003) *Special Needs and Early Years: A Practitioner's Guide*. Paul Chapman, London

Whitehead, M. (1999) *Supporting Language and Literacy Development in the Early Years*, Open University Press, Milton Keynes

Winston, R. and Livingstone, T. (2005) *Child of Our Time*, Bantam, London

Journals

Child Education
Early Years Educator
Journal of Developmental Psychology (British Psychological Society)
Nursery Education
Nursery World
The Psychologist
Times Educational Supplement Primary

Websites

www.achondroplasia.co.uk

www.askbaby.com (advice for parents)

www.babycentre.co.uk (advice for parents)

www.battens.org

www.behaviour.org.uk (child behaviour resource)

www.bfi.org.uk/education/teaching/disability (teaching resource)

www.bounty.com (advice for parents)

www.bps.org.uk (British Psychological Society)

www.cafamily.org.uk (Contact a Family)

www.cftrust.org.uk (Cystic Fibrosis Trust)

www.childrensworkforce.org.uk

www.c-r-y.org.uk (CRY: Cardiac Risk in the Young)

www.dfes.gov.uk/everychildmatters

www.direct.gov.uk (UK government)

www.drc-gb.org (Disability Rights Commission)

www.dsa-uk.com (Down's Syndrome Association)

www.earlysupport.org.uk

www.familytherapy.org.uk

www.haemophilia.org.uk

www.home-start.org.uk

www.inclusive.co.uk (Inclusive Technology Ltd, for special needs)

www.kidshealth.org

www.lovaas.com (Lovaas Institute: behaviour treatment/ autism)

www.luckyduck.co.uk (Lucky Duck Publishers)

www.marfan.org.uk

www.meningitis-trust.org/disease

www.muscular-dystrophy.org

www.nas.org.uk (National Autistic Society)

www.ncb.org.uk (National Children's Bureau)

www.nctpregnancyandbabycare.com

www.nidcd.nih.gov/health/hearing/usher.asp (Usher's syndrome)

www.nspku.org (National Society for Phenylketonuria)

www.pampers.com (advice for parents)

www.parentlineplus.com

www.parentpartnership.org.uk

www.patient.co.uk (health information)

www.pwsa.co.uk (Prader-Willi Syndrome Association UK)

www.rethink.org (mental illness)

www.sandy-green.com (for early years students, practitioners and parents)

www.strongbones.org.uk (Strongbones Children's Charitable Trust: brittle bone disease, arthritis, rheumatism)

www.supernanny.co.uk (parenting advice, etc.)

www.teachernet.gov.uk (site for teachers)

www.whizz-kids.org.uk (mobility equipment, training and advice)

Index